10

GERARD ANDERSON
922 - 12 ST.
BOULDER, COLO.

HI-2-7610

Notation —

(1) see preface

p. 218: $\vec{K}^2$, $\vec{k}_1^2$ are operators giving eigenvalue $L(L+1)\hbar$ and $l_1(l_1+1)\hbar$ respectively

$\vec{M}^2$ gives eigenvalue $J(J+1)\hbar$

QUANTUM MECHANICS OF ONE- AND TWO-ELECTRON ATOMS

BY

HANS A. BETHE AND EDWIN E. SALPETER

JOHN WENDELL ANDERSON PROFESSOR OF PHYSICS

PROFESSOR OF PHYSICS AND NUCLEAR STUDIES

CORNELL UNIVERSITY, ITHACA, NEW YORK

WITH 41 FIGURES

SPRINGER-VERLAG · BERLIN · GÖTTINGEN · HEIDELBERG · 1957

ACADEMIC PRESS INC · NEW YORK · NEW YORK

Distributors for the Western Hemisphere:
Academic Press Inc. 111 Fifth Avenue, New York 3, New York/USA.

Printed in Germany · Universitätsdruckerei H. Stürtz AG., Würzburg

DEDICATED TO THE MEMORY OF
ARNOLD SOMMERFELD

Preface.

Nearly all of this book is taken from an article prepared in 1956 for a recent volume of the Encyclopedia of Physics. This article, in turn, is partly based on Dr. Norbert Rosenzweig's translation of an older article on the same subject, written by one of us (HAB) about 25 years ago for the Geiger-Scheel Handbuch der Physik. To the article written last year we have added some Addenda and Errata. These Addenda and Errata refer back to some of the 79 sections of the main text and contain some misprint corrections, additional references and some notes.

The aim of this book is two-fold. First, to act as a reference work on calculations pertaining to hydrogen-like and helium-like atoms and their comparison with experiments. However, these calculations involve a vast array of approximation methods, mathematical tricks and physical pictures, which are also useful in the application of quantum mechanics to other fields. In many sections we have given more general discussions of the methods and physical ideas than is necessary for the study of the H- and He-atom alone. We hope that this book will thus at least partly fulfill its second aim, namely to be of some use to graduate students who wish to learn "applied quantum mechanics". A basic knowledge of the principles of quantum mechanics, such as given in the early chapters of Schiff's or Bohm's book, is presupposed.

Like its 1932 predecessor this book mainly gives "low-brow" explicit derivations rather than using more elegant and powerful, but more difficult, formalisms. However, in dealing with angular momentum and sum rules, etc., some operator manipulations are introduced, since these are now commonplace in the treatment of complex atoms. Since it is no longer necessary to "sell quantum mechanics", less space is devoted to the experimental verification of older quantum mechanical results. A large fraction of the present book is devoted to the Dirac theory of the electron and to radiative effects, including short discussions of the relevant experiments. These topics are also treated from the "low-brow" or "practical" point of view. In particular, no formal derivations of quantum-electrodynamics are presented, but the specific application to atomic systems of general field-theoretic results is described in detail.

Numbers in square brackets in the text, e.g. [*9*], refer to a short bibliography towards the end of the book, but most references are given as footnotes. References to "this Encyclopedia" refer to the recent Encyclopedia of Physics, edited by S. Flügge and published by Springer-Verlag; "this volume" refers to Vol. XXXV. In many sections atomic units are used, which are defined in the Introduction. The particular definitions of spherical harmonics we have used, as well as useful formulae, are given in an Appendix.

We are deeply grateful to many colleagues who have made suggestions, pointed out errors, communicated unpublished results and generally helped with the preparation of the manuscript or the proofreading. We are particularly indebted to Drs. J. F. Bird and N. Rosenzweig who read the proofs patiently and eradicated mistakes impatiently.

September 1957. H. A. Bethe · E. E. Salpeter.

Preface

√ = take these sections

Contents.

Quantum Mechanics of One- and Two-Electron Atoms.

Introduction. Units.

α) One of the simplest, and most completely treated, fields of application of quantum mechanics is the theory of atoms with one or two electrons. For hydrogen and the analogous ions He^+, Li^{++}, etc., the calculations can be performed exactly, both in SCHRÖDINGER's nonrelativistic wave mechanics and in DIRAC's relativistic theory of the electron. More specifically, the calculations are exact for a single electron in a fixed COULOMB potential. Hydrogen-like atoms thus furnish an excellent way of testing the validity of quantum mechanics. For such atoms the correction terms due to the motion and structure of atomic nuclei and due to quantum electrodynamic effects are small and can be calculated with high accuracy. Since the energy levels of hydrogen and similar atoms can be investigated experimentally to an astounding degree of accuracy, some accurate tests of the validity of quantum electrodynamics are also possible. Finally, the theory of such atoms in an external electric or magnetic field has also been developed in detail and compared with experiment.

For atoms and ions with two electrons, such as H^-, He, Li^+, etc., exact analytic calculations are not possible at the present time. But these atoms are still simple enough, so that various approximation methods can be used to carry out calculations to a high degree of accuracy. In fact, for the ground state of such atoms the accuracy of the theoretical calculations is of the same order of magnitude as that of spectroscopic measurements. Thus, helium-like atoms not only give further confirmation of the general validity of quantum mechanics, but provide an excellent testing ground for the various approximation methods which are commonly used in quantum mechanics. Finally, the relativistic effects for two-electron atoms (and especially for positronium) provide a simple field of application for present-day theories of the interaction between electrons.

We shall largely base our treatment on the standard wavemechanical form of quantum mechanics in the nonrelativistic theory and on the DIRAC theory for the relativistic treatment of electrons (particles of spin $\frac{1}{2}$). The fundamental principles of these theories are described in detail elsewhere, see for instance the works[1] by DIRAC [*1*], KRAMERS [*2*], PAULI [*3*] or SCHIFF [*4*]. Occasionally we shall use the more general methods of matrix manipulation, described, for instance, by CONDON and SHORTLEY [*5*]. We shall not treat quantum electrodynamics in any detail, but will refer to results obtained in this theory (see for instance, HEITLER [*6*]).

β) Units. To avoid carrying too many numerical factors, we shall in general use atomic units (a.u.), introduced by HARTREE[2]. These units are built up of various combinations of the charge e and mass m of the electron and of PLANCK's

[1] Numbers in italics, e.g., [*1*], refer to a bibliography at the end of this ~~article~~. book (p. 350)

[2] D. R. HARTREE: Proc. Cambridge Phil. Soc. **24**, 89 (1928).

constant h. In general we shall find it useful to introduce, instead of h, the "rationalized PLANCK's constant",

$$\hbar = \frac{h}{2\pi} = 1.0544_5 \times 10^{-27} \text{ erg sec}.$$

We shall also use SOMMERFELD's dimensionless "fine structure constant"

$$\alpha = \frac{e^2}{\hbar c} = \frac{1}{137.037},$$

where c is the velocity of light, $c = 299793$ km/sec. In our atomic units, $\hbar$ is also the unit of action and of angular momentum.

The atomic units are:

1. Unit of charge $= e =$ charge of the electron $= 4.8029 \times 10^{-10}$ e.s.u. $= 1.6021 \times 10^{-20}$ e.m.u.
2. Unit of mass $= m =$ mass of the electron $= 9.108_5 \times 10^{-28}$ gm.
3. Unit of length $= a =$ "radius of first BOHR orbit" (innermost circular orbit for H in the old quantum theory) $= \hbar^2/me^2 = 5.2917 \times 10^{-9}$ cm.
4. Unit of velocity $= v_0 =$ electron velocity in the first BOHR orbit $= e^2/\hbar = \alpha c = 2.1877 \times 10^8$ cm/sec.
5. Unit of momentum $= p_0 =$ electron momentum in the first BOHR orbit $= me^2/\hbar = mv_0 = 1.9926 \times 10^{-19}$ gm cm/sec.
6. Unit of energy $= e^2/a = me^4/\hbar^2 = p_0^2/m =$ twice the ionization potential of hydrogen (for nuclear mass ∞) $= 4.359_0 \times 10^{-11}$ erg.
7. Unit of time $= a/v_0 = \hbar^3/me^4 = 2.4189 \times 10^{-17}$ sec.
8. Unit of frequency $= v_0/a = me^4/\hbar^3 = 4\pi$ Ry $= 4.1341 \times 10^{16}$ sec^{-1} (Ry = RYDBERG frequency).
9. Unit of electric potential $= e/a = me^3/\hbar^2 = 0.09076$ e.s.u. $= 27.210$ Volt.
10. Unit of electric field strength $= e/a^2 = m^2e^5/\hbar^4 = 5.142 \times 10^9$ Volt/cm.

We have defined the "RYDBERG for infinite mass" Ry as a frequency, namely $1/4\pi$ atomic frequency units. We shall sometimes express energy in terms of "RYDBERG units", that is in units of (h Ry). This quantity is *one half* an atomic energy unit and numbers expressed in terms of it will carry the symbol "Ry" after them. In many experimental results, one obtains instead of an energy E, the equivalent wave number (E/hc), expressed in cm^{-1}, or the equivalent frequency (E/h), expressed in Mc/sec. The wave number corresponding to one "RYDBERG unit of energy" is[1]

$$R_\infty = \frac{e^2}{2ahc} = \frac{\alpha}{4\pi a} = 109737.3 \text{ cm}^{-1}.$$

The RYDBERG frequency itself, $\frac{v_0}{4\pi a} = \frac{e^2}{2ah}$, is equal to 3.28985×10^9 Mc/sec. One RYDBERG unit of energy, expressed in terms of electron volts, is 13.605_0 eV.

γ) Basis for numerical values used. The numerical values quoted above for the atomic units expressed in ordinary (C.G.S.) units were taken from DUMOND and COHEN's[2] Tables of the Physical Constants. DUMOND and COHEN's best numerical values of the physical constants are based on a large number of experiments, which measure different combinations of the fundamental constants. More experiments than unknown constants were available and the "best values" were derived by a method-of-least-squares analysis. Some of the most accurate

[1] This quantity R_∞ is often referred to simply as "the RYDBERG for infinite nuclear mass" in the literature.

[2] J. W. M. DUMOND and E. R. COHEN: Rev. Mod. Phys. **25**, 691 (1953); also first article in this volume.

experiments, used in this analysis, require for their interpretation a knowledge (and the validity) of the quantum theory of atomic energy levels. This theory, to be developed in the following chapters, is required in particular (a) to derive the "RYDBERG", R_∞, from the spectroscopic measurement of wave numbers of the BALMER lines for hydrogen, (b) to derive the fine structure constant α from microwave measurements of the fine structure (or hyperfine structure) splitting of energy levels of hydrogen.

To be able to discuss experimental tests for the validity of atomic theory, it is useful to consider the "best" values of the atomic constants which can be derived from experiments *without* any recourse to atomic theory. Besides the accurately known value for the velocity of light, c, we need numerical values for h, e and m. Enough experiments for such a determination are now available: In particular PLANK'S constant h can be derived from measurements of the short wave-length limit of the continuous X-ray spectrum without detailed knowledge of quantum theory, using only the postulate $E = h\nu$, relating energy E and frequency ν. An outline of some of the other experiments is as follows: X-ray diffraction experiments on crystals and gratings give the lattice constants of simple crystals in centimeters and hence AVOGADRO'S number N. The measurement of the Faraday then gives e. Mass-spectroscopy (and N) gives M_p, the proton mass. Experiments comparing (indirectly) the "cyclotron frequencies" of the electron and proton finally give m/M_p, and hence m.

The numerical values obtained from these experiments, which do *not* involve atomic theory for h, e and m (and hence for R_∞ and α) are, of course, less accurate than DUMOND and COHEN'S "best values" (using all experiments) which were quoted above. These "non-atomic" values[1] are

$$\begin{aligned} \hbar &= (1.0542 \pm 0.0002) \times 10^{-27}\,\text{erg sec}, \\ e &= (4.8026 \pm 0.0005) \times 10^{-10}\,\text{e.s.u.}, \\ m &= (9.107_8 \pm 0.001_0) \times 10^{-28}\,\text{gm}, \\ 1/\alpha &= 137.02 \pm 0.02, \\ R_\infty &= (109773 \pm 35)\,\text{cm}^{-1}. \end{aligned}$$

These non-atomic values agree with the more accurate ones, quoted above, to within (approximately) the experimental error (the discrepancy is less than 1.5 times the standard deviation in all cases)[2].

I. The hydrogen atom without external fields.

a) Nonrelativistic theory.

1. Separation of SCHRÖDINGER'S equation in spherical polar coordinates. Angularly dependent eigenfunctions and the angular momentum matrix. SCHRÖDINGER'S equation[3] in c.g.s. units for an electron in the field of a nucleus of charge Ze and of infinite mass is

$$\Delta u + \frac{2m}{\hbar^2}\left(E + \frac{Ze^2}{r}\right) u = 0, \tag{1.1}$$

[1] J. W. DUMOND and E. R. COHEN: In this volume and private communication.

[2] Numerical values, found in older theoretical references (including ref. [*10*] of our bibliography), which are based on the atomic constants, should be treated with great caution: The older values of some atomic constants were in error by much more than the statistical errors in the older experiments (due to systematic errors not expected at the time).

[3] We shall use throughout the symbol Δ for the LAPLACE operator $\left(\frac{\partial^2}{\partial x^2} + \frac{\partial^2}{\partial y^2} + \frac{\partial^2}{\partial z^2}\right)$, instead of the symbol ∇^2 which is more commonly used in English and American texts.

and in HARTREE's atomic units (see Introductory Remarks) is

$$\Delta u + 2\left(E + \frac{Z}{r}\right) u = 0. \tag{1.1'}$$

This equation can be separated in spherical polar coordinates. We choose the nucleus as origin of a polar coordinate system with some arbitrary z direction as polar axis. Let $r\vartheta\varphi$ be the coordinates of the electron. The LAPLACian operator Δ is given by

$$\Delta u = \frac{\partial^2 u}{\partial r^2} + \frac{2}{r}\frac{\partial u}{\partial r} + \frac{1}{r^2 \sin\vartheta}\frac{\partial}{\partial\vartheta}\left(\sin\vartheta\frac{\partial u}{\partial\vartheta}\right) + \frac{1}{r^2\sin^2\vartheta}\frac{\partial^2 u}{\partial\varphi^2}. \tag{1.2}$$

We try as solution

$$u = R(r)\, Y(\vartheta, \varphi) \tag{1.3}$$

and obtain

$$\frac{r^2}{R}\left[\frac{d^2R}{dr^2} + \frac{2}{r}\frac{dR}{dr} + 2\left(E + \frac{Z}{r}\right)R\right] = \lambda = -\frac{1}{Y}\cdot\left[\frac{1}{\sin\vartheta}\frac{\partial}{\partial\vartheta}\left(\sin\vartheta\frac{\partial Y}{\partial\vartheta}\right) + \frac{1}{\sin^2\vartheta}\frac{\partial^2 Y}{\partial\varphi^2}\right]. \tag{1.4}$$

The left side is a function of r only, the right side a function of ϑ and φ only. Therefore, λ is a constant. The equation on the right in (1.4), namely

$$\frac{1}{\sin\vartheta}\frac{\partial}{\partial\vartheta}\left(\sin\vartheta\frac{\partial Y}{\partial\vartheta}\right) + \frac{1}{\sin^2\vartheta}\frac{\partial^2 Y}{\partial\varphi^2} + \lambda Y = 0 \tag{1.5}$$

can be solved only if

$$\lambda = l(l+1). \qquad l = 0, 1, 2, \ldots \tag{1.6}$$

In this event there are the following $2l+1$ solutions:

$$Y_{lm} = \frac{1}{\sqrt{2\pi}}\mathcal{P}_{lm}(\vartheta)\, e^{im\varphi} = \sqrt{\frac{(l-m)!}{(l+m)!}\cdot\frac{2l+1}{4\pi}}\cdot P_l^m(\cos\vartheta)\, e^{im\varphi};\ m = -l, \ldots, l-1, l \tag{1.7}$$

Y_{lm} is a spherical harmonic, P_l^m the unnormalized associated LEGENDRE function (cf. Appendix).

The first few spherical harmonics are given explicitly:

$$\left.\begin{aligned}
&Y_{00} = \frac{1}{\sqrt{4\pi}}, \\
&Y_{10} = \sqrt{\frac{3}{4\pi}}\cos\vartheta, && Y_{11} = \sqrt{\frac{3}{8\pi}}\sin\vartheta\, e^{i\varphi}, \\
&Y_{20} = \sqrt{\frac{5}{4\pi}}\left(\frac{3}{2}\cos^2\vartheta - \frac{1}{2}\right), && Y_{21} = \sqrt{\frac{15}{8\pi}}\sin\vartheta\cos\vartheta\, e^{i\varphi}, \\
&Y_{22} = \frac{1}{4}\sqrt{\frac{15}{2\pi}}\sin^2\vartheta\, e^{2i\varphi}, \\
&Y_{30} = \sqrt{\frac{7}{4\pi}}\left(\frac{5}{2}\cos^3\vartheta - \frac{3}{2}\cos\vartheta\right), && Y_{31} = \frac{1}{4}\sqrt{\frac{21}{4\pi}}\sin\vartheta\,(5\cos^2\vartheta - 1)\, e^{i\varphi}, \\
&Y_{32} = \frac{1}{4}\sqrt{\frac{105}{2\pi}}\sin^2\vartheta\cos\vartheta\, e^{2i\varphi}, && Y_{33} = \frac{1}{4}\sqrt{\frac{35}{4\pi}}\sin^3\vartheta\, e^{3i\varphi}, \\
&Y_{40} = \sqrt{\frac{9}{4\pi}}\left(\frac{35}{8}\cos^4\vartheta - \frac{15}{4}\cos^2\vartheta + \frac{3}{8}\right), && Y_{41} = \frac{3}{4}\sqrt{\frac{5}{4\pi}}(7\cos^3\vartheta - 3\cos\vartheta)\sin\vartheta\, e^{i\varphi}, \\
&Y_{42} = \frac{3}{4}\sqrt{\frac{5}{8\pi}}\sin^2\vartheta\,(7\cos^2\vartheta - 1)\, e^{2i\varphi}, && Y_{43} = \frac{3}{4}\sqrt{\frac{35}{4\pi}}\sin^3\vartheta\cos\vartheta\, e^{3i\varphi}, \\
&Y_{44} = \frac{3}{8}\sqrt{\frac{35}{8\pi}}\sin^4\vartheta\, e^{4i\varphi}.
\end{aligned}\right\} \tag{1.8}$$

The normalized associated LEGENDRE functions $\mathscr{P}_{lm}$ for $l=1$ to 3 are graphed in Fig. 1 (i.e., the parts of the spherical harmonics depending on geographic latitude ϑ). As one can see, the associated LEGENDRE functions P_{lm} have $l-|m|$ zeros between the poles of the sphere. Thus, the spherical harmonic Y_{lm} has $l-|m|$ "parallels of latitude" as nodal lines. Furthermore, the real part of the spherical harmonic

$$\sqrt{\frac{1}{\pi}}\,\mathscr{P}_{lm}(\vartheta)\,{\cos \atop \sin}\, m\varphi$$

has $|m|$ meridians as nodal lines, resulting in a total of l nodal lines.

The eigenfunctions

$$u = R(r)\, Y_{lm}(\vartheta, \varphi)$$

are closely related to the angular momentum of the atom—it turns out that both the total angular momentum and the angular momentum about the z-axis are diagonal matrices. They are quantized; i.e., if the appropriate operators are applied to the eigenfunction u,

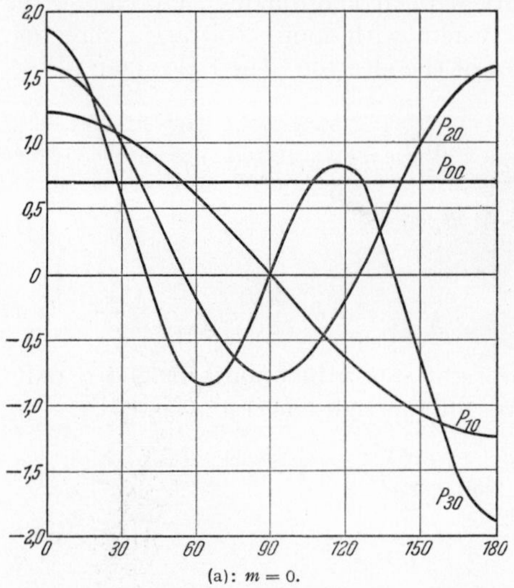

(a): $m = 0$.

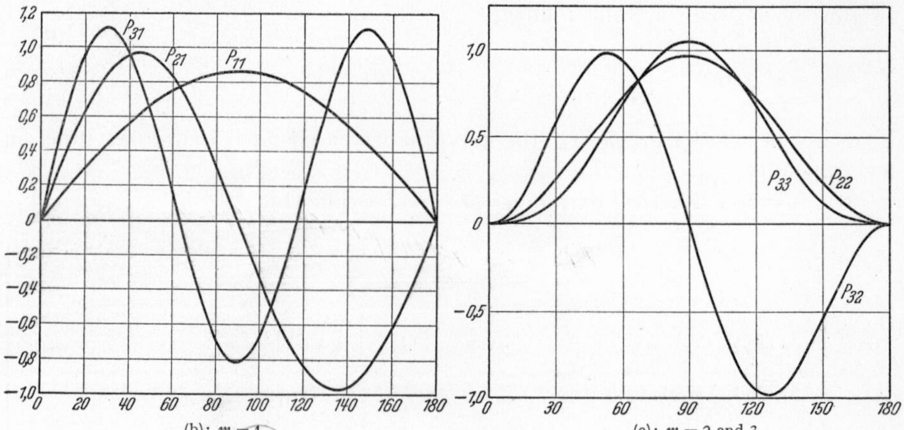

(b): $m = 1$. (c): $m = 2$ and 3.

Fig. 1 a—c. The normalized associated LEGENDRE function $\mathscr{P}_{lm}(\vartheta)$ plotted against ϑ (in degrees).

the result is the eigenfunction u multiplied by a constant. The operator belonging to the angular momentum about the z-axis is given by[1]

$$k_z = -i\left(x\frac{\partial}{\partial y} - y\frac{\partial}{\partial x}\right) = -i\frac{\partial}{\partial \varphi}. \tag{1.9}$$

Operating on u, one obtains

$$k_z u = -i\frac{\partial}{\partial \varphi}\left[R(r)\,\mathscr{P}_{lm}(\vartheta)\,\frac{1}{\sqrt{2\pi}}\,e^{im\varphi}\right] = m u, \tag{1.10}$$

m is a measure of the angular momentum in the z direction and is called the magnetic quantum number[2].

[1] k_z, x, and y are measured in atomic units.
[2] Cf. Theory of the ZEEMAN effect, Sect. 45.

The operator representing the total angular momentum is given by

$$k^2 u = -\left(x\frac{\partial}{\partial y} - y\frac{\partial}{\partial x}\right)^2 u - \left(y\frac{\partial}{\partial z} - z\frac{\partial}{\partial y}\right)^2 u - \left(z\frac{\partial}{\partial x} - x\frac{\partial}{\partial z}\right)^2 u$$
$$= r^2\left(\frac{\partial^2 u}{\partial r^2} + \frac{2}{r}\frac{\partial u}{\partial r} - \Delta u\right),$$

resulting from an elementary transformation. In view of (1.2) through (1.6) it follows that

$$k^2 u = r^2\left(\frac{\partial^2 u}{\partial r^2} + \frac{2}{r}\frac{\partial u}{\partial r} - \Delta u\right) = l(l+1)\,u. \tag{1.11}$$

We could have saved ourselves the trouble of calculating the angularly dependent eigenfunctions explicitly, by making use of some general theorems about the angular momentum. These theorems state: 1. The components and the absolute value of the total angular momentum of an electron in any central force field are constants of the motion. 2. The eigenvalues belonging to the square of the total angular momentum are equal to $l(l+1)$, where l is an integer. 3. The eigenvalues of the components in a fixed direction are equal to m, where m can assume all integral values from $-l$ to $+l$. 4. A quantum state is defined by specifying the magnitude and one of the components of the total angular momentum, i.e., by specifying l and m. Thus, by means of the generally valid formula (1.11) one can arrive at once at the differential equation for the radially dependent eigenfunction

$$\frac{d^2 R}{dr^2} + \frac{2}{r}\frac{dR}{dr} + 2\left(E + \frac{Z}{r}\right)R - \frac{l(l+1)}{r^2}R = 0, \tag{1.12}$$

which is identical with the left side of (1.4).

Before solving this equation, we shall calculate the matrix elements of the angular momenta k_x and k_y about the directions perendicular to the z-axis. By definition

$$\left.\begin{aligned} k_x &= -i\left(y\frac{\partial}{\partial z} - z\frac{\partial}{\partial y}\right) = i\sin\varphi\frac{\partial}{\partial\vartheta} + i\cot\vartheta\cos\varphi\frac{\partial}{\partial\varphi},\\ k_y &= -i\left(z\frac{\partial}{\partial x} - x\frac{\partial}{\partial z}\right) = -i\cos\varphi\frac{\partial}{\partial\vartheta} + i\cot\vartheta\sin\varphi\frac{\partial}{\partial\varphi}.\end{aligned}\right\} \tag{1.13}$$

Thus, in view of formulas (A. 25) and (A. 26) of our appendix,

$$\begin{aligned}(k_x + i k_y)\,Y_{lm}(\vartheta,\varphi) &= e^{i\varphi}\left(\frac{\partial}{\partial\vartheta} + i\cot\vartheta\frac{\partial}{\partial\varphi}\right)Y_{lm}(\vartheta,\varphi)\\ &= -\sqrt{(l-m)(l+m+1)}\,Y_{l,m+1}(\vartheta,\varphi),\\ (k_x - i k_y)\,Y_{lm}(\vartheta,\varphi) &= -e^{-i\varphi}\left(\frac{\partial}{\partial\vartheta} - i\cot\vartheta\frac{\partial}{\partial\varphi}\right)Y_{lm}(\vartheta,\varphi)\\ &= -\sqrt{(l+m)(l-m+1)}\,Y_{l,m-1}(\vartheta,\varphi),\end{aligned}$$

and the matrix elements of the components of the angular monentum become

$$\left.\begin{aligned}(m\,|\,k_x + i k_y\,|\,m-1) &= \int Y^*_{lm}(\vartheta,\varphi)\,(k_x + i k_y)\,Y_{l,m-1}(\vartheta,\varphi)\sin\vartheta\,d\vartheta\,d\varphi\\ &= -\sqrt{(l+m)(l-m+1)} = (m-1\,|\,k_x - i k_y\,|\,m).\end{aligned}\right\} \tag{1.14}$$

The matrix elements which correspond to transitions between states of different orbital quantum numbers or of different radially dependent eigenfunctions are zero. As is well known, the formulas (1.14), except for an indeterminancy in the sign of the square root, can be obtained from the general theory (ref. [3] of the bibliography).

We discuss finally the *parity* of our wave functions: For a one-electron atom the parity operation consists simply in the replacement of the position vector $\boldsymbol{r}$ of the electron by $-\boldsymbol{r}$. In spherical polar coordinates this means replacing (ϑ, φ) by $(\pi-\vartheta, \pi+\varphi)$. It follows from the properties of spherical harmonics, given in our appendix, that

$$Y_{lm}(\pi-\vartheta, \pi+\varphi) = (-1)^l Y_{lm}(\vartheta, \varphi). \tag{1.15}$$

For even l, then, our wave functions are unaffected by the parity operation and we say "the parity is even". For odd l, the wave functions change sign under the parity operation and "the parity is odd".

2. Derivation of BALMER's formula[1]. We shall now treat the differential equation satisfied by the radially dependent part of the eigenfunction

$$\frac{d^2R}{dr^2} + \frac{2}{r}\frac{dR}{dr} + \left[2E + \frac{2Z}{r} - \frac{l(l+1)}{r^2}\right] R = 0. \tag{2.1}$$

The last term in the above equation corresponds classically to the centrifugal force of the electron and increases with increasing angular momentum.

Let us begin by assuming that the energy E is negative. Since the potential energy vanishes at infinity, a negative energy corresponds to a bound electron which possesses a positive kinetic energy only by virtue of the nuclear attraction.

First, we study the asymptotic behavior by neglecting the terms in r which are of lower power compared to the ones that are kept, then

$$\frac{d^2R}{dr^2} + 2ER = 0, \qquad R = e^{\pm\sqrt{-2E}\,r}. \tag{2.2}$$

If $R(\infty)$ is to remain finite, we must select the minus sign. We introduce the notation

$$\varepsilon = +\sqrt{-2E} \tag{2.3}$$

and extend the asymptotic solution (2.2) to a solution valid for all r by putting

$$R = e^{-\varepsilon r} f(r), \tag{2.4}$$

where $f(r)$ is a function which varies slowly at infinity. Substitution of (2.4) into (2.1) results in a differential equation in f

$$f'' + 2\left(\frac{1}{r} - \varepsilon\right) f' + \left[2\left(\frac{Z-\varepsilon}{r}\right) - \frac{l(l+1)}{r^2}\right] f = 0. \tag{2.5}$$

Let us expand f in a power series,

$$f = r^\lambda \sum_{\nu=0}^{\infty} a_\nu r^\nu. \tag{2.6}$$

Substitution of (2.6) into (2.5) results in

$$\sum_{\nu=0}^{\infty} a_\nu \left[\left((\lambda+\nu)(\lambda+\nu+1) - l(l+1)\right) r^{\lambda+\nu-2} - 2\left(\varepsilon(\lambda+\nu+1) - Z\right) r^{\lambda+\nu-1}\right] = 0. \tag{2.7}$$

The coefficient of each power of r must vanish in the above equation. Setting the coefficient or $r^{\lambda-2}$ (the term of lowest power in r) equal to zero, one obtains an equation which determines λ:

$$\lambda(\lambda+1) = l(l+1),$$

---

[1] Compare, for example, ref. [7], A. SOMMERFELD, Wellenmechanischer Ergänzungsband, p. 70 and the original work of E. SCHRÖDINGER, Abhandlungen zur Wellenmechanik, p. 1.

from which

$$\lambda = \begin{cases} +l \\ -l-1. \end{cases} \tag{2.8}$$

The condition that f remain finite at $r=0$ forces one to the choice $\lambda = l$. Setting the coefficient of $r^{\lambda+\nu-2}$ equal to zero one obtains the recursion formula

$$a_\nu = 2a_{\nu-1} \frac{\varepsilon(l+\nu) - Z}{(l+\nu)(l+\nu+1) - l(l+1)}. \tag{2.9}$$

Next, we require that f be a polynomial in r, i.e., that the power series terminate, $a_{n-l-1} r^{n-1}$, say, being the last term. Then

$$a_{n-l} = 0.$$

This condition will be fulfilled if

$$\varepsilon = \frac{Z}{n}, \tag{2.10}$$

$$E = -\frac{1}{2}\frac{Z^2}{n^2}. \tag{2.11}$$

If the above requirement were not made, then for large values of ν:

$$a_\nu \approx \frac{2a_{\nu-1}\varepsilon}{l+\nu+1} \approx c\frac{(2\varepsilon)^{l+\nu+1}}{(l+\nu+1)!},$$

where c is a constant; $f(r)$ would behave as $e^{2\varepsilon r}$ for large r and $R = e^{-\varepsilon r} f(r)$ would increase as $e^{+\varepsilon r}$. Therefore, the breaking off of the series is necessary to assure that the eigenfunction be bounded at infinity.

(2.11) is the well-known BALMER formula for the discrete energy levels of hydrogen ($Z=1$) and for the ions having a single electron, such as He^+, Li^{++} etc. n is the principal quantum number. The energy does not depend on the other two quantum numbers m and l. The independence of the magnetic quantum number m has its origin in the fact that all directions in space enter on equal terms. This holds for all atoms in the absence of an external field and is called directional degeneracy. On the other hand, the fact that the energy is independent of the quantum number l is a special property of the hydrogen atom which must be attributed to the presence of the exact COULOMB potential Z/r. This degeneracy has the consequence that the hydrogen atom is particularly strongly influenced by external fields (first-order STARK effect instead of the usual second-order effect[1]).

The energy formula (2.11) has been verified to an extraordinary degree by spectroscopic measurements. The spectral line emitted in a transition of the atom from quantum state n to state n' has a frequency

$$\nu = \frac{1}{2\pi}(E_n - E_{n'}) = \frac{Z^2}{4\pi}\left(\frac{1}{n'^2} - \frac{1}{n^2}\right) \tag{2.12}$$

in atomic units[2], and is equal to

$$Z^2\left(\frac{1}{n'^2} - \frac{1}{n^2}\right) \mathrm{Ry}, \tag{2.13}$$

[1] The alkali atoms which are more closely related to hydrogen than any other atoms do not show this degeneracy. To be sure, the discrete energy levels of the alkali atoms can be calculated to a good approximation by considering only the motion of the valence electron in the field arising from a charge distribution of closed shells, but this field is a non-Coulomb central field and levels of like n and different l have entirely different energies.

[2] It should be noted that the atomic unit of action is $\hbar = h/2\pi$ and not h. The frequency of the spectral line may be obtained in c.g.s. units by dividing the energy difference (in c.g.s. units) between the initial and final states by h; or, if the energy difference is expressed in atomic units, by dividing by 2π.

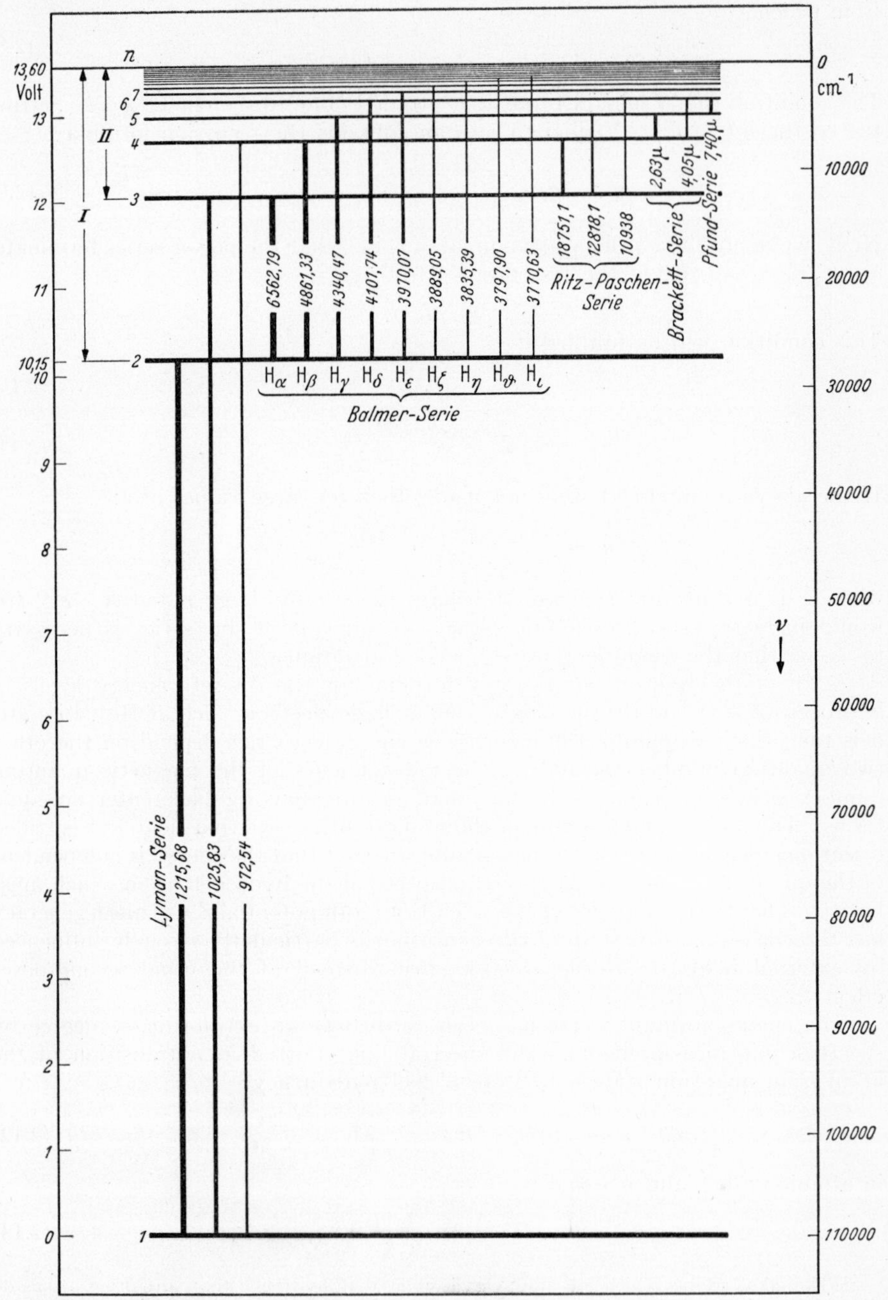

Fig. 2. The energy level scheme of hydrogen (both the energies in electron volts and the corresponding wave numbers in cm^{-1} are given).

where the RYDBERG frequency Ry was defined in the Introduction. The term scheme of hydrogen is shown in Fig. 2. The LYMAN, BALMER, PASCHEN, and BRACKET series, which have lowest levels corresponding respectively to the quantum numbers $n' = 1, 2, 3, 4$, are shown in Fig. 3. Figs. 2 and 3 are taken from

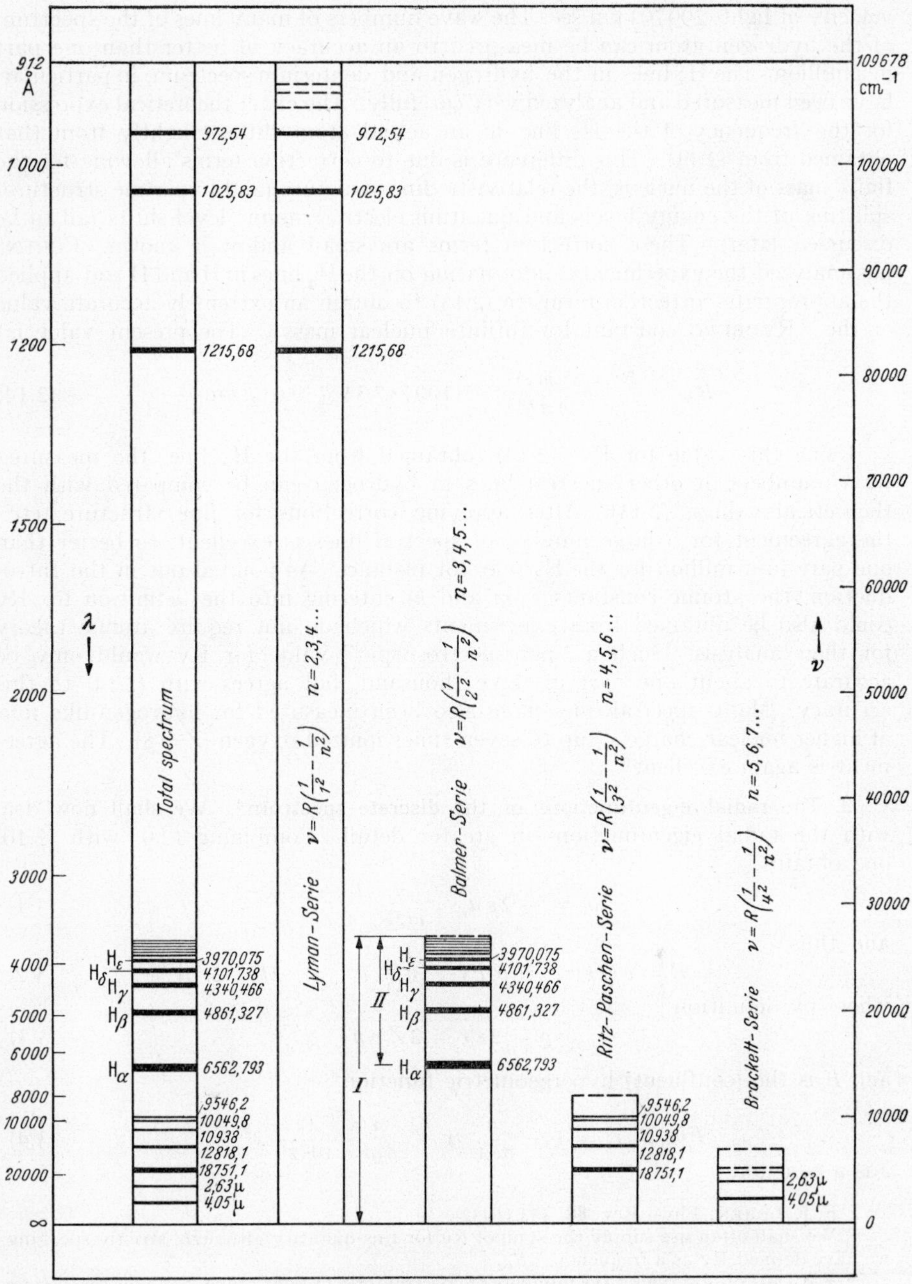

Fig. 3. The spectral lines of the hydrogen spectrum (the height of a line is proportional to its frequency, the number written next to a line is its wave length in ÅNGSTRÖM units).

GROTRIAN'S book "Graphische Darstellung der Spektren von Atomen und Ionen". It is apparent that the lines in the LYMAN series are more densely spaced than the lines in the higher series.

Usually, instead of its frequency ν, the wave number (inverse of the wave-length) of a spectral line is measured, which is simply (ν/c), where c is the velocity of light, 299793 km/sec. The wave numbers of many lines of the spectrum of the hydrogen atom can be measured to an accuracy of better than one part in a million. The H_α lines in the hydrogen and deuterium spectrum, in particular, have been measured and analyzed very carefully. The exact theoretical expression for the frequency of the H_α line in an actual atom differs slightly from that obtained from (2.13). This difference is due to correction terms allowing for the finite mass of the nucleus, the relativistic fine structure (and hyperfine structure) splitting of the energy levels and quantum electrodynamic level shifts (all to be discussed later). These correction terms are small and well known. COHEN[1] has analyzed the experimental information on the H_α lines in H and D and applied the appropriate correction terms to (2.13) to obtain an extremely accurate value or the "RYDBERG constant for infinite nuclear mass". The present value is[2]

$$R_\infty = \frac{\mathrm{Ry}}{c} = \frac{m e^4}{4\pi \hbar^3 c} = (109737.31 \pm 0.01_2)\ \mathrm{cm}^{-1}. \tag{2.14}$$

Using this value for Ry, (2.14), obtained from the H_α line, the measured wave numbers of other spectral lines in hydrogen can be compared with the theoretical values, (2.13). After applying corrections for fine structure, etc., the agreement for a large number of spectral lines is excellent, to better than one part in a million for the H_β line, for instance. As pointed out in the Introduction, the atomic constants e, m and h, entering into the definition for Ry could also be obtained from experiments which do not require atomic theory for their analysis. Such a "non-spectroscopic" value for Ry would only be accurate to about one part in three thousand, but agrees with (2.14) to this accuracy. Many spectral lines have also been measured for hydrogen-like ions of higher nuclear charge Z, up to seven-times ionized oxygen ($Z=8$). The agreement is again excellent[3].

3. The radial eigenfunctions of the discrete spectrum[4]. We shall now deal with the radial eigenfunctions in greater detail. Combining (2.9) with (2.10) one obtains

$$a_\nu = -2\varepsilon\, a_{\nu-1} \frac{n-l-\nu}{\nu(2l+1+\nu)}, \tag{3.1}$$

and thus

$$R = c\,(2\varepsilon)^{\frac{3}{2}} e^{-\frac{1}{2}\varrho} \varrho^l F(-(n-l-1),\ 2l+2,\ \varrho), \tag{3.2}$$ [5]

where by definition

$$\varrho = 2\varepsilon r = 2Z r/n \tag{3.3}$$

and F is the (confluent) hypergeometric function[6]

$$F(\alpha,\beta,x) = 1 + \frac{\alpha}{\beta\cdot 1!}x + \frac{\alpha(\alpha+1)}{\beta(\beta+1)\cdot 2!}x^2 + \cdots \tag{3.4}$$

c is a constant.

---

[1] E. R. COHEN: Phys. Rev. **88**, 353 (1952).

[2] We shall often use simply the symbol Ry for this quantity although, strictly speaking, we have defined Ry as a frequency, $c R_\infty$.

[3] For a list of observed wave numbers of spectral lines in light atoms and ions see: Atomic Energy Levels, Vol. 1, U.S. National Bureau of Standards, Circular 467, 1949.

[4] Cf. W. GORDON: Ann. d. Phys. **2**, 1031 (1929).

[5] The numerical factor $(2\varepsilon)^{\frac{3}{2}}$ is included only for the sake of convenience in later calculations.

[6] For properties of the confluent hypergeometric function see ref. [*8*], Chap. 16 or the article of J. MEIXNER, Vol. I of this Encyclopedia. We shall in general omit the word "confluent". We shall use the more general function $F(\alpha,\beta,\gamma,x)$ very rarely and will call it the "*general* hypergeometric function".

The radial eigenfunctions can also be expressed in terms of the associated LAGUERRE functions, which are defined by means of the relations[1]

$$L_\lambda^\mu = \frac{d^\mu}{d\varrho^\mu} L_\lambda(\varrho); \qquad L_\lambda(\varrho) = e^\varrho \frac{d^\lambda}{d\varrho^\lambda}(e^{-\varrho}\varrho^\lambda). \tag{3.5}$$

This may be seen by carrying out the indicated differentiations; then

$$L_\lambda(\varrho) = \sum_{\alpha=0}^{\lambda} (-1)^\alpha \binom{\lambda}{\alpha} \frac{\lambda!}{\alpha!} \varrho^\alpha, \tag{3.6}$$

$$L_\lambda^\mu(\varrho) = (-)^\mu \lambda! \sum_{\alpha=0}^{\lambda-\mu} \binom{\lambda}{\mu+\alpha} \frac{(-\varrho)^\alpha}{\alpha!} = (-)^\mu \lambda! \binom{\lambda}{\mu} F(-(\lambda-\mu), \mu+1, \varrho). \tag{3.7}$$

On comparison with (3.2) one finds that

$$R = -c \frac{(2\varepsilon)^{\frac{3}{2}}}{(n+l)!^2} (2l+1)!\,(n-l-1)!\, e^{-\frac{1}{2}\varrho} \varrho^l L_{n+l}^{2l+1}(\varrho). \tag{3.8}$$

Naturally, one can also prove directly that (3.8) satisfies the differential Eq. (2.1).

Next, we require that the eigenfunction be normalized according to the rule

$$\int R^2 r^2\, dr = 1, \tag{3.9}$$

i.e.,

$$\frac{c^2 (2l+1)!^2 (n-l-1)!^2}{(n+l)!^4} \int e^{-\varrho} \varrho^{2l+2} \left(L_{n+l}^{2l+1}(\varrho)\right)^2 d\varrho = 1. \tag{3.10}$$

R is now the normalized eigenfunction.

α) Evaluation of integrals over LAGUERRE *functions*[2]. Instead of evaluating (3.10), we evaluate the more general integral:

$$J_{\lambda\mu}^{(\sigma)} = \frac{1}{\lambda!^2} \int_0^\infty e^{-\varrho} \varrho^{\mu+\sigma} [L_\lambda^\mu(\varrho)]^2\, d\varrho. \tag{3.11}$$

For this purpose we substitute the representation (3.5) for one of the LAGUERRE functions:

$$\lambda!^2 J_{\lambda\mu}^{(\sigma)} = \int_0^\infty e^{-\varrho} \varrho^{\mu+\sigma} L_\lambda^\mu(\varrho) \frac{d^\mu}{d\varrho^\mu} \left[e^\varrho \frac{d^\lambda}{d\varrho^\lambda} (\varrho^\lambda e^{-\varrho})\right] d\varrho.$$

Integrating by parts μ times with respect to ϱ one obtains

$$\left.\begin{aligned} \lambda!^2 J_{\lambda\mu}^{(\sigma)} = \sum_{\beta=0}^{\mu-1} \Big| (-1)^\beta \frac{d^{\mu-\beta-1}}{d\varrho^{\mu-\beta-1}} \left(e^\varrho \frac{d^\lambda}{d\varrho^\lambda} (\varrho^\lambda e^{-\varrho})\right) \frac{d^\beta}{d\varrho^\beta} \left(e^{-\varrho} \varrho^{\mu+\sigma} L_\lambda^\mu(\varrho)\right) \Big|_0^\infty + \\ + (-1)^\mu \int_0^\infty e^\varrho \frac{d^\lambda}{d\varrho^\lambda} (\varrho^\lambda e^{-\varrho}) \frac{d^\mu}{d\varrho^\mu} \left(\varrho^{\mu+\sigma} e^{-\varrho} L_\lambda^\mu(\varrho)\right) d\varrho. \end{aligned}\right\} \tag{3.12}$$

We must now distinguish between two cases:

1. If σ is non-negative, then the integrated part goes to zero at least as fast as ϱ at the lower limit and at least as fast as $e^{-\varrho}$ at the upper limit. Thus, we are

[1] Cf., for example, A. SOMMERFELD and G. SCHUR, Ann. d. Phys. **4**, 409 (1930).

[2] Special cases treated, for example, by E. SCHRÖDINGER, Abhandlung zur Wellenmechanik, p. 133; I. WALLER, Z. Physik **38**, 635 (1926); L. PAULING, Proc. Roy. Soc. Lond., Ser. A **114**, 185 (1927).

left with the evaluation of the integral. We proceed by replacing the LAGUERRE function with its power series expansion (3.7) and then carry out the μ fold differentiation:

$$J_{\lambda\mu}^{(\sigma)} = \frac{1}{\lambda!}\int_0^\infty \frac{d^\lambda}{d\varrho^\lambda}(\varrho^\lambda e^{-\varrho}) \sum_{\alpha=0}^{\lambda-\mu} \binom{\lambda}{\mu+\alpha} \frac{(-)^\alpha}{\alpha!} \sum_{\gamma=0}^{\mu} (-)^\gamma \binom{\mu}{\gamma} \frac{(\mu+\sigma+\alpha)!}{(\gamma+\sigma+\alpha)!}\, \varrho^{\gamma+\sigma+\alpha}.$$

Integrating by parts λ more times results in

$$J_{\lambda\mu}^{(\sigma)} = (-)^\lambda \frac{(\mu+\sigma)!}{\lambda!}\int_0^\infty \varrho^\lambda e^{-\varrho}\, d\varrho \sum_{\alpha=0}^{\lambda-\mu}(-)^\alpha \binom{\mu+\sigma+\alpha}{\alpha}\binom{\lambda}{\mu+\alpha} \sum_{\gamma=\lambda-\sigma-\alpha}^{\mu} (-)^\gamma \frac{\varrho^{\gamma+\sigma+\alpha-\lambda}}{(\gamma+\sigma+\alpha-\lambda)!}\binom{\mu}{\gamma},$$

the factor $\varrho^\lambda e^{-\varrho}$ assuring the vanishing of the integrated parts. A final integration with respect to ϱ gives

$$J_{\lambda\mu}^{(\sigma)} = (-)^\lambda (\mu+\sigma)! \sum_{\alpha=0}^{\lambda-\mu} (-)^\alpha \binom{\mu+\sigma+\alpha}{\alpha}\binom{\lambda}{\mu+\alpha} \sum_{\gamma=\lambda-\sigma-\alpha}^{\mu} (-)^\gamma \binom{\mu}{\gamma}\binom{\gamma+\sigma+\alpha}{\lambda}.$$

The summation over γ can be accomplished by elementary means and gives

$$(-1)^\mu \binom{\sigma+\alpha}{\lambda-\mu}.$$

Introducing the notation $\beta = \alpha - \lambda + \mu + \sigma$ one finally gets

$$J_{\lambda\mu}^{(\sigma)} = (-)^\sigma \frac{\lambda!}{(\lambda-\mu)!}\,\sigma! \sum_{\beta=0}^{\sigma} (-)^\beta \binom{\sigma}{\beta}\binom{\lambda+\beta}{\sigma}\binom{\lambda+\beta-\mu}{\sigma}. \tag{3.13}$$

2. For negative σ the reverse is true. The integral vanishes, as is evident from (3.13), and the integrated terms make non-zero contributions at the lower limits (the upper limits still go to zero exponentionally). By means of (3.7) one obtains

$$\frac{d^{\mu-\beta-1}}{d\varrho^{\mu-\beta-1}}\left(e^\varrho \frac{d^\lambda}{d\varrho^\lambda}(\varrho^\lambda e^{-\varrho})\right)_{\varrho=0} = L_\lambda^{\mu-\beta-1}(0) = (-)^{\mu-\beta-1}\lambda!\binom{\lambda}{\mu-\beta-1},$$

$$\frac{d^\beta}{d\varrho^\beta}(e^{-\varrho}\varrho^{\mu+\sigma} L_\lambda^\mu)_{\varrho=0} = \lambda!\,(-)^{\beta-\sigma}\sum_{\alpha=0}^{\lambda-\mu}\binom{\beta}{\alpha+\mu+\sigma}\binom{\lambda}{\mu+\alpha}\frac{(\alpha+\mu+\sigma)!}{\alpha!}.$$

Substitution into (3.12) gives

$$J_{\lambda\mu}^{(\sigma)} = \sum_{\alpha=0}^{\lambda-\mu}\binom{\lambda}{\mu+\alpha}\frac{(\alpha+\mu+\sigma)!}{\alpha!}\sum_{\beta=1}^{\mu-1}\binom{\lambda}{\mu-\beta-1}(-)^{\mu-\beta-\sigma}\binom{\beta}{\mu+\sigma+\alpha}.$$

The summation over β can be accomplished by elementary means and gives

$$(-)^\alpha \binom{\lambda-\mu-(\alpha+\sigma+1)}{-(\alpha+\sigma+1)}.$$

Putting $-(\sigma+1) = s$ and $s-\alpha=\gamma$ one finally gets

$$J_{\lambda\mu}^{(\sigma)} = \frac{\lambda!}{(\lambda-\mu)!\,(s+1)!}\sum_{\gamma=0}^{s}(-)^{s-\gamma}\frac{\binom{s}{\gamma}\binom{\lambda-\mu+\gamma}{s}}{\binom{\mu+s-\gamma}{s+1}},\ (\sigma = -(1+s) \leq -1). \tag{3.14}$$

β) Discussion of the normalized eigenfunctions. The normalization integral (3.10) can now be evaluated by setting $\lambda = n + l$, $\mu = 2l + 1$ and $\sigma = 1$ in formula (3.13):

$$J^{(1)}_{n+l,\,2l+1} = \frac{(n+l)!}{(n-l-1)!} \cdot 2n; \qquad c = \sqrt{\frac{(n+l)!}{(n-l-1)! \cdot 2n}} \cdot \frac{1}{(2l+1)!}. \tag{3.15}$$

Thus, the normalized eigenfunction [cf. (3.2), (3.8), (3.10)] becomes:

$$R_{nl}(r) = -\frac{(n-l-1)!^{\frac{1}{2}}}{(n+l)!^{\frac{3}{2}}\,(2n)^{\frac{1}{2}}} \left(\frac{2Z}{n}\right)^{\frac{3}{2}} e^{-\frac{Zr}{n}} \left(\frac{2Zr}{n}\right)^{l} L^{2l+1}_{n+l}\left(\frac{2Zr}{n}\right) \tag{3.16}$$

$$= \frac{1}{(2l+1)!}\sqrt{\frac{(n+l)!}{(n-l-1)!\,2n}} \cdot \left(\frac{2Z}{n}\right)^{\frac{3}{2}} e^{-\frac{Zr}{n}} \left(\frac{2Zr}{n}\right)^{l} F\left(-(n-l-1),\, 2l+2,\, \frac{2Zr}{n}\right). \tag{3.17}$$

We write down explicit expressions for the first few radial eigenfunctions of hydrogen $(Z = 1)$:

$$\left.\begin{aligned}
R_{10} &= 2e^{-r},\\
R_{20} &= \frac{1}{\sqrt{2}}\, e^{-\frac{1}{2}r}\left(1 - \frac{1}{2}r\right),\\
R_{21} &= \frac{1}{2\sqrt{6}}\, e^{-\frac{1}{2}r}\, r,\\
R_{30} &= \frac{2}{3\sqrt{3}}\, e^{-\frac{1}{3}r}\left(1 - \frac{2}{3}r + \frac{2}{27}r^2\right),\\
R_{31} &= \frac{8}{27\sqrt{6}}\, e^{-\frac{1}{3}r}\, r\left(1 - \frac{1}{6}r\right),\\
R_{32} &= \frac{4}{81\sqrt{30}}\, e^{-\frac{1}{3}r}\, r^2,\\
R_{40} &= \frac{1}{4}\, e^{-\frac{1}{4}r}\left(1 - \frac{3}{4}r + \frac{1}{8}r^2 - \frac{1}{192}r^3\right),\\
R_{41} &= \frac{1}{16}\sqrt{\frac{5}{3}}\, e^{-\frac{1}{4}r}\, r\left(1 - \frac{1}{4}r + \frac{1}{80}r^2\right),\\
R_{42} &= \frac{1}{64\sqrt{5}}\, e^{-\frac{1}{4}r}\, r^2\left(1 - \frac{1}{12}r\right),\\
R_{43} &= \frac{1}{768\sqrt{35}}\, e^{-\frac{1}{4}r}\, r^3.
\end{aligned}\right\} \tag{3.18}$$

A few of the eigenfunctions are graphed as functions of ϱ in Fig. 4. Fig. 5 represents the charge distributions corresponding to these eigenfunctions. We have plotted $r^2 R^2_{nl}(r)$ as a function of r, i.e. the probability that the electron be found in the spherical shell between r and $r + dr$. It is apparent that the maximum charge density recedes from the nucleus with increasing principal quantum number n. For eigenfunctions which have the same n, the one with lowest l has the largest amplitude in the neighborhood of the nucleus. The radial eigenfunction has $n - l - 1$ zeros, and thus the complete eigenfunction

$$u = R_{nl}(r)\, \mathcal{P}_{lm}(\cos\vartheta) \frac{\cos}{\sin} m\varphi$$

has $n - 1$ nodal surfaces of which $n - l - 1$ are concentric spheres (r = const), $l - m$ are cones (ϑ = const) with common apex at the origin, and m are planes

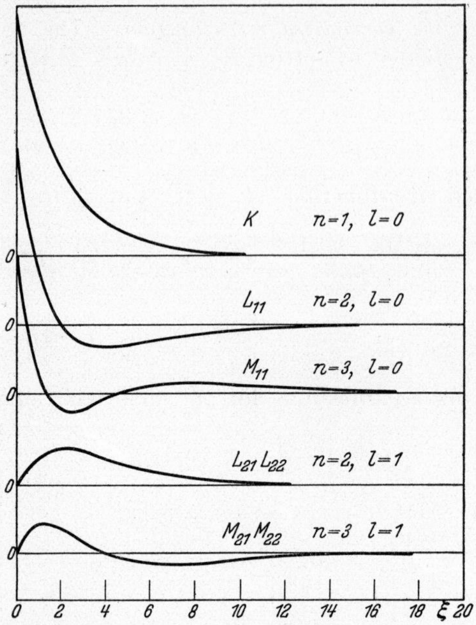

Fig. 4. The radial eigenfunctions (according to PAULING). The abscissa is $\varrho = 2r/n$, the ordinate is $n R_{nl}(r)$. The symbols K, etc. refer to the corresponding X-ray levels (in X-ray terminology the symbols L_{11}, L_{21}, L_{22} are usually replaced by L_{I}, L_{II}, L_{III}).

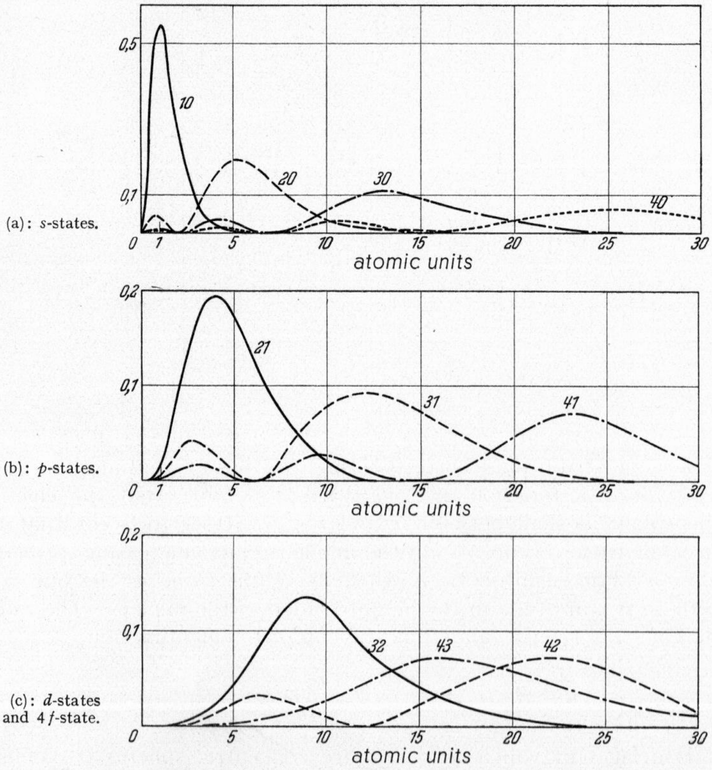

Fig. 5 a—c. The charge distribution in the first few states of the hydrogen atom. The abscissa is r in atomic units, the ordinate is the charge density $r^2 R_{nl}^2(r)$. The curves are labelled with the corresponding nl values (s-states in Fig. 5a, p-states in Fig. 5b and d- and f-states in Fig. 5c).

through the origin ($\varphi = \text{const}$)[1]. A particularly beautiful pictorial representation of the charge distribution in the various states of hydrogen is afforded by the silhouettes of WHITE[2].

γ) Mean values of powers of r. The differences between the various radial eigenfunctions become particularly apparent when we form the mean value of r, the distance between electron and nucleus, raised to various powers. The mean value $\overline{r^\nu}$ is given by

$$\overline{r^\nu} = \frac{\int r^\nu \psi_{nl}^2 r^2 \, dr}{\int \psi_{nl}^2 r^2 dr} = \left(\frac{n}{2Z}\right)^\nu \overline{\varrho^\nu} = \left(\frac{n}{2Z}\right)^\nu \frac{J_{n+l,\,2l+1}^{(\nu+1)}}{J_{n+l,\,2l+1}^{(1)}}\,, \tag{3.19}$$

in which $J_{\lambda\mu}^{(\sigma)}$ is the quantity given in (3.13) and (3.14). Assigning particular values to the indices results in the explicit formulas

$$\overline{r} = \frac{n}{2Z}\overline{\varrho} = \frac{1}{2Z}\left[3n^2 - l(l+1)\right], \tag{3.20}$$

$$\overline{r^2} = \frac{n^2}{2Z^2}\left[5n^2 + 1 - 3l(l+1)\right], \tag{3.21}$$

$$\overline{r^3} = \frac{n^2}{8Z^3}\left[35n^2(n^2-1) - 30n^2(l+2)(l-1) + 3(l+2)(l+1)\,l(l-1)\right], \tag{3.22}$$

$$\overline{r^4} = \frac{n^4}{8Z^4}\left[63n^4 - 35n^2(2l^2+2l-3) + 5l(l+1)(3l^2+3l-10) + 12\right], \tag{3.23}$$

$$\overline{r^{-1}} = \frac{Z}{n^2}\,, \tag{3.24}$$

$$\overline{r^{-2}} = \frac{Z^2}{n^3(l+\frac{1}{2})}\,, \tag{3.25}$$

$$\overline{r^{-3}} = \frac{Z^3}{n^3(l+1)(l+\frac{1}{2})\,l}\,, \tag{3.26}$$

$$\overline{r^{-4}} = \frac{Z^4 \cdot \frac{1}{2} \cdot \left[3n^2 - l(l+1)\right]}{n^5(l+\frac{3}{2})(l+1)(l+\frac{1}{2})\,l(l-\frac{1}{2})}\,. \tag{3.27}$$

The mean values for the first few states of hydrogen are given in Table 1.

Table 1. *Numerical values for the expectation values of r^ν.*

	$n=1$	$n=2$		$n=3$			$n=4$			
	$l=0$	$l=0$	$l=1$	$l=0$	$l=1$	$l=2$	$l=0$	$l=1$	$l=2$	$l=3$
$\nu=1$	$1\frac{1}{2}$	6	5	$13\frac{1}{2}$	$12\frac{1}{2}$	$10\frac{1}{2}$	24	23	21	18
2	3	42	30	207	180	126	648	600	504	360
3	$7\frac{1}{2}$	330	210	$3442\frac{1}{2}$	2835	1701	18720	16800	13104	7920
4	$22\frac{1}{2}$	2880	1680	$61357\frac{1}{2}$	49005	25515	570240	497280	362880	190080
−1	1	$\frac{1}{4}$		$\frac{1}{9}$			$\frac{1}{16}$			
−2	2	$\frac{1}{4}$	$\frac{1}{12}$	$\frac{2}{27}$	$\frac{2}{81}$	$\frac{2}{135}$	$\frac{1}{32}$	$\frac{1}{96}$	$\frac{1}{160}$	$\frac{1}{224}$
−3	∞	∞	$\frac{1}{24}$	∞	$\frac{1}{81}$	$\frac{1}{405}$	∞	$\frac{1}{192}$	$\frac{1}{960}$	$\frac{1}{2688}$
−4	∞	∞	$\frac{1}{24}$	∞	$\frac{10}{729}$	$\frac{2}{3645}$	∞	$\frac{23}{3840}$	$\frac{1}{3840}$	$\frac{1}{26880}$

[1] Cf. Sect. 1.
[2] H. E. WHITE: Phys. Rev. **37**, 1416 (1931).

The mean values of r raised to positive powers ν are determined essentially by the principal quantum number n, while for the mean values of r raised to negative powers ν (for $\nu < -1$) the orbital quantum number l becomes decisive. This is readily explained. For positive powers the important contributions to the integral come from the large values of r for which the eigenfunction behaves like $\varrho^{n-1} e^{-\varrho}$; for small r, important for negative powers, the eigenfunction behaves like ϱ^l. In terms of a picture this means that the probability of finding the electron at a large distance from the nucleus is essentially the same for both the circular ($l = n-1$) and the eccentric elliptical (small l) BOHR orbits. For fixed n the electron will be found more frequently in the immediate vicinity of the nucleus if its quantum state corresponds to an eccentric orbit than if its quantum state corresponds to a circular orbit. (It is even possible for $\overline{r^\nu}$ to diverge, as indeed happens if $\nu < -2l-2$; the mean value then becomes meaningless.)

The quantum mechanical analogue to BOHR orbits of large eccentricity (small l) is a large mean square deviation of the nucleus-electron separation:

$$\overline{(r-\bar{r})^2} = \overline{r^2} - \bar{r}^2 = \frac{n^2(n^2+2) - l^2(l+1)^2}{4Z^2}. \tag{3.28}$$

For example

$$\overline{r^2} - \bar{r}^2 = \begin{cases} \dfrac{n^2(n^2+2)}{4Z^2} & \text{for} \quad l = 0, \\[2ex] \dfrac{n^2(2n+1)}{4Z^2} & \text{for} \quad l = n-1. \end{cases}$$

As can be seen from (3.24) the expression for the mean value of r^{-1} is particularly simple. By means of it we can readily verify the well-known virial theorem[1] which states that the mean value of the potential energy $V = -\frac{Z}{r}$ is equal to twice the total energy. Thus,

$$\overline{V} = -Z\overline{r^{-1}} = -\frac{Z^2}{n^2} = 2E \qquad [\text{cf. } (2.11)]. \tag{3.29}$$

δ) Behavior of the eigenfunctions for large principal quantum number. WENTZEL-KRAMERS-BRILLOUIN *(WKB) method.* Aside from normalization, all eigenfunctions of a fixed orbital quantum number l and different principal quantum number n behave alike near the nucleus, provided $n \gg l$. This may be seen by neglecting l relative to n in formula (3.17), thus,

$$\left.\begin{aligned} R_{nl} &\approx \frac{n^l}{(2l+1)!\sqrt{2}}\left(\frac{2Z}{n}\right)^{\frac{3}{2}}\left(\frac{2Zr}{n}\right)^l e^{-\frac{Zr}{n}}\left[1 - \frac{n-l-1}{2l+2}\cdot\frac{2rZ}{n} + \frac{(n-l-1)(n-l-2)}{(2l+2)(2l+3)\,2!}\left(\frac{2rZ}{n}\right)^2 + \cdots\right] \\ &\approx 2\left(\frac{Z}{n}\right)^{\frac{3}{2}} \frac{(2Zr)^l}{(2l+1)!}\left[1 - \frac{2rZ}{2l+2} + \frac{(2rZ)^2}{(2l+2)(2l+3)\cdot 2!} - \cdots\right], \end{aligned}\right\} \tag{3.30}$$

or it can be seen, even more simply, directly from SCHRÖDINGER'S Eq. (2.1). If n is very large and r is of order 1 (more precisely, if $r \ll n^2/Z$), the energy $1/2n^2$ can obviously be neglected compared to $1/r$ and $l(l+1)/r^2$. Then (2.1) goes over into

$$\frac{d^2R}{dr^2} + \frac{2}{r}\frac{dR}{dr} + \left(\frac{2Z}{r} - \frac{l(l+1)}{r^2}\right)R = 0. \tag{3.31}$$

Since the differential Eq. (3.31) no longer contains n, its solution will also be independent of n. Its solution is

$$R_{\infty l} = \frac{c}{\sqrt{2Zr}} J_{2l+1}\left(\sqrt{8Zr}\right), \tag{3.32}$$

[1] Cf. A. SOMMERFELD: Wellenmechanischer Ergänzungsband, p. 292, ref. [7]; see also our Sect. 36ε.

where J_{2l+1} is the BESSEL function[1] of order $2l+1$ and c is a constant. If the power series expansion for J is used in (3.32), then the expansion (3.30) for R is again obtained. Using the asymptotic formula for the BESSEL function one obtains a solution valid for large r

$$R_{\infty l} = \frac{c}{(2Zr)^{\frac{3}{4}}\sqrt{\pi}} \cdot \cos\left(\sqrt{8Zr} - \frac{\pi}{4} - \frac{2l+1}{2}\pi\right). \tag{3.33}$$

One must be sure, however, that $r \ll n^2/Z$ (but $8Zr \gg 1$).

A useful approximate formula for the radial eigenfunction may be obtained by means of the WKB method when r becomes comparable to n^2/Z (cf. Sect. 53). First, we must get rid of the first derivative in Eq. (2.1). For this purpose we introduce $v = Rr$ in place of R. v satisfies the equation

$$\frac{d^2 v}{dr^2} + \left[-\frac{Z^2}{n^2} + \frac{2Z}{r} - \frac{l(l+1)}{r^2}\right] v = 0. \tag{3.34}$$

The coefficient of v represents the kinetic energy of the electron and is positive for $r_1 < r < r_2$, where

$$r_{1,2} = \frac{n^2}{Z} \pm \frac{n}{Z}\sqrt{n^2 - l(l+1)} \tag{3.35}$$

r_1 and r_2 are respectively the perihelion and aphelion of the classical electron orbit. In the region of the classical orbit $r_1 < r < r_2$ the eigenfunction may be represented according to (53.3) to a good approximation by[2]:

$$\left.\begin{aligned} v &= a\left(\frac{2Z}{r} - \frac{Z^2}{n^2} - \frac{(l+\frac{1}{2})^2}{r^2}\right)^{-\frac{1}{4}} \cos\left[\int_{r_1}^{r}\sqrt{\frac{2Z}{\varrho} - \frac{Z^2}{n^2} - \frac{(l+\frac{1}{2})^2}{\varrho^2}}\, d\varrho - \frac{\pi}{4}\right] \\ &= a\left(\frac{2Z}{r} - \frac{Z^2}{n^2} - \frac{(l+\frac{1}{2})^2}{r^2}\right)^{-\frac{1}{4}} \cos\left[\sqrt{2Zr - \frac{Z^2 r^2}{n^2} - (l+\tfrac{1}{2})^2} + \right. \\ &\quad \left. + n \arcsin\frac{Zr - n^2}{n\sqrt{n^2 - (l+\frac{1}{2})^2}} - (l+\tfrac{1}{2}) \arcsin\frac{n}{Zr} \cdot \frac{Zr - (l+\frac{1}{2})^2}{\sqrt{n^2 - (l+\frac{1}{2})^2}} + (n-l-1)\frac{\pi}{2}\right]. \end{aligned}\right\} \tag{3.36}$$

Although (3.36) looks rather complicated it turns out to be a useful formula in practice. For $(l+\frac{1}{2})^2 \ll Zr \ll n^2$, (3.36) becomes

$$v = a\left(\frac{r}{2Z}\right)^{\frac{1}{4}} \cdot \cos\left(\sqrt{8Zr} - (2l+1)\frac{\pi}{2} - \frac{\pi}{4}\right). \tag{3.37}$$

The radial eigenfunction $R = v/r$ thus becomes identical with (3.33), as must happen[3], and the constants are related through

$$c = \sqrt{2\pi Z}\, a. \tag{3.38}$$

v decays exponentially outside of the region of the classical orbit [see (53.4)]. Thus, if we wish to evaluate the normalizing integral

$$\int_0^\infty R_{nl}^2 r^2\, dr = \int_0^\infty v^2\, dr = 1\,,$$

---

[1] Cf. JAHNKE-EMDE: Tables of Functions, especially p. 166 (differential equation), p. 98 (asymptotic formula), p. 90 (series expansion).

[2] See Sect. 53.

[3] The asymptotic formula for the BESSEL function can thus be looked upon as a special case of the WKB procedure.

we only need to consider the region $r_1 < r < r_2$. In addition, we can make use of the fact that the cosine in (3.36) is a rapidly varying function compared to the other factor, and replace $\cos^2$ by its mean value $\frac{1}{2}$. Then

$$\int_0^\infty v^2\,dr = \frac{1}{2}\,a^2 \int_{r_1}^{r_2} \frac{dr}{\sqrt{\frac{2Z}{r} - \frac{Z^2}{n^2} - \frac{(l+\frac{1}{2})^2}{r^2}}} = \frac{1}{2}\,a^2 \pi Z^{-2} n^3,$$

$$a = 2^{\frac{1}{2}} \pi^{-\frac{1}{2}} Z\, n^{-\frac{3}{2}}, \qquad c = 2Z^{\frac{3}{2}} n^{-\frac{3}{2}}. \tag{3.39}$$

The eigenfunction is thus proportional to $1/n^{\frac{3}{2}}$ for $r \ll n^2/Z$ and, furthermore, this is the only factor through which u depends on n. For large n the normalization (3.39) is, of course, identical with the one previously derived. If the value for c is substituted into (3.32) and the series expansion for the BESSEL function (as given, for example, in JAHNKE-EMDE) is used, then exactly (3.30) is obtained.

ε) Generating function for LAGUERRE *functions*[1]. Occassionally a representation of the LAGUERRE polynomials different from (3.5) is preferable, particularly when we are dealing with a calculation of transition probabilities[2]. It turns out that the LAGUERRE polynomials can be defined by means of the generating function

$$e^{-\frac{xt}{1-t}} \cdot \frac{1}{1-t} = \sum_k L_k(x)\,\frac{t^k}{k!}\,. \tag{3.40}$$

Proof: Differentiating (3.40) with respect to t and setting the coefficient of t^k equal to zero gives

$$L_{k+1} - (2k+1-x)\,L_k + k^2 L_{k-1} = 0\,. \tag{3.41}$$

Differentiating (3.40) with respect to x, one obtains

$$L_k' = k\,(L_{k-1}' - L_{k-1})\,. \tag{3.42}$$

By means of a short calculation the differential equation

$$x\,L_k'' + (1-x)\,L_k' + k\,L_k = 0 \tag{3.43}$$

follows from (3.41), (3.42). If we set $k = n + l$ and differentiate $2l+1$ times with respect to x, we arrive at the equation

$$x\,(L_{n+l}^{2l+1})'' + (2l+2-x)\,(L_{n+l}^{2l+1})' + (n-l-1)\,L_{n+l}^{2l+1} = 0\,. \tag{3.44}$$

Putting $x = \varrho = 2\varepsilon r$ and $f = r^l L_{n+l}^{2l+1}$, the differential equation (2.5) follows without difficulty in view of (2.10).

(3.40) agrees with (3.5) also with respect to normalization as can be shown by calculating the constant term in L_k, i.e., the term which is free of x, thus

$$L_k(x) = \frac{d^k}{dt^k}\left(e^{-\frac{xt}{1-t}} \cdot \frac{1}{1-t}\right)_{t=0} = \left(\frac{k!}{(1-t)^{k+1}} + x \ldots\right)_{t=0} = k! + \cdots$$

which is in agreement with (3.6). The associated LAGUERRE functions can also be represented by a generating function. Differentiating (3.40) r times with respect to x we obtain

$$\frac{(-1)^r}{(1-t)^{r+1}}\, e^{-\frac{xt}{1-t}} = \sum L_k^r(x)\,\frac{t^{k-r}}{k!}\,. \tag{3.45}$$

---

[1] See, for example, E. SCHRÖDINGER, Ann. d. Phys. **80**, 131 (1926).
[2] Cf. Sec. 63 and particularly W. GORDON, Ann. d. Phys. **2**, 1031 (1929).

We finally quote the value at the origin of the squares of the normalized radial and total wave functions for $l=0$ and any principal quantum number n. From (1.8) and (3.2) to (3.4) we have

$$R_{n0}^2(0) = \frac{4Z^2}{n^3}, \qquad u_{n00}^2(0) = \frac{Z^2}{\pi n^3}. \tag{3.46}$$

4. The eigenfunctions of the continuous spectrum[1]. α) We shall now treat the case $E > 0$. The quantity ε, defined in (2.3), is now purely imaginary

$$\varepsilon = i\sqrt{2E} = i k. \tag{4.1}$$

In every other respect there is no change in the derivation of Sect. 2 up to the recursion formula (2.9). The ratio $a_\nu/a_{\nu-1}$ becomes complex, and it is no longer possible to terminate the series (2.6) through a particular choice of ε. On the other hand, there is no need for that now because both $e^{+\varepsilon r}$ and $e^{-\varepsilon r}$ remain finite for $r=\infty$. Thus, there is a solution for every positive E, and a continuous spectrum of positive eigenvalues adjoins the discrete levels of negative energy.

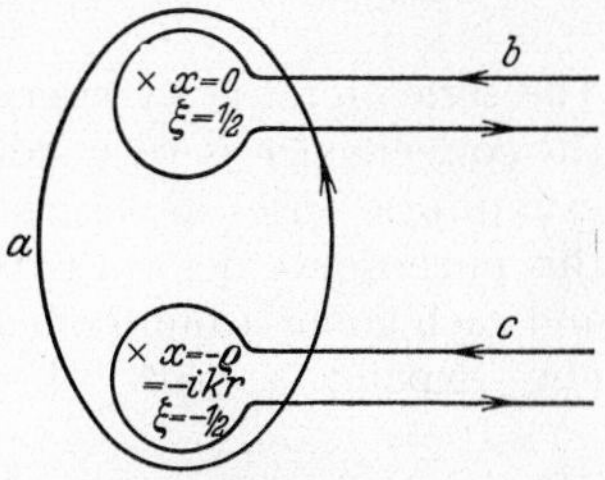

Fig. 6. Integration contour for the continuous eigenfunctions. The path a encloses both branch points $\xi = +\frac{1}{2}\,(x=0)$ and $\xi = -\frac{1}{2}\,(x=-\varrho)$ of the integrand. Integration along the path b gives (for large r) the asymptotic incoming wave $R^{(2)}$, the path c gives the outgoing wave $R^{(1)}$.

The eigenfunctions belonging to the states of the continuous spectrum are, in accordance with (3.2) and (3.4), expressible in terms of hypergeometric functions since the recursion formula (2.9) is still valid. However,

$$n = \frac{Z}{\varepsilon} = -i\frac{Z}{\sqrt{2E}} = -i\frac{Z}{k} \tag{4.2}$$

is imaginary.

Accordingly, the definition (3.5) of the LAGUERRE polynomials has no longer any apparent meaning. However, it is possible, using CAUCHY's theorem,

$$\frac{d^\lambda f(x)}{dx^\lambda} = \frac{\Gamma(\lambda+1)}{2\pi i}\int \frac{f(z)}{(z-x)^{\lambda+1}}\,dz, \tag{4.3}$$

to obtain a representation of the LAGUERRE polynomials,

$$L_\lambda(\varrho) = \frac{\Gamma(\lambda+1)}{2\pi i}\, e^{\varrho}\int \frac{e^{-z} z^\lambda}{(z-\varrho)^{\lambda+1}}\,dz = \frac{\Gamma(\lambda+1)}{2\pi i}\int e^{-x}(x+\varrho)^\lambda x^{-(\lambda+1)}\,dx, \tag{4.4}$$

which is valid for all λ. In the second of the above representations the variable of integration z has been replaced by $x+\varrho$. The path of integration consists of the simple loop a (Fig. 6) around the two branch points $x=-\varrho$ and $x=0$ of the integrand. μ-fold differentiation of (4.4) results in the integral representation of the associated LAGUERRE functions (μ is integral and positive):

$$L_\lambda^\mu(\varrho) = \frac{(\Gamma(\lambda+1))^2}{2\pi i\,\Gamma(\lambda-\mu+1)}\int e^{-x}(x+\varrho)^{\lambda-\mu} x^{-(\lambda+1)}\,dx. \tag{4.5}$$

Finally, the radial eigenfunction is obtained by setting $\lambda = n+l$, $\mu = 2l+1$, multiplying by $e^{-\varrho/2} r^l$, and including all constant factors in the constant c:

$$R = c(-i\varrho)^l e^{-\varrho/2}\cdot\frac{1}{2\pi i}\int (x+\varrho)^{n-l-1} x^{-n-l-1} e^{-x}\,dx, \tag{4.6}$$

$$= c\,\frac{(i\varrho)^{-l-1}}{2\pi}\cdot\int e^{-\varrho\xi}\left(\xi+\frac{1}{2}\right)^{n-l-1}\left(\xi-\frac{1}{2}\right)^{-n-l-1} d\xi. \tag{4.7}$$

---

[1] We shall follow the treatment of A. SOMMERFELD and G. SCHUR, Ann. d. Phys. **4**, 409 (1930); see also E. FUES, Ann. d. Phys. **87**, 281 (1926), W. GORDON, Ann. d. Phys. **2**, 1031 (1929), and other authors.

The representation (4.7) is obtained from (4.6) by substituting $x=\varrho(\xi-\frac{1}{2})$, the path of integration going around the branch points $\xi=\pm\frac{1}{2}$ in the positive sense. From (4.7) it is at once apparent that the radial eigenfunctions will be real if ϱ and n are pure imaginaries.

Expanding (4.6) in powers of ϱ and carrying out the integrations by means of CAUCHY's theorem, the representation (3.2) for the radial eigenfunction is again obtained (within a numerical factor):

$$\left.\begin{aligned} R_{nl}(\varrho) &= c\frac{(-i\varrho)^l e^{-\varrho/2}}{2\pi i}\sum_{\alpha=0}^{\infty}\binom{n-l-1}{\alpha}\varrho^\alpha\int\frac{e^{-x}}{x^{2l+2+\alpha}}\,dx \\ &= (-i\varrho)^l\cdot\frac{c}{(2l+1)!}\,e^{-\varrho/2}\cdot F(-(n-l-1),\,2l+2,\,\varrho)\,. \end{aligned}\right\} \tag{4.8}$$

The series for the hypergeometric function F [cf. (3.4)] converges for all ϱ, but the convergence is very slow for large ϱ. Therefore, it is necessary to look for an asymptotic series in descending powers of ϱ, which will be useful for large ϱ. For this purpose we deform path a (Fig. 6) into two loops b and c coming from infinity and each going around one of the branch points in the positive sense. Along path b we expand $(x+\varrho)^{n-l-1}$ in decreasing powers of ϱ:

$$(x+\varrho)^{n-l-1}=\sum_\alpha\binom{n-l-1}{\alpha}\varrho^{n-l-1-\alpha}\,x^\alpha.$$

This expansion diverges for the remote portions ($|x|>|\varrho|$) of the path of integration; the resulting asymptotic expansion for R_{nl} is, therefore, only semi-convergent. For the actual integrations we refer the reader to the work of SOMMERFELD and SCHUR and simply state here the results: The contribution of path b to the asymptotic representation of the eigenfunction is

$$R^{(2)}=c\frac{e^{-\frac{1}{2}\varrho-i\pi(n+\frac{3}{2}l+n\log\varrho}}{\Gamma(n+l+1)\cdot\varrho}\,G\left(n+l,\,l+1-n,\,\frac{1}{\varrho}\right), \tag{4.9}$$

where

$$G(\alpha,\beta,x)=1+\frac{\alpha\beta}{1!}x+\frac{\alpha(\alpha+1)\beta(\beta+1)}{2!}x^2+\cdots$$

is a hypergeometric function[1]. Along path c it is convenient to replace x by z [cf. (4.4)]. The contribution to the asymptotic representation of the eigenfunction turns out to be exactly the complex conjugate of $R^{(2)}$.

Collecting the contributions and substituting the values of ϱ and n from (3.3), (4.1) and (4.2), the asymptotic expression for the wave-function is obtained:

$$R=\frac{c\,e^{-\frac{\pi}{2}\frac{Z}{k}}}{|\Gamma(l+1-iZ/k)|\,kr}\cos\left[kr+\frac{Z}{k}\log 2kr-\frac{\pi}{2}(l-1)-\sigma_l\right], \tag{4.10}$$

where

$$\sigma_l=\arg\Gamma\left(l+1+i\frac{Z}{k}\right)$$

is the complex phase of the Γ-function. Thus, asymptotically, the eigenfunctions go over into spherical waves.

We must now normalize the eigenfunction R. The well-known rule for the normalization of eigenfunctions belonging to the continuous spectrum is

$$\int_0^\infty r^2\,dr\,R_{Tl}(r)\int_{T-\Delta T}^{T+\Delta T}R_{T'l}(r)\,dT'=1\,. \tag{4.11}$$

---

[1] See also M. STOBBE: Ann. d. Phys. 7, 661 (1930).

In the above, T is any function of the wave number k, e.g. the energy $W = \frac{1}{2}k^2$ or k itself. ΔT is a small interval. If condition (4.11) is fulfilled and the eigenfunctions belonging to the discrete spectrum are normalized in the usual fashion,

$$\int R_{nl}^2(r)\, r^2\, dr = 1,$$

then an arbitrary function of the space coordinates $f(r, \vartheta, \varphi)$ can be expanded in terms of our eigenfunctions as follows:

$$\left.\begin{aligned} f(r,\vartheta,\varphi) &= \sum_{l=0}^{\infty}\sum_{m=-l}^{+l} Y_{lm}(\vartheta,\varphi)\left(\sum_{n=l+1}^{\infty} a_{nlm} R_{nl}(r) + \int_{k=0}^{\infty} dT(k)\, a_{Tlm} R_{Tl}(x)\right)\\ &= \sum_{nlm} a_{nlm} u_{nlm}(r,\vartheta,\varphi) + \int dT \sum_{lm} a_{Tlm} u_{Tlm}\end{aligned}\right\} \quad (4.12)$$

and the coefficients in the expansion are given by

$$\left.\begin{aligned} a_{nlm} &= \int_0^\infty r^2 dr \int_0^\pi \sin\vartheta\, d\vartheta \int_0^{2\pi} d\varphi\, f(r,\vartheta,\varphi)\, R_{nl}(r)\, Y_{lm}^*(\vartheta,\varphi) = \int d\tau\, f\, u_{nlm}^*,\\ a_{Tlm} &= \int_0^\infty r^2 dr \int_0^\pi \sin\vartheta\, d\vartheta \int_0^{2\pi} d\varphi\, f(r,\vartheta,\varphi)\, R_{Tl}(r)\, Y_{lm}^*(\vartheta,\varphi).\end{aligned}\right\} \quad (4.13)$$

The eigenfunctions R_{Tl} are said to be normalized in the T-scale. The eigenfunctions normalized in the T-scale and k-scale respectively are related through

$$R_T = \left(\frac{dT}{dk}\right)^{-\frac{1}{2}} R_k, \quad (4.14)$$

as follows directly from (4.11).

We calculate the normalizing factor in the k-scale by putting

$$R = \frac{b}{r}\cdot\cos\left(kr + \frac{Z}{k}\log 2kr - \delta_l\right), \quad (4.15)$$

in accordance with (4.10); b is the normalizing constant to be determined, and δ_l is independent of r. If we neglect quantities of order $1/kr$ and $\Delta k/k$ we obtain

$$\int_{k-\Delta k}^{k+\Delta k} dk' \cos\left(k'r + \frac{Z}{k'}\log 2k'r - \delta\right) = 2\cos\left(kr + \frac{Z}{k}\log 2kr - \delta\right)\frac{\sin \Delta k r}{r}. \quad (4.16)$$

Substitution of (4.15) and (4.16) into (4.11), setting $T = k$, and replacing the rapidly oscillating $\cos^2$ by its mean value $\frac{1}{2}$ results in

$$2b^2 \int_0^\infty \frac{\sin\Delta k r}{r}\, dr \cos^2\left(kr + \frac{Z}{k}\log 2kr - \delta\right) = b^2\cdot\frac{\pi}{2} = 1. \quad (4.17)$$

Thus, in the k-scale

$$b = \sqrt{\frac{2}{\pi}}, \qquad R_k = \sqrt{\frac{2}{\pi}}\cdot\frac{1}{r}\cdot\cos\left[kr + \frac{Z}{k}\log 2kr - \frac{\pi}{2}(l-1) - \sigma_l\right]. \quad (4.18)$$

Normalizing in the energy-scale we get, correspondingly,

$$\left.\begin{aligned} W &= \frac{1}{2}k^2, \qquad \frac{dW}{dk} = k,\\ R_W &= \sqrt{\frac{2}{\pi k}}\cdot\frac{1}{r}\cdot\cos\left[kr + \frac{Z}{k}\log 2kr - \frac{\pi}{2}(l+1) - \sigma_l\right].\end{aligned}\right\} \quad (4.19)$$

Comparing the normalized eigenfunction (4.18) with the asymptotic representation (4.10) for the unnormalized eigenfunction we find that

$$c_k = \sqrt{\frac{2}{\pi}}\, k \left|\Gamma\left(l+1-i\frac{Z}{k}\right)\right| e^{\frac{\pi}{2}\frac{Z}{k}}, \qquad c_W = \frac{c_k}{\sqrt{k}}. \tag{4.20}$$

At this point we can find both the integral and, for small r, the series representations of the normalized eigenfunction, the former by going back to (4.6) and (4.7) and the latter by substituting (4.20) into (4.8). In doing this it is practical to write the Γ-function in terms of elementary functions by means of the well known recursion relation

$$\Gamma(x+1) = x\,\Gamma(x)$$

and the formula

$$\Gamma(x)\,\Gamma(1-x) = \frac{\pi}{\sin \pi x};$$

then[1]

$$|\Gamma(l+1-i n')| = \sqrt{\pi n'} \prod_{s=1}^{l} \sqrt{s^2+n'^2}\,(\mathrm{Sin}\,\pi n')^{-\frac{1}{2}} \quad \text{with} \quad n' = \frac{Z}{k}. \tag{4.21}$$

We thus obtain our final integral (4.22) and series (4.23) representations:

$$\left.\begin{aligned} R_W &= (-)^{l+1} \frac{2\sqrt{Z}}{\sqrt{1-e^{-2\pi n'}}} \prod_{s=1}^{l} \sqrt{s^2+n'^2}\cdot(2kr)^{-(l+1)} \times \\ &\quad \times \frac{1}{2\pi}\int e^{-\varrho\xi}\cdot\left(\xi+\frac{1}{2}\right)^{-in'-l-1}\left(\xi-\frac{1}{2}\right)^{+in'-l-1} d\xi. \end{aligned}\right\} \tag{4.22}$$

$$R_W = \frac{2\sqrt{Z}}{\sqrt{1-e^{-2\pi n'}}} \prod_{s=1}^{l} \sqrt{s^2+n'^2}\,\frac{(2kr)^l}{(2l+1)!}\, e^{-ikr} F(in'+l+1,\, 2l+2,\, 2ikr). \tag{4.23}$$

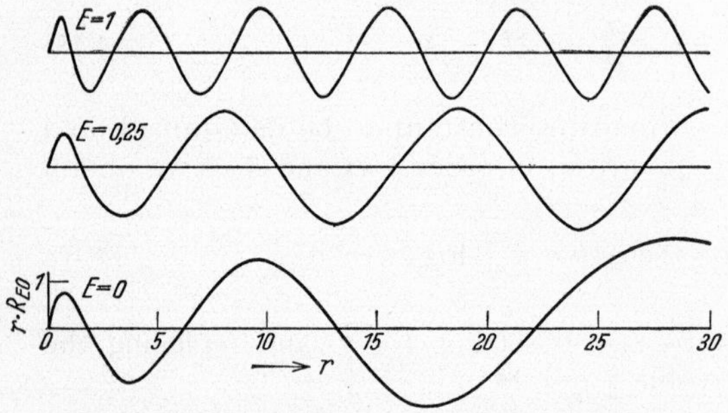

Fig. 7. The continuous eigenfunction of hydrogen for s-states ($l=0$) for three different energies E (in Ry units). Abscissa is r in atomic units, ordinate is $r R_{E0}$. Note that the "wave length" and amplitude increase rapidly with increasing r for $E=0$, but are almost constant for $E=1$.

Fig. 7 shows the eigenfunctions belonging to the continuous spectrum for $E=0$, 0.25 and 1 (in Ry units).

β) The irregular functions. In this section we have discussed wave functions for the continuous spectrum in the form of a radial wave function $R(r)$ multiplied by a spherical harmonic Y_{lm}. For *any* central potential (function of the radial distance r only) the SCHRÖDINGER equation can be separated in spherical polar coordinates and wave functions of the form $R_l(r)\,Y_{lm}$ exist. We have only calculated the radial wave functions for the special case of the COULOMB potential Zr^{-1}. Further, we have only treated radial wave functions which are finite at the origin, the "regular COULOMB functions". There exists another set of solutions forthe radial wave functions which diverge at the origin. These "irregular COULOMB functions" have an asymptotic form representing spherical standing waves, similar to that of the regular functions (4.10), but with *cosine* replaced by *sine*. These irregular functions do not arise in physical problems involving only *pure* COULOMB potentials, since physical

[1] We use the symbol Sin instead of sinh for the hyperbolic function.

wave functions must remain finite at the origin. They are of use, however, in problems involving central potentials which approximate a COULOMB potential at large distances, but deviate from it for small distances. These irregular functions occur[1], for instance, in nuclear problems but *not* in atomic theory and we shall not consider them further.

5. Motion of the nucleus. So far we have pretended (see Sect. 1) that the atomic nucleus has infinite mass and, therefore, remains at rest. We shall now correct for this. Calculating to begin with, in c.g.s. units, let M be the mass and $\xi_1 \eta_1 \zeta_1$ the coordinates of the nucleus, the quantities with index 2 referring to the electron of mass m. The HAMILTONian of the system is

$$H = \frac{p_1^2}{2M} + \frac{p_2^2}{2m} - \frac{Z e^2}{\varrho}$$

and SCHRÖDINGER's equation is

$$\frac{\hbar^2}{2M} \Delta_1 u' + \frac{\hbar^2}{2m} \Delta_2 u' + \left(E' + \frac{Z e^2}{\varrho}\right) u' = 0. \tag{5.1}$$

$\Delta_1 = \frac{\partial^2}{\partial \xi_1^2} + \frac{\partial^2}{\partial \eta_1^2} + \frac{\partial^2}{\partial \zeta_1^2}$ is the LAPLACian in the configuration space of the electron. u' depends on the six coordinates of nucleus and electron. Introducing the coordinates of the center of mass

$$X = \frac{M \xi_1 + m \xi_2}{M + m} \quad \text{(and similarly for } Y \text{ and } Z)$$

and the relative coordinates

$$x = \xi_2 - \xi_1 \quad \left(\text{and similarly for } y \text{ and } z,\ \varrho = \sqrt{x^2 + y^2 + z^2}\right)$$

we have

$$\frac{\partial^2 u'}{\partial \xi_1^2} = \left(\frac{M}{M+m}\right)^2 \frac{\partial^2 u'}{\partial X^2} - 2 \frac{M}{M+m} \frac{\partial^2 u'}{\partial X \partial x} + \frac{\partial^2 u'}{\partial x^2},$$

$$\frac{1}{M} \Delta_1 u' + \frac{1}{m} \Delta_2 u' = \frac{1}{M+m} \left(\frac{\partial^2}{\partial X^2} + \frac{\partial^2}{\partial Y^2} + \frac{\partial^2}{\partial Z^2}\right) u' + \frac{1}{\mu} \left(\frac{\partial^2}{\partial x^2} + \frac{\partial^2}{\partial y^2} + \frac{\partial^2}{\partial z^2}\right) u',$$

where

$$\mu = \frac{M m}{M + m} \tag{5.2}$$

is the reduced mass. (5.1) can be separated by means of a solution of the form

$$u' = u(x, y, z)\, u''(X, Y, Z), \qquad E' = E + E'', \tag{5.3}$$

The motion of the center of mass of the atom is governed by the equation

$$\Delta u'' + \frac{2(M+m)}{\hbar^2} E'' u'' = 0, \tag{5.4}$$

while for the relative motion of the electron the following equation holds:

$$\Delta u + \frac{2\mu}{\hbar^2} \left(E + \frac{Z e^2}{\varrho}\right) u = 0 \tag{5.5}$$

(5.5) differs from (1.1') only in that μ appears in the place of m. Thus, we need only to alter the atomic units defined in the Introduction in order to take into account the motion of the nucleus. Adopting μ as the new atomic unit of mass,

[1] For details, see the work by MOTT and MASSEY, ref. [7] of the bibliography. For tables of COULOMB wave functions see N.B.S. Appl. Math. Circ. No. 17, Vol. 1, Washington, D.C. 1952.

the previously used unit of energy becomes multiplied by

$$\frac{\mu}{m} = \frac{M}{M+m} = \left(1 + \frac{1}{1{,}836A}\right)^{-1}, \tag{5.6}$$

where A is the atomic weight of the nucleus. In terms of the new atomic units Schrödinger's equation again assumes the old form (1.1). In terms of the new units the energy of the n-th discrete state of a hydrogen-like ion is again given by Balmer's formula (2.11); in terms of the old units, which we shall retain in general, we accordingly get:

$$E_n = -\frac{Z^2}{2n^2}\frac{M}{M+m}. \tag{5.7}$$

According to (5.7) the absolute value of the energy, as a consequence of the motion of the nucleus, decreases with decreasing nuclear mass. (The unit of length a is increased by a factor of m/μ, i.e. the electrons are on the average more distant from a light nucleus than from a heavy nucleus of the same charge.)

This effect of nuclear motion has been of importance historically both for the detection of isotopes, in particular of deuterium[1], and for the "spectroscopic determination of the atomic mass of the electron". Consider, for instance, the various fine structure components of the H_α line in hydrogen and in deuterium ($Z=1$, atomic mass about 2). After applying small corrections for hyperfine structure and relativistic effects, the wave numbers of each line for hydrogen and for deuterium differ from the wave number for infinite nuclear mass only by a multiplicative factor of form (5.6). In (5.6), M is replaced by the proton and deuteron mass, respectively, for hydrogen and deuterium. The difference in wave numbers ν_H and ν_D for the two isotopes is then given by

$$\frac{\nu_D - \nu_H}{\nu_H} = \frac{m(M_D - M_H)}{(M_H - m)\,M_D} \tag{5.8}$$

where M_H, M_D are the mass of a *neutral* hydrogen and deuterium atom, respectively (including the electron mass).

The difference in wave number (5.8), has been measured by various authors[2] to an accuracy of about 1 in 5000. To get a feeling for the order of magnitude of the effect, the difference in wavelength of the H_α line in hydrogen ($\lambda = 6560$ Å) and in deuterium is about 1.75 Å, or about one-third the doublet separation of the D-lines in sodium. The values of M_H and M_D are known very accurately from mass spectroscopy and from data on nuclear reactions. In physical atomic mass units (referred to O^{16}) they are $M_H = 1.00814_2$ a.m.u., $M_D = 2.01473_7$ a.m.u. From (5.8) and the experimental values for $(\nu_D - \nu_H)$ one can then calculate the atomic mass of the electron to an accuracy of about 1 in 5000. Actually the electron's atomic mass is known more accurately from other types of experiments, in particular measurements of the "cyclotron frequency" of an electron and a proton in a constant magnetic field, giving directly the proton-electron mass ratio. The best "non-spectroscopic" value[3] for the electron mass is

$$M_H/m = 1837.13 \pm 0.05, \qquad m = (548.76 \pm 0.01_5) \times 10^{-6} \text{ a.m.u.} \tag{5.9}$$

The "spectroscopic" value for m, obtained by Cohen, is larger than the more accurate one given in (5.9) by about 1 part in 2500, i.e., by slightly more than its experimental error.

[1] Urey, Brickwedde and Murphy: Phys. Rev. **40**, 1, 464 (1932).
[2] For a detailed analysis see E. R. Cohen, Phys. Rev. **88**, 353 (1952).
[3] J. W. DuMond and E. R. Cohen: Rev. Mod. Phys. **25**, 691 (1953). — Cf. the preceding article in this volume.

The relation between the RYDBERG constant R_{H} for an actual hydrogen (or deuterium) atom and R_∞, Eq. (2.14), is

$$\left.\begin{aligned} R_{\mathrm{H}} = R_\infty (M_{\mathrm{H}} - m)/M_{\mathrm{H}} &= (109677.58 \pm 0.01_2)\,\mathrm{cm}^{-1}, \\ R_{\mathrm{D}} &= (109707.42 \pm 0.01_2)\,\mathrm{cm}^{-1}. \end{aligned}\right\} \tag{5.10}$$

Of course, R_{H} and R_{D} are the quantities which are measured directly and R_∞ is derived from them with the help of (5.9).

6. Separation of SCHRÖDINGER's equation in parabolic coordinates[1]. SCHRÖDINGER's equation for an electron moving in any central force field can always be separated in spherical polar coordinates. If the central field is of the COULOMB type, then a separation can also be carried out in parabolic coordinates. This alternative is connected with the degeneracy of the eigenvalues belonging to like principal and different orbital quantum numbers (cf. Sect. 2). A separation in parabolic coordinates turns out to be useful in the treatment of all kinds of perturbation problems in which a particular direction in space is distinguished by some external force, e.g., STARK effect, photo-electric effect, COMPTON effect, and collision of electrons.

α) Discrete spectrum. The parabolic coordinates ξ, η, φ are defined through the relations[2]

$$\left.\begin{aligned} x &= \sqrt{\xi\eta}\cos\varphi, & \xi &= r + z, \\ y &= \sqrt{\xi\eta}\sin\varphi, & \eta &= r - z, \\ z &= \tfrac{1}{2}(\xi - \eta), & \varphi &= \arctan\frac{y}{x}, \\ r &= \tfrac{1}{2}(\xi + \eta). \end{aligned}\right\} \tag{6.1}$$

The surfaces $\xi = \mathrm{const}$ and $\eta = \mathrm{const}$ are paraboloids of revolution about the z-axis having the nucleus at the origin $(x = y = z = 0)$ as focus. The coordinate system is orthogonal. The element of arc is given by

$$ds^2 = \frac{\eta + \xi}{4\xi}\,d\xi^2 + \frac{\eta + \xi}{4\eta}\,d\eta^2 + \xi\eta\,d\varphi^2, \tag{6.2}$$

and the volume element by

$$d\tau = \tfrac{1}{4}(\xi + \eta)\,d\xi\,d\eta\,d\varphi. \tag{6.3}$$

From (6.2) follows the expression for the LAPLACian operator, viz.

$$\Delta = \frac{4}{\xi + \eta}\frac{d}{d\xi}\left(\xi\frac{d}{d\xi}\right) + \frac{4}{\xi + \eta}\frac{d}{d\eta}\left(\eta\frac{d}{d\eta}\right) + \frac{1}{\xi\eta}\frac{d^2}{d\varphi^2}. \tag{6.4}$$

We deal with SCHRÖDINGER's equation by setting

$$u = u_1(\xi)\,u_2(\eta)\,e^{\pm im\varphi}, \qquad Z = Z_1 + Z_2 \quad (m \geq 0). \tag{6.5}$$

Multiplying the differential equation by $\frac{1}{4}(\xi + \eta)$ and carrying out the separation we obtain

$$\frac{d}{d\xi}\left(\xi\frac{du_1}{d\xi}\right) + \left(\frac{1}{2}E\xi + Z_1 - \frac{m^2}{4\xi}\right)u_1 = 0 \tag{6.6}$$

and also an exactly equivalent equation for $u_2(\eta)$. A procedure analogous to that in Sect. 4 leads us to conclude that u_1 behaves as $e^{-\frac{1}{2}\varepsilon\xi}$ for large ξ and as $\xi^{\frac{1}{2}m}$ for small ξ. We put

$$u_1 = e^{-\frac{1}{2}\varepsilon\xi}\,\xi^{\frac{1}{2}m}\,f_1(\xi) \quad \text{and} \quad x = \varepsilon\xi, \tag{6.7}$$

[1] Cf. E. SCHRÖDINGER, Abhandlungen III, p. 85.
[2] Cf., e.g., E. SCHRÖDINGER, Abhandlungen, p. 105.

so that

$$x\frac{d^2 f_1}{dx^2} + (m+1-x)\frac{d f_1}{dx} + \left(\frac{Z_1}{\varepsilon} - \frac{m+1}{2}\right) f_1 = 0.$$

On comparison with (3.45) it becomes apparent that the solutions of this equation are

$$f_1 = L^m_{n_1+m}(x),$$

where

$$n_1 = Z_1/\varepsilon - \tfrac{1}{2}(m+1) \tag{6.8}$$

must be a non-negative integer (in the case of real ε) if f_1 is to remain finite for large ξ. A corresponding result may be obtained for f_2. Finally, putting

$$n = n_1 + n_2 + m + 1 \tag{6.9}$$

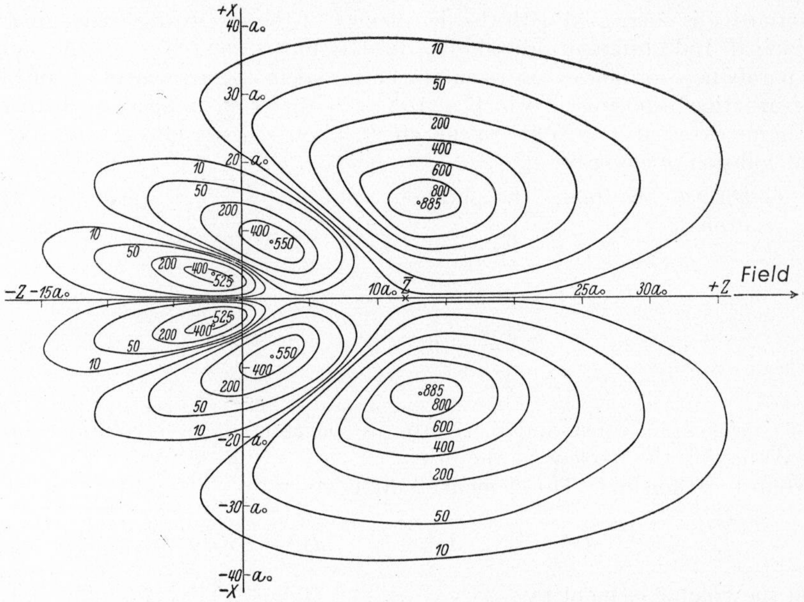

Fig. 8. Charge distribution of the state $n_1=2$, $n_2=0$, $m=1$ in parabolic quantization (according to F. G. SLACK): The figure shows a cross-section through the atom, the nucleus being at the center of the coordinate system The curves are lines of constant charge density, where charge density means the charge in a circular ring with the quantization direction (z-axis) as axis. Note the strong concentration of charge towards positive values of z

and solving (6.8) for ε, we obtain our previous energy formula (2.10), viz.,

$$E = -\frac{1}{2}\varepsilon^2 = -\frac{1}{2}\frac{Z^2}{n^2}. \tag{6.10}$$

The degree of degeneracy of the n-th eigenvalue is, as it must be, the same as in our previous calculation in polar coordinates. If m is fixed, n_1 can assume the $n-m$ values $0, 1, \ldots, n-m-1$. m itself can go from 0 to $n-1$, the non-zero values having to be counted twice because one can choose either the plus of the minus sign in $e^{\pm i m\varphi}$ of (6.5). Thus, one arrives again at exactly n^2 different eigenfunctions.

We must also normalize the eigenfunctions. Since the volume element is given by (6.3), we require

$$\tfrac{1}{4}c^2\int_0^\infty d\xi\int_0^\infty d\eta\int_0^{2\pi} d\varphi\, u_1^2(\xi)\, u_2^2(\eta)\cdot(\xi+\eta) = 1. \tag{6.11}$$

The value of the integral can be taken from (3.16). The normalized eigenfunction becomes

$$u_{n_1 n_2 m} = \frac{e^{\pm i m\varphi}}{\sqrt{\pi n}} \cdot \frac{n_1!^{\frac{1}{2}}\, n_2!^{\frac{1}{2}}\, \varepsilon^{m+\frac{3}{2}}}{(n_1+m)!^{\frac{3}{2}}\,(n_2+m)!^{\frac{3}{2}}}\, e^{-\frac{1}{2}\varepsilon(\xi+\eta)}\,(\xi\eta)^{\frac{1}{2}m}\, L^m_{n_1+m}(\varepsilon\xi)\, L^m_{n_2+m}(\varepsilon\eta)\,. \tag{6.12}$$

These eigenfunctions, contrary to the eigenfunctions in polar coordinates, are asymmetrical with respect to the plane $z=0$. For $n_1 > n_2$, the larger portion of the charge distribution of the electron lies on the positive side of z; for $n_1 < n_2$, on the negative side of z. This is best seen by examining the eigenfunctions for very large distances from the nucleus, i.e., for large arguments of the LAGUERRE functions. For large x, $L^\mu_\lambda(x)$ behaves [cf. (3.7)] as $x^{\lambda-\mu}$, and in view of the definitions (6.1) of parabolic coordinates we have

$$u_{n_1 n_2 m} \sim e^{i m\varphi}\, \xi^{n_1+\frac{1}{2}m}\, \eta^{n_2+\frac{1}{2}m}\, e^{-\frac{1}{2}\varepsilon(\xi+\eta)};$$

$$|u_{n_1 n_2 m}|^2 \sim r^{n-1}\, e^{-\varepsilon r}\,(1+\cos\vartheta)^{n_1+\frac{1}{2}m}\,(1-\cos\vartheta)^{n_2+\frac{1}{2}m}.$$

Fig. 8 gives contours of constant charge density for the state $n=3$, $n_1=2$, $n_2=m=0$. The large eccentricity in the charge distribution is quite evident.

The parabolic eigenfunctions can, naturally, be built up from the eigenfunctions in polar coordinates; e.g., for $n=2$, $n_1=1$, $n_2=m=0$ we have

$$u = \frac{1}{\sqrt{2\pi}} \cdot \left(\frac{1}{2}Z\right)^{\frac{3}{2}} \left[-1 + \frac{1}{2} Z r (1+\cos\vartheta)\right] e^{-\frac{1}{2}Zr}$$

$$= -\frac{1}{\sqrt{2}} R_{20}(r)\, Y_{00}(\vartheta,\varphi) + \frac{1}{\sqrt{2}} R_{21}(r)\, Y_{10}(\vartheta,\varphi),$$

in view of (3.7), (3.21), (1.8) and (6.1).

Generally, any of the $(n-m)$ wave functions in parabolic coordinates for a fixed value of n and m (and fixed sign in $e^{\pm i m\varphi}$) is a linear superposition of the $(n-m)$ spherical harmonics wave functions for the same values of n and m (and sign). For the non-degenerate ground state with $n=1$ ($n_1=n_2=m=0$) the "parabolic" and spherical harmonics wave functions are identical.

β) Continuous spectrum. For the continuous spectrum, with positive energy E, we find that

$$n = -i n' = -i Z/k, \qquad (k^2 = +2E) \tag{6.13}$$

is again a pure imaginary and

$$n_1 = -\tfrac{1}{2}(m+1) - \tfrac{1}{2} i (n'+\lambda); \qquad n_2 = -\tfrac{1}{2}(m+1) - \tfrac{1}{2} i (n'-\lambda) \tag{6.14}$$

are complex. λ can assume continuously all values from $-\infty$ to $+\infty$. The LAGUERRE functions with the complex indices n_1+m and n_2+m can again be represented by the integrals (4.6) and (4.7), from which a series expansion corresponding to (4.8) and an asymptotic representation corresponding to (4.10) may be derived. If the normalization is performed in the k and λ scales one obtains[1]:

$$u_{k\lambda m} = \frac{k}{\sqrt{\pi}}\, f_{k\lambda m}(k\xi)\, f_{k,-\lambda,m}(k\eta)\, e^{\pm i m\varphi} \tag{6.15}$$

where

$$f_{k\lambda m}(x) = C_{k\lambda} \frac{x^{\frac{1}{2}m}}{2\pi i} \int d\zeta\, e^{i x\zeta} \left(\zeta - \frac{1}{2}\right)^{-\frac{1}{2}+\frac{m}{2}-\frac{1}{2} i (n'+\lambda)} \left(\zeta + \frac{1}{2}\right)^{-\frac{1}{2}+\frac{m}{2}+\frac{1}{2} i (n'+\lambda)},$$

$$C_{k\lambda} = \prod_{\varrho=\frac{1}{2},\frac{3}{2},\ldots,\frac{m-1}{2}} \frac{1}{\sqrt{\varrho^2 + \frac{1}{4}(n'+\lambda)^2}} \cdot \frac{1}{\sqrt{1+e^{-\pi(n'+\lambda)}}},$$

[1] Cf. J. FISCHER, Ann. d. Phys. **8**, 821 (1931) paragraph 1; G. WENTZEL, Z. Physik **58**, 348 (1929).

when m is even,

$$C_{k\lambda} = \frac{1}{\sqrt{1+e^{-\pi(n'+\lambda)}}} \cdot \sqrt{\frac{2}{n'+\lambda}} \prod_{\varrho=1,2,\ldots,\frac{m-1}{2}} \frac{1}{\sqrt{\varrho^2+\frac{1}{4}(n'+\lambda)^2}},$$

when m is odd.

The path of integration in f consists, exactly as in (4.7), of a simple loop around the two branch points $\xi = \pm\frac{1}{2}$ (cf. Fig. 6). At large distances from the atom u behaves like a spherical wave, i.e., u falls off[1] as $1/r$.

γ) Eigenfunctions which behave asymptotically like plane waves. RUTHERFORD'S *scattering formula*[2]. In the theory of scattering of electrons and of other charged particles by bare nuclei it is convenient to construct a wave function which behaves asymptotically like an incident plane wave, with amplitude independent of r, plus an outgoing spherical wave. Such a wave function was first discussed by GORDON.

We try a wave function[3] of the form

$$u = e^{ikz} F(\eta) = e^{\frac{1}{2}ik\xi}\left[e^{-\frac{1}{2}ik\eta} F(\eta)\right], \tag{6.16}$$

where $k = +\sqrt{2E}$. We shall see that such a wave function has the required asymptotic behavior. Substituting (6.16) into the wave equation, we find that $F(\eta)$ is indeed a function of η only and satisfies the equation

$$\eta \frac{d^2F}{d\eta^2} + (1 - ik\eta)\frac{dF}{d\eta} + ZF = 0. \tag{6.17}$$

Comparison of (6.17) with (3.43) shows that $F(\eta)$ is, except for a normalization factor c, a LAGUERRE function

$$F(\eta) = c\,L_{-in'}(ik\eta); \quad n' = Z/k. \tag{6.18}$$

The solution u, (6.16) with (6.18), is mathematically similar to (6.15), but for a *complex* value of λ,

$$m = 0,\ \lambda = -(n'+i); \quad n_1 = 1,\ n_2 = -in'.$$

$F(\eta)$ can also be expressed in terms of a (confluent) hypergeometric function. Apart from a normalization constant it is

$$F(\eta) = F(in', 1, ik\eta) \tag{6.19}$$

where $n' = Z/k$.

Normalizing the wave function to unit charge density at large distance from the nucleus, we obtain the integral representation for u,

$$u = \sqrt{\frac{2\pi n'}{1-e^{-2\pi n'}}} \cdot e^{\frac{1}{2}ik\xi} \cdot \frac{1}{2\pi i}\int d\zeta\, e^{-ik\eta\zeta}\left(\zeta+\frac{1}{2}\right)^{-in'}\left(\zeta-\frac{1}{2}\right)^{in'-1}, \tag{6.20}$$

in which the path of integration, as before and exactly as in (4.7), consists of a simple loop going around the branch points $\xi = \pm\frac{1}{2}$. In view of (6.1), u is

[1] Cf. e. g., G. WENTZEL, Z. Physik **58**, 348 (1929), Eq. (22). More precisely, u falls off as $(r^2 - z^2)^{-\frac{1}{2}}$.

[2] W. GORDON: Z. Physik **48**, 180 (1928), cf. also G. TEMPLE, Proc. Roy. Soc. Lond., Ser. A **121**, 673 (1928); A. SOMMERFELD, Ann. d. Phys. **11**, 257 (1931), paragraph 6. See also p. 47 of ref. [9].

[3] See also ref. [9], p. 47.

represented asymptotically by

$$u = e^{i(kz - n' \log k(r-z) + \sigma_{n'})} + \frac{Z}{k^2(r-z)}\, e^{i(kr + n' \log k(r-z) - \sigma_{n'})}, \tag{6.21}$$

where $\sigma_{n'} = \arg \Gamma(1 + in')$ is the complex phase of the Γ-function.

The first term in (6.21) represents a plane wave incident in the z direction which is slightly modified by the COULOMB potential of the nucleus. Its amplitude does not depend on the separation r between electron and nucleus. The amplitude of the second term, on the other hand, is inversely proportional to r and thus represents a spherical wave; that the spherical wave is outgoing may be seen by including in (6.21) the time factor e^{-iEt}. The spherical wave is necessarily linked to the plane wave and represents the scattering of the electron by the nucleus.

Since the amplitude of the incident wave is unity and the velocity of each electron is k (atomic units), it is clear that k electrons per unit time enter the region of interaction with the nucleus through unit area of a surface which is perpendicular to the z-axis and is located at a great distance from the nucleus. The number of electrons scattered into the solid angle $d\Omega$ per unit time, i.e., the number leaving the field of force of the nucleus through an element of area $r^2\, d\Omega$ of a distant spherical surface per unit time, is given, in view of (6.21), by

$$k r^2\, d\Omega \cdot \left[\frac{Z}{k^2(r-z)}\right]^2 = k \cdot \frac{Z^2\, d\Omega}{k^4(1-\cos\vartheta)^2}.$$

In the above, $\vartheta = \arccos\frac{z}{r}$ is the angle of deviation of the electrons caused by scattering. The coefficient for scattering at the angle ϑ thus becomes:

$$\left.\begin{aligned} S^2(\vartheta) &= \frac{\text{number of particles scattered into the solid angle } d\Omega \text{ per unit time}}{\text{number of particles incident per unit area per unit time}} \\ &= \frac{Z^2\, d\Omega}{k^4(1-\cos\vartheta)^2} \text{ at. un.} \end{aligned}\right\} \tag{6.22}$$

S^2 has the dimensions of an area and is measured in atomic units (a^2). To change to c.g.s. units we must put

$$k^2 = E/\mathrm{Ry} \tag{6.23}$$

where E is the energy of the incident particles in c.g.s. units and thus (cf. Introduction):

$$S^2(\vartheta) = \frac{Z^2 \sin\vartheta\, d\vartheta\, d\varphi}{E^2(1-\cos\vartheta)^2} \cdot \mathrm{Ry}^2\, a^2 = \frac{e^4 Z^2 \sin\vartheta\, d\vartheta\, d\varphi}{16 E^2 \sin^4 \frac{1}{2}\vartheta}. \tag{6.24}$$

This is the well-known scattering formula of RUTHERFORD.

It is often useful to normalize (6.20) and (6.21) in some particular one of a number of different ways. Most frequently the normalization is such that one particle is incident on unit area per unit time; this requires multiplication of (6.20) and (6.21) by $\frac{1}{\sqrt{v}}$, where v is the velocity (k atomic units).

SOMMERFELD employs as eigenfunctions the system of functions

$$u_{\boldsymbol{k}} = e^{\frac{1}{2}i(kr + \boldsymbol{k}\cdot\boldsymbol{r})} \sqrt{\frac{n'}{1-e^{-2\pi n'}}} \cdot \frac{1}{(2\pi)^2 i} \cdot \int d\zeta \cdot \left(\zeta + \frac{1}{2}\right)^{-in'} \left(\zeta - \frac{1}{2}\right)^{in'-1} e^{-i(kr - \boldsymbol{k}\cdot\boldsymbol{r})\zeta} \tag{6.25}$$

in his theory of the continuous X-ray spectrum. $\boldsymbol{k}$ is a vector of variable direction and magnitude. The asymptotic formula for large r is

$$u_{\boldsymbol{k}} = (2\pi)^{-\frac{3}{2}} \left\{ e^{i[\boldsymbol{k}\cdot\boldsymbol{r} - n' \log(kr - \boldsymbol{k}\cdot\boldsymbol{r}) + \sigma_{n'}]} - \frac{n'}{kr - \boldsymbol{k}\cdot\boldsymbol{r}} \cdot e^{i[kr + n' \log(kr - \boldsymbol{k}\cdot\boldsymbol{r}) - \sigma_{n'}]} \right\}. \tag{6.26}$$

The system $u_{\boldsymbol{k}}$ makes the intuitive meaning of the eigenfunctions particularly clear. $u_{\boldsymbol{k}}$ is a simple plane wave incident in the $\boldsymbol{k}$ direction plus an associated scattered wave. The eigenfunction (6.26) is normalized in the k scale. Expanding an arbitrary function of the spatial coordinates in terms of the system (6.26)[1] one has

$$f(\boldsymbol{r}) = \int d k_x \, d k_y \, d k_z \, a_{\boldsymbol{k}} \, u_{\boldsymbol{k}}(\boldsymbol{r}) + \sum_{n_1 n_2 m} a_{n_1 n_2 m} \, u_{n_1 n_2 m}(\boldsymbol{r}), \tag{6.27}$$

and the coefficients in the expansion are given by

$$a_{\boldsymbol{k}} = \int u_{\boldsymbol{k}}^*(\boldsymbol{r}) \, f(\boldsymbol{r}) \, d\tau. \tag{6.28}$$

Finally, $u_{\boldsymbol{k}}$ can be normalized also per energy interval E and element of solid angle $d\Omega$. $d\Omega$ is the element of solid angle into which the vector $\boldsymbol{k}$ points and $E = \frac{1}{2} k^2$ atomic units. Thus, $dk_x \, dk_y \, dk_z = \sqrt{2E} \, dE \, d\Omega$. This change in normalization requires a division of (6.25) and (6.26) by $\sqrt[4]{2E} = \sqrt{k}$.

We have only discussed wave functions in the continuum which behave asymptotically like a plane wave plus spherically *outgoing* waves. For a physical problem involving *only* scattering by a pure COULOMB field, only these wave functions will occur. But in problems where the matrix element of some operator is required between an arbitrary initial state of the electron and a *final* state in the continuum, another set of wave functions is useful[2]. These other wave functions behave asymptotically like a plane wave plus spherical *incoming* waves. They can be obtained in an analogous manner, but the substitution (6.16) is replaced by

$$u = e^{ikz} G(\xi) = e^{-\frac{1}{2} i k \eta} \left[e^{\frac{1}{2} i k \xi} G(\xi) \right]. \tag{6.29}$$

An *alternative* complete set of eigenfunctions, analogous to (6.26), can be formed from wave functions of type (6.29).

The wave function (6.20), separated in parabolic coordinates, for positive energy E can also be expressed as a superposition of all the wave functions, separated in spherical polar coordinates, for the same energy E. This expansion for u, defined in (6.20) is[3]

$$u = \sqrt{\frac{\pi}{2k}} \sum_{l=0}^{\infty} (2l+1) \, i^l \, e^{-i\sigma_l} R_{Wl}(r) \, P_l(\cos\vartheta), \tag{6.30}$$

where $R_{Wl}(r)$ is the radial wave function for a particular value of l, given by (4.22) or (4.23), and $\sigma_l = \arg \Gamma(l + 1 + i n')$. Expansions of form similar to (6.30), but for a general central potential, will be discussed in Sect. 7.

7. Methods for the continuous spectrum for a general central potential. *α) General.* The separation of the SCHRÖDINGER wave equation in spherical polar coordinates (cf. Sect. 1) is possible for *any central* potential $V(r)$ (the potential V a function of the radial distance r only). The radial wave function $R_{nl}(r)$ satisfies a one-dimensional differential equation analogous to (2.1) (with $-Z/r$ replaced by V). For the continuous spectrum the radial wave function R_{El}, which is regular at the origin, is characterized by a positive value E of the total energy and by the orbital quantum number l. It has the asymptotic behavior of a standing spherical wave. The asymptotic form is similar to (4.10), but the logarithmic term is missing for a potential which falls off more rapidly than the COULOMB potential at large distances. For such a potential the asymptotic form of R

[1] To make the system $u_{\boldsymbol{k}}$ complete, the eigenfunctions of the discrete spectrum must, of course, be included.

[2] G. BREIT and H. A. BETHE: Phys. Rev. **93**, 888 (1954).

[3] W. GORDON: Z. Physik **48**, 180 (1928).

([9], p. 22) is

$$R_{El}(r) \sim (k\,r)^{-1} \sin\left(k\,r - \tfrac{1}{2}\pi\,l + \delta_l\right) \tag{7.1}$$

where $k = \sqrt{2E}$ and δ_l is a dimensionless constant, the "phase-shift for the partial wave l". The phase-shift δ_l depends on the energy E and is determined uniquely by the differential equation for R_{El} and the requirement that R be regular at the origin. For a few potential shapes (square well, exponential, MORSE potentials, etc.) the wave function R, and hence δ_l, can be obtained in analytic form, but for most potential shapes approximation methods have to be used.

The separation of the wave equation in parabolic coordinates, on the other hand, is possible *only* for the special case of the COULOMB potential (Sect. 6). Nevertheless, for *any* central potential $V(r)$ and for positive energy E, a superposition of the "spherical harmonic (partial wave) wave functions" can be found, which behaves asymptotically like a plane wave plus scattered spherical outgoing waves. This wave function is[1] ([9], p. 24)

$$u(r, \vartheta, \varphi) = \sum_{l=0}^{\infty} (2l+1)\, i^l\, e^{i\delta_l}\, R_{El}(r)\, P_l(\cos\vartheta) \tag{7.2}$$

where R_{El} is a radial wave function, normalized so that its asymptotic expression is given by (7.1), and δ_l is the phase-shift defined by (7.1). The asymptotic form of the wave function (7.2) is

$$u \sim e^{ikz} + r^{-1}\, e^{ikr} f(\vartheta), \tag{7.3}$$

where

$$f(\vartheta) = \frac{1}{2ik} \sum_{l=0}^{\infty} (2l+1)\left(e^{2i\delta_l} - 1\right) P_l(\cos\vartheta). \tag{7.4}$$

The quantity $|f(\vartheta)|^2$ has the dimension of an area and is called the "differential cross section", in complete analogy with the $S^2(\vartheta)$ of (6.22). The quantity $f(\vartheta)$ is called the scattering amplitude.

Some crude "order of magnitude" observations on the behavior of the infinite sum (7.4) can be made for potentials which have a certain "range" R_0, i.e. for potentials which are negligibly small for radial distances much larger than R_0: If $kR_0 \ll 1$, then all the higher phase shifts are small compared with δ_0 (the S-state phase-shift). In this case only the first (constant) term in (7.4) is important and $f(\vartheta)$ is approximately independent of ϑ (isotropic angular distribution). If, on the other hand, $kR_0 \gg 1$, then all the phase-shifts δ_l for $l \lesssim kR_0$ may be appreciable, but the terms in (7.4) with $l \gg kR_0$ can still be neglected. Now, for $l \neq 0$, $P_l(\cos\vartheta)$ is approximately equal to unity for $\vartheta < l^{-1}$, but oscillates rapidly for $\vartheta > l^{-1}$ if $l \gg 1$. If we cut the series (7.4) off at $l \sim kR_0$, then $f(\vartheta)$ will be approximately constant (and *finite*) for $\vartheta < (kR_0)^{-1}$. For $\vartheta \gg (kR_0)^{-1}$ there will be strong cancellations in (7.4), due to the oscillatory nature of the LEGENDRE functions with $\vartheta^{-1} < l < kR_0$. Thus $|f(\vartheta)|^2$ will decrease with increasing angle ϑ.

β) COULOMB potential. For the special case of a COULOMB potential the wave function[2] (7.2) represents a modified plane plus scattered wave. The asymptotic form of both the plane and scattered wave is modified by the presence of the logarithmic term and is given by (6.21) instead of (7.3). It was shown by GORDON[3] that for a COULOMB potential the sum (7.2) or (6.30) is identical with (6.20)

---

[1] For a potential falling off more rapidly than r^{-1} at large distances.

[2] With δ_l replaced by $-\sigma_l$, where σ_l is defined in (4.10). With this substitution (7.2) and (6.30) are identical except for a change in sign [see normalization of R_W, Eq. (4.19)].

[3] W. GORDON: Z. Physik **48**, 180 (1928).

and the square of the sum (7.4) for $f(\vartheta)$ identical with (6.22). Although we have already derived the expression (6.22) in closed form, it is instructive to consider the qualitative behavior of the sum (7.4) for a COULOMB potential. This sum is of importance for potentials which deviate only slightly from a COULOMB potential.

For a potential differing from a COULOMB potential only at small distances (e.g. electrostatic potential of a small, but finite, charged sphere) the radial wave functions have an asymptotic form similar to (4.10), including the logarithmic term. Only for the lowest few values of l do the values of σ_l differ appreciably from those given in (4.10). Consider next a potential which differs from (and is smaller than) a COULOMB potential only at *large* distances, e.g. the atomic HARTREE potential which falls off more rapidly than r^{-1} for r large compared with some screening radius R_0 (due to the screening by the atomic electrons). In this case the radial wave function has the asymptotic ($kr \gg 1$ *and* $r \gg R_0$) form (7.1), without any logarithmic term. But, if $kR_0 \gg 1$, the phase shifts δ_l for all but very large values of l are nearly equal to $(C-\sigma_l)$, where σ_l is given by (4.10) and C is a *constant* of the order of magnitude of $n' \log(2kR_0)$. Only for $l \gg kR_0$ do the phase shifts δ_l differ appreciably from $(C-\sigma_l)$. For these large values of l, δ_l decreases with increasing l without changing sign (see also Sect. 7γ).

In the relativistic DIRAC theory, finally, even for a *pure* COULOMB field separation of the wave equation in parabolic coordinates is impossible and infinite series analogous to (7.4) have to be summed (the equivalent phase-shifts in the relativistic case resemble the nonrelativistic σ_l for large values of l) (see Sect. 15).

We consider a general infinite series of form (7.4),

$$k\,f(\vartheta) = -\tfrac{1}{2} i \sum_{l=0}^{\infty} (2l+1)\, a_l\, P_l(\cos\vartheta). \tag{7.5}$$

For the special case of a COULOMB potential in the nonrelativistic theory we have, using (4.10),

$$a_l = e^{-2i\sigma_l} - 1 = \frac{\Gamma(l+1-i n')}{\Gamma(l+1+i n')} - 1, \tag{7.6}$$

where $n' = Z/k = Ze^2/\hbar v$. In this case we also have a closed analytic expression for $f(\vartheta)$, namely

$$k\,f(\vartheta) = \frac{n'}{(1-\cos\vartheta)} \exp\left[i n' \log(1-\cos\vartheta) - 2i\sigma_0\right]. \tag{7.7}$$

The function $f(\vartheta)$ has a singularity at $\vartheta = 0$ and the corresponding series (7.5) converges very poorly for small ϑ. Unlike the case of potentials with a finite range, for an unscreened COULOMB potential the phase-shifts σ_l, and hence a_l, do *not* decrease rapidly with increasing l for large l. For instance, if we restrict ourselves for the moment to the case of $n' \ll 1$ (energy E large compared with ground state binding energy), (7.6) reduces approximately to

$$a_l \approx -2i n' \psi(l+1), \quad \psi(z) = \frac{d}{dz} \log \Gamma(z). \tag{7.8}$$

For large l, (7.8) reduces further to the approximate expression

$$a_l \approx -2i n' \log\left(l + \tfrac{1}{2}\right), \tag{7.9}$$

which actually *increases* (in absolute magnitude) with l.

A convenient method for dealing with poorly convergent series of the type (7.5) was proposed recently[1]: For the COULOMB field and similar cases the poor

[1] YENNIE, RAVENHALL and WILSON: Phys. Rev. 95, 500 (1954).

convergence is due to a singularity of $f(\vartheta)$ at $\vartheta=0$. Much more rapidly convergent series can be obtained by multiplying the left and right sides of (7.5) by positive powers of $(1-\cos\vartheta)$, which removes (or at least lessens) the singularity of the left side. For instance, multiplying merely by the first power of $(1-\cos\vartheta)$ and rearranging the right hand side of (7.5) with the help of Eq. (A.22) of the appendix, we get

$$\left.\begin{aligned} k(1-\cos\vartheta)\,f(\vartheta) &= -\tfrac{1}{2}\,i\sum_{l=0}^{\infty}(2l+1)\,a_l'\,P_l(\cos\vartheta)\,;\\ (2l+1)\,a_l' &= (2l+1)\,a_l-(l+1)\,a_{l+1}-l\,a_{l-1}.\end{aligned}\right\}\tag{7.10}$$

For large l and for coefficients a_l of similar form to (7.6), one usually finds that a_l' is smaller than a_l by a factor of the order of l^2. For the special case where the coefficients a_l are given by the approximation (7.8), the coefficients a_l', defined by (7.10), vanish exactly for all l except for $l=0$. In this case we would have

$$k(1-\cos\vartheta)\,f(\vartheta)=n',\tag{7.7a}$$

which is just the first term in an expansion of (7.7) in powers of n'. If the exact expression (7.6) is used, a_l' decreases only as l^{-2} for large l. This is due to the fact that the *argument* of the exponential in the expression (7.7) for $(1-\cos\vartheta)\,f(\vartheta)$ still has a singularity at $\vartheta=0$, and it is convenient to apply the transformation (7.10) once more (or even twice).

γ) Born *approximation*[1]. Although no closed exact expression exists for $f(\vartheta)$ for a general central potential $V(r)$, an approximate expression for $f(\vartheta)$ in closed form can be derived, the "Born approximation". This approximation is valid only when the potential is "weak enough". Consider the Schrödinger wave Eq. (1.1) with Z/r replaced by $-V(r)$, the potential energy in atomic units of energy. We consider the potential as a small perturbation and take as our unperturbed wave function a single plane wave with momentum $\boldsymbol{k}_0$, where $k_0^2/2=E$, the total energy. We then apply first order perturbation theory to (1.1), obtaining the first order wave function as a superposition of eigenstates of the unperturbed Hamiltonian. These eigenstates are plane waves with momentum $\boldsymbol{k}$ for arbitrary direction of $\boldsymbol{k}$ but with $k^2=k_0^2=2E$. The coefficient in this superposition for a particular value of $\boldsymbol{k}\neq\boldsymbol{k}_0$ then represents the probability amplitude for scattering in the direction of $\boldsymbol{k}$. Finally, one obtains the Born approximation expression for $f(\vartheta)$, Eq. (7.3), in the form

$$\left.\begin{aligned} f(\vartheta) &= -\frac{1}{2\pi}\int d\tau\, e^{i(\boldsymbol{k}_0-\boldsymbol{k})\cdot\boldsymbol{r}}\,V(r) = -2\int_0^{\infty} dr\,r^2\,\frac{\sin Kr}{Kr}\,V(r)\,,\\ K &= 2k\sin\left(\tfrac{1}{2}\,\vartheta\right),\end{aligned}\right\}\tag{7.11}$$

where ϑ is the angle between the incident and scattered directions, $\boldsymbol{k}_0$ and $\boldsymbol{k}$.

An equivalent Born approximation expression can be obtained for the radial wave function $R_{El}(r)$ and the phase shift for the "partial wave" eigenstate for any value of the quantum number l. This is accomplished by solving the differential equation for R, analogous to (2.1), by first order perturbation theory. The Born approximation for the phase-shift ([9], p. 28) is

$$\delta_l^{(B)} = -\pi\int_0^{\infty} dr\,r\,[J_{l+\frac{1}{2}}(kr)]^2\,V(r)\,,\tag{7.12}$$

[1] See Sect. 9 and 70, also ref. [9], pp. 116—119.

where J is a BESSEL function. This expression is a good approximation if δ_l is small compared with $\pi/2$. It can be shown that the substitution of the approximation (7.12) for δ_l into (7.4) gives (after replacing $e^{2i\delta_l}$ by $1+2i\,\delta_l$) exactly the BORN approximation (7.11) for $f(\vartheta)$. (7.11) is thus a good approximation only if *each* δ_l is small. For potentials of short range usually all the δ_l are small except for the lowest few values of l. In such cases one can obtain a good and fairly simple approximation by evaluating δ_l exactly for the lowest few values of l and using the BORN approximation for all larger values of l. Making use of the relation between (7.11) and (7.12) one then obtains for $f(\vartheta)$ the expression (7.11) plus a series of a few terms, which involve $(e^{2i\delta_l}-1-2i\,\delta_l^{(B)})$.

For the special case of a COULOMB potential, the BORN approximation formula (7.11) for the scattering amplitude $f(\vartheta)$ gives the expression (7.7a). This expression differs from the exact one, (7.7), only by a phase factor which is small at high enough energies and reasonably large angles $\left(k \gg Z\,|\log(1-\cos\vartheta)|\right)$. On the other hand, the BORN approximation (7.12) for the partial wave phase shift δ_l is *not* useful for a COULOMB potential. In view of the logarithmic term in the asymptotic expression (4.10), the concept of a phase shift is somewhat ambiguous: Consider a screened COULOMB potential, e.g. $V(r)=-Z/r$ for $r<R_0$, $V=0$ for $r>R_0$, where $kR_0 \gg 1$. The phase shift is then given approximately by $\delta_l=(n'\log 2kR_0-\sigma_l)$ for $l<kR_0$. Even for small $n'=Z/k$, the first term in this expression is large compared with σ_l. It should be noted that for a weak attractive potential of short range the scattering amplitude $f(\vartheta)$ and the S-state phase shift δ_0 are positive and that δ_l decreases with increasing l. This is still true for a screened COULOMB potential for large k/Z, even though $(-\sigma_l)$, Eq. (4.10), is *negative* (σ_l is positive and increases with increasing l, $\delta_l=C-\sigma_l$ is positive and decreases with increasing l for $l<kR_0$. For $l>kR_0$, the phase shift δ_l depends on the details of the screening).

8. Wave functions in momentum space. Discrete spectrum. The wave function in momentum space, $\psi(\boldsymbol{p})$, is defined as the FOURIER transform of the ordinary "position space" wave function, $u(\boldsymbol{r})$. We shall use atomic units for momentum (see Introduction), the unit being the BOHR momentum, $p_0=mv_0=\hbar/a$. Explicitly, we have

$$\left.\begin{aligned}\psi(\boldsymbol{p}) &= (2\pi)^{-\frac{3}{2}}\int d^3r\, e^{-i\boldsymbol{r}\cdot\boldsymbol{p}}\, u(\boldsymbol{r}),\\ u(\boldsymbol{r}) &= (2\pi)^{-\frac{3}{2}}\int d^3r\, e^{i\boldsymbol{r}\cdot\boldsymbol{p}}\, \psi(\boldsymbol{p}).\end{aligned}\right\} \tag{8.1}$$

The wave function $\psi(\boldsymbol{p})$ satisfies the normalization condition

$$\int d^3p\, |\psi(\boldsymbol{p})|^2 = 1, \tag{8.2}$$

if $u(\boldsymbol{r})$ is normalized to unity.

Instead of first solving the SCHRÖDINGER equation in position space for $u(\boldsymbol{r})$ and then evaluating the FOURIER transform (8.1), it is often more convenient to rewrite the SCHRÖDINGER equation as an equation involving $\psi(\boldsymbol{p})$ directly. One possible method would be to use a representation of the quantum mechanical operators in which x is replaced by $i\,\partial/\partial p_x$, etc. The SCHRÖDINGER equation would then take the form of a differential equation in momentum space. Since one usually deals with potentials which depend on $\boldsymbol{r}$, but not on $\boldsymbol{p}$, such an equation usually is not easy to handle[1]. A more convenient approach[2] involves rewriting the SCHRÖDINGER equation in the form of an *integral* equation in momentum space.

---

[1] This method has, however, been used to obtain the momentum space wave functions for the discrete spectrum of hydrogen, E. A. HYLLERAAS, Z. Physik **74**, 216 (1932).

[2] H. WEYL: Z. Physik **46**, 1 (1928). — V. FOCK: Z. Physik **98**, 145 (1935).

Let $V(\boldsymbol{r})$ be an arbitrary potential in position space and $V'(\boldsymbol{p})$ its FOURIER transform [multiplied by $(2\pi)^{-\frac{3}{2}}$],

$$V'(\boldsymbol{p}) = (2\pi)^{-3} \int d^3r\, e^{-i\boldsymbol{r}\cdot\boldsymbol{p}}\, V(\boldsymbol{r}),$$
$$V(\boldsymbol{r}) = \int d^3p\, e^{i\boldsymbol{r}\cdot\boldsymbol{p}}\, V'(\boldsymbol{p}).$$

Let $u(\boldsymbol{r})$ and $\psi(\boldsymbol{p})$ be the wave function in position space and the momentum space, respectively, for an electron in this potential in a (bound) state of the discrete spectrum. By taking the FOURIER transform of the ordinary SCHRÖDINGER wave equation for $u(\boldsymbol{r})$ in position space, one obtains an integral equation for $\psi(\boldsymbol{p})$. For a state of negative energy E this equation is (in atomic units)

$$(p^2 - 2E)\,\psi(\boldsymbol{p}) = -2 \int d^3p'\, \psi(\boldsymbol{p}')\, V'(\boldsymbol{p} - \boldsymbol{p}'). \tag{8.3}$$

We are restricting ourselves to the case of "ordinary spatial potentials", which are represented in position space by a "local operator" $V(\boldsymbol{r})$, which simply multiplies the wave function $u(\boldsymbol{r})$ at each point $\boldsymbol{r}$ by a number $V(\boldsymbol{r})$. For such potentials the kernel of the integral equation (8.3), $V'(p-p')$, is a function of a *single* vector variable $(\boldsymbol{p}-\boldsymbol{p}')$. In some problems, such as in meson field theory and in the calculation of radiative corrections (see Sect. 19 and 28), more general types of "potentials" occur. These "velocity dependent" or "non-local" potentials are represented in position space by integral and/or differential operators. In many cases, however, these generalized potentials still lead to integral equations in momentum space for $\psi(\boldsymbol{p})$ of form (8.3), but $V'(\boldsymbol{p}-\boldsymbol{p}')$ is replaced by a kernel $K(\boldsymbol{p}, \boldsymbol{p}')$ which depends on *two* vector variables, $\boldsymbol{p}$ and $\boldsymbol{p}'$. We shall not consider such velocity dependent potentials further.

The potential operator ordinarily is HERMITian and $V(\boldsymbol{r})$ is real. In this case one can show[1] that $V'(\boldsymbol{q}) = V'^*(-\boldsymbol{q})$. If, further, the potential $V(\boldsymbol{r})$ is a central one (function of the radial distance r only), then the "momentum space potential" $V'(\boldsymbol{p})$ is a function of the absolute value of $\boldsymbol{p}$ only and is real.

For a central potential $V'(p)$, the "wave equation" (8.3) is separable in spherical polar coordinates. If (p, ϑ, φ) are the polar coordinates of the momentum $\boldsymbol{p}$, solutions exist of the form

$$\psi_{lm}(\boldsymbol{p}) = F_l(p)\, Y_{lm}(\vartheta, \varphi). \tag{8.4}$$

In this case (8.3) can be reduced, at least in principle, to a one-dimensional integral equation for $F_l(p)$ of form

$$\left.\begin{aligned}(p^2 - 2E)\, F_l(p) &= -\lambda \int_0^\infty dp'\, p'^2\, K_l(p, p')\, F_l(p');\\ \lambda K_l(p, p') &= 4\pi \int_{-1}^{1} dx\, V'\left(\sqrt{p^2 + p'^2 - 2pp'x}\right) P_l(x).\end{aligned}\right\} \tag{8.5}$$

The kernel K_l is symmetric in p and p' and depends on the value of l and on the *shape* of the potential $V(r)$. For convenience, the *strength* of the potential is contained in the multiplying factor λ. For mathematical purposes it is often convenient to consider the energy E as given and λ, the "potential strength parameter", as the eigenvalue to be determined. The integral equation (8.5) can be solved exactly only for a few specially simple potential shapes. For other potential shapes some approximation methods, notably iteration and variational methods,

---

[1] More generally, let $f(\boldsymbol{r})$ and $g(\boldsymbol{r})$ be two functions, which are complex conjugates of each other, $f^*(\boldsymbol{r}) = g(\boldsymbol{r})$. If $F(\boldsymbol{p})$ and $G(\boldsymbol{p})$ are the FOURIER transforms of f and g, respectively, one finds that $F^*(\boldsymbol{p}) = G(-\boldsymbol{p})$.

are available, but these procedures usually give good results only for the ground state and, possibly, for low excited states[1].

The expression $|pF_l(p)|^2$ is called the momentum distribution function. The probability for the absolute value of the momentum of the electron (irrespective of direction) to lie between p and $p+dp$ is $|pF_l(p)|^2\,dp$.

We return now to the special case of a COULOMB potential, $V(r)=-Z/r$. The momentum space potential is then

$$V'(p) = -\frac{Z}{2\pi^2 p^2}. \tag{8.6a}$$

The singularity of $V'(p)$ at $p=0$ is a characteristic of the "infinite range" of the COULOMB potential. Consider, for instance, a "screened COULOMB potential" $V(r)$ which deviates appreciably from the COULOMB potential only at *large* distances and falls off more rapidly for $r \gg R_0$, say. $V'(p)$ for such a potential deviates from the COULOMB expression only for *small* momenta and remains finite and practically constant for $pR_0 \ll 1$. For a potential of YUKAWA shape, for instance, we have

$$V(r) = -\frac{Z}{r}\,e^{-r/R_0}, \qquad V'(p) = -\frac{Z}{2\pi^2(p^2+R_0^{-2})}. \tag{8.6b}$$

To avoid ambiguities arising from the singularity of (8.6a) it is sometimes convenient to consider it as the limiting case of (8.6b) and to proceed to the limit only after integrations, etc., have been carried out.

Substituting the unscreened COULOMB potential (8.6a) into (8.3), this three-dimensional integral equation then is

$$(p^2-2E)\,\psi(\mathbf{p}) = \frac{Z}{\pi^2}\int d^3p\,\frac{\psi(\mathbf{p}')}{|\mathbf{p}-\mathbf{p}'|^2}. \tag{8.6}$$

(8.6) has "partial wave" solutions of form (8.4) and the radial wave function $F_l(p)$ satisfies a one-dimensional integral equation of form (8.5). Using the addition theorem of the spherical harmonics and the orthogonality properties of the LEGENDRE polynomials, the kernel K_l in (8.5) can be evaluated explicity. (8.5) then reduces to

$$(p^2-2E)\,F_l(p) = \frac{2Z}{\pi p}\int_0^\infty dp'\,p'\,Q_l\left(\frac{p^2+p'^2}{2pp'}\right)F_l(p') \tag{8.7}$$

where Q_l is a LEGENDRE function of the second kind[2], related to the unnormalized LEGENDRE function of the first kind, P_l, by

$$Q_l(z) = \frac{1}{2}\int_{-1}^{1} dt\,\frac{P_l(t)}{z-t}.$$

For negative values of E, (8.7) has solutions, $F_{nl}(p)$, for a discrete spectrum of energy eigenvalues E_n. The spectrum E_n is, of course, identical with that obtained by solving (Sect. 2) the SCHRÖDINGER differential wave equation in position space (n is again the principal quantum number). The radial momentum space wave function $F_{nl}(p)$ depends on n and the orbital quantum number

---

[1] N. SVARTHOLM: Thesis, Lund 1945. — R. MCWEENY and C. A. COULSON: Proc. Phys. Soc. Lond. A **62**, 509 (1949). — M. LÉVY: Proc. Roy. Soc. Lond. **204**, 145 (1950). — E. E. SALPETER: Phys. Rev. **84**, 1226 (1951).

[2] See, for instance, JAHNKE and EMDE, Funktionentafeln, 4th Ed., p. 109. Berlin: Springer 1945.

$l (l \gtrless n-1)$ but not on the magnetic quantum number m. The Eq. (8.7) has been solved directly by FOCK[1]. The wave functions $F_{nl}(p)\, Y_{lm}$ had been obtained previously[2] by carrying out the FOURIER transformation on the position space wave functions (Sect. 3).

The explicit expressions for the radial momentum space wave functions $F_{nl}(p)$ for a COULOMB potential follow. We give the wave functions for hydrogen $(Z=1)$, normalized such that

$$\int_0^\infty dp\, p^2 |F_{nl}(p)|^2 = 1$$

and p is expressed in atomic units[3] $(p_0 = \hbar/a)$

$$F_{nl}(p) = \left[\frac{2}{\pi} \frac{(n-l-1)!}{(n+l)!}\right]^{\frac{1}{2}} n^2\, 2^{2(l+1)}\, l!\, \frac{n^l p^l}{(n^2 p^2+1)^{l+2}}\, C_{n-l-1}^{l+1}\left(\frac{n^2 p^2-1}{n^2 p^2+1}\right), \tag{8.8}$$

where $C_N^\nu(x)$ is the GEGENBAUER function, defined as the coefficient of h^N in the expansion of $(1-2hx+h^2)^{-\nu}$ in powers of h. Recurrence formulae for C_N^ν will be found in [8], p. 329. The explicit expressions for C_N^ν for a few values of N are

$$\left.\begin{aligned} C_0^\nu(x) &= 1, \quad C_1^\nu(x) = 2\nu x, \\ C_2^\nu(x) &= 2\nu(\nu+1)\, x^2 - \nu. \end{aligned}\right\} \tag{8.9}$$

The first three radial wave functions $F_{nl}(p)$ are

$$\left.\begin{aligned} F_{10} &= 4\sqrt{\frac{2}{\pi}}\, \frac{1}{(p^2+1)^2}, \\ F_{20} &= \frac{32}{\sqrt{\pi}}\, \frac{4p^2-1}{(4p^2+1)^3}, \\ F_{21} &= \frac{128}{\sqrt{3\pi}}\, \frac{p}{(4p^2+1)^3}. \end{aligned}\right\} \tag{8.10}$$

The expressions (8.8) simplify if $np \ll 1$ or $np \gg 1$: For $np=0$, the argument of the GEGENBAUER function C is -1, for $np=\infty$ the argument is $+1$, and

$$C_N^\nu(1) = (-1)^N C_N^\nu(-1) = \frac{(2\nu+N-1)!}{(2\nu-1)!\, N!}.$$

For $l=0$ and 1, for instance, the radial functions approach the following values as $np \to \infty$

$$F_{n0}(p) = \sqrt{\frac{2}{n^3 \pi}}\, \frac{4}{p^4}, \quad F_{n1}(p) = \sqrt{\frac{2(n^2-1)}{n^5 \pi}}\, \frac{8}{3p^5}. \tag{8.11}$$

More generally we have, as $np \to \infty$,

$$F_{nl}(p) \to 4\, \frac{2^{2l}\, l!}{(2l+1)!} \sqrt{\frac{2}{n^3 \pi}} \left(\prod_{s=0}^{l} \sqrt{1-\frac{s^2}{n^2}}\right) \frac{1}{p^{4+l}}. \tag{8.12}$$

The ratio of two radial functions with the same value of l, but different values of n, is thus independent of p for large values of p. As np approaches zero, the radial function F_{nl} approaches zero for all non-zero values of l. For $l=0$ (S-states) it approaches

$$F_{n0}(0) = (-1)^{n-1}\, 4n^3 \sqrt{\frac{2}{n\pi}}. \tag{8.13}$$

---

[1] V. FOCK: Z. Physik **98**, 145 (1935).

[2] B. PODOLANSKI and L. PAULING: Phys. Rev. **34**, 109 (1929).

[3] The expressions for arbitrary nuclear charge Z are *identical* with those for hydrogen if p is expressed in units of (Zp_0).

The momentum space wave function at $p=0$ is $(2\pi)^{-\frac{3}{2}}$ times the volume integral of the position space wave function $u(\boldsymbol{r})$.

Using the known properties of the GEGENBAUER functions, one can evaluate the expectation value of the square of the momentum. It is

$$\overline{p^2} = \int_0^\infty dp\, p^2 \, |F_{nl}(p)|^2 \, p^2 = (Z\, p_0/n)^2, \tag{8.14}$$

where p_0 is the BOHR momentum for hydrogen ($\overline{p^2}$ for general nuclear charge Z). This relation could also have been derived from the virial theorem, (3.29), from which it follows that the expectation value of the kinetic energy $(p^2/2m)$ equals minus the total energy E.

Omit this section (§9) for now

9. Wave functions in momentum space. Continuous spectrum[1]. *α) General theory.* For positive total energy E the treatment of the integral equation (8.3) for the wave function in momentum space has to be modified. This is due to the fact that the left hand side of (8.3) vanishes if $|\boldsymbol{p}| = \sqrt{2E}$ and remains unchanged if any function is added to $\psi(\boldsymbol{p})$ on the left side, which is non-zero only for $p=\sqrt{2E}$. Before discussing (8.3), an equation in the explicit momentum space representation, we shall note some more general results.

We consider the equation of state for an eigenstate ψ of a HAMILTONian H which consists of two parts. Written in symbolic operator notation this equation is

$$(E-H)\,\psi = 0, \qquad H = H_0 + V,$$

where both H_0 and V are HERMITian. We assume that H_0 has a continuous spectrum of eigenstates, which we consider as known, and that E coincides with one of the eigenvalues in this spectrum. Let u_0 be *any* eigenstate of H_0 with energy eigenvalue E. We can then write ψ in the form

$$\psi = u_0 + \chi, \qquad (E-H_0)\,u_0 = 0,$$

where χ satisfies the equation

$$(E - H_0 - V)\,\chi - V\,u_0 = 0. \tag{9.1}$$

If we want to multiply Eq. (9.1) by the inverse operator of either $(E-H_0)$ or $(E-H)$ the resulting equations would not be well-determined unless we give an explicit prescription for handling the singularity of the "energy denominator". Two possible prescriptions are to add a positive or negative infinitesimally small quantity $\pm i\,\varepsilon$ to E in (9.1). We denote the eigenstates ψ, defined by these prescriptions, by $\psi_\pm = u_0 + \chi_\pm$. The modified Eq. (9.1) can then be rewritten in either of two forms,

$$\chi_\pm = \frac{1}{(E - H \pm i\,\varepsilon)}\, V\,u_0 \tag{9.2}$$

or

$$\chi_\pm = \frac{1}{(E - H_0 \pm i\,\varepsilon)}\, V(u_0 + \chi_\pm). \tag{9.3$^\pm$}$$

We can now show that there is one unique state ψ_+ (and ψ_-) corresponding to *each* eigenstate u_0 of H_0: Consider $(V\,u_0)$ expanded in terms of some complete set of eigenstates of the *total* HAMILTONian H. Since H is HERMITian, all its eigenvalues are real and hence the energy denominator in (9.2) can never vanish and $\chi_\pm$ is, therefore, determined uniquely. For many practical problems Eq. (9.2)

---

[1] B. A. LIPPMANN and J. SCHWINGER: Phys. Rev. **79**, 469 (1950). — M. L. GOLDBERGER: Phys. Rev. **82**, 757; **84**, 929 (1951). — E. E. SALPETER: Phys. Rev. **84**, 1226 (1951).

is not a suitable starting point, since the denominator contains H, the *total* HAMILTONian[1]. We shall use, instead, Eq. (9.3) and expand $\chi_\pm$ as well as $V(u_0+\chi_\pm)$ in terms of a complete set of eigenstates of H_0. Since H_0 is HERMITian, its eigenvalues are real and the denominator in (9.3) also cannot vanish. (9.3) can then be reduced to an explicit inhomogeneous integral equation for the expansion coefficient of $\chi_\pm$, with the expansion coefficient of $V u_0$ providing the inhomogeneous term. In Sects. 9β and 9γ we shall consider the special case of $H_0 = p^2/2m$, the kinetic energy operator, with V standing for an ordinary potential. In Sect. 9β we shall further specialize the complete set of eigenfunctions of H_0 to the set of all "plane wave" states of a free electron. The expansion coefficients of $\chi_\pm$ then reduce to the momentum space wave functions.

The prescriptions used in (9.3) are, of course, not the only possible ones for handling the singularity of $(E-H_0)^{-1}$. One other prescription is to use the principal value $\mathscr{P}$ of this denominator. To show the connection between the various prescriptions we first define two functions by

$$\mathscr{P}\left(\frac{1}{y}\right) = \frac{y}{y^2+\varepsilon^2}\,, \qquad \delta(y) = \frac{1}{\pi}\,\frac{\varepsilon}{y^2+\varepsilon^2} \tag{9.4}$$

where ε is an infinitesimally small real and positive quantity. We then have the relations

$$\left.\begin{aligned} \mathscr{P}\left(\frac{1}{y}\right) &= \frac{1}{2}\left(\frac{1}{y-i\varepsilon} + \frac{1}{y+i\varepsilon}\right), \\ \delta(y) &= \frac{1}{2\pi i}\left(\frac{1}{y-i\varepsilon} - \frac{1}{y+i\varepsilon}\right). \end{aligned}\right\} \tag{9.5}$$

The functions defined in (9.4) represent the principal value of y^{-1} and the DIRAC delta-function, respectively, in the following sense: If y is finite, then $\mathscr{P}(1/y)$ and $\delta(y)$ tend to y^{-1} and zero, respectively, as ε tends to zero. Further, if $f(y)$ is a function which is continuous at the origin but otherwise arbitrary and a and b are positive constants, we have

$$\int_{-a}^{b} dy\,\mathscr{P}\left(\frac{1}{y}\right) f(y) \to \mathscr{P}\int_{-a}^{b} \frac{dy}{y} f(y), \qquad \int_{-a}^{b} dy\,\delta(y)\,f(y) \to f(0)$$

where the arrows indicate the limiting expressions as ε tends to zero. For any particular eigenstate u_0 of H_0 we can then define a unique eigenstate $\psi_{(1)}$ of H by the following equation [instead of $(9.3^\pm)$]

$$\psi_{(1)} = u_0 + \chi_{(1)}; \qquad \chi_{(1)} = \mathscr{P}\left(\frac{1}{E-H_0}\right) V\,\psi_{(1)}. \tag{9.3a}$$

This principal value prescription is particularly useful in discussing the "partial wave" solutions. As will be shown in Sect. 9γ, it results in wave functions which behave asymptotically like *standing* spherical waves.

We have now given three different prescriptions for defining particular eigenstates ψ_+, ψ_- and $\psi_{(1)}$ of H, which correspond to a *particular* eigenstate u_0 of H_0. The states ψ_+, ψ_- and $\psi_{(1)}$, corresponding to the *same* state u_0, differ from each other in general. It should be noted, however, that the set of states ψ_+, which corresponds to a complete set of eigenstates u_0 of H_0, is by itself a complete[2] set of eigenstates of H. An example of such a set of states was discussed in Sect. 6γ with $H_0 = p^2/2m$ and V equal to the COULOMB potential. There each u_0 represented

[1] Eq. (9.2) has been used recently, however, as the starting point of calculations in meson field theory. See, e.g., G. F. CHEW and F. E. LOW, Phys. Rev. **101**, 1570 (1956).

[2] Actually, the bound states must be included to complete the set.

a plane wave and the corresponding ψ_+ that plane wave plus outgoing spherical waves, scattered by the potential. (6.25) is the position space wave function for such a state and its momentum space wave function will be discussed in Sect. 9β, (9.12). Quite generally, *each* of the sets of states ψ_+, ψ_-, and $\psi_{(1)}$, corresponding to a set u_0, forms an *alternative* complete set of eigenstates of H.

Further, definite relations exist between the various states ψ_+, ψ_- and $\psi_{(1)}$, all belonging to the *same* energy eigenvalue E. First, any state ψ_+ of energy E can be written as a linear superposition of states ψ_- (or $\psi_{(1)}$), all of the same energy E. Second, for any eigenstate u of H_0 we can find another eigenstate u' of H_0 with the *same* energy eigenvalue, such that ψ_+ corresponding to u is *identical* with $\psi_{(1)}$ (or ψ_-) corresponding to u'. This can be seen as follows. Let $\psi_+[u]$ be a particular solution of (9.3$^\pm$),

$$\psi_+[u] = u + \frac{1}{E - H_0 + i\varepsilon} V \psi_+[u].$$

With the help of (9.5) we can rewrite this equation in the form

$$\psi_+[u] = u' + \mathcal{P}\left(\frac{1}{E - H_0}\right) V \psi_+[u],$$

where

$$u' = u - \pi i \,\delta(E - H_0)\, V \psi_+[u].$$

Consider $V\psi_+[u]$ expanded in terms of eigenstates of H_0. The presence of the delta-function $\delta(E - H_0)$ then ensures that u' is some eigenstate of H_0 which belongs to the same energy eigenvalue E. We see then that the solution $\psi_+[u]$ of (9.3$^\pm$) corresponding to u is identical with the solution $\psi_{(1)}[u']$ of (9.3a) corresponding to the eigenstate u' of H_0. Similarly one finds that $\psi_+[u]$ is identical with $\psi_-[u'']$, where

$$u'' = u - 2\pi i \,\delta(E - H_0)\, V \psi_+[u],$$

and so on.

β) Plane wave solutions. We return now to our explicit momentum space representation for a single particle moving in an "ordinary" potential $V(\boldsymbol{r})$ with Fourier transform $V'(\boldsymbol{p})$. We can obtain from the general theory of Sect. 9α an integral equation analogous to (8.3) in the following manner. We take for H_0 the kinetic energy operator $p^2/2m$. The "plane wave" states of the particle form a complete set of eigenstates of the momentum operator, and hence also of H_0. We can then consider the momentum space wave function $\psi(\boldsymbol{p})$ of an eigenstate of the total Hamiltonian H as the expansion coefficient of this state in terms of the plane wave states. To define a definite eigenstate ψ of the total Hamiltonian, we must still choose one of the prescriptions (9.3$^\pm$) or (9.3a) and a particular eigenstate u_0 of H_0 with positive energy eigenvalue E. We discuss first the equation for a state ψ_+ obtained from (9.3$^+$) with u_0 chosen as a *single* plane wave with momentum $\boldsymbol{k}$.

We use again atomic units and consider a definite momentum $\boldsymbol{k}$ with $k^2 = 2E$. Except for a normalization factor, the momentum space wave function of a plane wave state of this momentum is the three-dimensional Dirac delta-function $\delta^{(3)}(\boldsymbol{p} - \boldsymbol{k})$. Expanding both sides of the Eq. (9.3$^+$) in terms of plane waves and considering the expansion coefficient for momentum $\boldsymbol{p}$, we obtain the equation

$$\left.\begin{aligned} \psi_+(\boldsymbol{p}) &= \delta^{(3)}(\boldsymbol{p} - \boldsymbol{k}) + \chi_+(\boldsymbol{p}), \\ \chi_+(\boldsymbol{p}) &= \frac{2}{(k + i\varepsilon)^2 - p^2} \int d^3p' \, \psi_+(\boldsymbol{p}') \, V'(\boldsymbol{p} - \boldsymbol{p}'). \end{aligned}\right\} \tag{9.6}$$

(9.6) is an integral equation for the momentum space wave function $\psi_+(\boldsymbol{p})$ in analogy with (8.3) for the discrete spectrum, but differs from it in the presence of the delta-function as an inhomogeneous term and in the presence of the infinitesimal positive imaginary part $i\varepsilon$. The prescription (9.3⁻) with the same plane wave for u_0 leads to a similar equation for $\psi_-(\boldsymbol{p})$, the momentum space wave function for the state ψ_-. This equation for $\psi_-(\boldsymbol{p})$ or $\chi_-(\boldsymbol{p})$ is identical with (9.6) except that $(k+i\varepsilon)$ is replaced by $(k-i\varepsilon)$. For a central potential, $V'(\boldsymbol{p})$ is a real function and hence $\psi_-(\boldsymbol{p})$ is the complex conjugate of $\psi_+(\boldsymbol{p})$, $\chi_-(\boldsymbol{p})$ that of $\chi_+(\boldsymbol{p})$. Finally, the prescription (9.3a) gives an equation for $\psi_{(1)}(\boldsymbol{p})$ which is again identical with (9.6) except that $[(k+i\varepsilon)^2-p^2]^{-1}$ is replaced by the principal value of $(k^2-p^2)^{-1}$.

(9.6) can also be rewritten in terms of a function $f_+(\boldsymbol{p})$ as follows

$$\left.\begin{aligned} \psi_\pm(\boldsymbol{p}) - \delta^{(3)}(\boldsymbol{p}-\boldsymbol{k}) &\equiv \chi_\pm(\boldsymbol{p}) = -\frac{f_\pm(\boldsymbol{p})}{2\pi^2(k\pm i\varepsilon-p)(k+p)}, \\ f_\pm(\boldsymbol{p}) &= -(2\pi)^2\left[V'(\boldsymbol{p}-\boldsymbol{k}) + \int d^3p'\,\chi_\pm(\boldsymbol{p}')\,V'(\boldsymbol{p}-\boldsymbol{p}')\right]. \end{aligned}\right\} \tag{9.7}$$

In (9.7) the positive subscripts refer to (9.6), the negative subscripts to the analogous equation for ψ_-. The function $f_+(\boldsymbol{p})$ [and $f_-(\boldsymbol{p})$], unlike $\psi_+(\boldsymbol{p})$ and $\chi_+(\boldsymbol{p})$, in general[1] has *no* singularity for $|\boldsymbol{p}|=k$. We shall see, in fact, that the values of $f_+(\boldsymbol{p})$ for $|\boldsymbol{p}|=k$ ("on the energy shell") are related to the scattering amplitude $f(\vartheta)$, discussed in Sect. 7. To show this we consider next the asymptotic forms of the (position) spatial wave functions corresponding to $\psi_+(\boldsymbol{p})$ and $\psi_-(\boldsymbol{p})$.

For the moment we consider (9.6) or (9.7) as solved (we discuss methods of solution later) and hence $f_+(\boldsymbol{p})$ and $f_-(\boldsymbol{p})$ as known. We shall assume further that $f_\pm(\boldsymbol{p})$ is a smoothly varying function without singularities. To obtain the spatial wave function we have to evaluate the FOURIER transform of $\psi_\pm(\boldsymbol{p})$. We shall need the integral

$$\mathcal{J}_\pm(\boldsymbol{r}) = \int \frac{d^3p\, e^{i\boldsymbol{r}\cdot\boldsymbol{p}} f_\pm(\boldsymbol{p})}{(k\pm i\varepsilon-p)(k+p)} = \int_0^\infty \frac{dp\, p^2}{(k\pm i\varepsilon-p)(k+p)} \int_0^{2\pi} d\varphi \int_{-1}^{1} dx\, e^{irpx} f_\pm(p,x,\varphi), \tag{9.8}$$

where we have used spherical polar coordinates for $\boldsymbol{p}$ with the vector $\boldsymbol{r}$ as axis and x is the cosine of the angle between $\boldsymbol{r}$ and $\boldsymbol{p}$. We are mainly interested in the asymptotic form of $\mathcal{J}_\pm(\boldsymbol{r})$, i.e. the limit as $kr\to\infty$. We can then carry out the integration over x first, using the relation

$$\int_{-1}^{1} dx\, e^{irpx} f(x) \approx \frac{1}{irp}\left[e^{irp} f(1) - e^{-irp} f(-1)\right].$$

This relation, obtained by integrating by parts, is true for any $f(x)$ without singularities in the limit of $pr\to\infty$ and is also exact for all pr if $f(x)$ is a constant. We substitute this relation into (9.8) and carry out the integration over φ by noting that, if a function $f(\boldsymbol{p})=f(p,x,\varphi)$ is single-valued and well-behaved, then $f(p,\pm 1,\varphi)$ is independent of φ. Denoting this function by $f(p,\pm 1)$, the asymptotic expression for $\mathcal{J}_\pm(\boldsymbol{r})$ reduces to a one-dimensional integral,

$$\mathcal{J}_\pm(\boldsymbol{r}) = \frac{2\pi}{ir}\int_0^\infty \frac{dp\, p}{(k\pm i\varepsilon-p)(k+p)}\left[e^{irp} f_\pm(p,1) - e^{-irp} f_\pm(p,-1)\right].$$

Next we change the variable of integration from p to $-p$ in the second term in this integral. The function f occuring in either part of the transformed integral

[1] For a COULOMB potential, f_+ still has a singularity at $\boldsymbol{p}=\boldsymbol{k}$.

is then of form $f(\boldsymbol{r}p/r)$, the value of the function $f(\boldsymbol{p})$ for a vector $\boldsymbol{p}$ which has absolute magnitude $|\boldsymbol{p}|$ and the direction of $\boldsymbol{r}$ if p is positive, of $-\boldsymbol{r}$ if p is negative. Finally we can convert this integral into a contour integral by adding a "semi-circle at infinity" in the upper-half complex plane, which gives a vanishingly small contribution to the integral. The position of the poles, which are different for $\mathcal{J}_+$ and $\mathcal{J}_-$, as well as the contour C are shown in Fig. 9. Evaluating this contour integral, we find

$$\left.\begin{aligned}\mathcal{J}_\pm(\boldsymbol{r}) &= \frac{2\pi}{i\,r}\oint\limits_C \frac{dp\,p\,f_\pm(\boldsymbol{r}p/r)\,e^{irp}}{(k^2-p^2)}\\ &= -2\pi^2 f_\pm\left(\pm\frac{\boldsymbol{r}k}{r}\right)\frac{e^{\pm irk}}{r}.\end{aligned}\right\}\qquad(9.9)$$

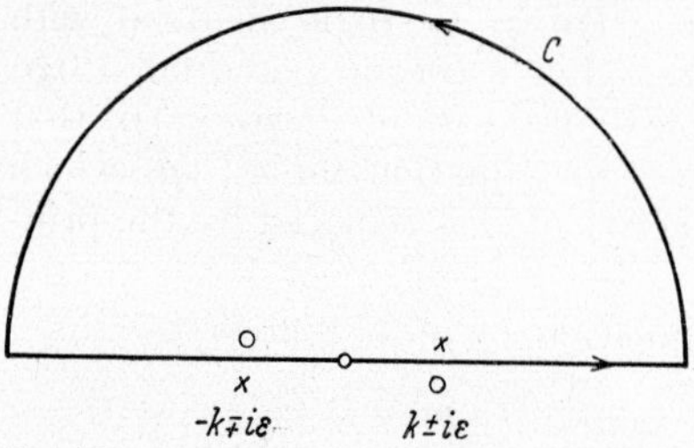

Fig. 9. The integration contour C for the integral occuring in Eq. (9.9). The first order poles for the integral $\mathcal{J}_+$ are marked by crosses, those for $\mathcal{J}_-$ by circles.

The expression (9.9) holds only asymptotically as $kr\to\infty$ in general, but is exact if $f_\pm$ is a constant.

Using (9.9) we obtain the asymptotic forms of the spatial wave functions $u_\pm(\boldsymbol{r})$, which are the FOURIER-transforms [multiplied by $(2\pi)^{\frac{3}{2}}$] of $\varphi_+(\boldsymbol{p})$ and $\varphi_-(\boldsymbol{p})$,

$$\left.\begin{aligned}u_+(\boldsymbol{r}) &\equiv \int d^3p\,e^{i\boldsymbol{r}\cdot\boldsymbol{p}}\,\varphi_+(\boldsymbol{p}) = e^{i\boldsymbol{k}\cdot\boldsymbol{r}} + f_+\left(\frac{\boldsymbol{r}k}{r}\right)\frac{e^{ikr}}{r},\\ u_-(\boldsymbol{r}) &= e^{i\boldsymbol{k}\cdot\boldsymbol{r}} + f_-\left(-\frac{\boldsymbol{r}k}{r}\right)\frac{e^{-ikr}}{r}.\end{aligned}\right\}\qquad(9.10)$$

The first part of the asymptotic expression (9.10) for both $u_+(\boldsymbol{r})$ and $u_-(\boldsymbol{r})$ represents an unperturbed plane wave with momentum $\boldsymbol{k}$. The second part of u_+ represents a spherical outgoing wave, the effect of the scattering by the potential of the incident plane wave. The angular distribution of the scattering is determined by $f_+(\boldsymbol{r}k/r)$, called the scattering amplitude. Note that the amplitude for scattering into any direction is determined completely by the value of the function $f_+(\boldsymbol{p})$, Eq. (9.7), "on the energy-shell" i.e. for a vector $\boldsymbol{p}$ pointing in this direction, but of absolute magnitude k. For the special case of a central potential, the scattering amplitude $f_+(\boldsymbol{r}k/r)$ depends only on the angle ϑ between the scattering direction ($\boldsymbol{r}$) and $\boldsymbol{k}$. In this case $f_+(\boldsymbol{r}k/r)$ is identical with the function $f(\vartheta)$, Eq. (7.3).

The wave function $u_-(\boldsymbol{r})$, on the other hand, represents a state in which spherically incoming waves are incident on the potential with phase and amplitude relations such that the result of the scattering is a single plane wave of momentum $\boldsymbol{k}$. For the special case of a central potential, $f_-(\boldsymbol{p}) = f_+^*(\boldsymbol{p})$. In this case the spatial wave function u_+ corresponding to an incident plane wave with momentum $\boldsymbol{k}$ is the complex conjugate of the function u_- corresponding to an emergent plane wave with momentum *minus* $\boldsymbol{k}$. Our third prescription, involving the "principal value" Eq. (9.3a), is not of general use in connection with "plane wave" solutions.

For most forms of the potential function V', no exact solutions of the integral Eq. (9.6) or (9.7) are available at present. (9.7) differs from (8.3), the equation for negative energy E, by being an inhomogeneous integral equation. There is no eigenvalue to be determined but, once the inhomogeneous term $V'(\boldsymbol{p}-\boldsymbol{k})$ is given, the solution of (9.7) gives uniquely not only the shape of the function $\chi_+(\boldsymbol{p})$, but also its absolute value for all $\boldsymbol{p}$. For a weak enough potential one can use the following simple perturbation method, equivalent to the BORN approximation which was discussed in Sect. 7: If V' contains a *small* multiplicative factor λ, then χ_+ and f_+ will be approximately linear in λ and the integral on the right side of (9.7) approximately quadratic in λ. First order BORN approximation consists in simply omitting the integral on the right side of (9.7),

$$f_{\pm}^{(B)}(\boldsymbol{p}) = -(2\pi)^2 V'(\boldsymbol{p}-\boldsymbol{k}). \tag{9.11}$$

As discussed before, the differential scattering cross section $|f(\vartheta)|^2$ is determined completely by the value of $f_+(\boldsymbol{p})$ "on the energy shell", i.e. for $|\boldsymbol{p}|=k$. For a central potential, the expression (9.11) on the energy shell, $-(2\pi)^2 V'(2k\sin\frac{1}{2}\vartheta)$, is identical with our previous BORN approximation expression (7.11) (ϑ is the angle between $\boldsymbol{p}$ and $\boldsymbol{k}$). (9.11) and the first line of (9.7) also give $\chi_+^{(B)}(\boldsymbol{p})$ "off the energy shell" (for general $\boldsymbol{p}$) and one could obtain second order BORN approximation (accurate to order λ^2) by substituting $\chi_+^{(B)}(\boldsymbol{p})$ into the integral on the right side of (9.7).

For the special case of the COULOMB potential an exact FOURIER transform of (6.20), the spatial COULOMB wave function representing a plane wave plus scattered outgoing waves, has been obtained by GUTH and MULLIN[1]. This momentum space wave function, analogous to $\psi_+(\boldsymbol{p})$ defined above, is

$$\psi_+(\boldsymbol{p}) = -\frac{1}{2\pi^2}\lim_{\varepsilon\to 0}\frac{d}{d\varepsilon}\left\{\frac{[p^2-(k+i\varepsilon)^2]^{-in'}}{[(\boldsymbol{p}-\boldsymbol{k})^2+\varepsilon^2]^{1-in'}}\right\}, \tag{9.12}$$

where $n' = +Z/k = Ze^2/\hbar v$ and ε is real and positive. This expression takes on an even simpler form if we carry out the differentiation of the numerator and denominator of (9.12) and, in each of these two terms, retain only the leading term in an expansion in powers of n'. Using the relation

$$\delta^{(3)}(\boldsymbol{y}) = \frac{1}{\pi^2}\lim_{\varepsilon\to 0}\frac{\varepsilon}{(y^2+\varepsilon^2)^2},$$

this approximation to (9.12), for $n'\ll 1$, is

$$\psi_+(\boldsymbol{p}) \approx \delta^{(3)}(\boldsymbol{p}-\boldsymbol{k}) - \frac{1}{\pi^2}\frac{1}{(k+i\varepsilon-p)(k+p)}\frac{Z}{(\boldsymbol{p}-\boldsymbol{k})^2}. \tag{9.13}$$

(9.13) is identical with the BORN approximation expression for $\psi_+(\boldsymbol{p})$ for a COULOMB potential as obtained from (9.11), (8.6a) and (9.7).

γ) *Partial wave solutions.* In Sect. 9α we have discussed general prescriptions for defining an eigenstate of the total HAMILTONian which is related to a particular eigenstate u_0 of the kinetic energy operator. In Sect. 9β we treated the special case of u_0 representing one single plane wave. For a central potential, wave functions exist which are separable in spherical polar coordinates, both in position and momentum space. These "partial wave" solutions are obtained from our general prescription by choosing for u_0 the simultaneous eigenstate of the kinetic energy operator (with eigenvalue $E=k^2/2$) and of the z-component and absolute square of the angular momentum operator, Eqs. (1.9) and (1.11) (with orbital and magnetic quantum numbers l and m). The momentum space wave function for u_0 is simply $\delta(p-k)\,Y_{lm}(\vartheta,\varphi)$. We use, for the moment, the principal value prescription (9.3a) to obtain an equation for $\psi_{lm}(\boldsymbol{p})$, the momentum space wave function of the required eigenstate of the total HAMILTONian. This equation, analogous to (8.5), is

$$\left.\begin{aligned}\psi_{lm}(\boldsymbol{p}) &= F_l(p)\,Y_{lm}(\vartheta,\varphi), \qquad F_l(p) = \delta(p-k)+\chi_l(p)\\ \chi_l(p) &= \lambda\,\mathscr{P}\left(\frac{1}{k^2-p^2}\right)\int_0^\infty dp'\,p'^2 K_l(p,p')\,F_l(p')\end{aligned}\right\} \tag{9.14}$$

[1] E. GUTH and C. J. MULLIN: Phys. Rev. **83**, 667 (1951).

where the kernel K_l is defined in (8.5). This integral equation for χ_l is an inhomogeneous one, like (9.7), but one-dimensional. Once the potential (and hence λK_l) and k are given, χ_l is determined uniquely by this equation.

In Sect. 9α we had discussed the relation between the three prescriptions (9.3±) and (9.3a). For our present case of the partial wave solutions, for fixed values of l, m and E there exists only *one* eigenstate of H_0, and hence only one eigenstate of the total HAMILTONian. In this case then the three prescriptions (9.3±) and (9.3a) should lead to physically *identical* wave functions. We can show this explicitly as follows. Using (9.3+) instead of (9.3a) we obtain instead of (9.14) the equation

$$\left.\begin{aligned} F_l^{(+)}(p) &= \delta(p-k) + \frac{1}{(k+i\varepsilon)^2 - p^2} f_l^{(+)}(p), \\ f_l^{(+)}(p) &= \lambda \int_0^\infty dp'\, p'^2 K_l(p,p')\, F_l^{(+)}(p'). \end{aligned}\right\} \tag{9.14+}$$

Using (9.5) we can rewrite the first line of (9.14+) as

$$F_l^{(+)}(p) = \left[1 - \frac{\pi i}{2k} f_l^{(+)}(k)\right] \delta(p-k) + \mathscr{P}\left(\frac{1}{k^2-p^2}\right) f_l^{(+)}(p).$$

Comparison with (9.14) shows that $F_l^{(+)}(p)$ is simply $F_l(p)$ times the *constant* factor in square brackets above. We can restrict ourselves to (9.14) then without loss of generality.

We evaluate next the asymptotic behavior of the spatial wave function $u_{lm}(\mathbf{r})$, the FOURIER transform of $\psi_{lm}(\mathbf{p})$, Eq. (9.14). Using (9.5), (9.9) and the relation $Y_{lm}(\vartheta,\varphi) = (-1)^l Y_{lm}(\pi-\vartheta, \pi+\varphi)$, we find the following asymptotic expressions (for $kr \to \infty$),

$$\left.\begin{aligned} \int d^3p\, e^{i\mathbf{r}\cdot\mathbf{p}} f(p)\, Y_{lm}(\vartheta_p,\varphi_p)\, \mathscr{P}\left(\frac{1}{k^2-p^2}\right) &= -2\pi^2 \frac{f(k)}{r} Y_{lm}(\vartheta,\varphi) \begin{cases} \cos kr, & \text{if } l \text{ even} \\ i\sin kr, & \text{if } l \text{ odd}, \end{cases} \\ \int d^3p\, e^{i\mathbf{r}\cdot\mathbf{p}} f(p)\, Y_{lm}(\vartheta_p,\varphi_p)\, \delta(p-k) &= -4\pi \frac{k\, f(k)}{r} Y_{lm}(\vartheta,\varphi) \begin{cases} -\sin kr, & \text{if } l \text{ even} \\ i\cos kr, & \text{if } l \text{ odd}. \end{cases} \end{aligned}\right\} \tag{9.15}$$

In (9.15), $f(p)$ is any continuous function, (ϑ_p, φ_p) are the spherical polar coordinates of $\mathbf{p}$ and (ϑ, φ) those of $\mathbf{r}$. With the help of (9.15) we then get for the asymptotic behavior of $u_{lm}(r)$ (except for a normalization constant)

$$\left.\begin{aligned} u_{lm}(r) &\sim r^{-1} \sin\left(kr + \tfrac{1}{2}\pi l + \delta_l\right) Y_{lm}(\vartheta) \\ \tan\delta_l &= -\frac{\pi\lambda}{2k} \int_0^\infty dp'\, p'^2 K_l(p,p')\, F_l(p'). \end{aligned}\right\} \tag{9.16}$$

The first line of (9.16) shows that the constant δ_l is the phase shift, defined in (7.1). The second line of (9.16) shows that δ_l is determined by the value of $\chi_l(p)$ on the energy shell[1]. The exact spatial wave function $u_{lm}(\mathbf{r})$ has the same angular dependence as the asymptotic form (9.16).

---

[1] The same physical wave function and the *same* phase shift δ_l would, of course, be obtained from Eq. (9.14+) in place of (9.14). With $F_l^{(+)}$ defined by (9.14+), the phase shift δ_l is given by the expression

$$e^{i\delta_l} \sin\delta_l = -\frac{\pi\lambda}{2k} \int_0^\infty dp'\, p'^2 K_l(p,p')\, F_l^{(+)}(p').$$

For most potential shapes even the one-dimensional integral Eq. (9.14) cannot be solved exactly, but iteration and variational methods are available[1] for approximate solutions even when the potential is not very weak. If the potential is very weak, BORN approximation can again be applied, i.e. F_l is replaced by $\delta(p-k)$ in the integral on the rigth side of (9.14). The BORN approximation for the phase shift is then[2]

$$\delta_l^{(B)} = -2\pi^2 k \int_{-1}^{1} dx\, V'\left(k\sqrt{2-2x}\right) P_l(x). \tag{9.17}$$

As discussed in Sect. 7, the BORN approximation breaks down completely for the special case of a pure COULOMB potential. For this case the integral (9.17) diverges logarithmically at $x=1$.

b) DIRAC theory.

10. General properties of the DIRAC theory[3]. *α) Non-covariant notation.* The energy levels of an actual hydrogen atom exhibit the well known fine structure splitting which is not contained in the nonrelativistic SCHRÖDINGER theory of the previous sections. This fine structure is partly due to the relativistic variation of mass with velocity, partly due to the spin of the electron. The variation of the mass alone would be predicted by the relativistic SCHRÖDINGER equation for spin-less particles (the KLEIN-GORDON equation, see Sect. 45), but would not give correct results for the fine structure, the ZEEMAN effect and other phenomena which depend on the spin of the electron. The DIRAC wave equation, on the other hand, forms the basis of a fully relativistic theory for particles "of spin $\frac{1}{2}$". We shall now apply the DIRAC theory to an electron placed in a given electromagnetic field. In the next few sections, we shall use absolute (C.G.S.) units, instead of atomic units.

Let $\varphi(\boldsymbol{r})$, $\boldsymbol{A}(\boldsymbol{r})$ be the scalar and vector potentials of the given external electromagnetic field and $(-e)$ the charge of an electron. The DIRAC wave equation for a stationary state of *total* energy E is then

NOTE

$$\left.\begin{aligned} H u &= +i\hbar\frac{\partial}{\partial t} u = E u,\\ H &= -e\varphi + \beta E_0 + \alpha\cdot(c\boldsymbol{p} + e\boldsymbol{A}), \end{aligned}\right\} \tag{10.1}$$

where E_0 and $\boldsymbol{p}$ are the rest-mass energy and the momentum operator, respectively, of the electron,

$$\boldsymbol{p} = -i\hbar\,\mathrm{grad}, \qquad E_0 = m c^2. \tag{10.2}$$

The vector $\boldsymbol{\alpha}$ is a vector operator, whose CARTESian components $(\alpha_1, \alpha_2, \alpha_3)$, together with the operator $\beta \equiv \alpha_4$, satisfy the commutation relations

$$\alpha_i\alpha_k + \alpha_k\alpha_i = 2\delta_{ik} \quad (i, k = 1, 2, 3, 4). \tag{10.3}$$

The DIRAC operators α_i operate on the wave function u, but do not depend on the spatial coordinates $\boldsymbol{r}$ of the electron.

Most properties[4] of the DIRAC operators could be derived directly from the commutation rules (10.3), but for our purposes it will be more convenient to use

[1] See references at the beginning of Sect. 9.

[2] A necessary, but not sufficient, condition for the validity of BORN approximation is $\tan\delta_l \approx \delta_l \ll 1$.

[3] See references [1], [2], [3] and [12] of the bibliography.

[4] A detailed discussion of the properties of the DIRAC operators is given by R. H. GOOD, Rev. Mod. Phys. **27**, 187 (1955).

an explicit representation for them. The usual representation is one in terms of four-by-four matrices with the matrices for α_1, α_2 and $\beta=\alpha_4$ being diagonal. We shall write these DIRAC matrices in the following "split notation" (see [2], Chap. 6).

$$\boldsymbol{\alpha}=\begin{pmatrix}0 & \sigma^P\\ \sigma^P & 0\end{pmatrix},\qquad \beta=\begin{pmatrix}I & 0\\ 0 & -I\end{pmatrix}, \tag{10.4}$$

where the three CARTESian components of σ^P are two-by-two matrices, called the PAULI spin matrices, and I is the unit two-by-two matrix. The PAULI matrices satisfy the following operator relations

$$(\sigma_i^P)^2=I,\qquad \sigma_i^P\sigma_k^P=-\sigma_k^P\sigma_i^P=i\,\sigma_l^P, \tag{10.5}$$

where (i, k, l) are cyclic permutations of the Cartesian coordinates $(1, 2, 3)$. Our explicit representation for the PAULI matrices is

$$\sigma_1^P=\begin{pmatrix}0 & 1\\ 1 & 0\end{pmatrix},\quad \sigma_2^P=\begin{pmatrix}0 & -i\\ i & 0\end{pmatrix},\quad \sigma_3^P=\begin{pmatrix}1 & 0\\ 0 & -1\end{pmatrix};\quad I=\begin{pmatrix}1 & 0\\ 0 & 1\end{pmatrix}. \tag{10.6}$$

We shall also need later on the DIRAC spin operator $\boldsymbol{\sigma}$, whose Cartesian components are defined by

$$\sigma_i\equiv-i\,\alpha_k\alpha_l\quad (i, k, l=\text{cycl. perm. } 1, 2, 3). \tag{10.7}$$

The DIRAC spin matrices σ_i satisfy exactly the same operator relations (10.5) as the PAULI matrices and in our "split notation"

$$\boldsymbol{\sigma}=\begin{pmatrix}\sigma^P & 0\\ 0 & \sigma^P\end{pmatrix}. \tag{10.8}$$

Written out in full, our explicit representation for the DIRAC operators is one in terms of four-by-four matrices with the matrix for σ_3 and that for β diagonal. Some examples of these matrices are

$$\alpha_3=\begin{pmatrix}0 & 0 & 1 & 0\\ 0 & 0 & 0 & -1\\ 1 & 0 & 0 & 0\\ 0 & -1 & 0 & 0\end{pmatrix},\quad \sigma_3=\begin{pmatrix}1 & 0 & 0 & 0\\ 0 & -1 & 0 & 0\\ 0 & 0 & 1 & 0\\ 0 & 0 & 0 & -1\end{pmatrix},\quad \beta=\begin{pmatrix}1 & 0 & 0 & 0\\ 0 & 1 & 0 & 0\\ 0 & 0 & -1 & 0\\ 0 & 0 & 0 & -1\end{pmatrix}. \tag{10.8a}$$

From (10.7) and (10.3) also follow the relations

$$\sigma_i\alpha_i=\alpha_i\sigma_i,\qquad \sigma_i\alpha_k-\alpha_k\sigma_i=2i\,\alpha_l. \tag{10.7a}$$

The wave function u is then not merely a single function of position $\boldsymbol{r}$, but a "matrix" with one column and 4 rows (a spinor), on which the DIRAC matrices act. The four components $u_\sigma\,(\sigma=1, 2, 3, 4)$ of u are themselves functions of position (unlike the matrices α_i and β). The multiplication of u by a DIRAC operator follows the usual rules of matrix multiplication. The result is again a 1 column—4 row matrix, just like u:

$$(\alpha_i u)_\varrho=\sum_{\sigma=1}^{4}(\alpha_i)_{\varrho\sigma}u_\sigma.$$

For instance, if

$$u=\begin{pmatrix}u_1\\ u_2\\ u_3\\ u_4\end{pmatrix},\quad\text{then}\quad \alpha_2 u=i\begin{pmatrix}-u_4\\ u_3\\ -u_2\\ u_1\end{pmatrix}.$$

The differential equation (10.1) holds, of course, for each of the four rows of the eigenfunction separately and gives four simultaneous coupled equations for the four functions u_σ. For instance

$$\left.\begin{array}{l}\frac{1}{c}(E+E_0+e\varphi)\,u_3-\left[\hbar\left(\frac{1}{i}\frac{\partial}{\partial x}-\frac{\partial}{\partial y}\right)+\frac{e}{c}(A_x-i\,A_y)\right]u_2-\\ \qquad -\left(\frac{\hbar}{i}\frac{\partial}{\partial z}+\frac{e}{c}A_z\right)u_1=0\end{array}\right\}\tag{10.9}$$

plus three similar equations.

The inner product of two DIRAC wave functions u and v is defined as the scalar quantity

$$\langle v^* u\rangle=\sum_{\varrho=1}^{4}\int d^3r\,v_\varrho^*(\boldsymbol{r})\,u_\varrho(\boldsymbol{r}),$$

and the wave functions are usually normalized so that $\langle u^* u\rangle$ equals unity. Perturbation theory can be developed in a manner analogous to the nonrelativistic theory, except that matrix elements now also contain sums over spinor indices. Consider a HAMILTONian $H=(H_0+H')$, where both H_0 and H' are built up of DIRAC matrices and of the four-by-four unit matrix, and let u be an eigenfunction of the operator H_0 alone. Following the rules of perturbation theory and matrix multiplication, the first order perturbation, $\Delta E^{(1)}$, to the energy eigenvalue is then given by

$$\Delta E^{(1)}=\langle u^* H' u\rangle=\sum_{\varrho,\sigma=1}^{4}\int d^3r\,u_\varrho^*\,H_{\varrho\sigma}\,u_\sigma.\tag{10.10}$$

Eq. (10.1) is the exact wave equation for an electron in a given external classical electromagnetic field, according to DIRAC's *original* theory. This theory is fully LORENTZ-invariant ([*3*], Part B), although (10.1) is not written in a fully covariant form. It was shown by PAULI [*3*] that the original DIRAC theory can be extended by adding certain terms to the wave equation, without violating the gauge invariance and LORENTZ invariance of the theory. For this purpose it will be convenient to rewrite the DIRAC equation in a covariant form.

β) Covariant notation[1]. We introduce relativistic four-vectors for the electromagnetic potentials, the space-time coordinates of the electron and its momentum plus energy:

$$\left.\begin{array}{l}A_\mu=(\boldsymbol{A},i\,\varphi),\qquad x_\mu=(\boldsymbol{r},i\,c\,t),\qquad (\mu=1,2,3,4),\\ p_\mu=-i\,\hbar\frac{\partial}{\partial x_\mu}=\left(-i\,\hbar\,\mathrm{grad},\,-\frac{\hbar}{c}\frac{\partial}{\partial t}\right)=\left(\boldsymbol{p},\frac{i}{c}E\right).\end{array}\right\}\tag{10.11}$$

We further define a four-vector γ_μ built up of DIRAC matrices, whose components satisfy a commutation relation equivalent to (10.3),

$$\left.\begin{array}{l}\gamma_\mu=(-i\,\beta\,\boldsymbol{\alpha},\beta),\qquad (\mu=1,2,3,4),\\ \gamma_\mu\gamma_\nu+\gamma_\nu\gamma_\mu=2\delta_{\mu\nu}.\end{array}\right\}\tag{10.12}$$

In this notation the DIRAC equation (10.1), multiplied by $i\beta/c$ takes the form [*using* (10.2), (10.3), (10.11) and (10.12)],

$$\left.\begin{array}{l}\left[\sum_{\mu=1}^{4}\pi_\mu\gamma_\mu-i\,m\,c\right]u=0,\\ \pi_\mu=p_\mu+\left(\frac{e}{c}\right)A_\mu.\end{array}\right\}\tag{10.13}$$

[1] See ref. [*3*], [*12*], and [*13*] of the bibliography.

It will be convenient to derive from (10.13) a second order differential equation which contains the DIRAC matrices only in terms which vanish in the absence of an electromagnetic field. This is accomplished by multiplying both sides of Eq. (10.13) by the operator $(\sum \pi_\mu \gamma_\mu + i m c)$.

We first rewrite the electric and magnetic fields, $\mathcal{E}$ and $\mathcal{H}$, in terms of the antisymmetric tensor[1]

$$F_{\mu\nu} = \frac{\partial A_\nu}{\partial x_\mu} - \frac{\partial A_\mu}{\partial x_\nu}$$

$$\mathcal{H}_i = F_{kl}, \quad \mathcal{E}_i = i F_{i4}.$$

We further note that the electromagnetic potentials satisfy the LORENTZ gauge condition

$$\sum_{\mu=1}^{4} \frac{\partial A_\mu}{\partial x_\mu} = 0$$

and the following commutation rule, which follows from the definition (10.11) of p_μ in terms of differentiation operators,

$$[\pi_\mu, \pi_\nu] \equiv \pi_\mu \pi_\nu - \pi_\nu \pi_\mu = \frac{\hbar e}{i c} F_{\mu\nu}.$$

Using this last relation and the commutation relations (10.12) for γ_μ, one finally obtains the desired second order differential equation.

This equation is

$$\left\{\left[\sum_{\mu=1}^{4} \pi_\mu^2 + m^2 c^2\right] + \frac{\hbar e}{2 i c} \sum_{\mu,\nu} \gamma_\mu \gamma_\nu F_{\mu\nu}\right\} u = 0. \tag{10.14}$$

In (10.14) the expression in square brackets is the operator which appears in the KLEIN-GORDON equation, the relativistic theory for spin-less particles. The last term in (10.14) is characteristic of the DIRAC theory, appropriate for particles of "spin $\frac{1}{2}$". We shall see later that this term represents the interaction of the electromagnetic field with an electric and a magnetic dipole moment, collectively called the "DIRAC moment of the electron". This "DIRAC moment" term is the only term in (10.14) which involves DIRAC matrices. If the electromagnetic field is sufficiently weak, the effect of this term on the energy eigenvalue is small and can be calculated by approximation methods which involve first order perturbation theory and an expansion in inverse powers of c, the velocity of light. Such evaluations will be carried out in Sect. 12 and 13. Eq. (10.14) will be written out in full in terms of the less elegant and less symmetric but conventional notation in (12.9). Of course, (12.9) can also be derived directly from (10.1) in conventional notation.

γ) Modified DIRAC *equation.* We now consider possible modifications of the DIRAC theory, which still give a LORENTZ- and gauge invariant theory. This can be achieved by adding some LORENTZ-invariant (scalar) combinations of the DIRAC operator γ_μ and of derivatives of the electromagnetic potentials to the operators occurring in (10.13). We consider, in particular, two such combinations which give the following modified DIRAC equation

$$\left(\sum_\mu \pi_\mu \gamma_\mu - i m c\right) u = \left[g_1 \left(\frac{\hbar e}{4 m c^2}\right) \sum_{\mu,\nu} \gamma_\mu \gamma_\nu F_{\mu\nu} - g_2 \frac{e}{c} \left(\frac{\hbar}{m c}\right)^2 \sum_\mu \gamma_\mu \Box^2 A_\mu\right] u, \tag{10.15}$$

[1] The indices (i, k, l) are cyclic permutations of the first three ("space-like") values of the index μ, and 4 denotes the "time-like" value of μ.

where

$$\square^2 A_\mu \equiv \sum_{\nu=1}^{4} \frac{\partial^2}{\partial x_\nu^2} A_\mu = -\frac{4\pi}{c} j_\mu$$

and j_μ is the current-charge four-vector for the *source* of the given electromagnetic field. The parameters g_1, and g_2 on the right side of (10.15) are dimensionless.

The unmodified DIRAC Eq. (10.1) represents the interaction of an electron with an external field only if we treat all electromagnetic fields *classically*. If we use quantum electrodynamics, even the interaction of the electron with a given field (i.e. even in the absence of the emission or absorption of "real" radiation) is modified. To a good approximation, these modifications can be accounted for by adding so-called "radiative correction" terms to the DIRAC equation (see Sect. 18 and 19), resulting in an equation of the form (10.15). The dimensionless constants g_1 and g_2 derived from quantum electrodynamics are small, of the order of the fine structure constant α, and we shall treat the effect of these extra terms on the energy eigenvalue only by first order perturbation theory (see Sect. 20). We shall also see that the right side of (10.15) is a good approximation to the radiative corrections only for nonrelativistic energies.

The term involving g_1, in (10.15),

$$G_1 = g_1 \left(\frac{\hbar e}{4 m c^2}\right) \sum_{\mu,\nu} \gamma_\mu \gamma_\nu F_{\mu\nu}, \tag{10.16}$$

is of very similar form as the "DIRAC moment" term in (10.14) and G_1 is often called a "PAULI moment" term. In fact, if both these terms are treated by first order perturbation theory, and to lowest order in $1/c$, their effects on the energy eigenvalue in a magnetic field are in the ratio $g_1:1$, except for terms of order g_1^2.

It should be noted, however, that this correspondence between the PAULI and DIRAC moments is *not* exact. This can be seen, for instance, by deriving an exact second order differential equation from (10.15) (with $g_2 = 0$) in analogy with the derivation of (10.14) from (10.13). The result is

$$\left\{\left[\sum_{\mu=1}^{4} \pi_\mu^2 + m^2 c^2\right] + (1+g_1)\frac{\hbar e}{2 i c} \sum_{\mu,\nu} \gamma_\mu \gamma_\nu F_{\mu\nu}\right\} u = \left\{G_1^2 + \left[\sum_\mu \gamma_\mu \pi_\mu, G_1\right]\right\} u, \tag{10.17}$$

where $[A, B] = +AB - BA$. The terms on the right side involve only the PAULI, but not the DIRAC moment. They contain higher powers of $1/c$ than the term involving g_1 on the left side and one might expect them to be small in an essentially nonrelativistic case (see also Sect. 12γ). However these terms on the right side contain higher derivatives of the electromagnetic potentials and can give rise to divergence difficulties not encountered with the DIRAC moment alone, if the potentials are singular and if the expansion in $1/c$ is carried to higher terms. These difficulties again show that (10.15) cannot be an exact self-consistent equation for very high energies (or momenta).

The addition of the term involving g_2 on the right side of (10.15) can be considered as equivalent to a modification of the external potential A_μ. In fact, (10.15) with $g_1 = 0$ reduces to (10.13) if, in the definition of π_μ in (10.13), A_μ is replaced by

$$A'_\mu = A_\mu + g_2 \left(\frac{\hbar}{m c}\right)^2 \square^2 A_\mu. \tag{10.18}$$

11. Angular momentum[1]. *α) Definitions.* According to the DIRAC theory, the electron is endowed with an intrinsic magnetic moment. We shall show that the electron is also endowed with an intrinsic angular momentum, the so-called spin, which is represented by the operator $\frac{1}{2}\hbar\sigma$, Eq. (10.7). First we review briefly some general properties of angular momentum operators.

---

[1] See ref. [*1*], Ch. VI; ref. [*5*], Ch. III and G. PAKE and E. FEENBERG, Quantum Theory of Angular Momentum. Cambridge: Addison-Wesley Co. 1953.

We shall call any vector operator $\boldsymbol{J}$ an "angular momentum operator" if its three CARTESian components J_i are HERMITian operators and satisfy the fundamental commutation relation

$$[J_i, J_i] = 0, \quad [J_i, J_k] = i\hbar J_l, \tag{11.1}$$

where (i, k, l) are cyclic permutations of the indices (1, 2, 3) and $[a, b] = (ab - ba)$ is the commutator of a and b. We denote the operator for the square of the angular momentum by $\boldsymbol{J}^2 = \sum_{i=1}^{3} J_i^2$. It follows from (11.1) that $\boldsymbol{J}^2$ commutes with each of the three components J_i and that simultaneous eigenstates u of $\boldsymbol{J}^2$ and, say, J_z $(i=3)$ can be found. Using only (11.1) and the HERMITian nature of J_i, one can show by general operator manipulation[1] that the simultaneous eigenvalues must be of the form

$$\left.\begin{aligned} \boldsymbol{J}^2 u &= j(j+1)\hbar^2 u, & J_z u &= m\hbar u, \\ j &= 0, \tfrac{1}{2}, 1, \tfrac{3}{2}, 2, \ldots; & m &= -j, -j+1, \ldots, +j. \end{aligned}\right\} \tag{11.2}$$

The CARTESian components of the quantum mechanical operators for position and momentum, $\boldsymbol{r}$ and $\boldsymbol{p}$, satisfy the commutation rules

$$[r_i, r_k] = [p_i, p_k] = 0, \quad [r_i, p_k] = i\hbar\,\delta_{ik}. \tag{11.3}$$

The explicit definition for the *orbital* angular momentum operator [see (1.9)], is

$$\boldsymbol{J}_{\text{orb}} \equiv \hbar\boldsymbol{k} = \boldsymbol{r}\times\boldsymbol{p}, \quad ([\boldsymbol{r}\times\boldsymbol{p}]_i = r_k p_l - r_l p_k). \tag{11.4}$$

$\hbar\boldsymbol{k}$ satisfies the commutation rule (11.1) and it follows [see (1.11)] from the special form of (11.4) that the eigenvalues of $\boldsymbol{k}^2$ are $l(l+1)$, where l can only be an integer or zero (*not* half-integral). From (11.3) and (11.4) we can also derive

$$[p_i, k_i] = 0, \quad [p_i, k_k] = i\,p_l, \quad \boldsymbol{p}\times\boldsymbol{k} + \boldsymbol{k}\times\boldsymbol{p} = 2i\,\boldsymbol{p}. \tag{11.5}$$

Further, using the identity

$$[a, b^2] = [a, b]\,b + b\,[a, b], \tag{11.6}$$

we also have

$$[\boldsymbol{p}, \boldsymbol{k}^2] = i(\boldsymbol{k}\times\boldsymbol{p} - \boldsymbol{p}\times\boldsymbol{k}). \tag{11.7}$$

One can also derive relations, identical with (11.5) and (11.7) except that $\boldsymbol{p}$ is replaced by $\boldsymbol{r}$ throughout.

In (10.7) we have defined, in terms of the DIRAC matrix $\boldsymbol{\alpha}$, a vector operator $\boldsymbol{\sigma}$, whose CARTESian components satisfy the operator relations (10.5). If we write

$$\boldsymbol{J}_{\text{spin}} = \hbar\,\boldsymbol{s}, \quad \boldsymbol{s} = \tfrac{1}{2}\boldsymbol{\sigma}, \tag{11.8}$$

it follows from (10.5) that $\boldsymbol{J}_{\text{spin}}$ satisfies (11.1) and we call it the spin angular momentum operator. It follows further from (10.5) that the square of each component s_i of $\boldsymbol{s}$ equals $\frac{1}{4}$ times the unit operator. Hence

$$\boldsymbol{s}^2 u = \sum_{i=1}^{3} s_i^2 u = s(s+1)\,u, \quad s = \tfrac{1}{2} \tag{11.9}$$

for *any* state u and the 2 possible eigenvalues of s_i are $\pm\frac{1}{2}$. Since the DIRAC matrices commute with $\boldsymbol{r}$ and $\boldsymbol{p}$, any component of $\boldsymbol{s}$ also commutes with every component of $\boldsymbol{k}$. We finally define as the operator for the "total angular mo-

[1] Ref. [*1*], p. 144 or ref. [*5*], p. 46.

mentum" the sum of the orbital and spin operators,

$$\boldsymbol{J}_{\text{tot}} = \hbar \boldsymbol{M}, \qquad \boldsymbol{M} = \boldsymbol{k} + \boldsymbol{s}. \tag{11.10}$$

$\boldsymbol{J}_{\text{tot}}$ also satisfies (11.1) and further, since $\boldsymbol{k}$ commutes with $\boldsymbol{s}$,

$$[k_i, M_k] = i\, k_l, \qquad [s_i, M_k] = i\, s_l. \tag{11.11}$$

It also follows [e.g. from (11.6) and (11.11)] that each component of $\boldsymbol{M}$ (and therefore also $\boldsymbol{M}^2$) commutes with both $\boldsymbol{k}^2$ and $\boldsymbol{s}^2$. The three types of angular momentum operators, expressed in atomic (instead of C.G.S.) units are simply $\boldsymbol{k}$, $\boldsymbol{s}$ and $\boldsymbol{M}$. It should be noted that the commutation rules of the DIRAC and PAULI spin operators are the same and the general discussion of the present section holds for either type of operator.

β) Central fields. The physical significance of the spin operator $\boldsymbol{s}$ can be seen as follows. Consider an electron in any central field with scalar potential $\varphi(r)$ and zero vector potential $\boldsymbol{A}(\boldsymbol{r})$. In the nonrelativistic SCHRÖDINGER theory every component of $\boldsymbol{k}$, as well as $\boldsymbol{k}^2$, commutes with the total HAMILTONian H (or "is a constant of the motion") and simultaneous eigenstates of H, $\boldsymbol{k}^2$, and k_z exist with eigenvalues E, $l(l+1)$ and m_l, respectively. In the DIRAC theory, however, *none* of the components of $\boldsymbol{k}$ or $\boldsymbol{s}$ individually, nor $\boldsymbol{k}^2$, commute with the HAMILTONian H, Eq. (10.1). In fact, one can show that

$$[\boldsymbol{k}, H] = -[\boldsymbol{s}, H] = i\, c\, \boldsymbol{\alpha} \times \boldsymbol{p}. \tag{11.12}$$

The first part of (11.12) represents the commutator of $\boldsymbol{k}$ with the term in $\boldsymbol{\alpha} \cdot \boldsymbol{p}$ in (10.1), rewritten with the help of (11.5). The second part represents the commutator of $\frac{1}{2}\sigma$ with the $\boldsymbol{\alpha} \cdot \boldsymbol{p}$ term, rewritten with the help of (10.7a). (11.12) shows that every component of $\boldsymbol{M}$, the *total* angular momentum, commutes with the HAMILTONian H. Using (11.6) we then see that $\boldsymbol{M}^2$ also commutes with H.

Since the orbital angular momentum $\boldsymbol{k}$ is no longer a constant of the motion in the DIRAC theory, no eigenstates of the HAMILTONian exist which are also eigenstates of $\boldsymbol{k}^2$ and k_z, i.e. l and m_l (eigenvalue of k_z) are no longer "good quantum numbers". In the DIRAC theory the total angular momentum $\boldsymbol{M}$ takes the place of $\boldsymbol{k}$, i.e. we can find simultaneous eigenstates of the HAMILTONian, of $\boldsymbol{M}^2$ and of M. We denote the eigenvalue of $\boldsymbol{M}^2$ by $j(j+1)$, that of M_z by m, where m is related to j by (11.2). j, which we shall call the "inner quantum number", takes the place of the orbital quantum number l in the DIRAC theory. It can be shown that j (and hence m) only takes on half-integral values and we shall also verify this explicitly in Sect. 13β. It follows from (11.9) that *any* state is an eigenstate of $\boldsymbol{s}^2$ with eigenvalue $\frac{3}{4}$ and that $s = \frac{1}{2}$, the "absolute value" of the spin, is always a good quantum number. On the other hand, the "direction" of the spin is not quantized, e.g. any eigenstate of the DIRAC HAMILTONian is a linear superposition of *two* eigenstates of s_z with eigenvalues $m_z = \frac{1}{2}$ and $-\frac{1}{2}$.

Although $\boldsymbol{k}^2$ is not strictly a constant of the motion in the DIRAC theory, for an electron in a weak central field, l is "almost a good quantum number". This means that we can find stationary states u, for which

$$\boldsymbol{k}^2 u = l(l+1)\, u + w \tag{11.13}$$

where l is a positive integer and w is a spinor whose "large components" w_1 and w_2 are zero. The "small components" (see Sect. 12α) both of u and of w are of order $\bar{v}/c$, where $\bar{v}$ is some average velocity of the electron Thus u and w are "almost orthogonal": w is of order $\bar{v}/c$, but the expectation value of the operator $\boldsymbol{k}^2$, taken over the eigenfunction u, differs from $l(l+1)$ only by a term of order $(\bar{v}/c)^2$. The properties of $\boldsymbol{k}^2$ are discussed further in Sects. 12 and 13.

Pauli approximation

12. PAULI theory of the spin-electron. α) *"Large" and "small" components.* Let $\bar{v}$ and $\bar{p}=m\bar{v}$ be the order of magnitude of the velocity and momentum of an electron in a particular stationary state (for instance, take for $\bar{p}$ the square root of the expectation value of the operator p^2). For an electron in a reasonably weak potential ($e\varphi \ll mc^2$), stationary states exist for which the average velocity $\bar{v}$ is nonrelativistic and the total energy E is close to the rest-mass energy $E_0=mc^2$ of the electron. I.e.

$$\bar{v} \ll c, \quad \bar{p} \ll mc, \quad |E-E_0| \sim \bar{p}^2/m \ll \bar{p}\,c \ll E_0.$$

For such states the DIRAC theory can be simplified considerably, as follows.

We have seen that the DIRAC equation (10.1) can be written in the form of four simultaneous differential equations for the four components u_σ of the spinor wave function u and have given one of these equations in (10.9). For a weak potential and a state with $E \approx E_0$, the factors multiplying the spinor components u_3 and u_4 are larger than those multiplying u_1 and u_2 by factors of order $c/\bar{v}$, in each of these equations. For instance, in (10.9) the factor of u_3 is of order $2mc$, those of u_1 and u_2 of order $\bar{p}$; in another equation the factor of u_1 is of order $(E-E_0)/c \sim \bar{p}^2/mc$, the factors of u_3 and u_4 of order $\bar{p}$, etc. It then follows that u_3 and u_4 are *smaller*[1] than u_1 and u_2 by factors of the order of $\bar{v}/c$. This conclusion forms the basis of our approximation method.

We can obtain a first approximation for u_3, one of the two "small" components, in terms of the two "large" components u_1 and u_2 from (10.9) by putting E equal to E_0 and by neglecting the potentials φ and $\boldsymbol{A}$ altogether. This approximate equation (and a similar one for u_4) reads

$$u_3 = -i\frac{\hbar}{2mc}\left(\frac{\partial u_2}{\partial x} - i\frac{\partial u_2}{\partial y} + \frac{\partial u_1}{\partial z}\right), \tag{12.1}$$

$$u_4 = -i\frac{\hbar}{2mc}\left(\frac{\partial u_1}{\partial x} + i\frac{\partial u_1}{\partial y} - \frac{\partial u_2}{\partial z}\right). \tag{12.2}$$

These two equations appear combined in a more compact form, if we use the split notation, discussed in Sect. 10, also for the wave function u. We write

$$u = \begin{pmatrix} U_A \\ U_B \end{pmatrix}; \quad U_A = \begin{pmatrix} u_1 \\ u_2 \end{pmatrix}, \quad U_B = \begin{pmatrix} u_3 \\ u_4 \end{pmatrix}. \tag{12.3}$$

Using (10.4), the exact DIRAC equation (10.1) takes the form

$$\left.\begin{aligned} (E - E_0 + e\varphi)\, U_A &= \boldsymbol{\sigma}^P \cdot (c\,\boldsymbol{p} + e\boldsymbol{A})\, U_B, \\ (E + E_0 + e\varphi)\, U_B &= \boldsymbol{\sigma}^P \cdot (c\,\boldsymbol{p} + e\boldsymbol{A})\, U_A. \end{aligned}\right\} \tag{12.4}$$

Replacing E by E_0 and neglecting φ in the second line of (12.4), we again obtain an approximate expression for the small components U_B in terms of the large components U_A. This expression, identical with (12.1) and (12.2) if $\boldsymbol{A}=0$, is

$$U_B = (2mc)^{-1}\left[\boldsymbol{\sigma}^P \cdot (\boldsymbol{p} + e\boldsymbol{A}/c)\right] U_A. \tag{12.5}$$

If we substitute the approximation (12.5) into the first line of (12.4), we obtain an approximate equation involving only the large components U_A. This equation (of the same form as the nonrelativistic SCHRÖDINGER equation) is

$$\left[E - E_0 + e\varphi - \frac{1}{2m}\left(\boldsymbol{p} + \frac{e}{c}\boldsymbol{A}\right)^2\right] U_A = 0. \tag{12.6}$$

[1] In older books and in ref. [9] the large components are labelled 3, 4 and the small components 1, 2. In these references the term in the HAMILTONian which involves β differs from ours by a change in sign.

With the help of (12.5) and (12.6) one can then derive a more accurate expression for U_B in terms of U_A from (12.4) and finally a more accurate (but still not exact) equation[1] involving only U_A. We shall derive this more accurate equation for U_A by a slightly different method.

It will be seen from the explicit representation of the DIRAC operators in our split notation, (10.4) and (10.8), that β and $\boldsymbol{\sigma}$ only couple the large components u_1 and $u_2 (U_A)$ with each other and the small components u_3 and $u_4 (U_B)$ with each other (operators diagonal in the split notation). The CARTESian components of $\boldsymbol{\alpha}$, on the other hand, couple the components U_A with the components U_B. For a wave function u satisfying the DIRAC equation (10.1) or (12.4) we can get an approximate relation involving $\boldsymbol{\alpha}\, u$, by using (10.4) and the approximation (12.5),

$$(\boldsymbol{\alpha}\, u)_A = \boldsymbol{\sigma}^P\, U_B \approx \frac{1}{2mc}\, [\boldsymbol{p} + i(\boldsymbol{p} \times \boldsymbol{\sigma}^P)]\, U_A, \tag{12.7}$$

(12.7) holds, even approximately[2], only for the first components $(\boldsymbol{\alpha}\, u)_1$ and $(\boldsymbol{\alpha}\, u)_2$ of $(\boldsymbol{\alpha}\, u)$. For the last two components $(\boldsymbol{\alpha}\, u)_3$ and $(\boldsymbol{\alpha}\, u)_4$, the right side of (12.7) would be of a completely wrong order of magnitude, the correct expression being

$$(\boldsymbol{\alpha}\, u)_B = \boldsymbol{\sigma}^P\, U_A \gg U_B .$$

The extent of the error made in the approximation (12.7) can best be seen by deriving an exact relation involving $\boldsymbol{\alpha}\, u$, as follows. We multiply the DIRAC equation (10.1) on the left by $\boldsymbol{\alpha}$,

$$\boldsymbol{\alpha}\, (E + e\varphi - \beta\, m c^2 - c\, \boldsymbol{\alpha} \cdot \boldsymbol{\pi})\, u = 0, \qquad \boldsymbol{\pi} = \boldsymbol{p} + e\boldsymbol{A}/c .$$

Using the relations (10.3) and the definition (10.7) of $\boldsymbol{\sigma}$, we can rewrite this equation in the form

$$(E + e\varphi)\, \boldsymbol{\alpha}\, u = (-\, m c^2 \beta\, \boldsymbol{\alpha} + c\, \boldsymbol{\pi} + i\, c\, \boldsymbol{\pi} \times \boldsymbol{\sigma})\, u .$$

Adding $mc^2 \boldsymbol{\alpha} u$ to both sides and dividing by the factor appearing on the left side, we obtain the required *exact* relation

$$\boldsymbol{\alpha}\, u = \frac{c}{m c^2 + E + e\varphi}\, [\boldsymbol{\pi} + i\, \boldsymbol{\pi} \times \boldsymbol{\sigma} + m c\, (1 - \beta)\, \boldsymbol{\alpha}]\, u . \tag{12.8}$$

The first two components of the term involving $(\beta - 1)$, $[(1-\beta)\, \boldsymbol{\alpha}\, u]_A$ vanish exactly (whereas the last two components are large). If E is replaced by mc^2, $e\varphi$ neglected compared with mc^2 and $(e/c)\boldsymbol{A}$ compared with $\boldsymbol{p}$, the first two components of the Eq. (12.8) reduce to (12.7). In many problems the non-relativistic energy, $W = E - E_0$, and $e\varphi$ are of the order of magnitude of $(\overline{v}/c)^2 \times mc^2 \ll mc^2$ and the vector potential eA is either zero or at least very small compared with $c\,p$.

β) Quadratic equation. We return now to the exact quadratic equation (10.14), which we had derived from the DIRAC equation using covariant notation. We rewrite (10.14) in terms of the conventional non-covariant notation, noting in particular that

$$\gamma_k \gamma_l = +\, i\, \sigma_i, \qquad \gamma_k \gamma_4 = i\, \alpha_k ,$$

[1] See ref. [2], Sect. 65.

[2] It should also be remembered that (12.7) only holds for a wave function u, which satisfies the DIRAC equation. Consider, for instance, the expression $(\boldsymbol{\alpha} f(\boldsymbol{r})\, u)_A$ where $f(\boldsymbol{r})$ is an arbitrary function of position, not involving DIRAC operators. Although $\boldsymbol{\alpha}$ commutes with f, $\boldsymbol{p}$ does *not*, and a valid approximation for $(\boldsymbol{\alpha}\, f\, u)_A$ is obtained from (12.7) only if we write $f(r)$ *to the left* of $\boldsymbol{p}$.

where (i, k, l) are cyclic permutations of the three "space-like" indices (1, 2, 3). Dividing (10.14) through by $-2m$, we obtain

$$\left.\begin{aligned}&\Big[W + e\varphi + \frac{\hbar^2}{2m}\Delta + \frac{1}{2mc^2}(W+e\varphi)^2 + i\frac{e\hbar}{mc}(\boldsymbol{A}\cdot\text{grad}) - \frac{e^2}{2mc^2}A^2 - \\ &\qquad - \frac{e\hbar}{2mc}(\sigma\cdot\mathcal{H}) + i\frac{e\hbar}{2mc}(\boldsymbol{\alpha}\cdot\mathcal{E})\Big]u = 0.\end{aligned}\right\} \tag{12.9}$$

If we disregard all but the first three members of this equation we obtain the ordinary SCHRÖDINGER equation. The next three terms are peculiar to the relativistic SCHRÖDINGER theory. This may be inferred from the fact that these terms, while containing the velocity of light, do not contain the operators σ and $\boldsymbol{\alpha}$. The fourth term represents the relativistic correction due to the change in mass with velocity. The fifth and sixth terms describe the effect of the external vector potential on the electron (cf. Sects. 45 and 47). Finally, the last two members are characteristic of the DIRAC theory. The seventh term may be interpreted as an interaction between the magnetic field and a magnetic moment

$$\mu_s = -\mu_0\sigma, \qquad \mu_0 = \frac{e\hbar}{2mc}. \tag{12.10}$$

The last term represents an interaction between the electric field and an electric moment $-i\dfrac{e\hbar}{2mc}\boldsymbol{\alpha}$.

The exact quadratic equation (12.9) looks less elegant than the linear DIRAC equation, but is more useful for our present aim of deriving an approximate, but fairly accurate, equation which involves only the large components U_A of the wave function. This is due to the fact that σ is diagonal in our split (U_A, U_B) notation and only $\boldsymbol{\alpha}$ couples U_A with U_B. Now the factor multiplying $\boldsymbol{\alpha}$ in (10.1) is of order $c\bar{p}$ or $W(c/\bar{v})$, but the factor in (12.9) only of order $(e\hbar\mathcal{E}/mc)$ which is much smaller (in many problems $e\hbar\mathcal{E}$ is of order $\bar{p}\,e\varphi$, $e\varphi$ of order W, the nonrelativistic energy, and hence $e\hbar\mathcal{E}/mc$ of order $W\bar{v}/c$). Hence, the replacement of $(\boldsymbol{\alpha}\,u)_A$ by the approximation (12.7) results in a much smaller error in Eq. (12.9) than in (10.1). If we make this substitution we get an equation, involving only the large components U_A, which forms the basis of the approximate PAULI theory for the spin-electron[1],

$$\left.\begin{aligned}&\Big[W + e\varphi + \frac{\hbar^2}{2m}\Delta + \frac{1}{2mc^2}(W+e\varphi)^2 + i\frac{e\hbar}{mc}\boldsymbol{A}\cdot\text{grad} - \frac{e^2}{2mc^2}A^2 + \\ &\qquad + i\frac{\mu_0}{2mc}\mathcal{E}\cdot\boldsymbol{p} - \frac{\mu_0}{2mc}\sigma^P\cdot(\mathcal{E}\times\boldsymbol{p}) - \mu_0\sigma^P\cdot\mathcal{H}\Big]U_A = 0,\end{aligned}\right\} \tag{12.11}$$

where

$$\mu_0 = \frac{e\hbar}{2mc}$$

is the "BOHR magneton", a measure of the spin magnetic moment of the electron.

Note that (12.11) is now an equation for a two-row, one-column wave function U_A (the "PAULI spinor wave function") with components u_1 and u_2, and that the DIRAC spin-matrix σ, (10.8), has been replaced by the PAULI spin-matrix σ^P, Eq. (10.6). We define, in analogy with (11.8), $\boldsymbol{s}^P = \frac{1}{2}\sigma^P$ and (11.9) holds for $\boldsymbol{s}^P$ as well as for $\boldsymbol{s}$. We can see the physical significance of u_1 and u_2 by noting that the two ortho-normal PAULI spinors α and β,

$$\alpha(s_z) = \begin{pmatrix}1\\0\end{pmatrix}, \qquad \beta(s_z) = \begin{pmatrix}0\\1\end{pmatrix}, \tag{12.12}$$

[1] W. PAULI: Z. Physik 43, 601 (1927).

are eigenstates of the z-component of the spin-operator $\mathbf{s}^P$ with eigenvalues $+\frac{1}{2}$ and $-\frac{1}{2}$, respectively. In the PAULI theory a state of the electron is thus specified by a two-component wave function, $u_\sigma(\mathbf{r})$, where $\sigma = 1, 2$ plays the role of a coordinate additional to $\mathbf{r}$ which specifies if the spin (in the z-direction) is "up" or "down". Instead of writing wave functions explicitly as spinors, we shall sometimes write wave functions as linear superpositions of products of a spatial and a spin wave function, $u = f(\mathbf{r})\,\alpha + g(\mathbf{r})\,\beta$, where f and g are ordinary spatial functions.

γ) Interpretation. We have discussed the physical significance of all the terms occuring in (12.11) [see Eq. (12.9)], except for the two terms involving the electric field $\mathcal{E}$, which were derived from (12.7). The term involving $\mathcal{E} \times \mathbf{p}$ is connected with the fact that, for a *moving* electron, an electric field $\mathcal{E}$ is equivalent with an extra magnetic field

$$\mathcal{H}_0 = \frac{1}{c}\,\mathcal{E} \times \mathbf{v} = \frac{1}{m\,c}\,\mathcal{E} \times \mathbf{p}.$$

If we add $\mathcal{H}_0$ to the external magnetic field $\mathcal{H}$ [last term in (12.11)] we get exactly *twice*[1] the second-last term in (12.11). The term involving $(\mathcal{E} \cdot \mathbf{p})$ has no classical analogue.

We consider next how (12.11) would be modified if we modify the DIRAC equation by the addition of a "PAULI-moment" term: In Sect. 19 we show that, according to quantum electrodynamics, the electron behaves (to a good approximation) as though its magnetic moment were not simply given by (12.10), but by $(1 + g_1)$ times that quantity, where g_1 (the anomalous moment factor) is a small constant. We have seen in Sect. 10β that such a modification can be achieved, without destroying relativistic invariance, by adding a term (10.16) involving g_1 to the linear DIRAC equation [see (10.15)].

We outline briefly how to evaluate the change in the energy eigenvalue due to the PAULI moment term, considering this term as a small perturbation. In conventional notation the inclusion of the term in g_1 in (10.15) means that we add to the HAMILTONian operator H in the linear DIRAC Eq. (10.1) a small operator

$$H' = g_1 \mu_0 \left[\beta\,\boldsymbol{\sigma} \cdot \mathcal{H} - i\,\beta\,\boldsymbol{\alpha} \cdot \mathcal{E}\right]. \tag{12.13}$$

The term involving the magnetic field $\mathcal{H}$ is simply $-g_1 \beta\,\boldsymbol{\mu}_s \cdot \mathcal{H}$, where $\boldsymbol{\mu}_s$ is defined in (12.10). The interaction energy between the spin magnetic moment of the electron and the magnetic field is simply $(1 + g_1)$ times the value in the unmodified DIRAC theory. We evaluate next the approximate expectation value E'_{el} of the second term in (12.13) over the DIRAC wave function u, using the approximation (12.7). We find

$$\begin{aligned}\langle u^* \beta\,\boldsymbol{\alpha} \cdot \mathcal{E}\,u\rangle &= \langle U_A^*\,\mathcal{E} \cdot \boldsymbol{\sigma}^P\,U_B\rangle - \langle U_B^*\,\boldsymbol{\sigma}^P \cdot \mathcal{E}\,U_A\rangle \\ &= \frac{1}{2m\,c}\,\langle U_A^*\,(\mathcal{E} \cdot \mathbf{p} - \mathbf{p} \cdot \mathcal{E} + 2i\,\mathcal{E} \cdot [\mathbf{p} \times \boldsymbol{\sigma}^P])\,U_A\rangle,\end{aligned}$$

where we have used the fact that curl $\mathcal{E} = 0$ and $p_x = -i\hbar\,\partial/\partial x$. We finally get

$$E'_{\mathrm{el}} = g_1 \frac{\mu_0}{2m\,c}\,\langle U_A^*\,(\hbar\,\mathrm{div}\,\mathcal{E} + 2\mathcal{E} \cdot [\mathbf{p} \times \boldsymbol{\sigma}^P])\,U_A\rangle. \tag{12.14}$$

One can show that (to within the accuracy of the PAULI approximation) the expression (12.14) is $2g_1$ times the expectation value of the sum of the two

[1] Regarding this factor of two, see L. H. THOMAS, Nature, Lond. **107**, 514 (1926).

terms involving $\mathcal{E}$ in (12.11). In establishing this identity the following relation is useful:

$$\langle U^* (\mathcal{E} \cdot \boldsymbol{p} + \boldsymbol{p} \cdot \mathcal{E})\, U \rangle = 0, \tag{12.15}$$

if U is an eigenstate of $(p^2/2m + V)$ and $\mathcal{E} = -\operatorname{grad} V$. (12.15) can be proved by writing $i\hbar\,\mathcal{E} = \boldsymbol{p} V - V \boldsymbol{p}$ and showing that $\langle U^* p^2 V U \rangle = \langle U^* V p^2 U \rangle$.

One can also derive an approximate equation involving only PAULI spinors and operators from the covariant quadratic Eq. (10.17). The derivation is somewhat similar to that of (12.11), but is very lengthy and involves dropping terms whose expectation values may diverge. The final result is the same as (12.11) [dropping terms in g_1^2 and terms which involve the operator occuring in (12.15)], except that the term involving $\mathcal{H}$ is multiplied by $(1+g_1)$ and the two terms involving $\mathcal{E}$ by $(1+2g_1)$.

13. PAULI theory for a central potential. We consider now the PAULI approximation (12.11) for the special case of an electron in a central electric field. We put the magnetic field $\mathcal{H}$ and vector potential $\boldsymbol{A}$ equal to zero and consider φ a function of the radial distance r only, so that

$$\mathcal{E} = -\frac{\boldsymbol{r}}{r}\frac{d\varphi}{dr}. \tag{13.1}$$

Making use of the definition (11.4) for the orbital angular momentum $\boldsymbol{k}$ and writing simply $\boldsymbol{s}$ for $\frac{1}{2}\sigma^P$, the spin, and u for the PAULI-spinor wave function, we obtain from (12.11)

$$W u = \left\{ -\left(e\varphi + \frac{\hbar^2}{2m}\Delta \right) - \frac{1}{2mc^2}(W + e\varphi)^2 + \frac{\mu_0 \hbar}{2mc}\frac{d\varphi}{dr}\left[\frac{\partial}{\partial r} - \frac{2}{r}\boldsymbol{k}\cdot\boldsymbol{s}\right]\right\} u, \tag{13.2}$$

where

$$\mu_0 = e\hbar/2mc$$

is the BOHR magnetic moment, (or magneton).

α) Energy eigenvalue. We do not consider, at the moment, the explicit dependence of the wave function u on the spin-coordinate (index $\sigma = 1, 2$) or on the angle variables ϑ, φ. We reduce, first, the differential equation (13.2) to a differential equation in the radial distance r alone, using general operator methods.

We can consider (13.2) as a generalized HAMILTONian equation with W, the nonrelativistic energy, as eigenvalue and the operator[1] on the right side as the HAMILTONian H. H depends on the angle variables and on the spin through the LAPLACE operator Δ and through $\boldsymbol{k}\cdot\boldsymbol{s}$, the "spin-orbit coupling" term. The Δ-operator we have already rewritten in (1.11) in terms of the operator $\partial/\partial r$ and the orbital angular momentum operator $\boldsymbol{k}$,

$$\Delta u = \left(\frac{\partial^2}{\partial r^2} + \frac{2}{r}\frac{\partial}{\partial r} - \frac{\boldsymbol{k}^2}{r^2} \right) u. \tag{13.3}$$

It further follows from the definition (11.10) for the operator $\boldsymbol{M}$ for the total angular momentum that

$$2\boldsymbol{k}\cdot\boldsymbol{s} = \boldsymbol{M}^2 - \boldsymbol{k}^2 - \boldsymbol{s}^2. \tag{13.4}$$

We see, therefore, that our approximate HAMILTONian operator H, Eq. (13.2), not only commutes with $\boldsymbol{M}^2$ and $\boldsymbol{s}^2$ (as does the exact DIRAC HAMILTONian), but *also* with $\boldsymbol{k}^2$ [with which the exact DIRAC HAMILTONian does *not* commute,

[1] Unlike the HAMILTONian in the nonrelativistic SCHRÖDINGER theory, H not only involves the spin operator, but also depends explicitly on the eigenvalue. We shall only consider cases where $|W| \ll mc^2$ and shall not encounter any difficulty from the dependence of H on W.

see (11.13)]. Since $\boldsymbol{M}^2$, $\boldsymbol{s}^2$ and $\boldsymbol{k}^2$ (and M_z) also commute with each other, we can find stationary states u which are simultaneous eigenstates of $\boldsymbol{M}^2$, $\boldsymbol{k}^2$, and $\boldsymbol{s}^2$ (and M_z) and hence also of $\boldsymbol{k}\cdot\boldsymbol{s}$, Eq. (13.4). For such a stationary state we can replace the angular momentum operators in (13.2) by their eigenvalues,

$$\left.\begin{array}{l} \boldsymbol{k}^2 \to l(l+1), \quad \boldsymbol{M}^2 \to j(j+1), \quad \boldsymbol{s}^2 \to s(s+1), \quad s=\tfrac{1}{2}; \\ 2\boldsymbol{k}\cdot\boldsymbol{s} \to X, \quad X \equiv j(j+1) - l(l+1) - s(s+1). \end{array}\right\} \tag{13.5}$$

We know that $s=\frac{1}{2}$ and that l is an integer or zero. We cannot yet specify j further, but we shall see later that $j=l+\frac{1}{2}$ or $j=l-\frac{1}{2}$.

On substituting (13.5) into (13.2) only the operator $\partial/\partial r$ remains, besides the quantum numbers j, l and s ,and we solve only for the radial wave function R (function of r only, not of ϑ, φ and the spin-index σ),

$$\left.\begin{array}{l} \left\{W + e\varphi + \dfrac{\hbar^2}{2m}\left[\dfrac{d^2}{dr^2} + \dfrac{2}{r}\dfrac{d}{dr} - \dfrac{l(l+1)}{r^2}\right] + \right. \\ \qquad \left. + \dfrac{1}{2mc^2}(W+e\varphi)^2 - \dfrac{\hbar\mu_0}{2mc}\dfrac{d\varphi}{dr}\left(\dfrac{d}{dr} - \dfrac{X}{r}\right)\right\} R = 0 \end{array}\right\} \tag{13.6}$$

where the constant X was defined in (13.5) and $\mu_0 = e\hbar/2mc$. If $\bar{v}$ is the order of magnitude of the electron velocity ($\bar{v} \ll c$), then the expectation values of the operators in the second line of (13.6) are of order $(\bar{v}/c)^2\, W$. If we neglect the operators in the second line completely, (13.6) reduces to the radial part of the non-relativistic SCHRÖDINGER equation (12.6)

$$\left[\frac{2m}{\hbar^2}(W_0 + e\varphi) + \frac{d^2}{dr^2} + \frac{2}{r}\frac{d}{dr} - \frac{l(l+1)}{r^2}\right] R_0 = 0. \tag{13.7}$$

If we solve (13.7) for W_0 and R_0, then W_0 differs from the correct W, and R_0 from the correct R, by terms of relative order $(\bar{v}/c)^2$. From a comparison of (12.7) and the exact (12.8) it follows that the approximate PAULI Eq. (13.2) or (13.6) is itself accurate up to (and including) terms of relative order $(\bar{v}/c)^2$. Thus even an exact solution of (13.6) for W would differ from the correct value given by the exact DIRAC equation (which we shall derive in Sect. 14) by terms[1] of relative order $(\bar{v}/c)^4$. For this reason we shall only calculate the eigenvalue W of (13.6) to relative order $(\bar{v}/c)^2$ by first order perturbation theory.

We consider the zero order equation (13.7) as solved for W_0 and R_0. The first order perturbation correction W_1, to be added to W_0, is then the expectation value of the operators in the second line of (13.6), using the zero order wave function R_0. To this approximation we can also replace W by W_0 in the second line of (13.6) and obtain

$$\left.\begin{array}{l} W_1 = W_a + W_b; \\ W_a = -\dfrac{1}{2mc^2}\displaystyle\int dr\, r^2 R_0^2 (W_0 + e\varphi)^2, \\ W_b = \dfrac{\mu_0\hbar}{2mc}\displaystyle\int dr\, r^2 R_0\left(\dfrac{dR_0}{dr} - X\dfrac{R_0}{r}\right)\dfrac{d\varphi}{dr}. \end{array}\right\} \tag{13.8}$$

We return now to atomic units, introduce the fine structure constant

$$\alpha = \frac{e^2}{\hbar c},$$

[1] The expansion parameter in the PAULI approximation scheme, roughly speaking, is $(\bar{v}/c)^2$, not $\bar{v}/c$.

write V for the electrostatic potential[1] in atomic units and note that $\mu_0 = e\hbar/2mc$ is equal to $\alpha/2$ in atomic units. In atomic units (13.8) then reduces to (dropping the subscript 0 from R_0)

$$\left.\begin{aligned} W_a &= -\tfrac{1}{2}\alpha^2 \overline{(W_0 + V)^2}, \\ W_b &= \frac{\alpha^2}{4}\int dr\, r^2 R\left(\frac{dR}{dr} - X\frac{R}{r}\right)\frac{dV}{dr}, \end{aligned}\right\} \tag{13.8a}$$

where the bar in the expression for W_a denotes the average over the zero-order wave function R. W_a represents the relativity correction due to the "variation of mass with velocity" and would also be obtained from the relativistic SCHRÖDINGER equation for spin-less particles. W_b, on the other hand, is characteristic of a particle with spin and its associated electromagnetic moment.

We return now to the special case of a COULOMB-potential,

$$V = \frac{Z}{r}.$$

Substituting the BALMER formula (2.11) for the zero-order energy W_0 and using (3.24), (3.25) for the expectation values of r^{-1} and r^{-2} in a hydrogen-like atom with principal quantum number n, the first term in (13.8a) reduces to

$$W_a = -\frac{\alpha^2}{2}\left(\frac{Z^4}{4n^4} - \frac{Z^3}{n^2}\overline{r^{-1}} + Z^2\overline{r^{-2}}\right) = -\frac{\alpha^2 Z^4}{2n^3}\left(\frac{1}{l+\frac{1}{2}} - \frac{3}{4n}\right). \tag{13.9}$$

In the first term in the expression for W_b we have $r^2\, dV/dr = -Z$. Integrating by parts, we get

$$W_b = \tfrac{1}{8}\alpha^2 Z\left[R^2(0) - R^2(\infty)\right] + \tfrac{1}{4}\alpha^2 XZ\,\overline{r^{-3}}. \tag{13.10}$$

For states of non-zero orbital angular momentum ($l \neq 0$), the wave function at the origin (and hence the term in square brackets) vanishes. Using (3.26) for the expectation value of r^{-3} and writing out the explicit form of the constant X, (13.5), we get, for $l \neq 0$,

$$W_b = +\frac{\alpha^2 Z^4}{4n^3}\,\frac{j(j+1) - l(l+1) - s(s+1)}{l(l+\frac{1}{2})(l+1)}. \tag{13.11}$$

For $l = 0$ (S-states) the term in square brackets in (13.10) is non-zero and finite, but $X\overline{r^{-3}}$ is indeterminate: For $l = 0$, j must equal s and X is zero, but the expectation value of r^{-3} diverges. This difficulty can be overcome as follows: The term involving $\overline{r^{-3}}$ was derived by using the approximation (12.7) instead of the exact expression (12.8), in particular we have replaced $(mc^2 + E + e\varphi)$ simply by $2mc^2$. For distances r of the order of the BOHR radius a/Z for nuclear charge Z, the error made in this neglect of $E - mc^2$ and of $e\varphi(r)$ is only of relative order $(Z\alpha)^2$. In all integrals used in the evaluation of the expectation values W_a and W_b, *except* in the integral leading to $\overline{r^{-3}}$, the important range of integration comes from r of the order of a/Z and the error made in our approximations is of relative order $(Z\alpha)^2$. For the $\overline{r^{-3}}$ term for $l = 0$, the wave function is finite at the origin, where the COULOMB potential diverges and the neglect of $e\varphi$ compared with mc^2 is no longer justified for $r \gtrsim e^2 Z/mc^2$. For this term then we use $(2mc^2 + e\varphi)$ instead of $2mc^2$ and instead of $\overline{r^{-3}}$ we get, in atomic units, the integral $\int dr\, r^2 R^2 [r^3(1 + Z\alpha^2/2r)]^{-1}$. This integral is finite, even for $l = 0$, but X vanishes *exactly* for $l = 0$, so the last term in (13.10) vanishes for $l = 0$. Using (3.46) for the value of $R(0)$, we then get, for $l = 0$, instead of (13.11) the expression

$$W_b = \alpha^2 Z^4/2n^3. \tag{13.12}$$

[1] *Not* the potential energy of the electron, i.e. $V = Z/r$, not $-Z/r$ for a nucleus of charge Z.

We shall prove soon that, for each value of l, there are two possible values of j, the inner quantum number, namely $l+\frac{1}{2}$ or $l-\frac{1}{2}$ (except for $l=0$, when $j=\frac{1}{2}$). (13.11) can then be written in the form

$$W_b = + \frac{\alpha^2 Z^4}{2n^3} \frac{1}{2l+1} \begin{Bmatrix} (l+1)^{-1} & \text{if } j = l + \frac{1}{2} \\ -l^{-1} & \text{if } j = l - \frac{1}{2}. \end{Bmatrix} \tag{13.13}$$

(13.13) also reduces to the correct expression (13.12) if $l=0$, $j=\frac{1}{2}$. Combining (13.9) and (13.13) we then get our final result for $W_1 = W_a + W_b$, the PAULI approximation for the shift in the energy eigenvalue,

$$W_1 = -\frac{\alpha^2 Z^4}{2n^3}\left(\frac{1}{j+\frac{1}{2}} - \frac{3}{4n}\right). \tag{13.14}$$

Eq. (13.14) is valid for all l and j and we note the important fact that W_1 depends only on j and n, but *not* on l. The two states with the same value of j and n and with $l=j+\frac{1}{2}$ and $l=j-\frac{1}{2}$ are thus *completely degenerate.*

β) PAULI eigenfunctions and values of the inner quantum number j. We now return to the wave equation (13.2) in the PAULI approximation and investigate the angle and spin dependence of the wave function u, which is a two-component spinor. In (13.2) we again consider $H_0 = -(e\varphi + \hbar^2 \Delta/2m)$ as the unperturbed HAMILTONian. For fixed values of n and l, the most general eigenfunction of H_0 is

$$u_{nl} = R_{nl}(r) \begin{pmatrix} a\, Y_{l m_l}(\vartheta, \varphi) \\ b\, Y_{l m_l'}(\vartheta, \varphi) \end{pmatrix}, \tag{13.15}$$

where ϑ, φ are the spherical polar angle coordinates of the electron, a and b are *arbitrary* constants and m_l, m_l' are independent of each other (chosen from the integers $-l, -l+1, \ldots, +l$). Only the ratio a/b is of physical significance and, if u is to be normalized, we take $|a|^2+|b|^2=1$. The total HAMILTONian, as well as H_0, commutes with $M_z = k_z + s_z$, the component in the z-direction of the *total* angular momentum. We therefore restrict ourselves to wave functions u of type (13.15) which are also eigenstates of M_z with eigenvalue m. Using (1.10) and the explicit representation (10.6) for $\sigma_3^P = 2s_z$, we have, for u of form (13.15),

$$M_z \begin{pmatrix} u_1 \\ u_2 \end{pmatrix} = \begin{pmatrix} (m_l + \frac{1}{2})\, u_1 \\ (m_l' - \frac{1}{2})\, u_2 \end{pmatrix}.$$

u is thus an eigenstate of M_z if

$$m_l + \tfrac{1}{2} = m_l' - \tfrac{1}{2} = m \tag{13.16}$$

or if either of the coefficients a and b in (13.15) is zero.

So far the ratio a/b is arbitrary, any value leading to an eigenstate of H_0, $\boldsymbol{k}^2$ and M_z. The full HAMILTONian of (13.2), however, also contains the operator $\boldsymbol{k}\cdot\boldsymbol{s}$ and we now have to find the values of a/b for which u is also an eigenstate of $\boldsymbol{k}\cdot\boldsymbol{s}$. It further follows from (13.4) that an eigenstate of $2\boldsymbol{k}\cdot\boldsymbol{s}$ with eigenvalue X [defined in (13.5)] is also an eigenstate of $\boldsymbol{M}^2$ with eigenvalue $j(j+1)$. Using (1.10), (1.14) and (10.6) for the matrix elements of k_i and s_i and choosing u of form (13.15) with (13.16), we have

$$2\boldsymbol{k}\cdot\boldsymbol{s}\, u = X u = \begin{pmatrix} \left[a(m-\frac{1}{2}) - b\sqrt{(l+\frac{1}{2})^2 - m^2}\right] Y_{l,m-\frac{1}{2}} \\ \left[-a\sqrt{(l+\frac{1}{2})^2 - m^2} - b(m+\frac{1}{2})\right] Y_{l,m+\frac{1}{2}} \end{pmatrix} R_{nl}(r).$$

This equation is fulfilled for two possible values of the ratio a/b,

cf Cayley-Klein representation of spinors in Goldstein

$$\frac{a_+}{b_+} = -\sqrt{\frac{l+m+\frac{1}{2}}{l-m+\frac{1}{2}}}, \quad \frac{a_-}{b_-} = \sqrt{\frac{l-m+\frac{1}{2}}{l+m+\frac{1}{2}}}. \tag{13.17}$$

The values[1] of the quantum number j and the eigenvalue X, (13.5), of $2\boldsymbol{k}\cdot\boldsymbol{s}$ for the two solutions labelled + and − are

$$\left.\begin{aligned} X_+ &= l, & j_+ &= l+\tfrac{1}{2}, \\ X_- &= -(l+1), & j_- &= l-\tfrac{1}{2}, \end{aligned}\right\} \tag{13.18}$$

except for $l=0$, when $X_+ = X_- = 0$ and $j_+ = j_- = \frac{1}{2}$. The two normalized eigenfunctions are then

$$\left.\begin{aligned} u_{nl,j=l+\frac{1}{2},m} &= \frac{1}{\sqrt{2l+1}} R_{nl}(r) \begin{pmatrix} \sqrt{l+m+\frac{1}{2}}\, Y_{l,m-\frac{1}{2}}(\vartheta,\varphi) \\ -\sqrt{l-m+\frac{1}{2}}\, Y_{l,m+\frac{1}{2}}(\vartheta,\varphi) \end{pmatrix}, \\ u_{nl,j=l-\frac{1}{2},m} &= \frac{1}{\sqrt{2l+1}} R_{nl}(r) \begin{pmatrix} \sqrt{l-m+\frac{1}{2}}\, Y_{l,m-\frac{1}{2}}(\vartheta,\varphi) \\ \sqrt{l+m+\frac{1}{2}}\, Y_{l,m+\frac{1}{2}}(\vartheta,\varphi) \end{pmatrix}. \end{aligned}\right\} \tag{13.19}$$

It is interesting to note that the ratios a/b in (13.17) do not depend on the value of the fine structure constant α and that neither a nor b is zero (except if $j = l+\frac{1}{2}$ and $m = \pm j$). Hence, even if α were allowed to approach zero (extreme nonrelativistic limit), the wave functions (13.19) would *not* be eigenstates of the operator k_z (nor of s_z). This is due to the fact that the eigenvalues of the "zero-order" nonrelativistic HAMILTONian H_0 are exactly the same for the + and − solutions in (13.19). Thus, even an infinitesimally small coefficient multiplying $(\boldsymbol{k}\cdot\boldsymbol{s})$ in (13.2) is sufficient to remove the degeneracy[2].

Any of the total wave functions u given by (13.19) are not eigenstates of s_z nor of the component of the spin $\boldsymbol{s}$ in any other direction (i.e. the spin-direction is not quantized). Nevertheless, for any such wave function and for a *specific* position (r,ϑ,φ) of the electron we can ask for the "direction of the spin". By this statement we mean the following: We are considering the wave function (13.19) of a particular eigenstate of M_z, consisting of the two spinor components $u_1(r,\vartheta,\varphi)$ and $u_2(r,\vartheta,\varphi)$. For a fixed value of (ϑ,φ) (the electron's polar angle coordinates with z as polar axis and with $\varphi=0$ in the zx-plane), the ratio u_1/u_2 is a constant. The constant spinor (u_1, u_2) must then be an eigenstate of the components s_ξ of the spin $\boldsymbol{s}$ in some particular direction $\boldsymbol{\xi}$ with polar coordinates (Θ,Φ). It can be shown, both by general invariance arguments[3] and by explicitly evaluating[4] the matrix elements of s_ξ, that the direction ξ is given by the relation,

$$\tan\left(\frac{\Theta}{2}\right) e^{i\Phi} = \frac{u_2}{u_1}. \tag{13.20}$$

---

[1] The statement that $j = l \pm \frac{1}{2}$ is merely a specific case of a more general theorem on the eigenvalues $j(j+1)$ of the square of the sum of two commuting angular momentum operators, $\boldsymbol{k}_a + \boldsymbol{k}_b$: If the eigenvalues of $\boldsymbol{k}_a^2$, $\boldsymbol{k}_b^2$ are $l_a(l_a+1)$ and $l_b(l_b+1)$, then $j = |l_a - l_b|, |l_a - b_b| + 1, \ldots, l_a + l_b$. j is defined as the *positive* root of $j(j+1) = \text{const}$.

[2] We can, of course, find a linear superposition of the two solutions, + and −, for fixed l and m, for which a or b vanishes. Such wave functions are eigenstates of k_z and s_z but *not* of the HAMILTONian (13.2), since the eigenvalues X_+ and X_- are different. If α is considered very small, the two eigenvalues of the total HAMILTONian are approximately the same and such a wave function is "almost a stationary state".

[3] Ref. [*1*], p. 151.

[4] Ref. [*10*], p. 310.

By substituting the explicit values of u_2/u_1 from (13.19) into (13.20) one then finds the coordinates (Θ, Φ) of the spin-direction ξ corresponding to each electron position (ϑ, φ) (in particular, $\Phi = \varphi$, i.e. the spin direction lies in the plane containing $\boldsymbol{r}$ and the z-axis).

In our preceding discussion we have classified the stationary states, for a fixed value of the principal quantum number n, first according to the value of l and second according to the value of m. The orbital quantum number l can take on the values $(0, 1, 2, \ldots, n-1)$. For a fixed value of l, if neither a nor b in (13.15) vanishes, (13.16) holds. It follows from (13.16) and the inequalities $|m_l| \lesseqgtr l$, $|m_l'| \lesseqgtr l$, that the possible values of m are $(-l+\frac{1}{2}, -l+\frac{3}{2}, \ldots, l-\frac{1}{2})$. For each of these $2l$ values of m, both sets of solutions, $+$ and $-$, in (13.17) are possible. There are only two other solutions, satisfying all the requirements, both for $j = l+\frac{1}{2}$: (i) $a=0$ and $m = -(l+\frac{1}{2})$ and (ii) $b=0$ and $m = +(l+\frac{1}{2})$. We thus have $2(2l+1)$ linearly independent wave functions for a fixed value of n and l. The total number of wave functions for fixed n and any possible value of l is $2n^2$, *twice* as many as in the nonrelativistic SCHRÖDINGER theory (the factor of two stems from the two possible eigenvalues of s_z).

The same set of $2n^2$ wave functions for a fixed value of n can also be classified according to the values of j and m, where $j(j+1)$ and m are the eigenvalues of $\boldsymbol{M}^2$ and of M_z. The possible values of j are $(\frac{1}{2}, \frac{3}{2}, \ldots, n-\frac{3}{2}, n-\frac{1}{2})$. For a fixed value of j, the possible values of m are $(-j, -j+1, \ldots, +j)$. For each value of j, except $j = n-\frac{1}{2}$, there are two wave functions to each value of m: One (labelled $+$) with $l = j-\frac{1}{2}$, the other (labelled $-$) with $l = j+\frac{1}{2}$. For any $j \neq n-\frac{1}{2}$ we thus have $2(2j+1)$ linearly independent solutions. For $j = n-\frac{1}{2}$, only the wave functions (labelled $+$) with $l = j-\frac{1}{2} = n-1$ exist ($2n$ in number). The total number of wave functions is thus again

$$\sum_{j=\frac{1}{2}}^{n-\frac{3}{2}} 2(2j+1) + 2n = 2n^2.$$

14. The exact solution of the DIRAC equation[1]. *α) The angular dependence of the eigenfunctions.* Next, we shall obtain the exact solution to the DIRAC differential equation for an electron in a COULOMB field, for the discrete spectrum. Accordingly, we put

$$\boldsymbol{A} = 0, \qquad \varphi = Ze/r \tag{14.1}$$

in (10.1) and write down explicitly the DIRAC equations for the four components of the wave function:

$$\left.\begin{aligned}
-\frac{i}{\hbar c}\left(E + \frac{Ze^2}{r} - E_0\right) u_1 + \frac{\partial u_3}{\partial z} + \frac{\partial u_4}{\partial x} - i\frac{\partial u_4}{\partial y} &= 0,\\
-\frac{i}{\hbar c}\left(E + \frac{Ze^2}{r} - E_0\right) u_2 - \frac{\partial u_4}{\partial z} + \frac{\partial u_3}{\partial x} + i\frac{\partial u_3}{\partial y} &= 0,\\
-\frac{i}{\hbar c}\left(E + \frac{Ze^2}{r} + E_0\right) u_3 + \frac{\partial u_1}{\partial z} + \frac{\partial u_2}{\partial x} - i\frac{\partial u_2}{\partial y} &= 0,\\
-\frac{i}{\hbar c}\left(E + \frac{Ze^2}{r} + E_0\right) u_4 - \frac{\partial u_2}{\partial z} + \frac{\partial u_1}{\partial x} + i\frac{\partial u_1}{\partial y} &= 0.
\end{aligned}\right\} \tag{14.2}$$

As a point of departure we shall make use of the fact that we already know, approximately, the components u_1 and u_2 of the wave-function [PAULI functions

[1] Cf. C. G. DARWIN: Proc. Roy. Soc. Lond., Ser. A **118**, 654 (1928). — W. GORDON: Z. Physik **48**, 11 (1928).

(13.19)]. For the case $j=l+\frac{1}{2}$ we put

$$\left.\begin{aligned} u_1 &= g(r)\sqrt{\frac{l+m+\frac{1}{2}}{2l+1}}\,Y_{l,m-\frac{1}{2}}(\vartheta,\varphi),\\ u_2 &= -\,g(r)\sqrt{\frac{l-m+\frac{1}{2}}{2l+1}}\,Y_{l,m+\frac{1}{2}}(\vartheta,\varphi),\end{aligned}\right\} \tag{14.3}$$

The above differs from (13.19) only in that the radially dependent eigenfunction $g(r)$ is not set equal to the SCHRÖDINGER function $R_{nl}(r)$, but is left arbitrary. Inserting (14.3) into the last two DIRAC equations (14.2), and also making use of formulas (A.37) to (A.39) one obtains

$$\begin{aligned} \frac{i}{\hbar c}\left(E+\frac{Ze^2}{r}+E_0\right)u_3 &= \frac{\partial u_1}{\partial z}+\frac{\partial u_2}{\partial x}-i\,\frac{\partial u_2}{\partial y}\\ &= \sqrt{\frac{l-m+\frac{3}{2}}{2l+3}}\cdot\left(\frac{dg}{dr}-l\,\frac{g}{r}\right)Y_{l+1,m-\frac{1}{2}},\\ \frac{i}{\hbar c}\left(E+\frac{Ze^2}{r}+E_0\right)u_4 &= \sqrt{\frac{l+m+\frac{3}{2}}{2l+3}}\left(\frac{dg}{dr}-l\,\frac{g}{r}\right)Y_{l+1,m+\frac{1}{2}}.\end{aligned}$$

If we put

$$\left.\begin{aligned} u_3 &= -\sqrt{\frac{l-m+\frac{3}{2}}{2l+3}}\,i\,f(r)\,Y_{l+1,m-\frac{1}{2}}(\vartheta,\varphi),\\ u_4 &= -\sqrt{\frac{l+m+\frac{3}{2}}{2l+3}}\,i\,f(r)\,Y_{l+1,m+\frac{1}{2}}(\vartheta,\varphi),\end{aligned}\right\} \tag{14.4}$$

we find that the following relation must hold between g and f

$$\frac{1}{\hbar c}\left(E+\frac{Ze^2}{r}+E_0\right)f = \frac{dg}{dr}-l\,\frac{g}{r}. \tag{14.5}$$

Next, we insert (14.4) into the third and fourth equations of the set (14.2). Employing formulas (A.37) to (A.39) again, one obtains two equations which are identical and are satisfied only if the following relation holds between f and g:

$$\frac{1}{\hbar c}\left(E+\frac{Ze^2}{r}-E_0\right)g = -\frac{df}{dr}-(l+2)\,\frac{f}{r}. \tag{14.6}$$

For the case $j=l-\frac{1}{2}$ one obtains, in a similar manner,

$$\left.\begin{aligned} u_1 &= \sqrt{\frac{l-m+\frac{1}{2}}{2l+1}}\,g(r)\,Y_{l,m-\frac{1}{2}},\\ u_2 &= \sqrt{\frac{l+m+\frac{1}{2}}{2l+1}}\,g(r)\,Y_{l,m+\frac{1}{2}},\\ u_3 &= -\sqrt{\frac{l+m-\frac{1}{2}}{2l-1}}\,i\,f(r)\,Y_{l-1,m-\frac{1}{2}},\\ u_4 &= \sqrt{\frac{l-m-\frac{1}{2}}{2l-1}}\,i\,f(r)\,Y_{l-1,m+\frac{1}{2}},\end{aligned}\right\} \tag{14.7}$$

$$\left.\begin{aligned} \frac{1}{\hbar c}\left(E+\frac{Ze^2}{r}+E_0\right)f &= \frac{dg}{dr}+(l+1)\,\frac{g}{r},\\ \frac{1}{\hbar c}\left(E+\frac{Ze^2}{r}-E_0\right)g &= -\frac{df}{dr}+(l-1)\,\frac{f}{r}.\end{aligned}\right\} \tag{14.8}$$

Introducing a new quantum number $\varkappa$ by setting

$$\left.\begin{aligned} \varkappa &= -(j+\tfrac{1}{2}) = -(l+1), && \text{if } j = l+\tfrac{1}{2}, \\ \varkappa &= +(j+\tfrac{1}{2}) = +l, && \text{if } j = l-\tfrac{1}{2}, \end{aligned}\right\} \tag{14.9}$$

(14.5), (14.6) and (14.8) can be summarized as follows:

$$\left.\begin{aligned} \frac{1}{\hbar c}\left(E+\frac{Ze^2}{r}+E_0\right)f-\left(\frac{dg}{dr}+(1+\varkappa)\frac{g}{r}\right)&=0, \\ \frac{1}{\hbar c}\left(E+\frac{Ze^2}{r}-E_0\right)g+\left(\frac{df}{dr}+(1-\varkappa)\frac{f}{r}\right)&=0. \end{aligned}\right\} \tag{14.10}$$

Thus, $\varkappa$ is a positive or negative integer. $\varkappa=0$ is not possible, for were we to put $l=0$ and $m=\frac{1}{2}$ in (14.7), then the only non-vanishing spherical harmonic would be the one contained in u_1. However, the factor $l-m+\frac{1}{2}$ contained in u_1 vanishes. Thus, the eigenfunction would vanish identically. For $\varkappa\neq 0$ it is readily seen from (14.3), (14.5) and (14.7) that there are $2|\varkappa|$ eigenfunctions, for each $\varkappa$, having the magnetic quantum-numbers $m=-(|\varkappa|-\frac{1}{2}), -(|\varkappa|-\frac{3}{2}) \ldots |\varkappa|-\frac{3}{2}$, $|\varkappa|-\frac{1}{2}$.

This completes the demonstration that the functions (14.3) which were postulated for the large components of the DIRAC wave-function will indeed lead to the goal. This is not completely obvious from the beginning. It might have happened that insertion of (14.4) into the first and second DIRAC equations would require an angular dependence different from the one postulated in (14.3), or we might have been led to a contradiction in the two equations for g (see also [*4*], Chap. 44).

β) Solution of the radial differential equation. Next, we shall solve the radial differential equation (14.10), and we shall do this by following the treatment of GORDON[1]. First of all, we introduce the functions χ_1 and χ_2 in place of f and g as follows

$$\chi_1 = r f, \quad \chi_2 = r g. \tag{14.11}$$

Setting E_0 equal to its value mc^2, we obtain

$$\left.\begin{aligned} \frac{d\chi_1}{dr}-\varkappa\frac{\chi_1}{r}&=\left[\frac{mc}{\hbar}\left(1-\frac{E}{E_0}\right)-\alpha\frac{Z}{r}\right]\chi_2, \\ \frac{d\chi_2}{dr}+\varkappa\frac{\chi_2}{r}&=\left[\frac{mc}{\hbar}\left(1+\frac{E}{E_0}\right)+\alpha\frac{Z}{r}\right]\chi_1. \end{aligned}\right\} \tag{14.12}$$

In the above, $\alpha=\frac{e^2}{\hbar c}=1/137.037$ is SOMMERFELD's fine-structure constant. For large values of r, (14.12) has the asymptotic solution

$$\left.\begin{aligned} &\chi_1 = a_1 e^{-\lambda r}, \quad \chi_2 = a_2 e^{-\lambda r}, \quad \lambda = \frac{mc}{\hbar}\sqrt{1-\frac{E^2}{E_0^2}}, \\ &a_1 = -a\sqrt{1-\frac{E}{E_0}}, \quad a_2 = +a\sqrt{1+\frac{E}{E_0}}. \end{aligned}\right\} \tag{14.13}$$

In passing we note that the quantity $2\pi\hbar/mc = 2.43\times 10^{-10}$ cm is the COMPTON wavelength. The COMPTON wavelength equals the radius of the first BOHR orbit multiplied by $2\pi\alpha$. Thus, in atomic units

$$\lambda = \frac{1}{\alpha}\sqrt{1-\left(\frac{E}{E_0}\right)^2} = \frac{1}{\alpha}\sqrt{1-\alpha^4 E^2}. \tag{14.14}$$

---

[1] W. GORDON: Z. Physik **48**, 11 (1928).

Use has been made of the fact that the rest energy of the electron mc^2 equals $2/\alpha^2$ in atomic units, i.e., approximately equal to 37560 times the ionization potential of hydrogen.

The next step consists of writing down a functional form which is valid for all values of r. To this end one might be tempted to replace the constant a by a function of r (cf. Sect. 2). However, this would amount to the assumption, surely unjustified, that χ_1 and χ_2 have a constant ratio for all values of r. Instead, we must have at our disposal two functions of r, and we therefore put

$$\chi_1 = \sqrt{1-\varepsilon}\, e^{-\lambda r}(\varphi_1 - \varphi_2), \quad \chi_2 = \sqrt{1+\varepsilon}\, e^{-\lambda r}(\varphi_1 + \varphi_2), \tag{14.15}$$

$$\varepsilon = E/E_0. \tag{14.16}$$

In view of (14.13) it is clear that for large values of r, φ_2 is much greater than φ_1. Let us introduce the new independent variable

$$\varrho = 2\lambda r. \tag{14.17}$$

Then (14.12) becomes

$$\left.\begin{aligned} \frac{1}{\sqrt{1-\varepsilon}}\left(\frac{d\chi_1}{d\varrho} - \frac{\varkappa}{\varrho}\chi_1\right) &= \left(\frac{1}{2} - \sqrt{\frac{1+\varepsilon}{1-\varepsilon}}\,\alpha\frac{Z}{\varrho}\right)\frac{\chi_2}{\sqrt{1+\varepsilon}},\\ \frac{1}{\sqrt{1+\varepsilon}}\left(\frac{d\chi_2}{d\varrho} + \frac{\varkappa}{\varrho}\chi_2\right) &= \left(\frac{1}{2} + \sqrt{\frac{1-\varepsilon}{1+\varepsilon}}\,\alpha\frac{Z}{\varrho}\right)\frac{\chi_1}{\sqrt{1-\varepsilon}}. \end{aligned}\right\} \tag{14.18}$$

Inserting (14.15) into (14.18) we obtain

$$\left.\begin{aligned} \frac{d\varphi_1}{d\varrho} &= \left(1 - \frac{\alpha\varepsilon}{\sqrt{1-\varepsilon^2}}\frac{Z}{\varrho}\right)\varphi_1 + \left(-\frac{\varkappa}{\varrho} - \frac{\alpha}{\sqrt{1-\varepsilon^2}}\frac{Z}{\varrho}\right)\varphi_2,\\ \frac{d\varphi_2}{d\varrho} &= \left(-\frac{\varkappa}{\varrho} + \frac{\alpha}{\sqrt{1-\varepsilon^2}}\frac{Z}{\varrho}\right)\varphi_1 + \frac{\alpha\varepsilon}{\sqrt{1-\varepsilon^2}}\frac{Z}{\varrho}\varphi_2. \end{aligned}\right\} \tag{14.19}$$

Next, we expand φ_1 and φ_2 as power series in ϱ

$$\varphi_1 = \varrho^\gamma \sum_{\nu=0}^{\infty} a_\nu \varrho^\nu, \quad \varphi_2 = \varrho^\gamma \sum_{\nu=0}^{\infty} b_\nu \varrho^\nu. \tag{14.20}$$

Inserting the power series expansions into (14.19) and equating like powers of ϱ we obtain

$$\left.\begin{aligned} a_\nu(\nu+\gamma) &= a_{\nu-1} - \frac{\alpha\varepsilon Z}{\sqrt{1-\varepsilon^2}}a_\nu - \left(\varkappa + \frac{\alpha Z}{\sqrt{1-\varepsilon^2}}\right)b_\nu,\\ b_\nu(\nu+\gamma) &= \left(-\varkappa + \frac{\alpha Z}{\sqrt{1-\varepsilon^2}}\right)a_\nu + \frac{\alpha\varepsilon Z}{\sqrt{1-\varepsilon^2}}b_\nu. \end{aligned}\right\} \tag{14.21^1}$$

In particular, let us put $\nu=0$. This gives two homogeneous equations in the two unknowns a_0 and b_0 $(a_{-1}=0)$. In order that a solution exist it is necessary that

$$\begin{vmatrix} \gamma + \dfrac{\alpha\varepsilon Z}{\sqrt{1-\varepsilon^2}} & \varkappa + \dfrac{\alpha Z}{\sqrt{1-\varepsilon^2}} \\ \varkappa - \dfrac{\alpha Z}{\sqrt{1-\varepsilon^2}} & \gamma - \dfrac{\alpha\varepsilon Z}{\sqrt{1-\varepsilon^2}} \end{vmatrix} = 0$$

[1] At this point we can readily see the advantage which (14.15) has over a function of the form $\chi_i = e^{-\lambda r} f_i(r)$. As a result of the fact that the function φ_2 approaches a power for large values of r $\left(\frac{d\varphi_2}{d\varrho} \sim \frac{\varphi_2}{\varrho}\right)$, the second Eq. (14.21) contains only a_ν and b_ν; it does not contain $a_{\nu-1}$ or $b_{\nu-1}$, so that b_ν can be expressed in terms of a_ν only.

i.e., that

$$\gamma = \pm\sqrt{\varkappa^2 - \alpha^2 Z^2}. \tag{14.22}$$

In order that φ_1 and φ_2 be acceptable eigenfunctions, they must be quadratically integrable. More precisely, the integral

$$\int (|f|^2 + |g|^2)\, r^2\, dr = \int (\chi_1^2 + \chi_2^2)\, dr = \int e^{-\varrho} (\varphi_1^2 + 2\varepsilon\, \varphi_1 \varphi_2 + \varphi_2^2)\, dr$$

must exist. That will be the case only if we choose the positive square root in (14.22). The ratio of the coefficients a_ν/b_ν can now be obtained from the second Eq. (14.21),

$$\frac{b_\nu}{a_\nu} = -\frac{-\varkappa + \alpha Z/\sqrt{1-\varepsilon^2}}{n' - \nu}. \tag{14.23}$$

In the above, we have abbreviated

$$n' = \frac{\alpha Z \varepsilon}{\sqrt{1-\varepsilon^2}} - \gamma = \frac{\alpha Z \varepsilon}{\sqrt{1-\varepsilon^2}} - \sqrt{\varkappa^2 - \alpha^2 Z^2}. \tag{14.24}$$

Inserting (14.23) into the first of the Eq. (14.21) we obtain the following recursion formula for the coefficients a_ν:

$$a_\nu = -\frac{n' - \nu}{\nu(2\gamma + \nu)}\, a_{\nu-1} = (-)^\nu \frac{(n'-1)\ldots(n'-\nu)}{\nu!\,(2\gamma+1)\ldots(2\gamma+\nu)}\, a_0, \tag{14.25}$$

and, since (14.23) gives

$$\frac{b_\nu}{a_\nu} = \frac{b_0}{a_0}\,\frac{n'}{n'-\nu},$$

we obtain

$$b_\nu = (-)^\nu \frac{n'\ldots(n'-\nu+1)}{\nu!\,(2\gamma+1)\ldots(2\gamma+\nu)}\, b_0. \tag{14.26}$$

As in the nonrelativistic case of Sect. 3, we must require that the power series for φ_1 and φ_2 terminate for real values of λ, i.e., for $\varepsilon < 1$ and $E < E_0$ (discrete spectrum), otherwise the eigenfunctions χ_1 and χ_2 increase as $e^{+\lambda r}$ with increasing values of r. The series terminate only if n' is a non-negative integer. In this case the series for φ_2 goes up to the power $r^{n'}$, and the series for φ_1 up to $r^{n'-1}$.

The case $n'=0$ requires special consideration. It is readily seen from (14.25) that, unless $a_0 = 0$, the coefficients of all higher powers will not vanish. It should be noted, however, that according to (14.23)

$$\frac{a_0}{b_0} = -\frac{n'}{-\varkappa + \alpha Z/\sqrt{1-\varepsilon^2}}. \tag{14.27}$$

This vanishes provided the denominator is different from zero. However, for the case $n'=0$, (14.24) gives

$$\gamma^2 = \varkappa^2 - \alpha^2 Z^2 = \alpha^2 Z^2 \frac{\varepsilon^2}{1-\varepsilon^2}, \text{ hence } \varkappa = \pm\frac{\alpha Z}{\sqrt{1-\varepsilon^2}}.$$

Thus, the denominator in (14.27) differs from zero only for negative values of $\varkappa\, (j = l + \frac{1}{2})$ and $\varkappa = -(l+1)$. In this case $a_0 = 0$, b_0 is non-vanishing, and we have arrived at a solution to the problem. On the other hand, if $\varkappa$ is positive, the denominator goes to zero as n', the ratio a_0/b_0 has a non-vanishing value and the series for φ_1 does not terminate. The case $n'=0$, $\varkappa = l$ must thus be excluded. On the other hand, $n'=0$, $\varkappa = -(l+1)$ is permissible. n' replaces the radial quantum number $n_r = n - l - 1$ of the SCHRÖDINGER theory.

We finally introduce the principal quantum-number

$$n = n' + k, \qquad k = |\varkappa| = j + \tfrac{1}{2} \tag{14.28}$$

and solve (14.24) for the desired eigenvalue ε

$$\varepsilon = \frac{E}{E_0} = \frac{1}{\sqrt{1 + \frac{\alpha^2 Z^2}{(n'+\gamma)^2}}} = \frac{1}{\sqrt{1 + \left(\frac{\alpha Z}{n - k + \sqrt{k^2 - \alpha^2 Z^2}}\right)^2}}. \tag{14.29}$$

(14.29) is our final formula for the energy E of the hydrogen atom. The energy depends only on k, i.e., only on j; the energy is independent of the sign of $\varkappa$, [i.e., independent of l, cf. (13.14)]. For light atoms (small values of Z) the energy is only slightly less than the rest energy E_0 of the electron because of the small magnitude of the fine-structure constant α. A more detailed discussion of the energy formula is postponed until Sect. 17.

γ) *Discussion and normalization of the radial eigenfunctions of the* KEPLER *problem.* The functions φ_1 and φ_2 are essentially confluent hypergeometric functions as can be seen directly from the recursion formulas (14.25) and (14.26), namely

$$\left.\begin{aligned} \varphi_1 &= -c \frac{n'}{\sqrt{-\varkappa + \alpha Z/\sqrt{1-\varepsilon^2}}} \varrho^\gamma F(-n'+1,\ 2\gamma+1,\ \varrho), \\ \varphi_2 &= \quad c\sqrt{-\varkappa + \alpha Z/\sqrt{1-\varepsilon^2}}\ \varrho^\gamma F(-n',\ \ 2\gamma+1,\ \varrho). \end{aligned}\right\} \tag{14.30}$$

The constant c is as yet undetermined, and we shall use it to normalize the eigenfunction u. The condition of normalization for the DIRAC eigenfunctions is as follows:

$$\int |u|^2 d\tau = \int (|u_1|^2 + |u_2|^2 + |u_3|^2 + |u_4|^2)\, d\tau = 1. \tag{14.31}$$

Since the spherical harmonics Y_{lm} are already normalized, the integration over angles in view of (14.3), (14.4) and (14.7), simply gives

$$\int |u|^2 d\tau = \int (|f|^2 + |g|^2)\, r^2 dr = \int (\chi_1^2 + \chi_2^2)\, dr = 1. \tag{14.32}$$

The above holds both for $j = l + \frac{1}{2}$ and $j = l - \frac{1}{2}$. The somewhat tedious integration has been carried out by BECHERT[1] giving the following value for the constant c which occurs in (14.30),

$$c = \frac{\sqrt{\Gamma(2\gamma + n' + 1)}}{\Gamma(2\gamma+1)\sqrt{n'!}} \sqrt{\frac{\lambda\sqrt{1-\varepsilon^2}}{2\alpha Z}}. \tag{14.33}$$

The formulas can be further simplified by inserting the explicit value of the energy (14.29):

$$1 - \varepsilon^2 = \frac{(\alpha Z)^2}{(n'+\gamma)^2 + (\alpha Z)^2} = \frac{(\alpha Z)^2}{n^2 - 2n'\left(k - \sqrt{k^2 - \alpha^2 Z^2}\right)}. \tag{14.34}$$

Next, we define the "apparent principal quantum-number" N

$$N = \sqrt{n^2 - 2n'\left(k - \sqrt{k^2 - \alpha^2 Z^2}\right)}, \tag{14.35}$$

which clearly becomes equal to the actual principal quantum-number n if we neglect the relativistic correction, that is, if we set $\alpha = 0$ and thus [cf. (14.22)] $\gamma = k$. Then according to (14.13) and (14.14)

$$\lambda = \frac{mc}{\hbar}\frac{\alpha Z}{N} = \frac{1}{a_0}\frac{Z}{N}, \tag{14.36}$$

in which a_0 is the atomic unit of length. Introducing the above into (14.11), (14.15), (14.30), and (14.33), we obtain the following explicit expressions for the

[1] K. BECHERT: Ann. d. Phys. 6, 700 (1930).

normalized radial DIRAC eigenfunctions:

$$\left.\begin{aligned} f &= -\frac{\sqrt{\Gamma(2\gamma+n'+1)}}{\Gamma(2\gamma+1)\sqrt{n'!}}\sqrt{\frac{1-\varepsilon}{4N(N-\varkappa)}}\left(\frac{2Z}{Na_0}\right)^{\frac{3}{2}} e^{-\frac{Zr}{Na_0}}\left(\frac{2Zr}{Na_0}\right)^{\gamma-1}\times \\ &\quad\times\left[n' F\left(-n'+1, 2\gamma+1, \frac{2Zr}{Na_0}\right)+(N-\varkappa)F\left(-n', 2\gamma+1, \frac{2Zr}{Na_0}\right)\right], \\ g &= -\frac{\sqrt{\Gamma(2\gamma+n'+1)}}{\Gamma(2\gamma+1)\sqrt{n'!}}\sqrt{\frac{1+\varepsilon}{4N(N-\varkappa)}}\left(\frac{2Z}{Na_0}\right)^{\frac{3}{2}} e^{-\frac{Zr}{Na_0}}\left(\frac{2Zr}{Na_0}\right)^{\gamma-1}\times \\ &\quad\times\left[-n' F\left(-n'+1, 2\gamma+1, \frac{2Zr}{Na_0}\right)+(N-\varkappa)F\left(-n', 2\gamma+1, \frac{2Zr}{Na_0}\right)\right]. \end{aligned}\right\} \quad (14.37)$$

The various quantities occurring in (14.37) were previously defined: for $\varkappa$ see (14.9), γ (14.22), ε (14.16) and (14.29), n' (14.24) and (14.28), N (14.35), and $k=|\varkappa|$.

The functions (14.37) have an appearance which is quite similar to the SCHRÖDINGER eigenfunction (3.20). They differ only in the argument in that N replaces the actual principal quantum-number n, and either $\varkappa$ or k appears in the place of l. If the fine-structure constant α is neglected compared to unity throughout (14.37), this amounts to setting $l=k$, $N=n$ and $\varepsilon=1$ [cf. (14.22), (14.28), (14.34) and (14.35)]. Then f vanishes on account of the factor $1-\varepsilon$, and g becomes precisely, as it must, the normalized SCHRÖDINGER eigenfunction (3.17), provided we express $\varkappa$ in terms of l by means of (14.9) and use the recurrence relation

$$x F(a+1, b+1, x) = b F(a+1, b, x) - b F(a, b, x).$$

We give below the explicit forms[1] of the radial wave functions (14.37) for the K and L shells ($n=1$ and 2). We define

$$\left.\begin{aligned} &\gamma_1=\sqrt{1-\alpha^2 Z^2}, \qquad \gamma_2=\sqrt{4-\alpha^2 Z^2}; \\ &N_1=1, \quad N_2=\sqrt{2(1+\gamma_1)}, \quad N_3=2; \quad \varrho_i=\frac{2Zr}{N_i a_0}; \\ &\varepsilon_1=\left[1+\left(\frac{\alpha Z}{\gamma_1}\right)^2\right]^{-\frac{1}{2}}, \quad \varepsilon_2=\left[1+\left(\frac{\alpha Z}{1+\gamma_1}\right)^2\right]^{-\frac{1}{2}}, \quad \varepsilon_3=\left[1+\left(\frac{\alpha Z}{\gamma_2}\right)^2\right]^{-\frac{1}{2}}. \end{aligned}\right\} \quad (14.38)$$

We then get from (14.37):

(i) $1 S_{\frac{1}{2}}$-state ($n=1$, $l=0$, $j=\frac{1}{2}$):

$$\left.\begin{aligned} g &= \left(\frac{2Z}{a_0}\right)^{\frac{3}{2}}\sqrt{\frac{1+\varepsilon_1}{2\Gamma(2\gamma_1+1)}}\, e^{-\frac{1}{2}\varrho_1}\varrho_1^{\gamma_1-1}, \\ f &= -\sqrt{\frac{1-\varepsilon_1}{1+\varepsilon_1}}\, g. \end{aligned}\right\} \quad (14.39)$$

(ii) $2 S_{\frac{1}{2}}$-state ($n=2$, $l=0$, $j=\frac{1}{2}$):

$$\left.\begin{aligned} g &= \left(\frac{2Z}{N_2 a_0}\right)^{\frac{3}{2}}\sqrt{\frac{2\gamma_1+1}{\Gamma(2\gamma_1+1)}}\sqrt{\frac{1+\varepsilon_2}{4N_2(N_2+1)}}\, e^{-\frac{1}{2}\varrho_2}\left[N_2\varrho_2^{\gamma_1-1}-\frac{N_2+1}{2\gamma_1+1}\varrho_2^{\gamma_1}\right], \\ f &= -\sqrt{\frac{1-\varepsilon_2}{1+\varepsilon_2}}\,\frac{(2\gamma_1+1)(N_2+2)-(N_2+1)\varrho_2}{(2\gamma_1+1)N_2-(N_2+1)\varrho_2}\, g. \end{aligned}\right\} \quad (14.40)$$

---

[1] These expressions are taken from W. B. PAYNE, Ph. D. Thesis, Louisiana State University 1955 (unpublished). Payne has also tabulated the radial wave functions for the M and N shells. See also E. H. BURHOP and H. S. MASSEY, Proc. Roy. Soc. Lond., Ser. A **153**, 661 (1935). Graphs of the DIRAC wave functions are given by H. E. WHITE, Phys. Rev. **38**, 513 (1931). Expressions for the DIRAC wave functions in terms of generalized LAGUERRE polynomials are given by L. DAVIS, Phys. Rev. **56**, 186 (1939).

(iii) $2P_{\frac{1}{2}}$-state ($n=2,\ l=1,\ j=\frac{1}{2}$):

$$\left.\begin{aligned} g &= \left(\frac{2Z}{N_2 a_0}\right)^{\frac{3}{2}} \sqrt{\frac{2\gamma_1+1}{\Gamma(2\gamma_1+1)}} \sqrt{\frac{1+\varepsilon_2}{4N_2(N_2-1)}}\, e^{-\frac{1}{2}\varrho_2}\left[(N_2-2)\,\varrho_2^{\gamma_1-1} - \frac{N_2-1}{2\gamma_1+1}\,\varrho_2^{\gamma_1}\right]. \\ f &= -\sqrt{\frac{1-\varepsilon_2}{1+\varepsilon_2}}\, \frac{(2\gamma_1+1)\,N_2-(N_2-1)\,\varrho_2}{(2\gamma_1+1)(N_2-2)-(N_2-1)\,\varrho_2}\, g. \end{aligned}\right\} \tag{14.41}$$

(iv) $2P_{\frac{3}{2}}$-state ($n=2,\ l=1,\ j=\frac{3}{2}$):

$$\left.\begin{aligned} g &= \left(\frac{Z}{a_0}\right)^{\frac{3}{2}} \sqrt{\frac{1+\varepsilon_3}{2\Gamma(2\gamma_2+1)}}\, e^{-\frac{1}{2}\varrho_3}\,\varrho_3^{\gamma_2-1}, \\ f &= -\sqrt{\frac{1-\varepsilon_3}{1+\varepsilon_3}}\, g. \end{aligned}\right\} \tag{14.42}$$

δ) Comparison with SCHRÖDINGER *wave functions.* Some general remarks can be made about the order of magnitude of the deviation of the DIRAC radial wave functions (14.37) from the equivalent nonrelativistic wave function R. We restrict ourselves, at first, to relatively small values of the principal quantum number n and to reasonably small values of the nuclear charge, $Z \ll 137$: For $\varrho=(2Zr/Na_0)$ of order of magnitude unity (r of the order of the BOHR radius for charge Z, the important range in most integrals over r), the ratios $(g-R)/R$ and $(f/g)^2$ are of order $(Z\alpha)^2$. For the states with $j=l-\frac{1}{2}$ and for $\varrho \ll 1$, the ratios $(g-R)/R$ and $(f/g)^2$ are of order $(Z\alpha)^2\varrho^{-1}$. For $j=l+\frac{1}{2}$ these ratios increase much less rapidly with decreasing ϱ. Note that for r as small as the COMPTON wavelength of the electron, ϱ is of order $(Z\alpha)$ and $(f/g)^2$ and $(g-R)/R$ are still only of order $Z\alpha$ or smaller.

The DIRAC wave functions with $j=\frac{1}{2}$ ($l=0$ or 1), unlike the other DIRAC functions and all SCHRÖDINGER wave functions, are *singular* at the origin for all principal quantum numbers n. If $Z\alpha \approx Z/137$ is small, however, this singularity is a very weak one. Consider, for instance, the states with $j=\frac{1}{2}$ and $l=0$ (for any value of n). For small distances, $\varrho \ll 1$, the SCHRÖDINGER function $R(\varrho)$ is approximately equal to a constant $R(0)$, but the DIRAC function $g(\varrho)$ is given by

$$g(\varrho) \sim R(0)\,\varrho^{\gamma-1} \sim R(0)\exp\left[\frac{1}{2}(Z\alpha)^2\log\frac{1}{\varrho}\right].$$

Thus $g(\varrho)$ is infinite at the origin but, at finite distances ϱ larger than $\exp(-1/Z^2\alpha^2)$, $(g-R)/R$ is still only of order $\frac{1}{2}(Z\alpha)^2\log\varrho$. Only for exceedingly small distances, ϱ of the order of $\exp[-2(137/Z)^2]$, does $(g-R)/R$ become of order unity or greater. For all but very large Z, this distance is well inside the nucleus. For the $j=\frac{1}{2}$, $l=1$ states, the singular term is smaller by a factor of order $(Z\alpha)^2$ than for the $l=0$ states. Since $R(\varrho)$ is proportional to ϱ for small ϱ if $l=1$, in this case $(g-R)/R$ is of order $(Z\alpha)^2/\varrho$.

We have thus seen that, for all but extremely small values of the radial distance r, the large components of the radial DIRAC wave functions approximate the nonrelativistic ones closely if $Z\alpha \approx Z/137$ is small. For heavy atoms the parameter $Z\alpha$ is by no means negligible and the deviations between the relativistic and SCHRÖDINGER wave functions are important, at least for low values of j. These deviations (and the singularity of the DIRAC functions, in particular) are especially important for the hyperfine structure and other effects for the states with $j=\frac{1}{2}$ and low n in heavy atoms. Quite generally the deviations between the DIRAC and SCHRÖDINGER functions become less marked as the values of n and especially of j increase.

We finally discuss, in the light of the preceding remarks, the accuracy of the terms, obtained in the PAULI approximation (13.10), which involve the wave function at the origin, $u(0)$. In Sect. 13 we had replaced the DIRAC wave function $u(0)$ by the nonrelativistic expression $R_0(0)$ and have to justify this procedure for states with $j=\frac{1}{2}$ ($l=0$ or 1), for which the DIRAC wave function at the origin diverges. As in the discussion preceding (13.12) we note that we have replaced $(mc^2+E+e\varphi)$ by $2mc^2$ in the derivation of (13.10). Using again the more accurate expression $(2mc^2+e\varphi)$, we get in (13.10), instead of $u^2(0)$, the integral

$$\int_0^\infty d\varrho \left(1+\frac{Z\alpha^2}{2\varrho}\right)^{-1} \frac{d}{d\varrho}\, u^2(\varrho) \tag{14.43}$$

with ϱ the radial distance in atomic units. If $Z\alpha \ll 1$ and $u(\varrho)$ is not singular, $u^2(0)$ is an excellent approximation for the integral (14.42). If $u(\varrho)$ has the weak singularity $\varrho^{-\frac{1}{2}(Z\alpha)^2}$ of the DIRAC functions for $j=\frac{1}{2}$ (and $Z\alpha \ll 1$), the integral (14.42) is still finite and equal, say, to $u^2(\varrho_0)$ where ϱ_0 is some characteristic length of order $(Z\alpha)^2$ atomic units ($\sim Z^2 r_0$ in ordinary units, where $r_0 = e^2/mc^2 \sim 10^{-13}$ cm is the "classical radius of the electron"). We have discussed above the relation between the radial DIRAC functions (f and g) and the SCHRÖDINGER function R for small distances ϱ. Using these relations one can show that replacing $u^2(\varrho_0)$ by $R^2(0)$ in (13.10) gives an approximation to W_b which is in error at most by terms of relative order $(Z\alpha)^2 \log Z\alpha$, both for the $S_{\frac{1}{2}}$ and the $P_{\frac{1}{2}}$ states.

15. DIRAC equation. Continuous spectrum. For a DIRAC electron in the COULOMB field of a positively charged nucleus, we found a discrete spectrum of bound states for values E of the total energy (including the rest mass $E_0 = mc^2$) in the range $0 < E < mc^2$. For $E > mc^2$, the effective quantum number n', Eq. (14.24), is complex. In analogy with the nonrelativistic theory, Sect. 4, one finds a continuous spectrum of stationary states in the range $E > mc^2$ and the corresponding wave functions have oscillating forms at large distances from the nucleus. As in the nonrelativistic case, the wave equation can be separated in spherical polar coordinates. From the phase shifts for these partial wave solutions one can again calculate the differential cross sections for scattering (cf. Sect. 7). We shall not carry out such calculations in detail, but merely quote the main results. We shall also discuss briefly solutions of the DIRAC equation with negative total energy E, which have no nonrelativistic analogue.

α) Partial wave solutions. For $E > mc^2$, as well as for $E < mc^2$, and for any central potential, stationary states can be found which are also eigenstates of the total angular momentum operators $\boldsymbol{M}^2$ and M_z with corresponding quantum numbers j and m. For fixed values of E, j and m we still get two linearly independent solutions. The angular and spin dependence of the one solution, denoted by $j=l+\frac{1}{2}$, is still given by (14.3) and (14.4); that of the other solution, denoted by $j=l-\frac{1}{2}$, is given by (14.7). The radial wave functions g and f again satisfy the differential Eq. (14.10), but asymptotically have the oscillating behavior of spherical waves. Exact analytic expressions for these radial wave functions (for a COULOMB potential) in terms of hypergeometric functions were derived first by DARWIN[1]. Extensive discussions of these wave functions and of alternative forms are given elsewhere[2] and we shall only quote DARWIN's result for the "large component" $g(r)$ for the case $j=l-\frac{1}{2}$.

[1] C. G. DARWIN: Proc. Roy. Soc. Lond., Ser. A **118**, 654 (1928).

[2] L. K. ACHESON: Phys. Rev. **82**, 488 (1951). — L. R. ELTON: Proc. Phys. Soc. Lond. A **66**, 806 (1953). — YENNIE, RAVENHALL and WILSON: Phys. Rev. **95**, 500 (1954). See also ref. [9], p. 79.

According to the theory of relativity the momentum $\hbar k$ and velocity v of a free electron is related to its total energy E by the relations

$$\varepsilon \equiv \frac{E}{m c^2} = \sqrt{1 + \left(\frac{\hbar k}{m c}\right)^2} = \left(1 - \frac{v^2}{c^2}\right)^{-\frac{1}{2}}. \tag{15.1}$$

We define three further dimensionless parameters

$$\left.\begin{aligned} &\gamma_l = \sqrt{l^2 - \alpha^2 Z^2}, \qquad (\alpha = e^2/\hbar c), \\ &\eta = \frac{Z e^2}{\hbar v} = \frac{Z \alpha \varepsilon}{\sqrt{\varepsilon^2 - 1}}, \qquad \eta' = \frac{Z e^2}{\hbar v} \sqrt{1 - \frac{v^2}{c^2}} = \frac{Z \alpha}{\sqrt{\varepsilon^2 - 1}}. \end{aligned}\right\} \tag{15.2}$$

We denote the "large" radial function g for the $j = l - \frac{1}{2}$ solution, Eq. (14.7), by g_{-l-1}. DARWIN's result is

$$\left.\begin{aligned} g_{-l-1} = N_{-l-1} (2 k r)^{\gamma_l} r^{-1} e^{-i k r} \times& \\ \times \{(\gamma_l - i\eta) F(\gamma_l + i\eta, 2\gamma_l + 1, 2 i k r) -& \\ - (l - i\eta') F(\gamma_l + 1 + i\eta, 2\gamma_l + 1, 2 i k r)\}.& \end{aligned}\right\} \tag{15.3}$$

If we choose for the normalization factor N

$$N = \frac{1}{2} \frac{|\Gamma(\gamma_l + 1 + i\eta)|}{\Gamma(2\gamma_l + 1)} \frac{\exp\left(\frac{1}{2}\pi\eta\right)}{\sqrt{(i\eta' - l)(\gamma_l - i\eta)}},$$

then the asymptotic form of g is

$$g_{-l-1} = r^{-1} \sin\left(k r + \eta \log 2 k r - \tfrac{1}{2}\pi l - \sigma_{-l-1}\right). \tag{15.4}$$

The phase-shift σ in (15.4) is given by

$$\exp(-2 i \sigma_{-l-1}) = \frac{l - i\eta'}{\gamma_l - i\eta} \frac{\Gamma(\gamma_l + 1 - i\eta)}{\Gamma(\gamma_l + 1 + i\eta)} \exp\left[\pi i (l - \gamma_l)\right]. \tag{15.5}$$

A similar expression is obtained for g_l, the "large" radial function g for the case $j = l + \frac{1}{2}$. g_l has the same asymptotic form as (15.4), except that σ_{-l-1} is replaced by σ_l, where

$$\exp(-2 i \sigma_l) = \frac{l + 1 + i\eta'}{\gamma_{l+1} + i\eta} \frac{\Gamma(\gamma_{l+1} - i\eta)}{\Gamma(\gamma_{l+1} + i\eta)} \exp\left[\pi i (l + 1 - \gamma_{l+1})\right]. \tag{15.6}$$

The expressions above are exact and valid for all positive values of $(E - mc^2)$ and of $Z\alpha$. In the fully nonrelativistic limit ($Z\alpha \ll 1$ and $\varepsilon - 1 \ll 1$), the parameter [see (15.2)] γ_l approaches l and η' approaches η (in atomic units η approaches Z/k). In this nonrelativistic limit the small radial functions f are negligible compared with g and each of the two solutions $j = l \pm \frac{1}{2}$ for a fixed value of l approaches the nonrelativistic solution for the same l. In particular, the two phase shifts σ_l and σ_{-l-1}, defined in (15.5) and (15.6), both tend to the nonrelativistic expression (4.10).

The expressions for the radial wave functions also simplify somewhat in the "extreme relativistic" limit of very high energy, $\varepsilon \gg 1$. Unlike the nonrelativistic parameter Z/k, the parameter $\eta = Z e^2/\hbar v$ tends to a non-zero limit $Z\alpha$ as the energy E approaches infinity while the velocity v approaches the velocity of light c. The parameter η', on the other hand, approaches zero in this limit. It then follows from (15.5) and (15.6) that σ_{-l-1} and σ_{l-1} (for $l \geq 1$), the phase shifts for the two states of equal j ($j = (l-1) + \frac{1}{2} = l - \frac{1}{2}$), approach each other as $\varepsilon \to \infty$ for *any* value of $Z\alpha$. In this limit the radial wave functions themselves for these two states are closely related: The "large" and "small" radial wave functions g and f are of the same order of magnitude for relativistic energies. Further, if we can neglect $E_0 = mc^2$ compared with the total energy E in (14.10) it follows that

$$g_{l-1} = f_{-l-1}, \quad f_{l-1} = -g_{-l-1} \quad (\text{as} \quad \varepsilon \to \infty). \tag{15.7}$$

β) Plane wave solutions and scattering amplitude. We discuss first plane wave solutions of the DIRAC equation for a *free* electron. We start from (12.4), the DIRAC equation written in split notation, for the field-free case $\varphi = \boldsymbol{A} = 0$. In this case (12.4) has solutions which are eigenstates of the momentum $\boldsymbol{p}$ with eigenvalues $\hbar \boldsymbol{k}$. We can write such a solution in the following form

$$\left.\begin{aligned} u &= e^{i\boldsymbol{k}\cdot\boldsymbol{r}} \begin{pmatrix} U_A \\ U_B \end{pmatrix}, \qquad & U_B &= \frac{c\hbar}{E+E_0} (\boldsymbol{k}\cdot\boldsymbol{\sigma}^P)\, U_A, \\ E^2 &= E_0^2 + (\hbar k c)^2, \qquad & E_0 &= m c^2. \end{aligned}\right\} \tag{15.8}$$

For a fixed value of $\boldsymbol{k}$, the two components u_1 and u_2 of the PAULI spinor U_A are two arbitrary constants, but the two components u_3 and u_4 of the other PAULI spinor U_B are completely determined by U_A and $\boldsymbol{k}$. The energy E is determined, except for sign, by the absolute value of the vector $\boldsymbol{k}$. We restrict ourselves, at present, to the positive value of E.

The normalization of the DIRAC four-component spinor is determined by the normalization of the two-component U_A and the absolute value of $\boldsymbol{k}$: we write

$$\langle u^* u\rangle = \langle U_A^* U_A\rangle + \langle U_B^* U_B\rangle, \ \langle U_A^* U_A\rangle = |u_1|^2 + |u_2|^2, \ \langle U_B^* U_B\rangle = |u_3|^2 + |u_4|^2.$$

It then follows from the properties of the spin-matrices $\boldsymbol{\sigma}$, (10.5), that

$$(E+E_0)^2\, U_B^* U_B = (c\hbar k)^2\, U_A^* U_A. \tag{15.9}$$

The relation (15.9) also holds for any more general wave function made up by superposition of "plane wave" functions of type (15.8) with different directions, but the same absolute value, of the vector $\boldsymbol{k}$. For a fixed direction of $\boldsymbol{k}$, it is often convenient to write an arbitrary two-component spinor U_A as a superposition of the two linearly independent spinors which are eigenstates of the operator[1] $(\boldsymbol{k}\cdot\boldsymbol{\sigma}^P)$. Using (13.20), we can write these two spinors as

$$U_{A\uparrow} = \begin{pmatrix} \cos\frac{1}{2}\vartheta \\ \sin\frac{1}{2}\vartheta\, e^{i\varphi} \end{pmatrix}, \qquad U_{A\downarrow} = \begin{pmatrix} -\sin\frac{1}{2}\vartheta\, e^{-i\varphi} \\ \cos\frac{1}{2}\vartheta \end{pmatrix}, \tag{15.10}$$

where (ϑ, φ) are the angle coordinates of the vector $\boldsymbol{k}$ in a spherical polar coordinate system with polar axis in the z-direction and $\varphi = 0$ in the zx-plane. A wave function of type (15.8) with U_A given by $U_{A\uparrow}$ (or $U_{A\downarrow}$) then represents an electron with momentum $\hbar\boldsymbol{k}$ and with its spin directed parallel (or antiparallel) to $\boldsymbol{k}$. If $U = a_\uparrow U_{A\uparrow} + a_\downarrow U_{A\downarrow}$, then $|a_\uparrow|^2, |a_\downarrow|^2$ represent the relative probabilities for "spin up" and "spin down", respectively.

We return now to the problem of the scattering of an electron by a central potential $\varphi(r)$. As in the nonrelativistic case, solutions of the DIRAC equation exist which behave asymptotically like an incident plane wave plus scattered spherically outgoing waves. In the DIRAC case, however, we have to specify not only the directions and value of the momentum of the incident electron, but also the state of polarization of the incident electron. Consider the specific case of an electron incident in the z-direction with momentum $\hbar\boldsymbol{k}$ and with "spin up". Using (15.10), we then find for the asymptotic behavior of the first

[1] In this section $\boldsymbol{k}$ is linear momentum, *not* angular momentum.

two components of the total wave function

$$\left.\begin{aligned} u_1(\mathbf{r}) &\sim e^{ikz} + r^{-1} e^{ikr} g_1(\vartheta, \varphi), \\ u_2(\mathbf{r}) &\sim r^{-1} e^{ikr} g_2(\vartheta, \varphi), \end{aligned}\right\} \tag{15.11}$$

if the potential falls off rapidly enough for large radial distances r. Note that, in the asymptotic region, the potential is negligible and the total wave function can be considered as a superposition of plane waves all with the same absolute value of momentum $\hbar k$. Using (15.8), the asymptotic expressions for the other two components of the wave function u_3 and u_4 can then be obtained directly from (15.11). It further follows from (15.9) that, in the asymptotic region, the ratio of $|u_3|^2 + |u_4|^2$ to $|u_1|^2 + |u_2|^2$ is a constant independent of ϑ and φ. The scattering of the incident electron is then described completely by the two functions g_1 and g_2. The differential scattering cross section, in particular, is given by

$$|f(\vartheta, \varphi)|^2 \, d\Omega = [|g_1(\vartheta, \varphi)|^2 + |g_2(\vartheta, \varphi)|^2] \, d\Omega. \tag{15.12}$$

(15.12) determines only the total probability for the incident electron being scattered into the solid angle $d\Omega$ around the direction (ϑ, φ). The ratio g_1/g_2 for a particular ϑ and φ also determines, with the help of (15.10), the state of polarization of the electron scattered into this particular direction.

As in the nonrelativistic case, the exact wave function which has the asymptotic form (15.11) cannot be obtained in closed analytic form for most potentials. In the present relativistic problem this is the case even for a COULOMB potential. Nevertheless, such an exact wave function can be obtained in the form of an infinite series involving all the partial wave solutions discussed in Sect. 15α. For a potential which falls off rapidly enough with r the asymptotic form of the "large" radial functions for the two partial waves with $j = l - \frac{1}{2}$ and $j = l + \frac{1}{2}$ are [cf. Eq. (15.4)]

$$g_{-l-1} = r^{-1} \sin(kr - \tfrac{1}{2}\pi l + \delta_{-l-1}), \qquad g_l = r^{-1} \sin(kr - \tfrac{1}{2}\pi l + \delta_l).$$

The infinite series[1] for the wave function of asymptotic form (15.11) involves all the partial wave states with m, the total angular momentum in the z-direction, equal to $+\frac{1}{2}$. The functions g_1 and g_2, Eq. (15.11), are then given in terms of the phase shifts δ_l and δ_{-l-1} by

$$\left.\begin{aligned} g_1(\vartheta, \varphi) &= g_1(\vartheta), \qquad g_2(\vartheta, \varphi) = e^{i\varphi} g_2(\vartheta); \\ 2ik\, g_1(\vartheta) &= \sum_{l=0}^{\infty} [(l+1)(e^{2i\delta_l} - 1) + l(e^{2i\delta_{-l-1}} - 1)] P_l(\cos\vartheta), \\ 2ik\, g_2(\vartheta) &= \sum_{l=0}^{\infty} [e^{2i\delta_{-l-1}} - e^{2i\delta_l}] P_l^1(\cos\vartheta). \end{aligned}\right\} \tag{15.13}$$

On substituting (15.13) into (15.12) we find that the differential cross section $|f(\vartheta, \varphi)|^2$ is independent of the azimuthal angle φ, as might be expected from symmetry. In the nonrelativistic limit ($E - mc^2$ and the potential energy both small compared with mc^2), δ_l and δ_{-l-1} both approach the nonrelativistic phase shift (7.1), $g_1(\vartheta)$ approaches the nonrelativistic scattering amplitude $f(\vartheta)$, Eq. (7.4), and $g_2(\vartheta)$ approaches zero. Thus, in the nonrelativistic limit the spin of the scattered electron "points in the positive z-direction" ($g_2 = 0$), if the spin of the incident electron does so.

[1] For the explicit form of this series and for further details on scattering and polarization see ref. [9], pp. 74 to 82.

We have so far discussed only the scattering of an incident electron with "spin up", Eq. (15.11). The asymptotic form for an incident electron with "spin down" is, instead of (15.11),

$$u_1' \sim r^{-1}\, e^{ikr}\, g_2'; \qquad u_2' \sim e^{ikz} + r^{-1}\, e^{ikr}\, g_1'. \tag{15.11a}$$

The corresponding exact wave function can again be built up out of the partial wave solutions, this time with $m = -\frac{1}{2}$. The function g_1' is identical with $g_1(\vartheta)$, Eq. (15.13) and $g_2' = -e^{-i\varphi} g_2(\vartheta)$, in contrast to $g_2 = +e^{i\varphi} g_2(\vartheta)$. The differential scattering cross section for an incident electron with "spin down" [see (15.12)] is then identical with that for an electron with "spin up". This again is expected from symmetry.

Consider now an incident electron in a more general spin-state, characterized by

$$u_1 = a\, e^{ikz}, \qquad u_2 = b\, e^{ikz}; \qquad |a|^2 + |b|^2 = 1.$$

This incident electron beam is still "fully polarized", i.e. it has a definite spin direction for given values of a and b [see Eq. (13.20)]. The scattered wave is given simply by a linear superposition of the scattering *amplitudes* (15.11) and (15.11a) with coefficients a and b, respectively. The differential scattering cross section is then given by

$$\begin{aligned} |f(\vartheta, \varphi)|^2 &= |a\, g_1(\vartheta) - b\, g_2(\vartheta)\, e^{-i\varphi}|^2 + |b\, g_1(\vartheta) + a\, g_2(\vartheta)\, e^{i\varphi}|^2 \\ &= |g_1(\vartheta)|^2 + |g_2(\vartheta)|^2 + 4\, \mathrm{Im}\,(a\, b^*\, e^{i\varphi})\, \mathrm{Im}\,[g_1(\vartheta)\, g_2^*(\vartheta)]. \end{aligned}$$

This expression differs from (15.12) by the last term which depends on a/b and is *not* independent of the azimuthal angle φ. If, for instance, $a = b$, the spin of the incident electron points in the direction ($\Theta = \frac{1}{2}\pi$, $\Phi = 0$) and the scattered intensity has maxima and minima at $\varphi = \pm\frac{1}{2}\pi$.

However, under most experimental conditions one is dealing with an "unpolarized" beam of incident electrons. This means that each electron in the beam may have a non-zero value for a and b, but that the phase relation between a and b varies in a random fashion from one electron to the next in the beam. One then finds that the *average* scattering cross-section of all the electrons in the beam is again given by (15.12) and independent of φ. However, the electrons scattered into a particular direction will in general be "partially polarized", even if the incident beam was unpolarized. This is due to the fact that the scattering amplitude depends on the spin-state of the incident electrons and there will be some average phase relation between a and b in the scattered beam. Thus, if the scattered beam is scattered once more, there will, in general, be some dependence on φ in the scattering cross-section[1].

For the special case of a COULOMB potential, the asymptotic form of each partial wave solution is known analytically. The expression (15.13) is modified only slightly by the presence of the logarithmic phase factor and the functions g_1 and g_2 are given in the form of an infinite series of LEGENDRE polynomials $P_l(\cos\vartheta)$ with known coefficients. These series cannot be obtained in closed analytic form for general values of $Z\alpha$ and E, but numerical calculations are now available for various values of these parameters[2]. The labor involved in such numerical calculations can be reduced[3] by modifying the series to be summed,

[1] For a discussion of double scattering and expressions for the "assymetry factor" see ref. [9], p. 78 and 82.

[2] J. H. BARTLETT and R. E. WATSON: Phys. Rev. **56**, 612 (1939). — H. FESHBACH: Pbys. Rev. **84**, 1206 (1951); **88**, 295 (1953). — G. PARZEN and T. WAINWRIGHT: Phys. Rev. **96**, 188 (1954). — J. DOGGETT and L. SPENCER: Phys. Rev. **103**, 1597 (1956). — N. SHERMAN: Phys. Rev. **103**, 1601 (1956).

[3] YENNIE, RAVENHALL and WILSON: Phys. Rev. **95**, 500 (1954).

as outlined in Sect. 7β [see (7.10)]. However, if $Z\alpha$ is fairly small, and each term in the infinite series (15.13) is expanded in powers of $Z\alpha$, then the series for the coefficients of the first few powers of $Z\alpha$ can be summed analytically. The first two terms in this expansion in powers of $Z\alpha$ for the scattering cross-section of an unpolarized electron beam are[1]

$$|f(\vartheta)|^2\,d\Omega = \frac{e^4 Z^2\,d\Omega}{4\,(p\,v)^2 \sin^4(\frac{1}{2}\vartheta)} \left\{\left[1-\left(\frac{v}{c}\sin\frac{\vartheta}{2}\right)^2\right] + \pi Z\alpha \frac{v}{c}\sin\frac{\vartheta}{2}\left(1-\sin\frac{\vartheta}{2}\right)\right\} \qquad (15.14)$$

where the momentum p and velocity v are related to the energy E by (15.1). The expression (15.14) can also be obtained directly, without summing the partial wave series (15.13), by higher order BORN approximation if a limiting procedure is adopted (the scattering is calculated for a screened COULOMB potential and the screening radius allowed to tend to infinity[2]).

If the factor in curly brackets in (15.14) is replaced by unity and if pv is replaced by twice the kinetic energy, the nonrelativistic expression (6.24) is obtained. However, for $E \gg mc^2$, v approaches c and pv approaches E. (15.14) is valid, if $Z\alpha$ is small, for all values of the energy. Note that the second term in curly brackets in (15.14) is linear in $Z\alpha$ and the scattering cross section is thus less for negative $Z\alpha$ (i.e. for scattering of positrons from nuclei). Note also that the term in $Z\alpha$ (as well as all higher terms) contains positive powers of v/c, since in the nonrelativistic limit, $v/c \to 0$, Eq. (6.24) must be exact.

γ) Negative energy states. We have so far discussed only eigenstates of the DIRAC equation for which E, the total energy *including* the rest-mass energy mc^2, is positive. However, there also exist solutions of the DIRAC equation with negative total energy E, even if the potentials are weak and the characteristic momentum of the electron is small. In the field-free case, in particular, for a given momentum $\hbar k$ we have so far dealt with two linearly independent solutions of (15.8), with "spin up" and with "spin down", both with positive energy $E_+ = \sqrt{(mc^2)^2 + (\hbar k c)^2}$. (15.8) has two other linearly independent solutions with negative energy $E_- = -E_+$ with the roles of U_A and U_B reversed compared with the positive energy solutions. Loosely speaking, the DIRAC spinor wave functions have four components, compared with the one-component SCHRÖDINGER wave functions, and we should expect the DIRAC equation to have four times as many eigenstates as the SCHRÖDINGER equation. Physically, the extra degrees of freedom correspond to the possible signs of the total energy E and of the component of the spin in the z-direction.

Negative energy solutions of the DIRAC equation exist for an electron in any time-independent electromagnetic field, characterized by scalar and vector potentials φ and $\boldsymbol{A}$. Further, each negative energy solution can be related, mathematically, to a positive energy solution (in a different potential) by the following prescription: Let (U_A, U_B) be the components of a solution of the DIRAC Eq. (12.4) with negative energy $-|E|$ for a given φ and $\boldsymbol{A}$. Change the sign of the energy to $+|E|$, also the sign of the momentum operator $\boldsymbol{p}$ and of $e\varphi$ and $e\boldsymbol{A}$, and interchange U_A and U_B. The resulting wave function is then identical with a solution of (12.4) for a particle, of same mass and *opposite* sign of the charge, in the same field with positive energy $+|E|$. DIRAC[3] used this mathe-

[1] Such an expression was first derived by N. F. MOTT, Proc. Roy. Soc. Lond., Ser. A **124**, 425 (1929) but his term in $Z\alpha$ was incorrect. The expression quoted in ref. [9] is also wrong. The correct expression was obtained by W. A. MCKINLEY and H. FESHBACH, Phys. Rev. **74**, 1759 (1948).

[2] R. H. DALITZ: Proc. Roy. Soc. Lond., Ser. A **206**, 509 (1951).

[3] P. A. M. DIRAC: Proc. Roy. Soc. Lond., Ser. A **133**, 80 (1931).

matical relation to overcome the following physical difficulty in his theory for a single electron: Even if an electron is initially in a state of positive energy, according to the form of DIRAC's theory we have discussed so far ("single-electron theory"), the electron could make a transition to a state of negative energy and give up energy, by emitting radiation, in a collision with another particle, etc. No such transitions, nor any electrons with negative energy, have ever been observed. However, if we assume that electrons satisfy the PAULI exclusion principle, we can introduce a new postulate, namely that the physically observed vacuum consists of an infinite sea of electrons filling all the possible negative energy states. Transitions of a "real" electron from a state of positive to one of negative energy is then forbidden by the exclusion principle. Further, if an electron is missing from the sea of negative energy states, it follows from the relation discussed above that this "hole" has the physical properties of a particle of electronic mass, positive charge $+|e|$ and positive energy, called a positron.

We have only given a physical picture of DIRAC's "hole theory" (or "pair theory") of the electron. To put this theory on a rigorous footing, the electron has to be treated by the formalism of "second quantization" or quantum field theory. Field theoretic treatments of pair theory have been developed in great detail by many authors, using different mathematical formalisms but with the same physical content. For a discussion of these treatments the reader is referred to the standard works, including references [*1*], [*3*], [*6*], [*11*], [*12*] and [*13*]. The most direct experimental tests of the "hole theory" are furnished by high energy phenomena, such as electron-positron pair-creation. We shall merely state briefly (without proof) the differences in predictions of single-electron theory and pair theory, which are relevant to atomic theory.

Consider first a single electron of positive total energy in a time-independent electromagnetic field. If the field is considered as a classical and *given* field, then the results of single-electron and hole theory are *identical*. In practice, however, small differences do arise, as follows: (1) If an external field is introduced into a vacuum then, according to hole theory, the "sea of filled electron states" readjusts itself so that all the negative-energy states for electrons in *this* field are filled. This readjustment in general produces some change in the charge density of the "sea" and the resulting "vacuum polarization" acts on a real electron introduced into the vacuum like a small additional potential. (2) If virtual interactions of a real electron with the quantized electromagnetic field are taken into account, the electron's interaction with an external classical field is also modified. This modification, the so-called "radiative corrections", partly involves intermediate states for which the electron is in a negative energy state and the quantitative expression for these corrections is different on single electron and hole theory[1].

Consider next a process in which a single electron makes a transition between two states of positive total energy (in an arbitrary external field) with the emission or absorption of any number of real photons. If such a process is calculated by the lowest non-zero order of perturbation theory, single electron and hole theory again give identical results. The use of higher order perturbation theory (involving integrations over the momenta of virtual photons in intermediate states) again results in radiative corrections, which are different on single-electron and hole theory. For processes involving more than one real electron the two theories already give slightly different results even if radiative corrections are not considered (see Sect. 38).

[1] In fact, these corrections can be calculated in a consistent manner *only* according to hole theory.

The following general rule applies to a system with any numbers of electrons (*no* real positrons): If the potentials are fairly weak and the characteristic momenta fairly small, calculations up to (and including) the order of accuracy of the PAULI approximation (Sect. 12) are identical in single-electron and pair theory. For systems containing both electrons and positrons, single-electron theory leads to larger errors or fails completely (see Sect. 23).

16. The DIRAC equation in momentum space. We consider now the DIRAC equation (10.1) for an electron in an external time-independent electromagnetic field, transformed into an integral equation in momentum space. As in the nonrelativistic case, Sects. 8 and 9, this is accomplished simply by taking the FOURIER transform of (10.1). We put $\hbar=1$, as in atomic units, but carry the symbols for e, m, c, etc. at for the moment[1]. The DIRAC equation in momentum space then reads

$$(E - mc^2\beta - c\boldsymbol{\alpha}\cdot\boldsymbol{p})\,\psi(\boldsymbol{p}) = -e\int d^3k\,[\varphi(-\boldsymbol{k}) - \boldsymbol{\alpha}\cdot\boldsymbol{A}(-\boldsymbol{k})]\,\psi(\boldsymbol{p}+\boldsymbol{k}). \tag{16.1}$$

In (16.1), $\psi(\boldsymbol{p})$, the DIRAC wave function in momentum space, is a four-component column matrix (or spinor) on which the DIRAC matrices $\boldsymbol{\alpha}$ and β operate. $\varphi(\boldsymbol{k})$ and $\boldsymbol{A}(\boldsymbol{k})$ are the FOURIER transforms of the scalar and vector potentials of the electromagnetic field [times $(2\pi)^{-\frac{3}{2}}$]. For the special case of the COULOMB potential of a nucleus of atomic number Z,

$$A=0, \qquad \varphi(\boldsymbol{k}) = +\frac{Ze}{2\pi^2}\frac{1}{k^2}. \tag{16.2}$$

For the special case of a COULOMB potential (16.2), RUBINOWITZ has[2] obtained the exact DIRAC wave function in momentum space $\psi(\boldsymbol{p})$ for the discrete spectrum by taking the FOURIER transform of the position wave function, Eq. (14.37). LÉVY[3] has obtained the same $\psi(\boldsymbol{p})$ by solving (16.1) directly. LÉVY has also given prescriptions, for a general central potential, for reducing (16.1) to two uncoupled one-dimensional integral equations and has discussed various approximation methods for solving (16.1). We shall only discuss approximation methods suitable for any "weak" electromagnetic field and for a total energy E of the electron close to $+mc^2$.

α) Mixed representation. In the split notation, discussed in Sect. 10 and 12, the DIRAC equation (16.1) reads (with $E_0=mc^2$)

$$\left.\begin{aligned}(E-E_0)\,\psi_A(\boldsymbol{p}) &= c\,\sigma^P\cdot\boldsymbol{p}\,\psi_B(\boldsymbol{p}) - e\int d^3k\,[\varphi(-\boldsymbol{k})\,\psi_A(\boldsymbol{p}+\boldsymbol{k}) - \sigma^P\cdot\boldsymbol{A}(-\boldsymbol{k})\,\psi_B(\boldsymbol{p}+\boldsymbol{k})],\\ (E+E_0)\,\psi_B(\boldsymbol{p}) &= c\,\sigma^P\cdot\boldsymbol{p}\,\psi_A(\boldsymbol{p}) - e\int d^3k\,[\varphi(-\boldsymbol{k})\,\psi_B(\boldsymbol{p}+\boldsymbol{k}) - \sigma^P\cdot\boldsymbol{A}(-\boldsymbol{k})\,\psi_A(\boldsymbol{p}+\boldsymbol{k})].\end{aligned}\right\} \tag{16.3}$$

ψ_A and ψ_B are two PAULI two-component spinors, the FOURIER transforms of the "large" and "small" components U_A and U_B of the PAULI reduction (Sect. 12), and (16.3) is the FOURIER transform of (12.4). If, as a first approximation, we replaced E by E_0 and omitted φ and $\boldsymbol{A}$ in the second line of (16.3), we could eliminate ψ_B and obtain an equation in ψ_A alone which is the FOURIER transform of the nonrelativistic SCHRÖDINGER Eq. (12.6) and is equivalent to (8.3). On substituting the first approximation for ψ_B on the right hand side of the second line of (16.3) (without dropping φ and $\boldsymbol{A}$) one could then obtain a better approximation for ψ_B. Substituting this approximation for ψ_B into the first line of (16.3) gives a more accurate equation for ψ_A alone, the FOURIER transform of the approximate PAULI Eq. (12.11), etc. If the potentials are weak and if

[1] e is positive.
[2] A. RUBINOWITZ: Phys. Rev. **73**, 1330 (1948).
[3] M. LÉVY: Proc. Roy. Soc. Lond., Ser. A **204**, 145 (1950).

$\gamma^2/2m \equiv E - E_0 \ll E_0$, then the important values of the momentum p will be of order $\gamma \ll mc$. The ratio $\psi_B(\boldsymbol{p})/\psi_A(\boldsymbol{p})$ is of order p/mc, which is small, but only by one power of v/c. Instead of pursuing this method further, we shall outline an alternative method of successive approximation which involves, instead of ψ_A and ψ_B, two other PAULI spinors ψ_+ and ψ_-, for which the ratio ψ_-/ψ_+ is of order $(p/mc)^3$. Since $\psi_-/\psi_+ \ll \psi_B/\psi_A$, this alternative method is more convenient than the one outlined above (especially if the external magnetic field is weaker than the electric one).

We consider first "plane-wave" solutions of (16.3) for the field-free case, $\varphi = \boldsymbol{A} = 0$. We define

$$E(p) = +\sqrt{E_0^2 + (cp)^2}, \qquad \Gamma(\boldsymbol{p}) = \frac{c\,\boldsymbol{p}\cdot\boldsymbol{\sigma}^P}{E_0 + E(p)}, \tag{16.4}$$

where $\boldsymbol{\sigma}^P$ is the 2-by-2 PAULI spin matrix ($\hbar = 1$ in our units). In analogy with the position space solution (15.8) we have two types of eigenstates of the HAMILTONian corresponding to a plane wave of momentum $\boldsymbol{q}$ with positive and negative energy eigenvalue respectively. In our split notation the two types of DIRAC wave function $\psi_q^{(+)}$ and $\psi_q^{(-)}$ are of the form

$$\left.\begin{aligned} &(E_0\beta + c\,\boldsymbol{\alpha}\cdot\boldsymbol{p})\,\psi_q^{(\pm)}(\boldsymbol{p}) = \pm E(q)\,\psi_q^{(\pm)}(\boldsymbol{p});\\ &\psi_q^{(+)}(\boldsymbol{p}) = \begin{pmatrix}\psi_+\\ \Gamma(\boldsymbol{p})\,\psi_+\end{pmatrix}\delta^{(3)}(\boldsymbol{p}-\boldsymbol{q}), \quad \psi_q^{(-)}(\boldsymbol{p}) = \begin{pmatrix}-\Gamma(\boldsymbol{p})\,\psi_-\\ \psi_-\end{pmatrix}\delta^3(\boldsymbol{p}-\boldsymbol{q}).\end{aligned}\right\} \tag{16.5}$$

In (16.5) ψ_+ and ψ_- are any two constant (but otherwise arbitrary), two-component PAULI-spinors on which the PAULI matrix $\Gamma(\boldsymbol{p})$ operates.

We define next the CASIMIR projection operators Λ_+ and Λ_- by

$$\Lambda_\pm(\boldsymbol{p}) = \frac{1}{2E(p)}\left[E(p) \pm (E_0\beta + c\,\boldsymbol{\alpha}\cdot\boldsymbol{p})\right], \quad \Lambda_+ + \Lambda_- = 1. \tag{16.6}$$

These projection operators have the property that

$$\Lambda_\pm(\boldsymbol{p})\,\psi_q^{(\pm)}(\boldsymbol{p}) = \psi_q^{(\pm)}(\boldsymbol{p}), \qquad \Lambda_\pm(\boldsymbol{p})\,\psi_q^{(\mp)}(\boldsymbol{p}) = 0. \tag{16.7}$$

We further see that *any* arbitrary DIRAC wave function $\psi(\boldsymbol{p})$ can be written in the form

$$\psi(\boldsymbol{p}) = \begin{pmatrix}1\\ \Gamma(\boldsymbol{p})\end{pmatrix}\psi_+(\boldsymbol{p}) + \begin{pmatrix}-\Gamma(\boldsymbol{p})\\ 1\end{pmatrix}\psi_-(\boldsymbol{p}). \tag{16.8}$$

where $\psi_\pm(\boldsymbol{p})$ are two-component PAULI-spinors (with arbitrary dependence on $\boldsymbol{p}$ for each of the components) on which $\Gamma(\boldsymbol{p})$, Eq. (16.4), operates[1]. Any DIRAC wave function is then specified by these two PAULI spinors $\psi_\pm(\boldsymbol{p})$ and we derive next two coupled integral equations for ψ_+ and ψ_- from the DIRAC equation (16.1).

We first define four PAULI operators $I_{++}(\boldsymbol{p}_1, \boldsymbol{p}_2)$, which are functions of two momentum variables $\boldsymbol{p}_1$ and $\boldsymbol{p}_2$, by

$$\Lambda_+(\boldsymbol{p}_1)\begin{pmatrix}1\\ \Gamma(\boldsymbol{p}_2)\end{pmatrix} = \begin{pmatrix}1\\ \Gamma(\boldsymbol{p}_1)\end{pmatrix} I_{++}(\boldsymbol{p}_1, \boldsymbol{p}_2), \quad \Lambda_-(\boldsymbol{p}_1)\begin{pmatrix}1\\ \Gamma(\boldsymbol{p}_2)\end{pmatrix} = \begin{pmatrix}-\Gamma(\boldsymbol{p}_1)\\ 1\end{pmatrix} I_{-+}(\boldsymbol{p}_1, \boldsymbol{p}_2), \tag{16.9}$$

plus two similar relations for I_{+-} and I_{--}. We similarly define four vector PAULI operators $\boldsymbol{\alpha}_{\pm\pm}$ by

$$\left.\begin{aligned} &\Lambda_+(\boldsymbol{p}_1)\,\boldsymbol{\alpha}\begin{pmatrix}1\\ \Gamma(\boldsymbol{p}_2)\end{pmatrix} \equiv \Lambda_+(\boldsymbol{p}_1)\begin{pmatrix}\boldsymbol{\sigma}^P\Gamma(\boldsymbol{p}_2)\\ \boldsymbol{\sigma}^P\end{pmatrix} = \begin{pmatrix}1\\ \Gamma(\boldsymbol{p}_1)\end{pmatrix}\boldsymbol{\alpha}_{++}(p_1, p_2);\\ &\Lambda_-(\boldsymbol{p}_1)\,\boldsymbol{\alpha}\begin{pmatrix}1\\ \Gamma(\boldsymbol{p}_2)\end{pmatrix} = \begin{pmatrix}-\Gamma(\boldsymbol{p}_1)\\ 1\end{pmatrix}\boldsymbol{\alpha}_{-+}(\boldsymbol{p}_1, \boldsymbol{p}_2);\end{aligned}\right\} \tag{16.10}$$

---

[1] Note that $E_0\beta + c\,\boldsymbol{\alpha}\cdot\boldsymbol{p}$ operating on the first part of (16.8) results in a multiplying factor of $+E(p)$, and a factor of $-E(p)$ for the second part.

plus two similar relations for $\boldsymbol{\alpha}_{+-}$ and $\boldsymbol{\alpha}_{--}$. (16.9) and (16.10) are to be considered as operator equations: This means that each of the equations is satisfied if the left and right hand operate on the same PAULI spinor (otherwise arbitrary). Writing the projection operators (16.6) in the split notation given in (10.4) and using the usual rules of matrix multiplication one can obtain explicit expressions for $I_{\pm\pm}$ and $\boldsymbol{\alpha}_{\pm\pm}$ involving only the PAULI operator $\boldsymbol{\sigma}^P$. These expressions can be simplified further by using the following operator identities[1] which can be derived from (10.5),

$$\left.\begin{aligned}(\boldsymbol{\sigma}\cdot\boldsymbol{p})\,\boldsymbol{\sigma}+i\,\boldsymbol{p}\times\boldsymbol{\sigma}=\boldsymbol{\sigma}(\boldsymbol{\sigma}\cdot\boldsymbol{p})-i\,\boldsymbol{p}\times\boldsymbol{\sigma}=\boldsymbol{p},\\ (\boldsymbol{\sigma}\cdot\boldsymbol{p}_1)\,(\boldsymbol{\sigma}\cdot\boldsymbol{p}_2)=\boldsymbol{p}_1\cdot\boldsymbol{p}_2+i\,\boldsymbol{\sigma}\cdot(\boldsymbol{p}_1\times\boldsymbol{p}_2).\end{aligned}\right\}\tag{16.11}$$

Writing E_1 for $E(p_1)$, E_2 for $E(p_2)$ and $\boldsymbol{k}$ for $\boldsymbol{p}_2-\boldsymbol{p}_1$, we finally get

$$\left.\begin{aligned}I_{++}(\boldsymbol{p}_1,\boldsymbol{p}_2)&=I_{--}=\left\{1+\frac{c^2(\boldsymbol{\sigma}\cdot\boldsymbol{p}_1)\,(\boldsymbol{\sigma}\cdot\boldsymbol{k})+(E_1-E_0)\,(E_1-E_2)}{2E_1(E_0+E_2)}\right\},\\ I_{+-}(\boldsymbol{p}_1,\boldsymbol{p}_2)&=-I_{-+}=\frac{c}{2E_1}\left\{\boldsymbol{\sigma}\cdot\boldsymbol{p}_1-\frac{E_0+E_1}{E_0+E_2}\,\boldsymbol{\sigma}\cdot\boldsymbol{p}_2\right\},\\ \boldsymbol{\alpha}_{++}(\boldsymbol{p}_1,\boldsymbol{p}_2)&=-\boldsymbol{\alpha}_{--}=\frac{c}{2E_1}\left\{\boldsymbol{p}_1-i\,\boldsymbol{p}_1\times\boldsymbol{\sigma}+\frac{E_0+E_1}{E_0+E_2}(\boldsymbol{p}_2+i\,\boldsymbol{p}_2\times\boldsymbol{\sigma})\right\},\\ \boldsymbol{\alpha}_{+-}(\boldsymbol{p}_1,\boldsymbol{p}_2)&=\boldsymbol{\alpha}_{-+}=\frac{1}{2E_1}\left\{(E_0+E_1)\,\boldsymbol{\sigma}-c^2\,\frac{(\boldsymbol{\sigma}\cdot\boldsymbol{p}_1)\,\boldsymbol{\sigma}\,(\boldsymbol{\sigma}\cdot\boldsymbol{p}_2)}{E_0+E_2}\right\}.\end{aligned}\right\}\tag{16.12}$$

We now write $\psi(\boldsymbol{p})$, the solution of the DIRAC equation (16.1), in the form (16.8) and derive two equations involving ψ_+ and ψ_- from (16.1) in the following way[2]. We operate on both sides of the Eq. (16.1) with the projection operator $\Lambda_+(\boldsymbol{p})$, then rewrite the right side in terms of $I_{\pm\pm}$ and $\boldsymbol{\alpha}_{\pm\pm}$, using the definitions (16.9) and (16.10). We then repeat the procedure, using $\Lambda_-(\boldsymbol{p})$ instead of Λ_+ to obtain a second equation. This gives

$$\left.\begin{aligned}(E-E(p))\,\psi_+(\boldsymbol{p})&=-e\int d^3k\sum_{j=+,-}\big[\varphi(-\boldsymbol{k})\,I_{+j}(\boldsymbol{p},\boldsymbol{p}+\boldsymbol{k})-\\&\qquad-\boldsymbol{A}(-\boldsymbol{k})\cdot\boldsymbol{\alpha}_{+j}(\boldsymbol{p},\boldsymbol{p}+\boldsymbol{k})\big]\,\psi_j(\boldsymbol{p}+\boldsymbol{k}),\\ (E+E(p))\,\psi_-(\boldsymbol{p})&=-e\int d^3k\sum_{j=+,-}\big[\varphi(-\boldsymbol{k})\,I_{-j}(\boldsymbol{p},\boldsymbol{p}+\boldsymbol{k})-\\&\qquad-\boldsymbol{A}(-\boldsymbol{k})\cdot\boldsymbol{\alpha}_{-j}(\boldsymbol{p},\boldsymbol{p}+\boldsymbol{k})\big]\,\psi_j(\boldsymbol{p}+\boldsymbol{k}),\end{aligned}\right\}\tag{16.13}$$

where the suffix j stands for $+$ or $-$.

The Eqs. (16.13) for ψ_+,ψ_- have a somewhat similar form to the Eqs. (16.3) for ψ_A,ψ_B. (16.3) is the DIRAC equation written in our previous "split notation", i.e. in a representation in terms of the two possible eigenvalues of β, in which the operator $\boldsymbol{\alpha}$ is represented by the square matrix (10.4) and the wave function by the column matrix (ψ_A,ψ_B). Similarly we can consider (16.13) as the DIRAC equation in a new "mixed representation" in terms of the two possible eigenvalues of the operator $E_0\beta+c\boldsymbol{\alpha}\cdot\boldsymbol{p}$, in which the wave function is represented by the column matrix (ψ_+,ψ_-). Since the operator defining the representation, $E_0\beta+c\boldsymbol{\alpha}\cdot\boldsymbol{p}$, depends on the momentum $\boldsymbol{p}$, the unit operator is represented by the matrix with components $I_{\pm\pm}(\boldsymbol{p}_1,\boldsymbol{p}_2)$, *not* simply by the unit 2-by-2 matrix. Similarly the operator $\boldsymbol{\alpha}$ is represented by the matrix $\boldsymbol{\alpha}_{\pm\pm}(\boldsymbol{p}_1,\boldsymbol{p}_2)$. Our new representation looks more complicated than the old and (16.13) seems longer than (16.3), but is nevertheless advantageous for weak enough fields, as we shall see.

---

[1] We shall simply write $\boldsymbol{\sigma}$ for $\boldsymbol{\sigma}^P$.

[2] H. A. BETHE: Z. Naturforsch. 3a, 470 (1948). — E. E. SALPETER: Phys. Rev. 87, 328 (1952).

β) The PAULI *approximation.* We consider first the simplest approximation to (16.13), involving only $\psi_+(\boldsymbol{p})$, obtained by simply putting ψ_- equal to zero in the first equation in (16.13) and omitting the second equation altogether. We can further simplify the exact expressions (16.12) by expanding in powers of p_1/mc and p_2/mc. These expansions, up to second order for I_{++} and first order for the other components, are

$$\left.\begin{aligned} I_{++} &= I_{--} = 1 + \frac{(\boldsymbol{\sigma}\cdot\boldsymbol{p}_1)(\boldsymbol{\sigma}\cdot\boldsymbol{k})}{(2mc)^2}, \qquad I_{+-} = -I_{-+} = -\frac{\boldsymbol{\sigma}\cdot\boldsymbol{k}}{2mc};\\ \boldsymbol{\alpha}_{++} &= -\boldsymbol{\alpha}_{--} = \frac{2\boldsymbol{p}_1+\boldsymbol{k}+i\boldsymbol{k}\times\boldsymbol{\sigma}}{2mc}, \qquad \boldsymbol{\alpha}_{-+} = \boldsymbol{\alpha}_{+-} = \boldsymbol{\sigma}.\end{aligned}\right\} \tag{16.14}$$

Substituting the approximations (16.14) for I_{++} and $\boldsymbol{\alpha}_{++}$ into the Eq. (16.13) for ψ_+ (with ψ_- neglected) and replacing $E(p)$ by the first three terms in an expansion in powers of p/mc, we get

$$\left.\begin{aligned} &\left(W - \frac{p^2}{2m} + \frac{p^4}{8m^3c^2}\right)\psi_+(\boldsymbol{p})\\ &= -e\int d^3k\left\{\left[1+\frac{(\boldsymbol{\sigma}\cdot\boldsymbol{p})(\boldsymbol{\sigma}\cdot\boldsymbol{k})}{(2mc)^2}\right]\varphi(-\boldsymbol{k}) - \left[\frac{2\boldsymbol{p}+\boldsymbol{k}+i\boldsymbol{k}\times\boldsymbol{\sigma}}{2mc}\right]\cdot\boldsymbol{A}(-\boldsymbol{k})\right\}\psi_+(\boldsymbol{p}+\boldsymbol{k})\end{aligned}\right\} \tag{16.15}$$

where $W = E - E_0$.

We compare next the Eq. (16.15) for the PAULI 2-component spinor ψ_+ with the FOURIER transform of (12.11), the position space equation in the PAULI approximation. We shall see that they agree to the required order of accuracy if the magnetic field is considered small compared with the electric field: Consider first the case of no magnetic field, $\boldsymbol{A}=0$. We make use of the approximate relation

$$(W+e\varphi)\,u(\boldsymbol{r}) \approx (p^2/2m)\,u(\boldsymbol{r}), \quad \boldsymbol{p} = -i\,\mathrm{grad}$$

to find

$$\left[(W+e\varphi)^2 - \left(\frac{p^2}{2m}\right)^2\right]u \approx \frac{e}{2m}(\varphi p^2 - p^2\varphi)\,u = -\frac{ie}{2m}(\boldsymbol{p}\cdot\boldsymbol{\mathcal{E}}+\boldsymbol{\mathcal{E}}\cdot\boldsymbol{p})\,u \tag{16.16}$$

where $\boldsymbol{\mathcal{E}} = -\mathrm{grad}\,\varphi$ is the electric field[1]. In (12.11) we can then, to within the accuracy of the equation itself, rewrite the term in $(W+e\varphi)^2$ with the help of (16.16). Using (16.11) and the fact that $\mathrm{curl}\,\boldsymbol{\mathcal{E}}=0$, (12.11) then reduces to (with $\boldsymbol{A}=\boldsymbol{\mathcal{H}}=0$)

$$\left[W + e\varphi - \frac{p^2}{2m} + \frac{p^4}{8m^3c^2} - \frac{ie}{4m^2c^2}(\boldsymbol{\sigma}\cdot\boldsymbol{p})(\boldsymbol{\sigma}\cdot\boldsymbol{\mathcal{E}})\right]u = 0. \tag{16.17}$$

(16.17) is exactly the FOURIER transform of (16.15) (with $\boldsymbol{A}=0$). Similarly the terms involving $\boldsymbol{A}(\boldsymbol{k})$ in (16.15) are the FOURIER transforms[2] of the terms involving $(\boldsymbol{A}\cdot\mathrm{grad})$ and $\boldsymbol{\sigma}\cdot\boldsymbol{\mathcal{H}}$ in (12.11). Only the term in (12.11) involving A^2 is missing in (16.15).

γ) Improvements. The approximate Eq. (16.15) was obtained from (16.13) by omitting $\psi_-(\boldsymbol{p})$ altogether and by approximating the operators I_{++} and $\boldsymbol{\alpha}_{++}$. A simple approximation for ψ^- in terms of ψ_+ could be obtained from the second line of (16.13). On substituting this expression for ψ_- into the first line of (16.13)

[1] Although the operator $\boldsymbol{p}\cdot\boldsymbol{\mathcal{E}}+\boldsymbol{\mathcal{E}}\cdot\boldsymbol{p}$ is not zero itself, its expectation value with any real and bounded wave function u is $-i\int d\tau\,\mathrm{div}(\boldsymbol{\mathcal{E}}u^2)=0$. It then also follows that the expectation value of $2\boldsymbol{\mathcal{E}}\cdot\boldsymbol{p}$ equals that of $\boldsymbol{\mathcal{E}}\cdot\boldsymbol{p}-\boldsymbol{p}\cdot\boldsymbol{\mathcal{E}}=i\,\mathrm{div}\,\boldsymbol{\mathcal{E}}$.

[2] In carrying out the FOURIER transforms it is useful to write $\boldsymbol{\mathcal{E}} = -\mathrm{grad}\,\varphi = -i(\boldsymbol{p}\varphi - \varphi\boldsymbol{p})$ and $\boldsymbol{\mathcal{H}} = \mathrm{curl}\,\boldsymbol{A} = i(\boldsymbol{p}\times\boldsymbol{A}+\boldsymbol{A}\times\boldsymbol{p})$. Note also that, for time-independent potentials satisfying the LORENTZ gauge condition, $\mathrm{div}\,\boldsymbol{A}(\boldsymbol{r}) = \boldsymbol{k}\cdot\boldsymbol{A}(\boldsymbol{k}) = 0$.

and keeping more accurate expressions for I_{++} and $\boldsymbol{\alpha}_{++}$, one could obtain an equation more accurate than (16.15), but again involving only ψ_+. This equation would contain terms quadratic in $\boldsymbol{A}$, as does (12.11), and would be more accurate than the PAULI approximation (12.11) if $\boldsymbol{A}$ is less important than φ. We shall not discuss this equation further, but only the behavior of the wave functions $\psi_\pm(\boldsymbol{p})$ for large $\boldsymbol{p}$.

In discussing the PAULI approximation (13.2) for a central potential we used an approximate wave function in the form of a PAULI spinor, whose radial dependence was the same as that of the nonrelativistic SCHRÖDINGER wave function. Only the spin and angle dependence was chosen so that the wave function represented an eigenstate of $\boldsymbol{M}^2$ and of M_z. Let $\psi_0(\boldsymbol{p})$ be the FOURIER transform of this PAULI spinor wave function. We consider a state of the electron with total energy E fairly close to E_0 in a fairly weak potential φ (with $\boldsymbol{A}=0$). The PAULI approximation then gives a very good approximation for the binding energy (or the scattering amplitudes for $E>E_0$), but $\psi_0(\boldsymbol{p})$ is a *poor* approximation in the region $p \gtrsim mc$. However, an approximation for the wave function, which is fairly accurate for *all* values of p, can be obtained from (16.13), essentially by an iteration method, using $\psi_0(\boldsymbol{p})$ as starting point. On the right side of (16.13) we replace $\psi_+(\boldsymbol{p})$ by $\psi_0(\boldsymbol{p})$ and ψ_- by zero and replace E by the PAULI approximation to the energy. We then get for ψ_+ and ψ_- the better approximation

$$\psi_\pm(\boldsymbol{p}) = \frac{-e}{E \mp E(p)} \int d^3q\, \varphi(-\boldsymbol{q}+\boldsymbol{p})\, I_{\pm+}(\boldsymbol{p},\boldsymbol{q})\, \psi_0(\boldsymbol{q}), \tag{16.18}$$

where $I_{\pm+}$ is given in (16.12).

Consider the special case of (16.18) for $\psi_0(\boldsymbol{p})$ corresponding to an S-state ($l=0$) in a central potential $\varphi(k)$. Comparison with (13.19) then shows that $\psi_0(\boldsymbol{p})$ is a constant PAULI spinor times a function of $|\boldsymbol{p}|$ only. In general, $\psi_0(p)$ will be extremely small if p is large compared with some characteristic momentum $p_0 \ll mc$ (for the special case of the hydrogen atom p_0 is of order αmc, the BOHR momentum). For $p \gg p_0$ we then get a very simple approximation for $\psi_\pm$ by simply replacing $\varphi(|\boldsymbol{p}-\boldsymbol{q}|)$ by $\varphi(p)$ and $I(\boldsymbol{p},\boldsymbol{q})$ by $I(\boldsymbol{p},0)$. Also replacing E by E_0 we get, using (16.12),

$$\psi_+(p) = \frac{e\,\varphi(p)\,[E(p)+E_0]}{2E(p)\,[E(p)-E_0]}\, u_0(0), \qquad \psi_-(p) = \frac{e\,\varphi(p)\, c\,\boldsymbol{\sigma}\cdot\boldsymbol{p}}{2E(p)\,[E(p)+E_0]}\, u_0(0), \tag{16.19}$$

where

$$u_0(0) = \int d^3q\, \psi_0(q)$$

is the nonrelativistic position space wave function [times $(2\pi)^{\frac{3}{2}}$] evaluated at the origin. (16.19) is just the first term of (16.18) expanded in powers of p_0/p.

For a state of non-zero l value, the expression $u_0(0)$ and hence (16.19) vanishes. For such states, $\psi_\pm(\boldsymbol{p})$ does in fact decrease more rapidly with increasing p than for $l=0$. For $l \neq 0$ and $p \gg p_0$ a better approximation for $\psi_\pm(\boldsymbol{p})$ can be obtained from (16.18) by expanding $\varphi(\boldsymbol{p}-\boldsymbol{q})$ and $I(\boldsymbol{p},\boldsymbol{q})$ in positive powers of q/p. For $p \gtrsim p_0$, another approximation for $\psi_-(\boldsymbol{p})$ can be got from (16.18), using the approximation (16.14).

In Table 2 we give the orders of magnitude of $\psi_+\ p)$ and $\psi_-(p)$ for the special case of an S-state with low principal quantum number n in hydrogen, $\varphi(p) = e/2\pi^2 p^2$. Also given is the order of $\psi_+(p)-\psi_0(p)$, normalized to the same value for $p=0$. It will be seen that $\psi_-(p)$ is only of order α^3 for $p \sim p_0$, whereas $\psi_B(p)$, the "small" component of the PAULI reduction (16.3), is of order α. In the extreme relativistic region, $p \gg mc$, ψ_+ and ψ_- are of the same order of magnitude and are larger than the nonrelativistic approximation ψ_0 by about p/mc.

We finally mention a method introduced by FOLDY and WOUTHUYSEN[1], which is related to the above representation of the DIRAC wave function in terms of ψ_+ and ψ_- but is more general and elegant. They start from the DIRAC Eq. (10.1) with $\boldsymbol{\alpha}$, σ and β in the "split" representation (10.4), (10.8) but keep the representation of the momentum and position operators $\boldsymbol{p}$ and $\boldsymbol{r}$ general. In the split representation, DIRAC operators like β and σ are "even", i.e. diagonal, and $\boldsymbol{\alpha}$ is "odd", i.e. has only non-diagonal matrix elements connecting U_A with U_B. They then perform successive contact transformations, which transform the DIRAC spinor wave function u and all operators, including the HAMILTONian H, to a new representation. For a contact transformation, defined by a transformation operator S, the new representation of any operator O and the wave function u is given by the primed quantities

Table 2. *Orders of magnitude of ψ_+, ψ_- and ψ_0 for an S-state. $p_0 = \alpha m c$, where $\alpha = e^2/\hbar c$.*

	$p < p_0$	$p_0 < p < mc$	$mc < p$
$\psi_+(p)$	1	$(p_0/p)^4$	$\alpha^4 (mc/p)^3$
$\psi_-(p)$	α^3	$\alpha^3 (p_0/p)$	$\alpha^4 (mc/p)^3$
$\psi_0(p)$	$\psi_+(p)\,[1 + O(p^2/m^2c^2)]$		$\alpha^4 (mc/p)^4$

$$u' = e^{iS}\,u, \qquad O' = e^{iS}\,O\,e^{-iS}; \qquad H'u' = E\,u'. \tag{16.20}$$

The aim of these successive transformations is to eliminate odd operators from the HAMILTONian, i.e. each step reduces the off-diagonal elements of H by some power of $1/m$.

For the field-free HAMILTONian ($\varphi = \boldsymbol{A} = 0$) the complete transformation, diagonalzing H, is given by the transformation operator

$$S = -\frac{1}{2}\, i\beta\, \frac{\boldsymbol{\alpha}\cdot\boldsymbol{p}}{p}\, \operatorname{arc\,tan}\left(\frac{p}{m\,c}\right). \tag{16.21}$$

this transformation is exactly equivalent to our change of representation from (ψ_A, ψ_B) to (ψ_+, ψ_-), carried out explicitly in momentum space. In particular the HAMILTONian is transformed to the operator

$$H' = \beta\sqrt{(mc^2)^2 + (cp)^2}.$$

When the contact transformation (16.21) is applied to the general HAMILTONian (10.1), the DIRAC equation in the new representation is equivalent to (16.13). If the vector potential $\boldsymbol{A}$ is appreciable it is more convenient to start with a contact transformation, defined by an operator linear in $1/mc$,

$$S_1 = -\frac{i}{2mc}\,\beta\boldsymbol{\alpha}\cdot\left(\boldsymbol{p} + \frac{e}{c}\boldsymbol{A}\right). \tag{16.22}$$

If $\boldsymbol{A}$ were zero, (16.22) would be just the first term in an expansion of (16.21) in powers of (p/mc). The DIRAC equation, transformed by (16.22), contains all the even operators contained in the PAULI approximation (12.11) but is still exact and contains some odd operators involving the first or higher powers of $1/m$. These odd operators can be reduced further by additional contact transformations.

17. The fine structure formula. *α) Hydrogen.* We write again $W = E - E_0$ for the binding energy of an electron in a hydrogen-like atom. (14.29) then gives the exact DIRAC formula

$$\frac{W}{m\,c^2} = \left[1 + \left(\frac{\alpha Z}{n - k + \sqrt{k^2 - \alpha^2 Z^2}}\right)^2\right]^{-\frac{1}{2}} - 1. \tag{17.1}$$

[1] L. FOLDY and S. WOUTHUYSEN: Phys. Rev. **78**, 29 (1950).

In (17.1), n is the principal quantum number and $k=j+\frac{1}{2}$ is a quantum number which has as possible values $(1, 2, \ldots, n)$. To each value of k or j, except $k=n$, correspond two possible values of the orbital quantum number $l=j+\frac{1}{2}$ and $l=j-\frac{1}{2}$ (for $k=n$, only $l=j-\frac{1}{2}=n-1$). In the nonrelativistic SCHRÖDINGER theory for each value of n we have n^2 linearly independent eigenstates, all having the same energy. In the DIRAC theory we have $2n^2$ independent states, the factor 2 stemming from the two possible eigenvalues of a component of the electron spin. Here the degeneracy is partially removed and the SCHRÖDINGER level splits into n components, one for each value of k. Nevertheless, in the DIRAC theory the pairs of levels with $l=j\pm\frac{1}{2}$ still have *exactly* the same energy. We shall see in the following sections that radiative corrections (LAMB shift) remove this degeneracy of the $l=j\pm\frac{1}{2}$ levels, but the splitting is small and we neglect it at the moment. Remarkably enough, (17.1) had already been derived by SOMMERFELD from the "*old*" BOHR quantum theory, although the interpretation of the quantum numbers, statistical weights, etc. was different (and wrong) in the old theory[1].

Since the fine structure constant, $\alpha=e^2/\hbar c=1/137.037$, is small, the parameter $Z\alpha$ in (17.1) will be small compared with unity, except for very heavy atoms (large nuclear charge Z). If we expand (17.1) in ascending powers of $(Z\alpha)^2$, the first two terms in this expansion are

$$W=-\frac{Z^2\,\mathrm{Ry}}{n^2}\left[1+\frac{(\alpha Z)^2}{n}\left(\frac{1}{k}-\frac{3}{4n}\right)\right], \tag{17.2}$$

where $\mathrm{Ry}=e^4m/2\hbar^2=\frac{1}{2}\alpha^2mc^2$ is the RYDBERG energy unit. The first term in this expansion is W_0, the energy eigenvalue in the nonrelativistic SCHRÖDINGER theory. The second term is exactly equal to W_1, the correction obtained for the energy on the PAULI approximation, Eq. (13.14). Note that the expansion parameter in (17.2) is $(Z\alpha)^2$, *not* $Z\alpha$. The difference between the exact expression (17.1) and the PAULI approximation (17.2) is thus of order $(Z\alpha)^2W_1\sim(Z\alpha)^4W_0$. Radiative corrections, which are not contained in the DIRAC theory, on the other hand, are of order $\alpha(\log\alpha)W_1$. For fairly small values of the nuclear charge Z, to which hydrogen-like atoms are restricted in practice, $(Z\alpha)^2\ll\alpha\log\alpha$. The radiative corrections then are more important than the difference of (17.1) and (17.2), although both are small compared even with W_1. We therefore discuss at the moment only the PAULI approximation W_1.

To get an idea of the order of magnitude of the fine structure splitting, consider the levels with $n=2$ for hydrogen ($Z=1$). Let ΔW be the energy difference between the level with $k=1$ (both the $2S_{\frac{1}{2}}$- and $2P_{\frac{1}{2}}$- state) and with $k=2$ ($2P_{\frac{3}{2}}$). In various energy units, ΔW is approximately

$$\Delta W=\alpha^2W_0/2n=1.33\times10^{-5}W_0=0.365\ \mathrm{cm}^{-1}=1.10\times10^4\ \mathrm{Mc/sec}. \tag{17.3}$$

For any Z and n the energy separation between the two extreme components of the fine structure multiplet, i.e. between $k=1$ and $k=n$, is given by

$$\Delta W=W_0(Z\alpha)^2(n-1)/n^2, \tag{17.4}$$

where W_0 is the nonrelativistic energy for the level. Thus, even the ratio of the fine structure splitting ΔW to W_0 increases with increasing Z and decreases[2] with increasing n, just as $|W_0|$ itself does. This stems from the fact that the fine

[1] For a historical survey see ref. [*10*], p. 317, and A. SOMMERFELD, Naturwiss. **28**, 417 (1940).

[2] Except that there is no splitting for $n=1$ ($j=\frac{1}{2}$ only). Nevertheless the energy *shift* W_1 is larger for $n=1$ than for any other level.

structure increases sharply with the electron's velocity (for large l, at least, a large part of W_1 is due to relativistic variation of mass with velocity): These effects are large when the average kinetic energy is large which, in turn equals $-W_0$. For fixed values of Z and n the fine structure energy shift $|W_1|$ decreases with increasing l (i.e. with k), even though W_0 is independent of l. This is due to the fact that W_1 contains the expectation value of the *square* of the kinetic energy operator [see (16.16)], which is largest when the electron penetrates closest to the nucleus, i.e. for small l.

The absolute value of the fine structure splitting ΔW, Eq. (17.4), decreases rapidly with increasing n (except for $n=1$). The splitting of a spectral line due to the transition between two states of different n is mainly due to the splitting of the lower state, with finer fine structure due to the upper state. Thus each BALMER line (lower state $n=2$) essentially consists of a doublet with separation approximately given by (17.3). Each component of this doublet is again composite (splitting of the upper state) but with splitting smaller than (17.3). Each RITZ-PASCHEN line (lower state $n=3$) essentially consists of a triplet, etc.

Detailed investigations have been carried out on the fine structure of many spectral lines of hydrogen and ionized helium, by optical spectroscopy. All the experimental results are in good *semi*-quantitative agreement[1] with (17.2). Optical observations on fine structure components are rather complicated and their quantitative accuracy is not very great. Nevertheless some small deviations from (17.2) have been observed. In particular, careful observation on the H_α-line indicates that the energy difference of the $2S_{\frac{1}{2}}$- and $2P_{\frac{1}{2}}$-levels is not exactly zero, as predicted by (17.1) or (17.2), but is about 10% of the fine structure, Eq. (17.3). The theoretical explanation of this effect, and more accurate microwave experiments, will be discussed later.

β) Alkali atoms and screening. Before discussing the fine structure of alkali and X-ray spectra, we digress a moment to consider the various "central field approximations" in the nonrelativistic treatment of many-electron atoms[2].

If we are prepared to neglect correlations between the various electrons (polarization) in a complex atom, we can write the atomic wave function in the form of an antisymmetrized product of "single-particle" wave functions. If we further neglect exchange effects, the wave function is a single product of Z functions $u_i(\boldsymbol{r}_i)$, where $\boldsymbol{r}_i$ is the position of the i-th electron. The best form $u_i(\boldsymbol{r}_i)$ is then the solution of the SCHRÖDINGER equation for a single electron in an effective potential $V_i(\boldsymbol{r}_i)$. This effective potential V_i is the sum of the COULOMB potentials due to the nuclear charge at the origin and due to the charge cloud of all the electrons, except the i-th, averaged over their respective wave functions. For the valence electron in an alkali atom (a single electron outside closed shells) $V_i(\boldsymbol{r}_i)$ is automatically a central potential, i.e. a function of the radial distance r_i only. For fairly heavy atoms in general, most of the electrons are in closed shells and we can approximate V_i by a central potential $V_i(r_i)$.

Various approximation methods are available for finding $V_i(r_i)$, the effective central potential in which the i-th electron moves. The most accurate of these is HARTREE's self-consistent field method[3]. This method requires numerical evaluation of the wave function of each electron in any particular atom and $V_i(r_i)$ is finally given in numerical form, separately for each atom. HARTREE solutions are available for a number of atoms up to Hg. Another, less accurate, method for

[1] See ref. [*10*], p. 319 and W. E. LAMB, Rep. Progr. Physics **14**, 19 (1951).

[2] For details on this voluminous subject see ref. [*5*] or A. SOMMERFELD, Atombau und Spektrallinien, 5th Ed.; or ref. [*4*], Ch. 6; or Vol. XXXVI of this Encyclopedia.

[3] D. R. HARTREE: Proc. Cambridge Phil. Soc. **24**, 111 (1928).

evaluating $V_i(r_i)$ is the THOMAS-FERMI statistical model[1]. This method treats the charge distribution of the electrons in a semi-classical manner and only gives $V(r)$, the total electrostatic potential at radial distance r due to *all* the electrons (including the i-th). This method gives good results only for medium and heavy atoms (large Z), for light atoms it overestimates the potential and charge density of the electrons at small radial distances. It has the advantage, however, of giving $V(r)$ simultaneously for all values of the nuclear charge Z. The potential due to all the electrons alone, $V(r)$, approaches a finite limit $V(0)$ at $r=0$. $V(0)$ is equal to $\int\limits_0^\infty dr\, r\, \varrho(r)$, where ϱ is the charge density due to all the electrons. According to the THOMAS-FERMI theory this limit is $3.59 Z^{\frac{4}{3}}$ Ry.

$V_i(r_i)$ is in general not of COULOMB form and the SCHRÖDINGER equation for an electron in such a potential can usually not be solved analytically. For an electron with small principal quantum number n (and generally for small $n-l$) its wave function is concentrated over a reasonably small range of radial distances near some value r_0. If we do not require very high accuracy we can replace $V_i(r_i)$ by a simple analytic function, which is a good approximation for r near r_0. The most convenient form to choose is

$$V_i(r) = -\frac{(Z-s_i)}{r} + V_{0i}. \tag{17.5}$$

Roughly speaking, the "inner screening constant" s_i represents the total charge of the part of the electronic charge cloud which lies inside r_0. The "outer screening constant" V_{0i} represents the constant potential produced at small radial distances by the electronic charge cloud which lies outside r_0. The form (17.5) has the great advantage that the wave function of the i-th electron reduces to a hydrogen-like wave function with charge $(Z-s_i)$. The nonrelativistic ionization potential of the i-th electron is then, in our approximation [see (2.11)],

$$I_i = \left[\left(\frac{Z-s_i}{n_i}\right)^2 - 2V_{0i}\right] \text{Ry}. \tag{17.6}$$

The distance r_0, at which the charge distribution of the i-th electron has its maximum, increases strongly with the principal quantum number n_i. Hence the inner screening constant s_i (electronic charge inside r_0) also increases strongly with n_i. For an atom containing N electrons in closed shells and only very few electrons outside the closed shells, s_i for the outermost electrons is about equal to N, which is almost as big as Z, and the screening is very strong. For such an outer electron with fixed principal quantum number n_i, its wave function penetrates inside the closed shells (where the screening is much weaker) more if its orbital quantum number l_i is low. Thus, for fixed n_i, the effective screening constant increases with increasing l_i. For inner electrons the dependence of s_i on l_i is weaker.

For an electron in any shell, the inner screening comes mainly from electrons in the same shell and in shells of smaller principal quantum number. The screening constant s_i for an electron in a closed shell then is almost independent of the nuclear charge Z or the number of electrons outside this particular shell. SLATER[2] and others have obtained values of s_i for electrons in a closed shell by semi-

[1] E. FERMI: Z. Physik **48**, 73 (1928). — L. H. THOMAS: Proc. Cambridge Phil. Soc. **23**, 542 (1927). See also P. GOMBÁS, Statistische Theorie des Atoms, Vienna: Springer 1949, and Vol. XXXVI of this Encyclopedia.

[2] L. PAULING: Proc. Roy. Soc. Lond., Ser. A **114** (1927). — J. C. SLATER: Phys. Rev. **36**, 57 (1930).

empirical means: For an electron in the helium atom in its ground state, $s_i = \frac{5}{16}$ (see Sect. 26 and 32). For a $1s$ electron in all atoms heavier than helium, $s_1 \approx 0.3$ is still a good approximation. For a $2s$ or $2p$ electron in neon and heavier atoms, SLATER finds $s_2 \approx 4.15$ (although s_2 should be slightly lower for $2s$ than $2p$), etc.

For light atoms, especially for the outer electrons, the outer screening constant V_{0i} is unimportant. For medium-heavy and heavy atoms, especially for inner electrons, V_{0i} is quite large. However, V_{0i} only acts as an additive constant to the energy eigenvalue, but does not affect the wave function. For a $1s$ electron in a medium or heavy atom a crude, but simple, approximation for the central potential $V_i(r)$ can be obtained as follows: The effect of the second $1s$ electron is accounted for by choosing $s_1 = 0.3$. The potential due to all the other (outer) electrons is approximately constant over the region in which the $1s$ wave function is large. We therefore take for V_{0i} the THOMAS-FERMI electrostatic potential at the origin due to all the electrons, $1.79 Z^{\frac{4}{3}}$ a.u., minus the potential at the origin due to the two $1s$ electrons, which is about $2Z$ a.u. [see Eq. (3.29)]. We then have

$$\left.\begin{aligned} V_1(r) = -\frac{(Z-0.3)}{r} + \\ + (1.79 Z^{\frac{4}{3}} - 2Z) \end{aligned}\right\} \quad (17.7)$$

in atomic units. In this approximation the ionization potential of a $1s$ electron, (17.6), becomes roughly

$$\left.\begin{aligned} I_1 = (Z^2 - 3.59 Z^{\frac{4}{3}} + \\ + 3.4 Z)\,\text{Ry}. \end{aligned}\right\} \quad (17.8)$$

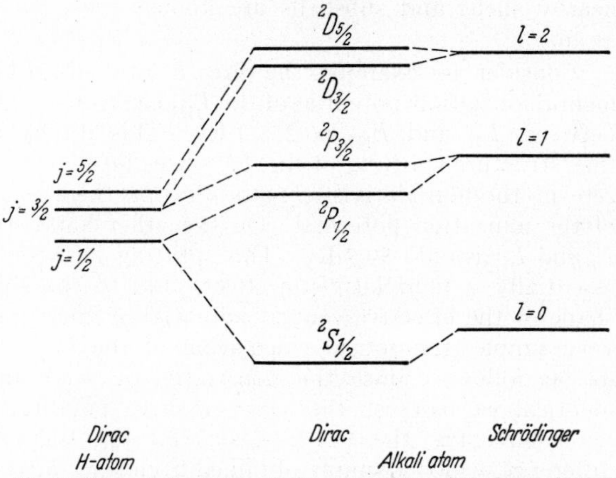

Fig. 10. Schematic level scheme for the states with $n=3$ of a DIRAC electron in an alkali atom. To the left is the level scheme for a DIRAC electron in a COULOMB potential, to the right the nonrelativistic levels in the alkali atom.

We finally return to the fine structure of energy levels in alkali atoms, containing one single electron outside closed shells. The central field approximation is then excellent for this valence electron. But, as discussed above, the shape of the effective potential $V_i(r)$ is far from the COULOMB form and, for fixed principal quantum number n, the binding energy decreases with increasing l. Thus unlike in hydrogen, there is no degeneracy between levels of different l in the nonrelativistic theory of alkali atoms. In addition, the relativistic fine structure corrections (13.8) have to be added to the nonrelativistic energy. These will result in a further splitting of any l-level (except $l=0$) into a doublet with $j = l \pm \frac{1}{2}$. The fine structure splitting of these familiar alkali doublets, being a relativistic effect, is very small compared with the (nonrelativistic) energy separation of levels of different l. The level scheme for a valence electron with $n=3$ in Li or Na is given schematically in Fig. 10.

γ) X-ray levels. For hydrogen-like atoms of reasonably low nuclear charge Z we have seen that the relativistic fine structure shifts W_1 are of order $(Z\alpha)^2 W_0$, where W_0 is the nonrelativistic energy of the level, and hence very small. Further, the difference between the exact DIRAC expression for W_1 and the PAULI approximation for it is of order $(Z\alpha)^2 W_1$, which is smaller even than the radiative corrections of order $W_1 \alpha \log \alpha$. For the heaviest atoms, however, $(Z\alpha)^2$ is not very much smaller than unity (about 0.45 for U) and the relativistic effects become very marked. For very large Z even the difference between the DIRAC and PAULI expressions is large compared with the radiative corrections and the experimental errors in the measurement of energy levels. In practice, of course, one-electron ions of heavy atoms are not available and we have to turn to the innermost electrons of neutral heavy atoms.

The relativistic effects are largest for electrons of low principal quantum number n, for which the inner screening is also weakest. We restrict ourselves therefore to the ionization potentials of electrons in the K and L shells of very heavy atoms (the K-shell contains the $1s$-electrons, the L_{I} subshell the $2s$-electrons, L_{II} and L_{III} the $2p_{\frac{1}{2}}$- and $2p_{\frac{3}{2}}$-electrons respectively; the M and N shells correspond to $n=3$ and 4, etc.). The ionization potentials of the various subshells are known experimentally to quite good accuracy from an analysis of the frequency measurements of X-ray spectra[1]. The energy differences of nearby shells and subshells are known even more accurately for most heavy atoms.

Consider, for example, the three L subshells of Uranium ($Z=92$). The experimental ionization potential of the L_{III} electrons is 1264 Ry. The energy difference between L_{II} and L_{III} is 278.4 Ry. This difference represents the relativistic fine structure splitting of the $2P$-states into $j=\frac{3}{2}$ and $\frac{1}{2}$, which would be exactly zero in the nonrelativistic SCHRÖDINGER theory, and is an appreciable fraction of the ionization potential. On the other hand, the energy difference between L_{I} and L_{II} is only 59.7 Ry. This splitting between the S and P levels of $j=\frac{1}{2}$ is essentially a nonrelativistic effect, due to the slight deviation from COULOMB shape of the effective central potential at small radial distances. A rough, but very simple, theoretical calculation of the $L_{\mathrm{II}}-L_{\mathrm{III}}$ difference can be carried out as follows. Since the nonrelativistic wave functions of $2P_{\frac{1}{2}}$ and $2P_{\frac{3}{2}}$ are identical we can use the *same* effective potential (17.5) for both states. The outer screening, the additive constant V_{0i}, then does not enter in the energy difference, which is simply obtained from the relativistic expressions for hydrogen-like ions with the same effective charge $(Z-s_2)$. With SLATER'S value of $s_2=4.15$, the energy difference for U obtained from the PAULI approximation (17.2) is 198 Ry, from the exact DIRAC expression (17.1) one gets 269 Ry, compared with the experimental value of 278 Ry. Note that the PAULI approximation would give too low a value (238 Ry) even with *no* screening ($s_2=0$).

In reality we should use a slightly lower value for s_2 for fine structure calculations than SLATER'S nonrelativistic value of 4.15: The "expectation value" integrals for the fine structure splitting weight small distances more heavily than the integrals for the nonrelativistic energy and the screening is smaller at smaller radial distances. SOMMERFELD has shown that, with an empirical value of $s_2=3.5$, the exact DIRAC expression (17.1) gives good agreement with the experimental $L_{\mathrm{II}}-L_{\mathrm{III}}$ splitting for all elements up to the heaviest. The PAULI approximation (17.2) gives good agreement only for small nuclear charge Z, for all elements of large Z (e.g. for 92 in U) it deviates appreciably from experiment (for *any* value of s_2). More accurate calculations for the $L_{\mathrm{II}}-L_{\mathrm{III}}$ splitting on the DIRAC theory have been carried out[2], including an explicit calculation of the effect of the other electrons (instead of SOMMERFELD'S empirical screening). The agreement with experiment is again good[3].

[1] LANDOLT and BÖRNSTEIN: Zahlenwerte und Funktionen, 6. Ed., Vol. I/1 Berlin: Springer 1950.

[2] R. CHRISTY and J. KELLER: Phys. Rev. **61**, 147 (1942).

[3] Small remaining discrepancies, due to the finite nuclear size, are discussed by A. SCHAWLOW and C. TOWNES, Science, Lancaster, Pa. **115**, 284 (1952) and Phys. Rev. **100**, 1273 (1955).

We consider next the ionization potential of the K-shell ($1S$-electrons) in heavy atoms. For $Z=92$ (Uranium) for instance, the nonrelativistic BALMER formula for a hydrogen-like ion (91-times ionized U!) would give $|W_0| = Z^2$ Ry $=$ 8464 Ry, the PAULI approximation (17.2) would increase this value by $0.113\,|W_0|$, the exact DIRAC expression (17.1) by $0.150\,|W_0|$. For neutral U let us use the rough, but simple, approximation (17.7) for the effective potential $V_i(r)$. The nonrelativistic ionization potential, given by (17.8), is then about 7290 Ry. With this effective potential the PAULI approximation gives about 8230 Ry, the DIRAC expression 8530 Ry, compared with the experimental value of 8515 Ry. This simple calculation, based on an effective potential derived from the non-relativistic THOMAS-FERMI model, is of course very crude, but already favors the DIRAC over the PAULI expression[1]. BRENNER and BROWN[2] have carried out similar, but more accurate, calculations for the K-shell ionization potential of a number of heavy atoms up to Hg. They take an effective potential, due to all but K-electrons, of similar form to (17.7), but calculate the best outer screening constant V_{0i} from the more accurate HARTREE potentials, corrected for relativistic effects. Further, they calculate the interaction energy between the two $1S$-electrons using more accurate relativistic expressions (see Sect. 43). Their results, using the DIRAC theory, agree with the experimental ionization potentials to within better than 20 Ry for all elements[3].

The most accurate calculation available is one by COHEN[4] on the $K-L_{\mathrm{I}}$ energy difference ($1S-2S$) in Hg ($Z=80$). Calculating this energy *difference* has the advantage that the contribution of electrons outside the K- and L-shells is fairly small. The tabulated nonrelativistic HARTREE potentials are used merely to calculate accurate relativistic wave functions for each of the atomic electrons. The interaction energy between the $1S$- or $2S$-electron with all the other electrons is then calculated numerically, using relativistic expressions. This calculation, based on the exact DIRAC theory, gives for the $K-L_{\mathrm{I}}$ energy difference 5025.2 Ry and the experimental value[5] is about 5022 Ry. The purely numerical errors in the calculation are about ± 0.5 Ry. The remaining small discrepancy of about 3 Ry is probably due to radiative corrections (e.g. LAMB shift) not included in the DIRAC theory. If the PAULI approximation (17.2) had been used, the discrepancy would have been of the order of 100 Ry. Even if the DIRAC expression (17.1) had been expanded in powers of $(Z\alpha)^2$ and terms up to $(Z\alpha)^8\,mc^2 \sim Z^8\alpha^6$ Ry (one order *higher* than the PAULI approximation) kept, the discrepancy would still be about 20 Ry.

c) Radiative and other corrections.

18. Radiative corrections. S-matrix theory. We discuss next the modifications to the DIRAC theory of an electron, which are introduced by the quantization of the electromagnetic radiation field, the so-called "radiative corrections". We shall not attempt to describe the techniques of modern quantum electrodynamics[6], but merely how its results affect atomic theory. skip

[1] The almost exact agreement of this crude calculation for U with experiment is fortuitous.

[2] S. BRENNER and G. E. BROWN: Proc. Roy. Soc. Lond., Ser. A **218**, 422 (1953).

[3] For a more detailed comparison of theory with the latest experimental data see D. SAXON Ph. D. Thesis, Univ. of Wisconsin and J. E. MACK, Phys. Rev. **87**, 225 (1952).

[4] S. COHEN: Ph. D. Thesis, Cornell 1955.

[5] Recent experimental work by D. SAXON indicates a slightly smaller value for the $K-L_{\mathrm{I}}$ difference, which would increase the discrepancy by a few Ry.

[6] For treatments of quantum electrodynamics see, for instance, refs. [*3*], [*6*] and [*11*] to [*14*] of the bibliography.

α) Expansion of the S-matrix. We consider a DIRAC electron under the influence of two interactions. One with an external, given, electromagnetic field, described by a four-vector potential $A_\mu(\boldsymbol{r}, t)$; the other with the electron's own (virtual) radiation field. It is this second interaction which is missing in the DIRAC theory, treated in the preceding sections. For the time being we treat both interactions as small perturbations, but later on we shall discuss the case of an arbitrarily large external potential A_μ. Further, we consider for the moment an unbound electron. First of all, the electron can be scattered any number of times by the potential A_μ. The interaction of the electron with the general radiation field then represents the possibility of the emission or absorption of any number of transverse electromagnetic quanta (photons) by the electron, one at a time. Any physical process is then described by the total transition amplitude for transitions between two "real" states A and B of the system, $S(A, B)$. Each "real" state consists of a free electron and some number of free ("real") quanta (and some number of electron-positron pairs). The states A and B have the same total energy and $S(A, B)$ is called the S-matrix. We shall only consider radiationless scattering, i.e. transitions between states A and B which contain *no* real quanta (and no pairs). For such transitions we can say that the electron interacts only with "its own virtual radiation field" (apart from its interaction with the potential).

We take, as initial and final states A and B, plane wave solutions, (15.8), with positive energy, of the field-free DIRAC equation. Let the momenta of the electron in the two states be $\boldsymbol{p}$ and $(\boldsymbol{p}+\boldsymbol{q})$, respectively, with $|\boldsymbol{p}| = |\boldsymbol{p}+\boldsymbol{q}|$ and energy $E = \sqrt{(mc^2)^2 + (pc)^2}$. The transition amplitude $S(A, B)$ is given as an infinite sum of terms, according to the rules of general perturbation theory. A general term in this perturbation expansion involves a number of intermediate states, each representing the electron in some plane wave state plus some number of virtual quanta. The total energy in the intermediate states is in general not equal to E. The overall matrix element for such a term contains the product of a number of energy denominators and of matrix elements involving the potential A_μ or the emission-absorption operators for virtual quanta. Each scattering with momentum change $\boldsymbol{k}$ by the potential introduces a factor $A_\mu(\boldsymbol{k})$, the FOURIER transform of the potential. Each emission or absorption of a quantum involves the coupling constant between the electron and field. The square of this coupling constant (itself proportional to e) is a simple multiple of α, the fine structure constant. Any quantum emitted by the electron must be subsequently reabsorbed (since A and B contain no quanta) and the number of interactions with virtual quanta is even. Thus the perturbation theory expression for the transition amplitude $S(A, B)$ consists of a double expansion in ascending powers both of α (number of virtual quanta) and of A_μ (number of scatterings by the external potential). Even though the formalism of perturbation theory is used, if one could sum the expansion for $S(A, B)$, the resulting expression would be exact (if the expansion converges).

The terms in this expansion which are of zero order in α (no virtual quanta) give simply the ordinary scattering amplitudes according to the unmodified DIRAC equation alone. Of the terms of first order in α (a single virtual quantum) we consider first the term linear in A_μ (one scattering by the potential). This term, of order α times smaller than the ordinary scattering amplitude, consists of the sum of three expressions. These expressions are described symbolically by "FEYNMAN diagrams[1]", shown in Fig. 11, diagrams 1,1a; 1,1b and 1,1c. The

[1] R. P. FEYNMAN: Phys. Rev. **76**, 749, 769 (1949).

"self-energy diagram", (1,1a), represents one scattering by the potential followed (or preceded) by the emission and reabsorption of a photon by the electron itself. The "LAMB shift diagram proper", (1,1b), represents one potential scattering *between* the emission and reabsorption of the photon. The "vacuum polarization diagram", (1,1c), refers to the emission of a virtual electron-positron pair by the external potential, followed by the annihilation of the pair under emission of a quantum which is absorbed by the electron (or a COULOMB interaction taking the place of the quantum exchange). Vacuum polarization terms are a feature of electron pair (or hole) theory and would be absent entirely if DIRAC single electron theory were used. A matrix element of a higher order in α and/or A_μ also consists of a sum of individual expressions, which can be described by FEYNMAN diagrams. The number and complexity of these expressions increases rapidly with the order of the matrix element. Some examples of the FEYNMAN diagrams of order $\alpha^2 A_\mu$ (2,1a and 2,1b) and of order αA_μ^2 (1,2a) are given in Fig. 11.

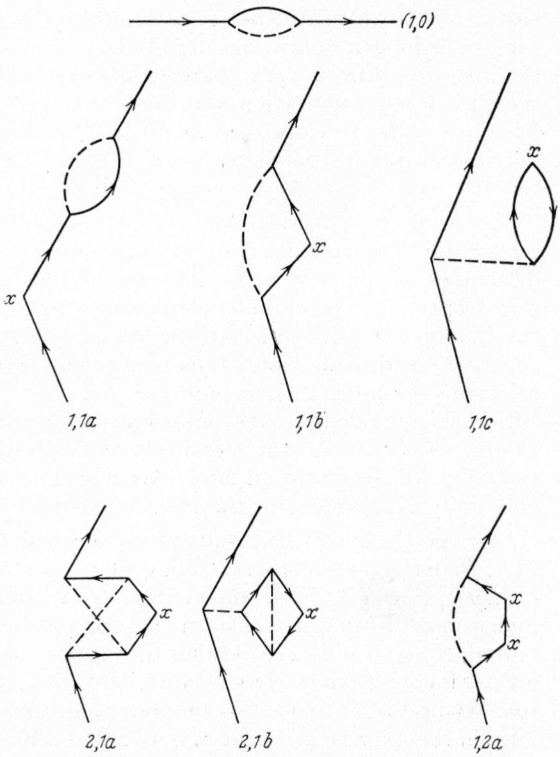

Fig. 11. Some FEYNMAN diagrams for radiative corrections to the scattering of an electron by an external electromagnetic field A_μ. The solid lines represent electrons (or positrons), the dotted lines virtual photons, the crosses the field A_μ.

β) Covariant calculation. Consider, for example, the mathematical expression for the term in the expansion which corresponds to diagram (1,1b). For a fixed momentum change $\boldsymbol{q}$ from the initial to the final state of the electron [involving the FOURIER transform $A_\mu(\boldsymbol{q})$ of the potential] this expression contains an integral over all values of $\boldsymbol{k}$, the momentum of the virtual quantum. This integral diverges as $k \to \infty$ (as do the integrals for most higher order expressions). These divergence difficulties are connected with some unobservable infinite quantities, such as the "transverse self-energy" of the electron. This self-energy, diagram (1, 0), stems from the term in the perturbation expansion of first order in α and zero order in A_μ, the simple emission and reabsorption of a quantum by the electron. Such a term does not contribute directly to the scattering of the electron, but it adds a "constant" self-energy to the "bare" rest mass energy of the electron and the observed electron mass corresponds to the sum of these terms. This "constant" self-energy also involves an integral over $\boldsymbol{k}$, which also diverges as $\boldsymbol{k} \to \infty$. To calculate correctly the total transition amplitude of order αA_μ one has to subtract from the infinite expressions for diagrams (1,1a, 1,1b and 1,1c) a multiple of $A_\mu(q)$ which is proportional to the infinite self energy.

If these subtraction procedures, called renormalizations[1], are carried out consistently the resulting transition amplitudes are finite.

Since the renormalizations involve the difference between two divergent integrals, great care must be taken to carry out the subtractions in an unambiguous manner. This can be achieved most elegantly by the use of modern, fully LORENTZ-covariant, techniques which were developed by DYSON, FEYNMAN and SCHWINGER[2]. These new covariant techniques are equivalent to "old-fashioned" perturbation theory, but are much more powerful. In principle, at least, they enable one to calculate the terms of any order in α and A_μ in the perturbation expansion for the transition amplitude. In practice, the calculation of any but the first few terms is very cumbersome even with this improved method. Both the idea of renormalization and the covariant formulations of quantum electrodynamics were developed in about 1947 to 1949, stimulated to a large extent by experiments on the LAMB shift in hydrogen and the anomalous moment of the electron.

Some of the integrals over the photon momentum $\boldsymbol{k}$, which occur in these relativistic S-matrix calculations, encounter some difficulties as $k \to 0$. These difficulties at the low-frequency end of the quantum spectrum (the infrared catastrophe) are purely nonrelativistic effects. They are not connected with the divergence difficulties at the high-frequency end which are removed by covariant renormalization. It is convenient to introduce a constant lower cut-off λ into the integrals over k in the covariant calculations, where $\lambda \ll m c$. This cut-off is equivalent to the omission of the influence of virtual quanta of momentum less than λ. The treatment of this low-frequency part of the quantum spectrum will be discussed later. With such a cut-off the covariant calculations give finite expressions for the transition amplitudes.

We merely quote the results of some calculations on the transition amplitude $S(A, B)$ for radiationless scattering of an electron in a potential A_μ for a fixed change $q_\nu = (\boldsymbol{q}, i\,q_0)$ in the momentum energy four-vector. Let $A_\mu(q_\nu)$ be the four-dimensional FOURIER transform of the potential (for a time-independent potential, $A_\mu(q_\nu)$ is non-zero only for the energy-change $q_0 = 0$, i.e. for elastic scattering). It follows from the DIRAC equation (10.13) that the first term in the perturbation expansion for $S(A, B)$ is simply proportional to $(e/c) \sum A_\mu(q_\nu)\,\gamma_\mu$. The second term in this expansion, linear in both α and $(e/c)\,A_\mu$, has been evaluated by various authors[3]. The result of these calculations, using a lower cut-off λ on the photon momentum, is to replace the first order term $\sum A_\mu \gamma_\mu$ by[4]

$$\sum_\mu \left[1 - g_2 \frac{\sum\limits_\nu q_\nu^2}{(m c)^2}\right] A_\mu(q_\nu)\,\gamma_\mu - g_1 \frac{i}{4 m c} \sum_{\mu,\sigma} \left[A_\sigma(q_\nu)\,q_\mu - A_\mu(q_\nu)\,q_\sigma\right] \gamma_\mu \gamma_\sigma. \tag{18.1}$$

In (18.1), $\sum q_\nu^2$ denotes $|\boldsymbol{q}|^2 - q_0^2$, and g_1 and g_2 are dimensionless constants given by

$$g_1 = \frac{\alpha}{2\pi}, \qquad g_2 = \frac{\alpha}{3\pi}\left[\left(\log\frac{m c}{\lambda} - \log 2 - \frac{3}{8} + \frac{5}{6}\right) - \frac{1}{5}\right]. \tag{18.2}$$

---

[1] H. A. BETHE: Phys. Rev. **72**, 339 (1947). See also our Sect. 19β.

[2] For a list of the classic papers of these authors on quantum electrodynamics see refs. [*6*], [*12*], [*13*] and [*14*].

[3] N. KROLL and W. LAMB: Phys. Rev. **75**, 388 (1949). — J. FRENCH and V. WEISSKOPF: Phys. Rev. **75**, 1240 (1949). — J. SCHWINGER: Phys. Rev. **76**, 790 (1949). — R. P. FEYNMAN: Phys. Rev. **76**, 769 (1949).

[4] The expression (18.1) holds only for a nonrelativistic change in momentum, $q_\nu^2 \ll (m c)^2$, but expressions have been evaluated which hold for all values of q_ν^2.

The term in g_2 involving $\frac{1}{5}$ comes from the vacuum polarization diagram (1, 1c), all other parts of g_2, and g_1 come from the FEYNMAN diagram (1, 1a) and (1, 1b) and the mass renormalization term.

The expression (18.1) can also be described in position space as follows: The scattering amplitude, including the effect of radiative corrections of order αA_μ, is obtained by: (i) Replacing A_μ in the DIRAC equation (10.13) by the expression

$$\left[1 + g_2 \left(\frac{\hbar}{m c}\right)^2 \square^2\right] A_\mu - g_1 \left(\frac{\hbar}{4 m c}\right) \sum_\nu F_{\mu\nu} \gamma_\nu . \tag{18.3}$$

(ii) Treating the part of (18.3) which involves g_1 or g_2 as a small perturbation in (10.13) and evaluating the transition amplitude (matrix element) between two plane wave states of the electron by *first* order perturbation theory. The modified DIRAC equation is then exactly of form (10.15). The physical significance of such a modification was discussed in Sect. 10γ. When the equation is treated by lowest order perturbation theory the effect is: (i) To multiply the electromagnetic moment of the electron, given by the DIRAC theory, by the factor $(1 + g_1)$. (ii) For a time-independent electrostatic potential φ, for instance, $(\boldsymbol{A} = 0, A_4 = i\varphi)$ the potential φ is replaced by

$$\varphi + g_2 \left(\frac{\hbar}{m c}\right)^2 \Delta\varphi = \varphi - 4\pi g_2 \left(\frac{\hbar}{m c}\right)^2 \varrho , \tag{18.4}$$

where ϱ is the charge density of the *external* charge distribution which gives rise to the potential φ.

Calculations of all radiative corrections of second order in α and first in A_μ, as well as of second order in A_μ and first in α, have been carried out by now. We shall give some of these results in Sect. 21. We merely quote here the result[1] of the terms of order $\alpha^2 A_\mu$ on the anomalous moment of the electron. The effective total magnetic moment is again $(1 + g_1)$ times the DIRAC moment, but g_1 is now not simply given by (18.2) but includes a term in α^2,

$$1 + g_1 = 1 + \frac{\alpha}{2\pi} - 2.973 \frac{\alpha^2}{\pi^2} = 1.0011453 . \tag{18.5}$$

Consider (18.1) for radiationless scattering of an electron from initial momentum $\boldsymbol{p}$ to final momentum $(\boldsymbol{p} + \boldsymbol{q})$ in a time-independent field (initial and final energies the same). The expression (18.2) for the factors g_1 and g_2 were obtained by evaluating integrals over the momentum $\boldsymbol{k}$ of the virtual photon, with a lower cut-off λ on k, where $\lambda \ll q \ll mc$. Even for such low values of λ, some of the integrals depend on λ and, in fact, g_2 diverges logarithmically as λ tends to zero. The numerical factor multiplying this divergence is small, e.g. if λ is decreased from λ_1 to λ_2, then the transition amplitude S is decreased by a multiplicative factor given approximately by

$$1 - b \log \frac{\lambda_1}{\lambda_2} , \qquad b = \frac{\alpha}{3\pi} \left(\frac{q}{m c}\right)^2 \ll \alpha \ll 1 . \tag{18.6}$$

This infrared catastrophe is connected with the fact that, besides the elastic radiationless scattering considered so far, the electron can also undergo inelastic scattering with the emission of one or more *real* photons (Bremsstrahlung, see Sect. 76 to 79). For very low photon momenta $k \ll q$, the total probability for scattering with the emission of one photon with k between λ_1 and λ_2 is given approximately by

$$P_1 = |S|^2 \, 2b \log \frac{\lambda_1}{\lambda_2} , \tag{18.7}$$

1 R. KARPLUS and N. KROLL: Phys. Rev. **77**, 536 (1950).

where S and $|S|^2$ are the transition amplitude and probability for radiationless scattering and b is given in (18.6). Hence, without any lower cut-off on the photon momentum the total number of real photons emitted in a physical scattering process will be infinite. But the momenta of most of these photons will be extremely small ("soft" quanta). Thus, on the average, only one photon will be emitted in the enormous range of momenta q to $q\,e^{-1/2b}$, another one in the range $q\,e^{-1/2b}$ to $q\,e^{-1/b}$, etc. (where $2b$ is a very small number). Further, for low photon momenta, the decrease in the probability $|S|^2$ for radiationless scattering due to radiative corrections involving virtual photons in a certain momentum range is almost exactly cancelled by the additional probability of scattering with the emission of a real photon in this range. Mathematically, if we decrease the cut-off from λ_1 to λ_2 the total probability for scattering with or without emission of a real photon changes from $|S|^2$ to [see Eqs. (18.6) and (18.7)]

$$P_{\text{tot}} = \left|S\left(1 - b\log\frac{\lambda_1}{\lambda_2}\right)\right|^2 + |S|^2\, 2b\log\frac{\lambda_1}{\lambda_2} \approx |S|^2; \tag{18.8}$$

i.e., if we neglect terms quadratic in b, the total probability is unchanged.

For a consistent treatment of the fact that the most probable number of "soft" photons emitted is *not* small, the formalism of perturbation theory has to be modified somewhat. In particular, terms in our perturbation expansion for S which involve more than one virtual photon cannot be neglected, nor processes involving the emission of more than one real photon. These formal difficulties were overcome some time ago[1] in the framework of "oldfashioned" quantum electrodynamics and, more recently[2], also for the modern, covariant formalism. The results are roughly as follows. The *total* probability P_{tot} of scattering, irrespective of the number of real photons emitted and including radiative corrections of all orders, remains finite even when the lower cut-off λ tends to zero. However, if λ is very small, the probability for all scattering processes in which *no* real photon of momentum greater than λ is emitted (but any number of photons of smaller momentum) is given, approximately, by

$$P_\lambda = P_{\text{tot}} \exp\left(-2b\log\frac{q}{\lambda}\right). \tag{18.9}$$

This expression tends to zero as λ does, which merely indicates that any scattering process is accompanied by the emission of at least some very soft photons. If in (18.2) we choose the cut-off λ such that $q\,e^{-1/2b} \ll \lambda \ll q$, then (18.1) is still a good approximation in the following sense. It furnishes the probability for an "almost elastic" scattering, i.e. for a process in which no real photons of momentum larger than λ are emitted. Although the total number of soft photons emitted is still infinite, their total energy (and hence the electron's energy loss) is finite and small.

19. Radiative corrections. Bound states. In Sect. 18 we have only discussed the perturbation expansion for the S-matrix for the scattering of *free* electrons. We are mainly interested in the effect of radiative corrections on the energy levels of an electron *bound* in a central potential, in particular in the fine structure of hydrogen-like atoms. We discuss next the extent to which the covariant formalism can be adapted to bound electrons and how the results are joined on to nonrelativistic calculations.

---

[1] F. BLOCH and A. NORDSIECK: Phys. Rev. **52**, 54 (1937). — W. PAULI and M. FIERZ: Nuovo Cim. **15**, 167 (1938).

[2] J. JAUCH and F. ROHRLICH: Phys. Rev. **98**, 181 (1955) and Helv. phys. Acta **27**, 613 (1954). — E. L. LOMON: Nuclear Physics **1**, 101 (1956).

α) Covariant calculation. The terms involving g_1 and g_2 in (18.1) hold strictly only for transitions between plane wave states of a free electron. If $p_\mu = (\boldsymbol{p}, i E_p/c)$ is the energy-momentum four-vector of the electron in its initial state then $\sum_\mu p_\mu^2 = (mc)^2$, i.e. the energy is

$$E(p) = \sqrt{(m c^2)^2 + (p c)^2}\,.$$

Similarly if $(p_\mu + q_\mu)$ is the final energy-momentum, $\sum_\mu (p_\mu + q_\mu)^2 = (mc)^2$. If these conditions are satisfied, (18.1) depends only on the momentum transfer q_μ, but not explicitly on p_μ. The wave function of a bound electron can be written as the superposition of plane wave eigenfunctions and the probability amplitude for a momentum $\boldsymbol{p}$ is simply $\psi(\boldsymbol{p})$, the momentum space wave function (see Sects. 8 and 16). However, the energy of each plane wave function of momentum $\boldsymbol{p}$ is E, the total energy of the electron's bound state (including the restmass energy mc^2), and *not* E_p, the free particle value. Hence $\sum p_\mu^2$ is not exactly $(mc)^2$ for such "bound plane waves" and (18.1) is not applicable rigorously.

The covariant formalism can, at least in principle, be modified to be applicable to such bound plane waves. It will be remembered that the calculations leading to the terms in g_1 and g_2 in (18.1) involve an integration over $\boldsymbol{k}$, the momentum of the virtual photon. Consider the transition amplitude for a transition between two "bound plane waves" of momentum $\boldsymbol{p}$ and $(\boldsymbol{p}+\boldsymbol{q})$, both with energy E. One then finds that the integrand in the integral over $\boldsymbol{k}$ has very nearly its free particle value for $q_\mu = (\boldsymbol{q}, 0)$, as long as both $E(p) - E$ and $E(|\boldsymbol{p}+\boldsymbol{q}|) - E$ are small compared with kc (the energy of the virtual photon). For an electron bound in a sufficiently weak potential the momentum space wave function $\psi(\boldsymbol{p})$ will be appreciable only for $p \ll mc$. For a hydrogen-like atom of low nuclear charge Z, for instance, only momenta of the order of $Z p_0 \sim Z \alpha m c$ are important, where p_0 is the BOHR momentum. For such an atom the important values of $E(p) - E$ are of the order of magnitude $Z^2\,\mathrm{Ry} \sim Z^2 \alpha^2 m c^2 \ll m c^2$. The free particle integrands will then be a good approximation as long as $k \gg (Z\alpha)^2\, mc$.

In the integrals leading to all the terms in (18.1), (18.2) (except possibly the term in $\log \lambda$) the important values of k are of order mc. For these terms then, if $Z\alpha \ll 1$ $(Z \ll 137)$, the modification due to the plane waves being bound is small. In the integral leading to the term in $\log \lambda$ in (18.2), however, all values of k down to the cut-off λ are important. If $Z\alpha \ll 1$, it is convenient to choose λ such that $(Z\alpha)^2 mc \ll \lambda \ll mc$. The contribution of virtual photons of $k > \lambda$ is then obtained from the covariant expressions neglecting the effect of the plane waves being bound (i.e. neglecting $Z^2\alpha^2 mc/\lambda$). The contribution of photons of $k < \lambda$ is then evaluated by a different, nonrelativistic, calculation which we discuss later. For the high-frequency part $k > \lambda$ we then simply use (18.1) with $q_4 = 0$ for the transition amplitude between any two FOURIER transforms of the spatial wave function of the bound state of the electron. In (18.1) the term involving unity in the first bracket is exactly the FOURIER transform of the position space potential [compare Eqs. (10.1), (10.13) and (16.1)]. The remaining terms in (18.1) involve g_1 and g_2 and are thus small. We can then treat these extra terms by first order perturbation theory. The perturbation to the energy eigenvalue is then

$$\Delta E_> = \int d^3 q \int d^3 p\, \psi^*(\boldsymbol{p})\, \Gamma(\boldsymbol{q})\, \psi(\boldsymbol{p}+\boldsymbol{q})\,, \tag{19.1}$$

where ψ is the momentum space wave function and $\Gamma(\boldsymbol{q})$ is $ie\beta$ times the part of (18.1) which involves g_1 or g_2. For any part of $\Gamma(q)$ which is a constant Γ, for instance, the double integral (19.1) reduces to Γ times the absolute square of $\int d^3 p\, \psi(\boldsymbol{p})$.

Instead of evaluating (19.1) directly in momentum space it is often more convenient to work in position space. As in Sect. 18 we simply replace $A_\mu(x_\mu)$ in the DIRAC equation (10.13) by the expression (18.3) and again use perturbation theory. For a time-independent potential this furnishes for $\Delta E_>$ the expression

$$\Delta E_> = \int d^3 r\, u_0^*(\boldsymbol{r})\, \Gamma(\boldsymbol{r})\, u_0(\boldsymbol{r}) \equiv \langle \Gamma(\boldsymbol{r}) \rangle_{00}, \tag{19.2}$$

where $u_0(\boldsymbol{r})$ is the position space wave function and $\Gamma(\boldsymbol{r})$ is $i e \beta \sum_\mu \gamma_\mu$ times the part of (18.3) which involves g_1 or g_2. The expression (19.2) is exactly equivalent to (19.1). If the vector potential $\boldsymbol{A}$ is zero, $\Gamma(\boldsymbol{r})$ reduces to

$$\Gamma(\boldsymbol{r}) = -g_2 \left(\frac{\hbar}{m c}\right)^2 e \Delta \varphi(\boldsymbol{r}) - g_1 \frac{i e \hbar}{2 m c} \beta \boldsymbol{\alpha} \cdot \mathcal{E}(\boldsymbol{r}), \tag{19.3}$$

where φ and $\mathcal{E}$ are the electrostatic potential and field.

In Sect. 21 we shall evaluate explicitly the first order perturbation $\Delta E_>$ to the energy eigenvalue for a COULOMB potential, given by the integrals (19.1) or (19.2). We shall do this by PAULI's method of "reduction to the large components". I.e. we use for the wave function $u(\boldsymbol{r})$ or $\psi(\boldsymbol{p})$ the approximate PAULI wave functions, whose radial parts are identical with the nonrelativistic SCHRÖDINGER expressions, *not* with the exact DIRAC expressions. We shall consider only the case of $Z\alpha \ll 1$, so the error due to this replacement should be small in general. For a COULOMB potential, however, some parts of the operator $\Gamma(\boldsymbol{q})$ to be substituted into (19.1) are equal to a constant Γ_c, independent of $\boldsymbol{q}$. The equivalent part of $\Gamma(\boldsymbol{r})$ in (19.3) is then a multiple of a DIRAC[1] delta-function, $\Gamma_c \delta^{(3)}(\boldsymbol{r})$. The corresponding contribution to the energy shift $\Delta E_>$ is then given by

$$\Delta E_{>,c} = \frac{\Gamma_c}{(2\pi)^3} \left| \int d^3 p\, \psi(\boldsymbol{p}) \right|^2 = \Gamma_c |u(0)|^2, \tag{19.4}$$

where $u(0)$ is the position space wave function at the origin.

We have already seen in Sect. 14 that, even for small $Z\alpha$, the PAULI and DIRAC wave functions at the origin are quite different, in fact the DIRAC wave function diverges. This apparent difficulty is resolved as follows. The expressions involving g_1 and g_2 in (18.1) are only valid if $q^2 \ll (mc)^2$ and further the expression (19.1) is strictly valid only if p and $|\boldsymbol{p}+\boldsymbol{q}|$ are small compared with mc. For p and/or $|\boldsymbol{p}+\boldsymbol{q}|$ large compared with mc one finds that the operator $\Gamma(\boldsymbol{q})$ in (19.1) is replaced by a more complicated operator which falls off much more rapidly with increasing momentum. Thus the integral in (19.1) should effectively be cut off for $p, q > mc$. A comparison with Table 2 (Sect. 16) shows that, if the nonrelativistic wave functions are used, the contribution from very large momenta is small even if the integrals are allowed to run to infinity with the unmodified operator $\Gamma(\boldsymbol{q})$. Further, the main contribution to the integral comes from values of p and q of the order of $Z p_0$ where the SCHRÖDINGER and DIRAC radial functions are nearly the same. We therefore get a good approximation to $\Delta E_>$ by using the integral (19.1) without modifying Γ as long as we use the PAULI wave functions and *not* the DIRAC ones (which are much larger for very large momenta).

For the position space integral (19.2) the equivalent argument runs as follows. The operator $\Gamma(\boldsymbol{r})$, Eq. (19.3), is a good approximation for all but very small radial distances r. For very small r, however, $\Gamma(\boldsymbol{r})$ has to be replaced by a complicated non-local operator. The part involving $\Gamma_c \delta^{(3)}(\boldsymbol{r})$ should then be replaced

[1] In (18.4), for instance, the term in g_2 is proportional to the charge distribution producing the field, which is a point charge $Ze\,\delta^{(3)}(\boldsymbol{r})$ for a COULOMB potential.

by an operator extending over small, but finite, distances and $\Gamma_c|u(0)|^2$ in (19.4) should be replaced by some complicated average of $\Gamma_c|u(\boldsymbol{r})|^2$ over small distances. As discussed in Sect. 14δ, a good approximation to $\Delta E_>$ is then obtained by using the integral (19.2) without modifying $\Gamma(\boldsymbol{r})$ but using the PAULI wave function $u(r)$.

We have discussed so far only the application to bound states of the terms in the perturbation expansion for the S-matrix which are linear both in the potential and in α (one virtual photon). All terms of higher order in α (two or more virtual photons), but still linear in the potential, can be applied to bound states in exactly the same manner. The radiative correction terms involving higher powers of the potential present more difficulties. The contribution of terms, quadratic in the potential and linear in α, to the energy eigenvalues of hydrogen-like atoms have nevertheless been calculated[1]. The vacuum polarization terms, which are linear in α, have even been calculated recently[2] for an arbitrarily strong potential (all powers of A_μ). At the present time, however, no methods are available for treating the radiative corrections in general for an arbitrarily strong potential. For the very heavy atoms, where $Z\alpha$ is not very small, the LAMB shift cannot yet be calculated with good accuracy.

β) Nonrelativistic calculations. The expression (19.1) or (19.2) gives the contribution to the lowest order radiative correction to the energy eigenvalue from virtual photons of momentum k larger than a certain cut-off value λ. We chose λ to be large compared with $(Z\alpha)^2\, mc$, small compared with mc ($Z\alpha$ is considered as small). The contribution from virtual photons of momentum k less than λ is best treated by a nonrelativistic method, proposed by BETHE[3]. An outline of this method is as follows.

We treat the electron nonrelativistically throughout and first solve (at least in principle) the SCHRÖDINGER equation for an electron in the external electrostatic potential $\varphi(\boldsymbol{r})$. Unlike the covariant *S-matrix* method, the electron's interaction with the potential is thus treated *exactly*. The electron's interaction with the virtual radiation field, on the other hand, is treated as a small perturbation. The perturbation HAMILTONian H', to be added to the SCHRÖDINGER HAMILTONian is obtained from "old fashioned" nonrelativistic quantum electrodynamics. H' can be written in the form

$$H' = N\frac{e}{m}\,\boldsymbol{p}\cdot\sum_\sigma\left[\boldsymbol{\pi}_\sigma e^{i\boldsymbol{k}_\sigma\cdot\boldsymbol{r}/\hbar} q_\sigma + \boldsymbol{\pi}_\sigma e^{-i\boldsymbol{k}_\sigma\cdot\boldsymbol{r}/\hbar} q_\sigma^*\right]. \tag{19.5}$$

In (19.5) e, m are the electronic charge and mass, $\boldsymbol{p}$ and $\boldsymbol{r}$ the momentum and position of the electron; the summation index σ denotes the direction of polarization $\boldsymbol{\pi}_\sigma$ and the momentum $\boldsymbol{k}_\sigma$ of the virtual photon and q_σ, q_σ^* are the absorption, emission operators for the photon (numerical constants have been absorbed into the symbol N). q_σ (and q_σ^*) have matrix elements proportional to $k_\sigma^{-\frac{1}{2}}$ for transitions involving the absorption (and emission, respectively) of one σ-photon.

We use as zero-order state-vectors those representing an electron in a particular atomic state, given by the SCHRÖDINGER (or rather PAULI) wave function for a potential φ, plus any number of photons. We label a general atomic state by n and are interested in the change in the energy eigenvalue for a particular atomic state, labeled 0, in the absence of any real photons. The contribution to this energy shift of lowest order in e (i.e. in $\sqrt{\alpha}$) is given by using second order

[1] R. KARPLUS, A. KLEIN and J. SCHWINGER: Phys. Rev. **86**, 288 (1952). — M. BARANGER, H. BETHE and R. FEYNMAN: Phys. Rev. **92**, 482 (1953).
[2] E. WICHMAN and N. M. KROLL: Phys. Rev. **101**, 843 (1956).
[3] H. A. BETHE: Phys. Rev. **72**, 339 (1947).

perturbation theory on H', Eq. (19.5). The first virtual transition in the two-stage process involves q_σ^*, the emission operator for a particular photon σ, the second step involves the absorption operator q_σ for the *same* photon. The perturbation of the energy then involves a double sum over intermediate states involving any atomic state n and a single (virtual) photon of any momentum $\boldsymbol{k}$ (with $k \lesssim \lambda$) and one of two directions of polarization perpendicular to $\boldsymbol{k}$. We shall neglect retardation at the moment (see Sect. 19γ for justification), i.e. we replace the exponential factors in (19.5) by unity. The sum over photon-momentum $\boldsymbol{k}$ can be converted into an integral and the integration over the direction of $\boldsymbol{k}$ and the sum over the polarization direction carried out. We use units in which $\hbar$ is unity (but carry the symbols for e, m and c). The energy change, i.e. the "self-energy of the electron in the bound state 0", is then given by ($\alpha = e^2/\hbar c$)

$$\Delta W = -\frac{2}{3\pi}\alpha\frac{1}{m^2}\int_0^\lambda dk\, k \sum_n \frac{\boldsymbol{p}_{0n}\cdot\boldsymbol{p}_{n0}}{(E_n - E_0 + kc)}. \tag{19.6}$$

E_0 and E_n are the SCHRÖDINGER energy eigenvalues for the two atomic states and $\boldsymbol{p}_{0n}$ is the matrix element of the momentum operator for transitions between them. The sum over n includes all states of the electron in the potential φ, both in the discrete and the continuous spectrum.

It is convenient to split the expression (19.6) into two parts, one of which does not involve $(E_n - E_0)$. For this term the sum over n can be eliminated by a simple sum rule and we have

$$\Delta W = -\frac{2}{3\pi}\alpha\frac{1}{m^2}\int_0^\lambda dk\, k\left[\frac{\langle p^2\rangle_{00}}{kc} + \sum_n \frac{\boldsymbol{p}_{0n}\cdot\boldsymbol{p}_{n0}(E_0 - E_n)}{kc(kc + E_n - E_0)}\right]. \tag{19.7}$$

We shall show next that the *observable* change $\Delta E_<$ in the energy eigenvalue is given *not* by the whole expression for ΔW, but only by the second term in (19.7). The first term is cancelled by a mass renormalization term, which can be evaluated as follows.

Consider, for a moment, a *free* electron (*no* external potential φ). Its experimentally observed mass m consists partly of the unobservable "bare" mass m_0 and partly of a correction δm, arising from the self energy. We consider δm as small (it involves α) and expand in powers of it. The HAMILTONian for the free electron is then

$$H_{\text{free}} = \frac{p^2}{2m_0} + H' = \frac{p^2}{2m} + \left(\frac{\delta m}{m}\frac{p^2}{2m} + H'\right), \tag{19.8}$$

where H' is given by (19.5). The operator H' leads, in second order perturbation theory, to a change in energy of the *free* electron. If retardation is neglected, this energy change is found to be identical[1] with the expectation value of the first term in (19.7). By definition, the experimental mass m is such that the total energy of a free electron of momentum p is exactly $p^2/2m$. The mass correction δm must then be chosen so that the expectation value of the term involving δm in (19.8) cancels the energy change due to H' for a free electron. Thus

$$\delta m = +\frac{4}{3\pi c}\alpha\int_0^\lambda dk.$$

---

[1] This follows from (19.7) as a special case. For a free electron, the momentum changes by $\boldsymbol{k}$ upon emission or absorption of a quantum. If retardation is neglected, this means that $\boldsymbol{k}$ is negligible compared with $\boldsymbol{p}$, and therefore the energy E_n after emission of the quantum, is the same as that before, E_0. Then the second term in (19.7) vanishes, q.e.d.

When we now consider an electron in a potential φ, the term in δm in (19.8) also has to be added to the HAMILTONian. The expectation value of this operator exactly cancels the first term in (19.7). The observable energy change $\Delta E_<$ is then given by the second term alone, which is, after carrying out the integration,

$$\Delta E_< = -\frac{2}{3\pi}\alpha\frac{1}{(mc)^2}\sum_n \boldsymbol{p}_{0n}\cdot\boldsymbol{p}_{n0}(E_0-E_n)\log\left(\frac{\lambda c + E_n - E_0}{|E_n-E_0|}\right). \tag{19.9}$$

The important values of $|E_n - E_0|$ will be of the order of the ground state binding energy or Z^2 Ry for a hydrogenic atom. This energy is thus very small compared with λc, so the logarithm in (19.9) is very large and not very sensitive to the exact value of $E_n - E_0$. In the numerator of this logarithm we neglect $(E_n - E_0)$ altogether and in the denominator replace it by an average energy K_0. K_0 will be of order Z^2 Ry and it is defined exactly by the relation

$$\log\left(\frac{K_0}{Z^2\,\mathrm{Ry}}\right)\sum_n \boldsymbol{p}_{0n}\cdot\boldsymbol{p}_{n0}(E_n-E_0) = \sum_n \boldsymbol{p}_{0n}\cdot\boldsymbol{p}_{n0}(E_n-E_0)\log\left|\frac{E_n-E_0}{Z^2\,\mathrm{Ry}}\right|. \tag{19.10}$$

The evaluation of K_0 will be discussed in Sect. 21 and 74γ.

With the logarithm in (19.9) replaced by the constant $\log(\lambda c/K_0)$, the remaining sum over states can be rewritten in the form

$$\sum_n \boldsymbol{p}_{0n}\cdot\boldsymbol{p}_{n0}(E_0-E_n) = \sum_n [(H\boldsymbol{p})_{0n}\cdot\boldsymbol{p}_{n0} - (\boldsymbol{p}H)_{0n}\cdot\boldsymbol{p}_{n0}] = \langle[H,\boldsymbol{p}]\cdot\boldsymbol{p}\rangle_{00}. \tag{19.11}$$

In the first line of (19.11), H is the HAMILTONian for the electron, excluding the interaction H' with the radiation field,

$$H = \frac{p^2}{2m} - e\varphi(\boldsymbol{r}), \tag{19.12}$$

which gives E_0 and E_n, respectively, when operating on the wave functions for the states 0 and n. The last member of (19.11) involving the commutator of H and $\boldsymbol{p}$, is obtained from the middle member by a simple sum rule. An equivalent expression to (19.11), but with $[H,\boldsymbol{p}]\cdot\boldsymbol{p}$ replaced by $\boldsymbol{p}\cdot[\boldsymbol{p},H]$, also holds. Adding these expressions we finally obtain (putting $\hbar = 1$)

$$\sum_n \boldsymbol{p}_{0n}\cdot\boldsymbol{p}_{n0}(E_0-E_n) = \tfrac{1}{2}\langle[[H,\boldsymbol{p}]\cdot,\boldsymbol{p}]\rangle_{00} = +\tfrac{1}{2}e\langle\Delta\varphi(\boldsymbol{r})\rangle_{00}, \tag{19.13}$$

where we have used the relation

$$[p_x, f(r)] = -i\frac{\partial f}{\partial x}. \tag{19.14}$$

Hence (19.9) reduces to

$$\Delta E_< = -\frac{\alpha}{3\pi}\frac{1}{(mc)^2}\log\left(\frac{\lambda c}{K_0}\right)\langle e\Delta\varphi(\boldsymbol{r})\rangle_{00}. \tag{19.15}$$

We can now add the expression (19.15) for $\Delta E_<$ to the expression (19.2) [with Eqs. (18.2) and (19.3)] for $\Delta E_>$ to get the total energy shift ΔE irrespective of the frequency of the virtual photon. This shift is given by

$$\left.\begin{aligned}\Delta E = &-\frac{\alpha}{3\pi}\left(\frac{\hbar}{mc}\right)^2\left[\log\frac{mc^2}{K_0} - \log 2 - \frac{3}{8} + \frac{5}{6} - \frac{1}{5}\right]\langle e\Delta\varphi(\boldsymbol{r})\rangle_{00} - \\ &-\frac{\alpha}{2\pi}i\left(\frac{e\hbar}{2mc}\right)\langle\beta\boldsymbol{\alpha}\cdot\mathcal{E}(\boldsymbol{r})\rangle_{00},\end{aligned}\right\} \tag{19.16}$$

where K_0 is defined in (19.10). Note that, after adding $\Delta E_>$ to $\Delta E_<$, the dependence on the arbitrary cut-off λ has dropped out[1] of the expression (19.16).

[1] In the covariant evaluation of $\Delta E_>$, great care must be taken that the definition of λ is equivalent to that in the nonrelativistic calculation of $\Delta E_<$; see footnote 13 of R. P. FEYNMAN, Phys. Rev. **76**, 769 (1949).

γ) Retardation. We finally outline briefly how the neglect of retardation, used above, can be justified: If retardation is not to be neglected, the exponential terms in (19.5) must be carried. If, for instance, we consider a photon of momentum $\boldsymbol{k}$ in the z-direction, polarized in the x-direction, then in (19.6) and (19.7) the operator p_x occurring twice is replaced by $p_x\, e^{ikz/\hbar}$ in one factor and by $p_x e^{-ikz/\hbar}$ in the other. Now we are considering an essentially nonrelativistic system in which the order of magnitude of momentum (p_0), of atomic radius (a_0) and of the energy difference $E_0 - E_n (K_0)$, satisfy the following inequalities

$$K_0 \ll p_0 c \sim \hbar c/a_0 \ll mc^2.$$

Now retardation will certainly be negligible unless the photon momentum k is of order p_0 or bigger. Although the upper limit λ of k is small compared with mc it is not necessarily smaller than p_0. In the region of $p_0 < k < \lambda$ we should then consider retardation and keep the exponential factors in (19.7), but in this region $E_n - E_0 \sim K_0 \ll kc$ and in the denominator of the second term in (19.7) we can neglect $E_n - E_0$. Using sum rules similar to those leading to (19.13), the integrand of the modified expression (19.7) in this region reduces to (except for some factors, and before summing over polarization directions)

$$\frac{\langle p_x^2 \rangle_{00}}{kc} + \frac{1}{2(kc)^2} \langle [[H, p_x e^{ikz/\hbar}], p_x e^{-ikz/\hbar}] \rangle_{00}, \tag{19.17}$$

where H is given by (19.12).

Now retardation also affects the mass-renormalization term [see (19.8)] which has to be subtracted from (19.17). This term involves, as a denominator, the "energy of the intermediate state" which is $(kc + k^2/2m)$, the photon energy plus recoil energy of the electron. Since $k \ll mc$ we can expand in powers of k/mc and keep only the first *two* terms (with retardation neglected the *second* term would be missing). With this approximation one finds, again using some sum rules, for the term to be subtracted from (19.17)

$$\frac{\langle p_x^2 \rangle_{00}}{kc} \left[1 - \frac{k^2/2m}{kc}\right] = \frac{\langle p_x^2 \rangle_{00}}{kc} + \frac{1}{2(kc)^2} \langle [[H_0, p_x e^{ikz/\hbar}], p_x e^{-ikz/\hbar}] \rangle, \tag{19.18}$$

where $H_0 = p^2/2m$. The difference of (19.17) and (19.18) is then

$$-\frac{e}{2(kc)^2} \langle [[\varphi(\boldsymbol{r}), p_x e^{ikz/\hbar}], p_x e^{-ikz/\hbar}] \rangle_{00} = \frac{e}{2(kc)^2} \left\langle \frac{\partial^2 \varphi(\boldsymbol{r})}{\partial x^2} \right\rangle_{00}$$

which finally leads again to (19.15), the result with retardation neglected.

20. Corrections for nuclear motion and structure. In Sects. 18 and 19 we have discussed radiative corrections to the atomic energy levels given by the DIRAC theory, but have still assumed that the atomic nucleus is a stationary and structureless point charge. In reality the electron's mass m is not negligibly small compared with the nuclear mass M and we have to consider the effect of nuclear motion on the energy levels. Actual nuclei also possess some internal structure, such as a finite (although small) size and a magnetic moment, which also affect the energy levels slightly.

We first summarize, for comparison, some orders of magnitude of energies. We shall express energies in terms of the equivalent frequency (see Introduction) in units of megacycles per second (Mc). In these units

$$1\ \text{Ry} = 3.2898 \times 10^9\ \text{Mc}, \qquad 1\ \text{cm}^{-1} = 29979\ \text{Mc}. \tag{20.1}$$

The fine structure separation (FS) is of order $(Z\alpha)^2$ Ry. The radiative corrections to lowest order (LS), the LAMB shift given by (19.16), are of order

$$\alpha \log \alpha (Z\alpha)^2 \,\mathrm{Ry} \sim \alpha \log \alpha \,(\mathrm{FS}).$$

Radiative corrections of the next order, i.e. of order α (LS) and $Z\alpha$ (LS) have also been calculated. For the levels with $n=2$ in hydrogen, for instance, (FS) is about 10^4 Mc, (LS) about 10^3 Mc and the higher order radiative corrections about 5 Mc.

α) Nuclear motion. In the nonrelativistic SCHRÖDINGER theory for a hydrogen-like atom the effect of the finite value M of the nuclear mass is accounted for exactly by replacing the electron's mass m by the reduced mass $\mathcal{M} = mM/(m+M)$ in all formulae evaluated for a fixed COULOMB potential (Sect. 5). For the energy of any atomic level this is achieved by replacing Ry_∞ by R_M, i.e. multiplying the energy for a fixed COULOMB potential by the factor

$$\frac{M}{M+m} = 1 - \frac{m}{M} + \left(\frac{m}{M}\right)^2 \ldots .$$

We consider next the effect of nuclear motion on the PAULI approximation to the energies of the fine structure components for a fixed principal quantum number n. This effect is discussed in Sect. 42 by an approximation method which is accurate up to (and including) energies of order (m/M) (FS). To this approximation it is shown that any nucleus can be treated as a nonrelativistic particle of mass M with a (phenomenological) magnetic moment μ. The correction terms involving m/M consist of the sum of one term involving μ (discussed in Sects. 20β and 22) and one independent of μ. This second term is quite independent of the internal structure of the nucleus. As shown in Sect. 42β, this term has the following two effects. 1. The PAULI approximation to the energy splitting of the fine structure components for any n (for a fixed nucleus) is multiplied by the factor $(1-m/M)$, i.e. the RYDBERG constant is again replaced by R_M (the reduced mass RYDBERG) in the PAULI approximation. 2. In addition, the energy of *all* fine structure components for fixed principal quantum number n are shifted by the *same* amount, given by (42.7). This shift is about -25 Mc for the hydrogen ground state (less for $n>1$), which is beyond the accuracy of optical spectroscopy, and does not contribute to the fine structure *splitting*. Correction terms of order $(m/M)^2$ (FS) have not been calculated yet, but should be extremely small ($\lesssim 0.01$ Mc).

We consider next the various correction terms to the energy of order

$$\alpha (m/M)\,(\mathrm{FS}) \sim (m/M)\,(\mathrm{LS}),$$

which have all been calculated. Some terms of this order come from the effect of nuclear motion on the quantum electrodynamic effects which lead to the LAMB shift, Eq. (19.16). The main part of this effect is due to a change of distance scale in the atomic wave functions which are used in the expectation value (19.16). The "atomic radius" is changed by a factor $(m/\mathcal{M})$. This can be shown[1] to result in a multiplicative factor of $(\mathcal{M}/m)^3 \approx (1-3m/M)$ to (19.16), at least for S-states[2]. An additional correction term stems from the fact that, in the logarithmic term in (19.16), K_0 is proportional to the reduced mass $\mathcal{M}$, whereas mc^2 refers to the real mass of the electron.

[1] E. E. SALPETER: Phys. Rev. **89**, 92 (1953).

[2] For P-states a term in (19.16), connected with the electron's anomalous magnetic moment, is multiplied by $(1-2m/M)$; see W. BARKER and F. GLOVER, Phys. Rev. **99**, 317 (1955).

Some additional corrections, also of order $\alpha(m/M)$ (FS), were calculated by SALPETER[1]. These corrections are first calculated for the electron-proton system, using the covariant two-body wave equation discussed in Sect. 42γ, under the assumption that the proton is a DIRAC particle. Complex nuclei are composed of protons and neutrons (each a DIRAC particle) interacting with each other. It is then shown that the proton calculations are also valid (to a good approximation, based on the fact that mc is smaller than the relative momenta of the neutrons and protons inside the nucleus) for complex nuclei. The main parts of these corrections, which are of order $\alpha \log \alpha (m/M)$ (FS), can also be obtained from conventional perturbation theory. One such term is essentially an addition to the operator used in Sect. 42 for the BREIT interaction between electron and proton, which corrects for the fact that in deriving this operator the energy denominator in (38.5) was replaced by kc or the expression (38.17) by unity. Another such term is connected with the exchange of *two* virtual photons between the electron and proton.

The terms of order $\alpha(m/M)$ (FS) have expectation values which depend on the quantum numbers l and j (as well as on n) and hence contribute to the fine structure splitting and LAMB shift. All terms of this order combined contribute -1.27 Mc to the energy difference $2\,{}^2S_{\frac{1}{2}} - 2\,{}^2P_{\frac{1}{2}}$ in hydrogen and half this amount in deuterium. Correction terms of order $\alpha^2(m/M)$ (FS) have not been calculated yet, but are expected to be less than ± 0.05 Mc for $n=2$ in hydrogen.

β) Nuclear structure. Complex nuclei, besides having a finite mass, are not point particles but show some structure. In particular they have a finite size (radii of the order of $A^{\frac{1}{3}} \times 10^{-13}$ cm, where A is the atomic mass number), an internal angular momentum or "spin" and a magnetic dipole moment and small electric quadrupole moment[2] associated with the spin.

The finite size of the nucleus affects the atomic energy levels in a very simple way. Inside the charge distribution of the nucleus its electrostatic potential deviates from (and is less than) a COULOMB potential of charge Z. Nuclear radii are much smaller than atomic radii and (if Z is not too large and nonrelativistic atomic wave functions are justified) the following approximate expression holds for the change ΔV of the energy of an atomic state.

shell model — see lecture March 17

$$\Delta V = \frac{2\pi Z e^2}{3} |u(0)|^2 \langle r^2 \rangle, \tag{20.2}$$

where $u(0)$ is the value of the atomic wave function at the origin and $\langle r^2\rangle$ is the mean squared radius of the nuclear charge distribution around its center of mass. In this approximation ΔV is zero for atomic states of non-zero l, whose wave function vanishes at the origin. For S-states, (20.2) gives a small upward shift of the energy. For the $2S$-state of deuterium[3], for instance, this shift is about $+0.73$ Mc. The ratio of ΔV to the binding energy of the atomic state (for $l=0$) is of the order of $\langle r^2\rangle/a_n^2$, where a_n is the "radius" of the atomic wave function. As Z (and hence the atomic weight of the nucleus) increases, $\langle r^2\rangle$ increases and a_n decreases. The effect of nuclear size thus increases with increasing Z. In fact, for very large Z the nonrelativistic approximation (20.2) is not very accurate and ΔV is appreciable not only for S-states but also for $P_{\frac{1}{2}}$-states, whose wave functions are reasonably large near the origin[4].

---

[1] E. E. SALPETER: Phys. Rev. **87**, 328 (1952). A small term in this paper, called ΔE_{cc}, should be doubled.

[2] No nuclei are known which have a finite electric dipole moment, see ref. [*16*], Chap. 2.

[3] E. E. SALPETER: Phys. Rev. **89**, 92 (1953).

[4] A. SCHAWLOW and C. TOWNES: Science, Lancaster, Pa. **115**, 284 (1952) and Phys. Rev. **100**, 1273 (1955).

Nuclei with non-zero "spin" usually have a non-zero magnetic moment parallel to its spin. The energy of the electron's interaction with this nuclear moment is quite large (compared with the other corrections discussed in this section) and leads to the hyperfine structure of each atomic fine structure component (discussed in Sect. 22). This hyperfine structure energy depends on the direction of the nuclear spin in a known manner and experimental results on the hyperfine structure components of a particular fine structure level can be analyzed to give the energy the level would have in the absence of hyperfine structure.

If we were to consider a nucleus as a Dirac particle with an anomalous magnetic moment of Pauli type [see (10.16)], this moment would contribute (besides the relatively large spin-dependent hyperfine structure) a small spin-*in*dependent shift in the atom's energy[1]. For ordinary hydrogen (with a single proton as nucleus) this shift would be $+0.02$ Mc for the $2S$-state and zero for states of $l \neq 0$. This term, however, is only of the same order of magnitude as other terms which depend on the detailed internal structure of a proton, which is not yet fully understood. For instance, although a proton is a single fundamental particle and does not have a "nuclear radius" in the strict sense, its interaction with the virtual meson field is likely to spread its charge over finite distances (but distances much smaller than the radius of any complex nucleus).

21. Fine structure and the Lamb shift. *α) Lowest order* Lamb *shift.* We now evaluate explicitly the expression (19.16) for the radiative correction (to lowest order) ΔE to the energy of a state (n, l, j) in a hydrogenlike atom. For an S-state $(n, 0, \frac{1}{2})$ we have

$$(e\,\Delta\varphi)_{nn} = -4\pi e^2 Z\left(\delta^{(3)}(\boldsymbol{r})\right)_{nn} = -4\pi e^2 Z\, u_{n0}^2(0) = -\frac{4Z^4}{n^3}\ \text{at. un.}, \tag{21.1}$$

where $u_{n0}(0)$ is the nonrelativistic Schrödinger wave function at the origin. The last term in (19.16) arises from the anomalous moment of the electron and corresponds to (12.13) with $g_1 = \alpha/2\pi$. To within the accuracy of the Pauli approximation this term is [see Sect. 12γ and (12.14)] simply $2g_1 = \alpha/\pi$ times the expression (13.13) for any value of the orbital quantum number l. Writing mc^2 as $2\,\text{Ry}/\alpha^2$ and using (21.1) and (13.13), expression (19.16) for S-states reduces to

$$\Delta E(n, 0) = \frac{8Z^4}{n^3}\,\frac{\alpha^3}{3\pi}\,\text{Ry}\left[2\log\frac{1}{Z\alpha} + \log\frac{Z^2\,\text{Ry}}{K_0(n, 0)} + \frac{19}{30}\right], \tag{21.2}$$

where K_0 is defined by (19.10).

For states with non-zero l, the last part of (19.16) is again α/π times (13.13). The nonrelativistic wave function at the origin, and hence $(\Delta\varphi)_{nn}$, vanishes for $l \neq 0$ and we would expect the first part of (19.16) to vanish. In fact this term is finite, although extremely small, since K_0, as defined by (19.10), diverges for $l \neq 0$. To remove this difficulty[2] one can modify the definition of K_0 for $l \neq 0$ by replacing the initial state in the sum on the left hand side of (19.10) by the S-state with the same principal quantum number. One then obtains, instead of (21.2),

$$\Delta E(n, l) = \frac{8Z^4}{n^3}\,\frac{\alpha^3}{3\pi}\,\text{Ry}\left[\log\frac{Z^2\,\text{Ry}}{K_0(n, l)} + \frac{3}{8}\,\frac{c_{lj}}{2l+1}\right], \tag{21.3}$$

where

$$c_{lj} = \begin{cases} (l+1)^{-1} & \text{for}\quad j = l + \frac{1}{2} \\ -l^{-1} & \text{for}\quad j = l - \frac{1}{2}. \end{cases}$$

[1] L. L. Foldy: Phys. Rev. **83**, 688 (1951).

[2] Bethe, Brown and Stehn: Phys. Rev. **77**, 370 (1950)

The numerical evaluation of the dimensionless ratio $K_0(n, l)/Z^2\,\mathrm{Ry}$ is discussed in Sect. 74γ. This ratio is independent of Z and varies rather slowly with n. For S-states, for instance, this ratio is about 19.8 for $n=1$, 15.7 for $n=4$, and not much smaller for $n=\infty$. For $l\neq 0$, this ratio is very close to unity for all n, e.g. for P-states it is about 0.97 for $n=2$ and 0.96 for $n=4$.

According to the DIRAC theory, the energy of any fine structure level for fixed n depends only on j, not l. In the PAULI approximation the energy is given by (17.2) and the only part depending on j is

$$\Delta W = -\frac{Z^4}{n^3}\frac{\alpha^2}{(j+\frac{1}{2})}\,\mathrm{Ry}. \tag{21.4}$$

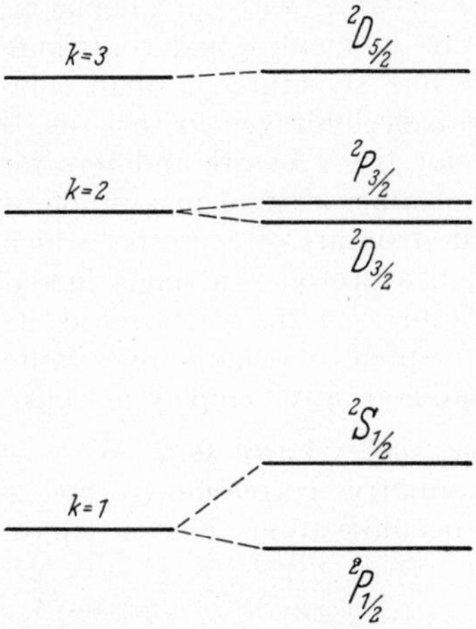

Fig. 12. Schematic energy level diagram for the states with $n=3$ in hydrogen. The levels on the left are according to the DIRAC theory without LAMB shift. The levels on the right show the level splitting due to radiative corrections (not accurately to scale, the actual $P_{\frac{3}{2}}-D_{\frac{3}{2}}$ splitting is much smaller than that on the diagram).

To this we now have to add the radiative correction ΔE, given by (21.2) or (21.3). Note that ΔW and ΔE have almost the same dependence on Z and on n [the logarithms in (21.2) and (21.3) vary slowly with Z and n]. A schematic picture of the energy level splitting is given in Fig. 12 for $n=3$.

For a fixed value of n, by far the largest radiative correction is the positive shift of the energy of the $S_{\frac{1}{2}}$-state, which is given by (21.2) and stems largely from the term in $\log\alpha$. This LAMB shift of the S-state is about 10% of the fine structure separation between the levels of $j=\frac{1}{2}$ and $\frac{3}{2}$ (for reasonably low Z and any n). For states with $l\neq 0$, the logarithmic term in (21.3) is extremely small. The last term in (21.3), which stems from the electron's anomalous moment, is sufficient to split the two levels of equal j (degenerate on the DIRAC theory), but the splitting is very small. The energy splitting of the two levels for any $j>\frac{1}{2}$ is only about 0.2% of the fine structure separation between the levels of j and $(j+1)$. Excited energy levels have a finite lifetime and hence a finite energy spread (natural line width). For $j=\frac{1}{2}$ this line width is always smaller than the LAMB shift, but for $j\geqq\frac{3}{2}$ it is larger than the energy splitting given by (21.3).

For the splitting of the $n=2$, $j=\frac{1}{2}$ levels very accurate microwave experiments are available and will be discussed below. But there is also (less accurate) confirmation for the level shift (21.2) of the S-states for various n from optical spectroscopy. In deuterium, for instance, the experimental shift[1] of the 1 S-state is $(0.26\pm 0.03)\ \mathrm{cm}^{-1}$ and of[2] the 3 S-state $(0.008\pm 0.003)\ \mathrm{cm}^{-1}$. The corresponding theoretical shifts from (21.2) are $0.271\ \mathrm{cm}^{-1}$ and $0.0103\ \mathrm{cm}^{-1}=309$ Mc/sec, respectively.

β) The LAMB *experiments.* Very accurate, careful and beautiful experimental work has been done by LAMB[3] and coworkers on the structure of the levels with $n=2$ in hydrogen, deuterium and singly ionized helium. This work is based on the fact that, even in hydrogen-like atoms, direct radiative (electric dipole) transitions are possible from any $n\,S_{\frac{1}{2}}$-state to both the $P_{\frac{1}{2}}$ and $P_{\frac{3}{2}}$-states with the *same* principal quantum number n. Since the energy differences are very

[1] G. HERZBERG: Proc. Roy. Soc. Lond., Ser. A **234**, 516 (1956).

[2] G. W. SERIES: Proc. Roy. Soc. Lond., Ser. A **208**, 277 (1951).

[3] For a description of the method see W. E. LAMB and R. C. RETHERFORD, Phys. Rev. **79**, 549 (1950); **81**, 222 (1951); **86**, 1014 (1951). A general review is given by W. E. LAMB, Rep. Progr. Phys. **14**, 19 (1951).

small, the probability for spontaneous transitions is negligibly small, but induced transitions can occur if a rotating (or oscillating) magnetic field of the appropriate frequency is applied to the atom (see Sect. 64γ). This frequency (of the order of 10^3 or 10^4 Mc/sec) can be measured very accurately and is simply the energy difference of the two levels divided by h. Now, the extremely accurate determinations of the RYDBERG by optical spectroscopy essentially measure a wave number which is (c/h) times the RYDBERG energy unit ($\frac{1}{2}$ a.u.), where c is the accurately known velocity of light. A measurement of the frequency of rotation in the LAMB experiment thus gives the energy separation of two levels with the *same* principal quantum number in terms of the RYDBERG (without requiring any knowledge of PLANCK's constant h).

In practice, the natural line width of the P-states and the hyperfine structure (for H and D) are very much larger than the error of measurement of the frequency of the inducing field. The line shape for each transitions is therefore measured very accurately and in great detail and compared with the theory of line shape and hyperfine structure[1]. The agreement is excellent and the energy separation of the S and P-states (as it would be in the absence of line width and hyperfine structure) can be inferred to within an error very much smaller than the line width.

The LAMB experiments can be most easily performed for the levels with $n=2$, for the following reason: The $2S$-state in hydrogen-like atoms is metastable and, in the absence of perturbations, has an extremely long lifetime compared with all other excited states (see Sect. 67α). An atomic beam apparatus can thus be designed, in which atoms in the beam in the $2S$-state can reach the detector, but atoms which initially were in other excited states (e.g. $2P_{\frac{1}{2}}$ or $2P_{\frac{3}{2}}$) make radiative transitions to the ground state long before reaching the detector. In turn, detectors can be devised which are sensitive to excited atoms in the $2S$-state, but not to atoms in the ground state. One can thus measure the depletion of a beam of $2S$-atoms, due to induced transitions to $2P_{\frac{1}{2}}$ or $2P_{\frac{3}{2}}$ in a rotating magnetic field, as a function of the applied frequency.

The experimental values for the $2S_{\frac{1}{2}}-2P_{\frac{1}{2}}$ separations are compared with the theoretical values for the LAMB shift in Sect. 21γ. But this experimental value, combined with the measurement of the $2S_{\frac{1}{2}}-2P_{\frac{3}{2}}$ separation, also gives a very accurate experimental value for the fine structure separation $2P_{\frac{1}{2}}-2P_{\frac{3}{2}}$. For deuterium[2] this separation F is (10971.59 ± 0.20) Mc/sec. The best theoretical expression for this separation is

$$F=\frac{c R_{\mathrm{D}}}{16}\alpha^2\left[1+\frac{5}{8}\alpha^2+\left(1-\frac{m}{M_{\mathrm{D}}}\right)\frac{\alpha}{\pi}-\frac{5.946}{\pi^2}\alpha^2\right], \tag{21.5}$$

where R_{D} is the "reduced mass RYDBERG" for deuterium and M_{D} is the deuteron's mass. The first two terms in (21.5) come from an expansion in powers of α of the DIRAC fine structure formula (17.1). The last two terms represent radiative corrections [cf. Eq. (21.3)], stemming from the anomalous magnetic moment of the electron (18.5). Terms of order α^5 Ry and $\alpha^4(m/M_{\mathrm{D}})$ Ry, effects of nuclear size, etc. have not yet been calculated. However, all these terms are expected to be very small (much smaller than for the $2S$-state) and introduce an error smaller than the present experimental one. The experimental value for F and (21.5) thus give a very accurate value for the fine structure constant,

$$\frac{1}{\alpha}=137.0371\pm0.0012, \tag{21.6}$$

[1] W. E. LAMB: Phys. Rev. **85**, 259 (1952).
[2] E. DAYHOFF, S. TRIEBWASSER and W. LAMB: Phys. Rev. **89**, 106 (1953).

if we use a value of

$$c = (299\,792.9 \pm 0.8)\ \text{km/sec} \tag{21.7}$$

for the velocity of light[1]. The value of (21.6) for α agrees well[1] with values obtained from other precision measurements.

γ) Comparison with theory[2]. We summarize now the various terms contributing to the theoretical value for the LAMB shift in hydrogen, i.e., the energy by which the $2S_{\frac{1}{2}}$-state lies higher than the $2P_{\frac{1}{2}}$. The main term, of order α^3 Ry, comes from (21.2) and (21.3) for the lowest order shift of the S- and P-states, respectively. Using the values (2.14), (21.6) and (21.7) for Ry (the RYDBERG for *infinite* nuclear mass), α and c we have the following value for the "LAMB constant" L,

$$L \equiv \frac{\alpha^3}{3\pi}\,\text{Ry}\,c = (135.641 \pm 0.004)\ \text{Mc/sec}. \tag{21.8}$$

The excitation energies K_0 in (21.2) and (21.3) have been evaluated very accurately[3] (see Sect. 74γ),

$$K_0(2,0) = 16.6398\,Z^2\,\text{Ry}, \qquad K_0(2,1) = 0.970430\,Z^2\,\text{Ry}.$$

Substituting into (21.2) and (21.3), one finds a value of $7.75703\,L$ for the LAMB shift to lowest order for $Z=1$ and a fixed nucleus, i.e.

$$S_\infty^{(1)} = (1052.17 \pm 0.04)\ \text{Mc/sec}.$$

As discussed in Sect. 18, the expression (21.2) or (21.3) is only the first term in an expansion in powers of $Z\alpha$ and of α. Numerically the largest of the higher terms in the expansion for the LAMB shift is the term of order $Z\alpha S_\infty^{(1)}$ (even for $Z=1$). This term[4] contributes $+7.14$ Mc/sec to the LAMB shift for hydrogen. All the various terms[5] of order $\alpha S_\infty^{(1)}$ have been calculated and together contribute (-0.94 ± 0.10) Mc/sec. The various corrections to the LAMB shift due to nuclear motion and structure have already been discussed in Sect. 20.

In Table 3 we compare the present theoretical values with the experimental[6] ones for H and D and those[7] for He^+. The probable errors quoted for the theoretical results do *not* include any allowance for higher order radiative corrections, which have not been calculated yet. The leading terms of these corrections are of order $\alpha^2 S_\infty^{(1)}$ for hydrogen and might be expected to be of order ± 0.10 Mc/sec or less, but the possibility of large numerical coefficients making these terms bigger cannot be ruled out. Table 3 shows that the experimental values for H and D (but, possibly, not for He^+) are about $\frac{1}{2}$ Mc/sec larger than the theoretical ones, a discrepancy of a few times the experimental error. It is not yet known whether this small discrepancy is due to some of the $\alpha^2 S_\infty^{(1)}$ terms or due to some other cause.

We thus see that the theoretical prediction for the energy splitting of the $2S_{\frac{1}{2}}$ and $2P_{\frac{1}{2}}$ levels in H and D is confirmed experimentally to an accuracy of about one part in 2000. The LAMB shift is thus an excellent confirmation of

[1] J. DuMOND and E. COHEN: This volume. — J. BEARDEN and J. THOMSEN: Atomic Constants. Baltimore: Johns Hopkins University 1955.

[2] E. E. SALPETER: Phys. Rev. **89**, 92 (1953). In this paper the notation used in this section is explained more fully.

[3] J. M. HARRIMAN: Phys. Rev. **101**, 594 (1956).

[4] M. BARANGER, H. BETHE and R. FEYNMAN: Phys. Rev. **92**, 482 (1953). — KARPLUS, KLEIN and SCHWINGER: Phys. Rev. **86**, 288 (1952).

[5] R. KARPLUS and N. KROLL: Phys. Rev. **77**, 536 (1950). — M. BARANGER, F. DYSON and E. SALPETER: Phys. Rev. **88**, 680 (1952). — BERSOHN, WENESER and KROLL: Phys. Rev. **91**, 1257 (1953).

[6] S. TRIEBWASSER, E. DAYHOFF and W. LAMB: Phys. Rev. **89**, 98 (1953).

[7] R. NOVICK, E. LIPWORTH and P. YERGIN: Phys. Rev. **100**, 1153 (1955).

Table 3. *The* LAMB *shift for hydrogen, deuterium and ionized helium (in Mc/sec).*

	H	D	He⁺
Theoretical	1057.13 ± 0.13	1058.47 ± 0.13	14043 ± 3
Experimental	1057.77 ± 0.10	1059.00 ± 0.10	14043 ± 13

present day quantum electrodynamics and of the relativistic theory of the electron. For instance, some time ago there was some doubt whether vacuum polarization effects should be included in quantum electrodynamic calculations. These effects contribute the term involving $-\frac{1}{5}$ to the expression (18.2) which gives a contribution of about -27 Mc/sec to the LAMB shift in H and D. The necessity of including this term is demonstrated by the excellent agreement in Table 3.

It should also be remembered that the LAMB shift itself is a very small fraction of the total binding energy of an electron in a $2S$ or $2P$-state and has been verified to an accuracy of better than 10^{-9} times this total binding energy: If, for instance, the COULOMB law Ze/r were modified by a multiplicative factor of form $(r/a_0)^\gamma$, a value for γ of more than about 10^{-9} would contribute to the $2S-2P$ splitting an amount larger than the present limit of error.

22. Hyperfine structure splitting. So far we have only considered electrons moving in a purely central electric field. In this case the energy of the atomic levels may depend on the absolute value of the total angular momentum j of the electrons, but *not* on its component in any direction. This degeneracy is removed not only by an external non-central field but also if the atomic nucleus has a magnetic moment. Many nuclei do, in fact, have non-zero magnetic moments which are roughly of order $e\hbar/M_p c$, where M_p is the proton mass. This is smaller than the magnetic moment of the electron by a factor of order one thousand. Consequently the level splitting due to the electron's interaction with the nuclear moment should be smaller than the ordinary fine structure splitting by a factor of the same order. We shall also find that this hyperfine structure splitting is largest if the distance between electron and nucleus is smallest.

α) Derivation of operators. We consider a hydrogen-like atom with a nucleus of charge $Z \ll 137$ and a magnetic moment $\boldsymbol{\mu}$. For such small values of Z one can consider the atom as nonrelativistic to lowest order, the ordinary fine structure as a perturbation and the hyperfine structure as an even smaller perturbation. In Sect. 42 we shall derive an approximate equation for a hydrogen-like atom which takes the motion and magnetic moment of the nucleus into account. The HAMILTONian Eq. (42.2), derived from the BREIT equation, contains a HAMILTONian which consists of three parts. The first part H_a is identical with the HAMILTONian of the PAULI equation (13.2) for an electron in a *fixed* COULOMB potential. The second part H_b only contributes a small level shift, which does not depend on the nuclear moment and is due merely to the nuclear recoil. The third part H_c, finally, takes account of the magnetic moment of the nucleus. We consider later the relation between the vector $\boldsymbol{\mu}$, which represents the nuclear magnetic moment, and the nuclear angular momentum. The part H_c in (42.2), which we consider as a small perturbation, reads[1]

$$H_c = -2\mu_0 \left[-\frac{8\pi}{3} (\boldsymbol{s}_1 \cdot \boldsymbol{\mu})\, \delta^{(3)}(\boldsymbol{r}) + \frac{1}{r^3} (\boldsymbol{s}_1 \cdot \boldsymbol{\mu} - 3 s_{1r} \mu_r) - \frac{1}{r^3} (\boldsymbol{k} \cdot \boldsymbol{\mu}) \right], \quad (22.1)$$

[1] In evaluating expectation values of H_c the following prescription must be used: In the expression (22.1) replace $1/r^3$ by zero for $r < \varepsilon$, evaluate all integrals, and *then* take the limit of ε tending to zero.

where $\mu_0 = e\hbar/2mc$ is the BOHR magneton (electron's magnetic moment), $\mathbf{s}_1 = \frac{1}{2}\sigma_1^P$ is the PAULI spin operator for the electron, s_{1r} the component of $\mathbf{s}_1$ in the direction $\boldsymbol{r}$, and $\boldsymbol{k}$ is the orbital angular momentum $(\boldsymbol{r}\times\boldsymbol{p})/\hbar$.

The expectation value of the operator H_c only gives the lowest order contribution to the hyperfine structure in an expansion in powers of α and of (m/M), where M is the nuclear mass. To calculate higher order terms one must start from the BREIT equation, as in Sect. 42, or some other relativistic theory for two interacting particles. The lowest order operator (22.1), however, can also be obtained in a semi-classical manner from the PAULI equation (12.11) for a single electron in a *fixed* external field, as follows.

We consider (12.11) for an electron in a fixed COULOMB potential plus a fixed external magnetic field, which we consider as weak. Neglecting terms quadratic in the vector potential $\boldsymbol{A}$, the interaction with the magnetic field is given by the perturbation HAMILTONian

$$H' = +2\mu_0\left[(\boldsymbol{A}\cdot\boldsymbol{p})\frac{1}{\hbar} + \mathbf{s}\cdot\mathcal{H}\right], \tag{22.2}$$

where $\mathbf{s}$ is the electron's spin operator (dropping the suffix 1) and $\mathcal{H} = \operatorname{curl}\boldsymbol{A}$ is the magnetic field. We now attribute to the nucleus a fixed classical magnetic dipole moment $\boldsymbol{\mu}$, which produces a magnetic field characterized by the vector potential

$$\left.\begin{aligned} \boldsymbol{A} &= \frac{\boldsymbol{\mu}\times\boldsymbol{r}}{r^3} = -\boldsymbol{\mu}\times\left(\operatorname{grad}\frac{1}{r}\right), \\ \mathcal{H} &= \operatorname{curl}\boldsymbol{A}. \end{aligned}\right\} \tag{22.3}$$

Substituting (22.3) into (22.2), using some simple vector identities and writing $\boldsymbol{k} = \boldsymbol{r}\times\boldsymbol{p}$ (using again units such that $\hbar = 1$) we get for $r \neq 0$ the same result as from (22.1),

$$H' = -\frac{2\mu_0}{r^3}\left[(\mathbf{s}\cdot\boldsymbol{\mu}) - 3 s_r \mu_r - \boldsymbol{k}\cdot\boldsymbol{\mu}\right]. \tag{22.4}$$

At $r = 0$, however, the operator $(\mathbf{s}\cdot\mathcal{H})$ has a strong singularity and care must be taken not to miss a part of the operator, which contains a delta function at the origin.

One simple way to isolate this delta-function singularity of $-2\mu_0\mathbf{s}\cdot\mathcal{H}$ is to consider the FOURIER transform of this expression, which is [using (22.3), (39.6) and some vector identities]

$$\frac{\mu_0}{\pi^2}\left\{\left[\frac{(\mathbf{s}\cdot\boldsymbol{q})(\boldsymbol{\mu}\cdot\boldsymbol{q})}{q^2} - \frac{1}{3}\mathbf{s}\cdot\boldsymbol{\mu}\right] - \frac{2}{3}\mathbf{s}\cdot\boldsymbol{\mu}\right\} \tag{22.5}$$

where $\boldsymbol{q}$ denotes the momentum change. We now use some arguments, to be given in Sect. 39, leading to (39.13): The expectation value of the term in square brackets in (22.5) is zero for any spherically symmetric wave function (S-state) and this term corresponds to the second term in round brackets in (22.1) with the prescription, explained in the footnote to (22.1), of excluding an infinitesimal sphere around the origin in position space. The last term in (22.5) corresponds to the first term in (22.1) and thus (22.2) plus (22.3) again leads[1] to (22.1).

---

[1] A more rigorous derivation of (22.1) could be obtained as follows: From the exact Eq. (16.13) an approximate integral equation for $\psi_+(\boldsymbol{p})$ could be derived which is more accurate than the PAULI equation in momentum space for an electron in an external field, Eq. (16.15). The integrand in this equation would differ appreciably from that of (16.15) only for q (called k in Sect. 16) and p of order $mc/\hbar$ or larger. The more accurate expression replacing (22.5) would be almost identical with (22.5) except that it decreases with increasing q for $q \gtrsim mc/\hbar$. In position space one would then get an operator almost identical with (22.1) except at very small distances, i.e. $1/r^3$ would be replaced by a function somewhat like $1/r^2(r+\varepsilon)$ and $\delta^{(3)}(\boldsymbol{r})$ by a function which is appreciable only for $r \lesssim \varepsilon$ and whose volume integral is unity, where ε is some length much smaller than one atomic radius.

For a different derivation of (22.1) see ref. [*10*], p. 385.

β) Expectation values. We evaluate next the expectation value of the operator H_c, Eq. (22.1), for a particular state of an electron in a central potential and interacting with the magnetic moment of the nucleus. We make use of the fact that the magnetic moment of the nucleus is much smaller than that of the electron, and, consequently, the hyperfine structure smaller than the fine structure. We use the PAULI approximation, so that $\boldsymbol{k}^2$ is a constant of the motion and l is a good quantum number. In the absence of H_c, $\boldsymbol{M}^2 = (\boldsymbol{k}+\boldsymbol{s})^2$ is also a constant of the motion and the spin-orbit coupling operator results in the dependence of the energy on the inner quantum number j (fine structure). Although the operator H_c does *not* commute with $\boldsymbol{M}^2$, $\boldsymbol{M}^2$ is still a constant of the motion to a good approximation since H_c is small compared with the spin-orbit coupling operator. On the other hand, M_z is *not* even approximately a constant of the motion, since the energy is exactly degenerate with respect to M_z in the absence of H_c and H_c does not commute with M_z.

The magnetic moment $\boldsymbol{\mu}$ of a nucleus is connected with its internal intrinsic angular momentum (or "spin") $\boldsymbol{i}$ by the relation

$$\boldsymbol{\mu} = +\mu_N g\, \boldsymbol{i} \tag{22.6}$$

where

$$\mu_N = \frac{|e|\hbar}{2M_p c} = \mu_0 \frac{m}{M_p} = \frac{\mu_0}{1836.1_3} \tag{22.7}$$

is the "nuclear magneton" (M_p is the proton mass). In (22.6), g is a dimensionless constant characteristic of a particular nucleus which is positive for some nuclei and negative for others. For each nucleus the quantum number I [$I(I+1)$ is the eigenvalue of $\boldsymbol{i}^2$] is fixed. The quantity gI is sometimes called the "nuclear moment" for short and lies between -3 and $+5$ for most nuclei[1]. For a proton, $I=\frac{1}{2}$ and gI would be unity if the proton were a pure DIRAC particle. The actual value of gI is about 2.8 for a proton (and about -1.9 for a neutron). If we call $\boldsymbol{f}=(\boldsymbol{i}+\boldsymbol{j})$ the total angular momentum operator for the whole atom, then f_z and $\boldsymbol{f}^2$ [with eigenvalue $f(f+1)$] are constants of the motion, as well as $\boldsymbol{s}^2$, $\boldsymbol{k}^2$, and $\boldsymbol{M}^2$.

We consider first a state with $l \neq 0$, whose wave function at the origin vanishes. The expectation value of the first term in (22.1) then vanishes. Using the relation (A.33) of the appendix, the expectation value of H_c then equals that of the operator

$$H_c' = \frac{2\mu_0}{r^3}\left[\frac{2k^2\, \boldsymbol{s}\cdot\boldsymbol{\mu} - 3(\boldsymbol{s}\cdot\boldsymbol{k})(\boldsymbol{\mu}\cdot\boldsymbol{k}) - 3(\boldsymbol{\mu}\cdot\boldsymbol{k})(\boldsymbol{s}\cdot\boldsymbol{k})}{(2l+3)(2l-1)} + \boldsymbol{k}\cdot\boldsymbol{\mu}\right].$$

For the expectation value over a state with fixed quantum numbers $s=\frac{1}{2}$, l and j, the operators $\boldsymbol{k}^2$ and $(\boldsymbol{s}\cdot\boldsymbol{k})$ are simply replaced by their eigenvalues $l(l+1)$ and $\frac{1}{2}X$, Eq. (13.5), respectively. For the remaining operators $(\boldsymbol{s}\cdot\boldsymbol{\mu})$ and $(\boldsymbol{k}\cdot\boldsymbol{\mu})$ we use the following relation [discussed in Sect. 46, see Eq. (46.3)]: For transitions between (or expectation values for) states of the *same* s, l and j, the operators $\boldsymbol{s}$ and $\boldsymbol{k}$ can be replaced by constant multiples of the operator $\boldsymbol{M}$,

$$\boldsymbol{s} \to \boldsymbol{M}\frac{\overline{(\boldsymbol{s}\cdot\boldsymbol{M})}}{\overline{\boldsymbol{M}^2}}, \qquad \boldsymbol{k} \to \boldsymbol{M}\frac{\overline{(\boldsymbol{k}\cdot\boldsymbol{M})}}{\overline{\boldsymbol{M}^2}}, \tag{22.8}$$

where the bars denote eigenvalues[2]. Using this relation, the fact that $s=\frac{1}{2}$ and $\boldsymbol{M}=\boldsymbol{k}+\boldsymbol{s}$, and explicit expressions for the eigenvalues of $(\boldsymbol{s}\cdot\boldsymbol{M})$, $(\boldsymbol{k}\cdot\boldsymbol{M})$,

[1] See ref. [*16*], Chap. 4.

[2] Classically speaking, $\boldsymbol{s}$ and $\boldsymbol{k}$ precess rapidly about the direction of $\boldsymbol{M}$. In turn, $\boldsymbol{M}$ precesses about the direction of $\boldsymbol{f}$, but much more slowly, and only the components of $\boldsymbol{s}$ and $\boldsymbol{k}$ parallel to $\boldsymbol{M}$ are important.

etc., one finds that the expectation value of H_c equals that of

$$H'_c = +2\mu_0 \frac{l(l+1)}{j(j+1)} \boldsymbol{\mu}\cdot\boldsymbol{M}\,\overline{\frac{1}{r^3}}\,. \qquad (22.9\text{a})$$

Using (22.6) and the fact that $\boldsymbol{f}=\boldsymbol{i}+\boldsymbol{M}$, we finally get for this expectation value

$$E_c = \mu_0\mu_N g\frac{l(l+1)}{j(j+1)}[f(f+1)-I(I+1)-j(j+1)]\overline{\frac{1}{r^3}}\,. \qquad (22.9)$$

For an S-state, the expression (22.9) vanishes, since l is zero and the expectation value of $1/r^3$ is to be evaluated by excluding a small sphere around the origin, which gives a finite (although large) result. The first term in (22.1), however, gives a non-vanishing contribution. Its expectation value is[1] [using Eq. (22.6)]

$$E_{c0} = \tfrac{4}{3}\mu_0\mu_N g\,\boldsymbol{i}\cdot\boldsymbol{s}\,R^2_{n0}(0)\,, \qquad (22.10)$$

where $R_{n0}(0)$ is the normalized radial wave function at the origin. Since $l=0$, $j=s=\frac{1}{2}$ and the only possible values of f are $I+\frac{1}{2}$ and $I-\frac{1}{2}$. Thus

$$2\boldsymbol{i}\cdot\boldsymbol{s} = f(f+1)-I(I+1)-s(s+1) = \begin{cases} I & \text{for } f=I+\frac{1}{2}, \\ -(I+1) & \text{for } f=I-\frac{1}{2}. \end{cases} \qquad (22.11)$$

The expressions (22.9) for $l\neq 0$ and (22.10) with (22.11) for $l=0$ hold for single-electron atoms with any central atomic potential. For the special case of hydrogen-like atoms (COULOMB potential) we have the expression (5.12) for $\overline{r^{-3}}$ and [see Eq. (3.46)]

$$R^2_{n0}(0) = \frac{4Z^3}{n^3}\ \text{at. un.}$$

In this case *both* (22.9) and (22.10) reduce to the following expression for any l (with $\mu_0=\frac{1}{2}\alpha$ and Ry $=\frac{1}{2}$ in atomic units),

$$E_c = \frac{Z^3\alpha^2 g}{n^3}\,\frac{m}{M_p}\,\frac{f(f+1)-I(I+1)-j(j+1)}{j(j+1)(2l+1)}\,\text{Ry}\,. \qquad (22.12)$$

A fine structure level with fixed l and j is thus split further into hyperfine structure components with the possible values of f being $(j+I)$, $(j+I-1)$, ..., $|j-I|$. The multiplicity of such a level is the smaller of the two numbers $(2j+1)$ and $(2I+1)$. From (22.12) the energy separation between the two outermost components ($f=j+I$ and $|j-I|$) is

$$\Delta E = \frac{m}{M_p}\,\frac{4Z^3\alpha^2 g}{n^3(2l+1)(j+1)}\,\text{Ry}\begin{cases} I+\frac{1}{2} & \text{if } j \gtrless I, \\ \frac{I(j+\frac{1}{2})}{j} & \text{if } j \lesseqgtr I. \end{cases} \qquad (22.13)$$

For a given atom the hyperfine splitting ΔE decreases very rapidly with increasing n and fairly rapidly with increasing l and j. For ordinary hydrogen, for instance, ($Z=1$, $I=\frac{1}{2}$, $g\approx 5.56$) we have

	$1S_{\frac{1}{2}}$	$2S_{\frac{1}{2}}$	$2P_{\frac{1}{2}}$	$2P_{\frac{3}{2}}$
$\frac{\Delta E}{1420\ \text{Mc/sec}}$	1	$\frac{1}{8}$	$\frac{1}{24}$	$\frac{1}{60}$

A schematic diagram of the level splitting for $n=2$ for ordinary hydrogen and for deuterium ($Z=1$, $I=1$, $g\approx 0.86$) is given in Fig. 13.

[1] This expression was first derived by E. FERMI, Z. Physik **60**, 320 (1930).

The expression (22.13) and the hyperfine splitting, as observed by optical spectroscopy, can be used to determine the spin I and magnetic moment of the nucleus (gI): The maximum multiplicity of levels with large j gives $(2I+1)$ and the amount of splitting gives the factor g. Nuclear moments of many atoms have been measured in this manner[1] [using a generalization of Eq. (22.13) for complex atoms], but with rather poor accuracy since the hyperfine splittings are very small for optical spectroscopy. More recently, accurate microwave techniques have been developed for investigating hyperfine structure. For excited atomic states accurate analyses of experiments are hampered somewhat by the fact that the natural line width of a level is usually not much less than the hyperfine splitting, but very accurate comparison of theory and experiment is possible for the ground states of hydrogen-like atoms.

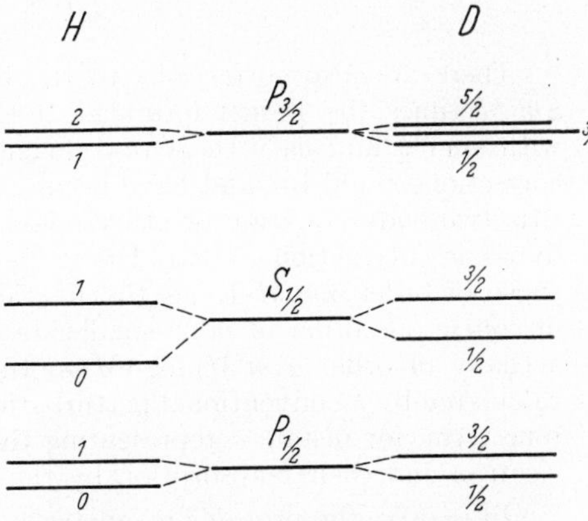

Fig. 13. Schematic energy level diagram for the hyperfine structure splitting of the states with $n=2$ in hydrogen (H) and deuterium (D). In the middle column are the levels without hyperfine structure. The number labeling each line is the value of the quantum number f.

γ) Higher order corrections for the ground state. For the ground state ($1\,S_{\frac{1}{2}}$) of hydrogen (with a proton of "spin" $\frac{1}{2}$ as nucleus), the simple FERMI formula (20.21) leads to the following expression [see (22.13)] for the hyperfine structure splitting

$$\Delta E = \frac{16}{3}\alpha^2\left(\frac{g_P\mu_N}{2\mu_0}\right)\text{Ry}, \tag{22.14}$$

where g_P is the g-factor for a proton in (22.6). For comparison with very accurate experiments we discuss various theoretical corrections to this formula.

We first consider the proton as a fixed structureless point charge with a given magnetic moment. The FERMI formula (22.14) was derived from the PAULI approximation to the DIRAC theory. From a more accurate treatment of the relativistic DIRAC theory (but *without* radiative corrections) BREIT[2] derived a small correction to (22.14) in the form of a multiplying factor $(1+\frac{3}{2}\alpha^2)$. However, much larger effects[3] come from radiative corrections, largely from the electron's anomalous magnetic moment g_s [discussed in Sect. 18β, Eq. (18.5) and in Sect. 49]. Besides the effect of this anomalous moment, other radiative corrections of relative order α^2, specific to hyperfine structure in a bound S-state, have also been calculated[4].

The result for the frequency $\nu_\infty = \Delta E/h$, assuming a fixed structureless proton, is

$$\left.\begin{aligned} \nu_\infty &= \frac{16}{3}\alpha^2\left(\frac{g_P\mu_N}{2\mu_0}\right)c\,R_\infty\left(1+\frac{3}{2}\alpha^2\right)\left[\frac{g_s}{2}+\alpha^2\left(\frac{5}{2}-\log 2\right)\right],\\ \frac{g_s}{2} &= 1+\frac{\alpha}{2\pi}-\frac{2.973}{\pi^2}\alpha^2, \end{aligned}\right\} \tag{22.15}$$

where R_∞ is the "RYDBERG for infinite mass" in wave numbers.

---

[1] S. TOLANSKI: Fine Structure In Line Spectra. London: Methuen & Co. 1935.

[2] G. BREIT: Phys. Rev. **35**, 1447 (1930).

[3] In fact, the anomalous magnetic moment of the electron was first inferred from a discrepancy between (22.14) and experiment. G. BREIT: Phys. Rev. **72**, 984 (1947).

[4] R. KARPLUS and A. KLEIN: Phys. Rev. **85**, 972 (1952). — N. M. KROLL and F. POLLOCK: Phys. Rev. **86**, 876 (1952).

We consider next the effect of nuclear motion and structure on hyperfine structure in the ground state. The largest and simplest of these effects depends only on the mass, but on no structural details, of the nucleus: The FERMI formula (22.10) is proportional to $R_{n0}^2(0)$, where $R_{n0}(r)$ is the normalized nonrelativistic radial atomic wave function. If the nucleus has a finite mass M, the distance scale of the wave function is altered by a factor $m/\mathcal{M}$, where $\mathcal{M}=mM/(m+M)$ is the reduced mass (see Sect. 5). Now the square of the normalized wave function is proportional to the minus third power of this scale factor. Thus $R_{n0}^2(0)$ and hence the FERMI formula (for a fixed nucleus) have to be multiplied[1] by a factor

$$\left(\frac{\mathcal{M}}{m}\right)^3 \approx 1 - 3\,\frac{m}{M}\,. \tag{22.16}$$

There are also corrections to the hyperfine structure of hydrogen of order $\alpha m/M$ times the FERMI formula. If the proton were simply a DIRAC particle with spin $\frac{1}{2}$ and *only* the DIRAC magnetic moment [$g=2$ in Eq. (22.6)], these corrections could be (and have been) evaluated unambiguously[2] using a relativistic two-body equation or other relativistic treatments of the quantum electrodynamic interaction of two DIRAC particles. These corrections are similar to those of order $\alpha m/M$ times the fine structure, discussed in Sect. 20α, but are of course one order of m/M smaller in absolute value. Some of these terms are actually of order $\alpha(m/M)\log(M/m)$ times the FERMI formula and can also be calculated by a conventional perturbation treatment of quantum electrodynamics (one term, for instance, representing the emission of two virtual photons by the electron and their reabsorption by the magnetic moment of the nucleus).

In reality, the proton's magnetic moment differs appreciably from the DIRAC value ($g=5.6$ instead of 2) although its spin is $\frac{1}{2}$. If the "extra" or anomalous moment $(g_P-2)\,\mu_N$ is treated as a point dipole moment of the PAULI type [see Eq. (10.16)], the corrections of relative order $\alpha m/M$ can again be calculated, in principle. In practice, in some of the terms referring to the PAULI moment, integrals over the momentum of a virtual photon diverge logarithmically at the high momentum side (see also end of Sect. 10γ). This divergence is due to the fact that a *point* magnetic moment was assumed. In reality, the proton's interaction with its virtual meson cloud, which is responsible for the proton's anomalous magnetic moment, also contributes a spatial spread and structure to this moment. If a consistent meson theory were available the equivalent integrals over photon momentum would presumably have convergence factors in them, but at the moment a completely unambiguous separation of correction terms due to nuclear motion and to nuclear structure is impossible. If, in the expressions of ARNOWITT, NEWCOMB and SALPETER, we simply omit all integrals proportional to $\int_{Mc}^{\infty} dp/p$ then the total nuclear motion corrections are only -0.2×10^{-5} times the FERMI formula for the hydrogen ground state. This very small number is due to some fortuitous cancellation; the corresponding number for individual terms is of relative order $\alpha(m/M)\log(M/m)=3.0\times10^{-5}$.

The effects of the internal structure of a proton cannot be calculated quantitatively at present, but presumably would contribute to the hyperfine structure (besides cancelling the divergent integrals mentioned above) a finite amount, say δ times the FERMI formula. On a naive picture of such structure effects, the

[1] G. BREIT and R. MEYEROTT: Phys. Rev. **72**, 1023 (1947).

[2] R. ARNOWITT: Phys. Rev. **92**, 1002 (1953). — W. NEWCOMB and E. SALPETER: Phys. Rev. **97**, 1146 (1955).

interaction of the proton's moment with a virtual photon of momentum k is modified if k is larger than some value K, which may lie between $m_\pi c$ and $M_p c$, where $m_\pi \approx 275\, m$ and $M_p = 1836\, m$ are the masses of a π-meson and a proton. Such effects would change the hyperfine structure by a term of relative order $\alpha(mc/K)$. If we simply omit all contributions from photon momenta $k > K$, then the structure correction δ is -5.6×10^{-5} and -0.7×10^{-5}, respectively, for $K = m_\pi c$ and $M_p c$. However, our present knowledge of meson theory is insufficient even to predict the *sign* of the correct value of δ.

Collecting all the correction terms, the theoretical expression for the frequency $\nu_H = \Delta E/h$ (for the hyperfine splitting of the hydrogen ground state) can be written in the form

$$\frac{\nu_H}{c R_\infty} = \frac{16}{3}\alpha^2 \left(\frac{M_p}{M_p + m}\right)^3 \left(\frac{g_p \mu_N}{g_s \mu_0}\right) \frac{g_s}{2} \left[\frac{g_s}{2} + \alpha^2 (4 - \log 2) - 0.2\times 10^{-5} + \delta\right], \quad (22.17)$$

where g_s is the expression defined in (22.15). Experimentally this frequency ν_H has been measured very accurately and directly by atomic beam and by microwave resonance absorption techniques, by which direct magnetic dipole transitions are induced between the two hyperfine structure components of the hydrogen ground state (see Sect. 49α). The experimental value[1] is

$$\nu_H = (1420.4057 \pm 0.0001)\ \text{Mc/sec}. \quad (22.18)$$

The ratio $(g_p \mu_N / g_s \mu_0)$ in (22.17) is simply the ratio of the magnetic moments of the proton and electron. This ratio has also been measured very accurately by microwave techniques (see Sect. 49γ) and is[2]

$$\frac{g_s \mu_0}{g_p \mu_N} = 658.2293 \pm 0.0006. \quad (22.19)$$

Using this value, the expression (21.7) for c and the accurately known value for R_∞, the theoretical and experimental expressions (22.17) and (22.18) give a relation between the fine structure constant α and the nuclear structure correction δ,

$$\frac{1}{\alpha} = 137.0368 \left(1 + \frac{1}{2}\delta \pm 2\times 10^{-6}\right). \quad (22.20)$$

The good agreement between (21.6) and (22.20) indicate that δ is rather small[3].

Another quantity of interest is the ratio of the hyperfine structure splitting in the ground states of ordinary hydrogen and of deuterium. The nucleus of deuterium, the deuteron, consists of a proton and neutron, rather loosely bound, with their spins "parallel" so that the "spin" I of the deuteron is unity. The g-factor in (22.6) for the deuteron is accurately known and is about 0.86 (compared with 2×2.79 for the proton and -2×1.91 for the neutron). The theoretical expression for ν_D is similar to (22.17) and radiative corrections drop out in the

[1] A. Prodell and P. Kusch: Phys. Rev. **88**, 184 (1952) and **100**, 1183 (1955). — J. Witke and R. Dicke: Phys. Rev. **96**, 530 (1954).

[2] S. Koenig, A. Prodell and P. Kusch: Phys. Rev. **88**, 191 (1952). — R. Beringer and M. Heald: Phys. Rev. **95**, 1474 (1954).

[3] The internal structure of the proton also contributes (unknown) corrections to the fine structure separation energy of the same *absolute* order of magnitude as to hyperfine structure. But, since the fine structure itself is very much larger than hyperfine structure, these corrections have a negligible effect on (21.6), but an appreciable one on (22.20). On the other hand, the purely experimental errors are larger in the experiments leading to (21.6) than in those leading to (22.20).

ratio ν_D/ν_H. Theoretically this ratio is

$$\frac{\nu_D}{\nu_H} = \frac{3}{4}\left(\frac{\mathcal{M}_D}{\mathcal{M}_H}\right)^3 \frac{2g_D}{g_p}(1+\Delta), \tag{22.21}$$

where $\mathcal{M}$ is the reduced mass and Δ is the effect of nuclear structure plus "relativistic recoil" corrections of order $\alpha m/M$. The loose structure of the deuteron, as built up from a proton and neutron, is reasonably well understood and contributes a rather large amount[1] to Δ. The $\alpha m/M$-corrections can be calculated[2] with similar limitations as for hydrogen. The present theoretical value for Δ is about 28×10^{-5}, compared with an experimental value of $(17.0\pm 0.1)\times 10^{-5}$. The poor agreement may be due to the rather large uncertainties in the calculation for deuterium.

23. The fine structure of positronium[3]. In Sect. 15γ we have discussed briefly the positron, the electron's antiparticle with the same mass m and spin $\frac{1}{2}$ as the electron, but equal and opposite charge. Since the electron and positron have opposite charge, a bound system can be formed which contains only one electron and one positron. This system, called positronium, is thus a hydrogen-like atom in which the positron takes the place of the nucleus. Experimentally positronium can be formed by radiative capture (recombination, see Sect. 75), if positrons are slowed down in a gas containing hydrogen.

Positronium differs radically from other hydrogen-like atoms in two respects: 1. Instead of having a nucleus much heavier than the electron, the two particles forming the "atom" have *equal* masses. The reduced mass of the system, $\mathcal{M} = m_1 m_2/(m_1+m_2)$ is thus $\frac{1}{2}m$, instead of being close to m. In nonrelativistic atomic theory this merely results in energy levels of exactly half the energy of levels in a hydrogen-like atom with $Z=1$ and a fixed nucleus, as well as a doubling of the distance scale in all wave functions (see Sect. 5). The equality of the two masses has a much more profound effect on the fine and hyperfine structure of positronium, which will be discussed below.

2. According to the DIRAC pair theory, an electron and a positron can annihilate each other, in which case the total rest mass energy, $2mc^2$, of the positronium atom is converted into photons. For states with non-zero orbital quantum number l the wave function at the origin is zero in nonrelativistic approximation, so that the electron and positron never overlap. In such states the probability for annihilation is very small and ordinary radiative transitions to lower atomic states are more probable. In S-states, however, the wave function at the origin is finite and the probability for annihilation may be greater than that for radiative transitions. Annihilation can also take place from the ground state of positronium, from which spontaneous radiative transitions are impossible.

From the requirement of conservation of energy and momentum, at least two photons must be produced when an electron-positron pair annihilates. For S-states of positronium in which the spins $\mathbf{s}_1$ and $\mathbf{s}_2$ of the two particles are "antiparallel" (singlet states), two-quantum annihilations are possible. The probability for such processes is of order α^3 atomic units of frequency. For S-states with parallel spin (triplet states) some general symmetry arguments show that two-quantum annihilations are forbidden. Thus triplet states annihilate mainly with

---

[1] A. BOHR: Phys. Rev. **73**, 1109 (1948). — F. E. LOW: Phys. Rev. **77**, 361 (1950). — F. LOW and E. SALPETER: Phys. Rev. **83**, 478 (1951).

[2] C. GREIFINGER: Ph. D. Thesis, Cornell 1954.

[3] For a more detailed account and a bibliography see a review article by S. DEBENEDETTI and H. C. CORBEN, Ann. Rev. Nuc. Sci. **4**, 191 (1954). Cf. also L. SIMONS in Vol. XXXIV of this Encyclopedia.

the emission of three photons with a probability of order α^4 atomic units of frequency. These probabilities can be calculated explicitly[1], using DIRAC pair theory and quantum electrodynamics. The mean lifetimes for annihilation of a singlet and a triplet S-state of positronium are

$$\tau_{\text{sing}} = 1.25 \times 10^{-10}\, n^3 \,\text{sec}, \qquad \tau_{\text{trip}} = 1.4 \times 10^{-7}\, n^3 \,\text{sec}. \tag{23.1}$$

α) The PAULI *approximation.* We consider now relativistic corrections to the energy levels of the positronium atom to the same accuracy as the PAULI approximation for hydrogen, i.e. to order α^2 Ry. In hydrogen the proton's mass is much larger, and its magnetic moment much smaller, than that of the electron. Thus the electron's spin-orbit coupling is much larger than the magnetic interaction between the spins of electron and nucleus and the fine structure much larger than the hyperfine structure. In positronium, however, the magnetic moments of the particles are equal (and opposite) and the hyperfine structure is of the *same* order as the fine structure, i.e. of order α^2 Ry.

We first omit any effects of the possibility of virtual pair annihilation on the energy levels. To the required accuracy (α^2 Ry) we can proceed from an approximately relativistic Eq. (42.1) for two DIRAC particles interacting with each other, to be derived in Sect. 42. In this approximate equation the wave function contains one PAULI spinor each for the electron and positron, on which the respective spin operators $\boldsymbol{s}_1$ and $\boldsymbol{s}_2$ operate. In this equation we merely substitute $m_1 = m_2 = m$,

$$e_1 = -\,e_2 = e \quad \text{and} \quad \mu_1 = -\,\mu_2 = \mu_0 .$$

The HAMILTONian H of this wave equation consists of the sum of six terms. Each term, and hence H, commutes with the operator $\boldsymbol{k}^2$, where $\boldsymbol{k}$ is the orbital angular momentum, and l is thus a good quantum number. The first term of the HAMILTONian, $H_0 = p^2/m - e^2/r$, is simply the nonrelativistic HAMILTONian for a fixed COULOMB potential and a reduced mass of $\frac{1}{2}m$. The other terms H_1 to H_5 are all smaller than H_0 by two powers of α and will be treated by first order perturbation theory. The terms H_2 and H_4 do not contain any spin-operators and their expectation values over a nonrelativistic eigenfunction of M_0 can be evaluated and depend only on the principal and orbital quantum numbers n and l.

The operator H_3 can be written in the form

$$H_4 = 3\,\frac{\mu_0\, e}{m\, c}\,\frac{\hbar}{r^3}\,\boldsymbol{k}\cdot\boldsymbol{S}, \quad \boldsymbol{S} = \boldsymbol{s}_1 + \boldsymbol{s}_2, \tag{23.2}$$

where $\boldsymbol{S}$ is the operator for the total spin of the atom. We are only interested in the expectation values of the operators H_1 to H_5 over wave functions for which l is a good quantum number. For this purpose we can replace H_5 by another operator H_5', using the relation (A.33) of the appendix. Using the relation (40.8), to be derived in Sect. 40, this operator can be further simplified to read

$$\left.\begin{aligned} H_5' &= 4\mu_0^2\Big\{\frac{8\pi}{3}\,\boldsymbol{s}_1\cdot\boldsymbol{s}_2\,\delta^{(3)}(\boldsymbol{r}) + \\ &+ \frac{1}{r^3(2l+3)(2l-1)}\Big[\Big(2\boldsymbol{s}_1\cdot\boldsymbol{s}_2+\frac{3}{2}\Big)\boldsymbol{k}^2 - \frac{3}{2}\,\boldsymbol{S}\cdot\boldsymbol{k} - \frac{3}{2}\,(\boldsymbol{S}\cdot\boldsymbol{k})^2\Big]\Big\}, \end{aligned}\right\} \tag{23.3}$$

where $1/r^3$ is again to be replaced by zero for $r < \varepsilon$ (and $\varepsilon \to 0$ after evaluating expectation values).

---

[1] A. ORE and J. POWELL: Phys. Rev. **75**, 1696, 1963 (1953).

The constants of the motion for the positronium atom are thus similar to those of the helium atom, discussed in Sect. 40: Since $\mathbf{s}_1^2$ and $\mathbf{s}_2^2$ are just numbers ($\frac{1}{2}\times\frac{3}{2}$ each), the spin-spin interaction operator $\mathbf{s}_1\cdot\mathbf{s}_2$ commutes with $\boldsymbol{S}^2$. Since any component of $\boldsymbol{S}$ also commutes with $\boldsymbol{S}^2$, H_3 and H_5 also commute with $\boldsymbol{S}^2$, which is then a constant of the motion. The possible eigenvalues of $\boldsymbol{S}^2$ are $S(S+1)$ with either $S=0$ (singlet state) or $S=1$ (triplet state). Let us call $\boldsymbol{M}=(\boldsymbol{k}+\boldsymbol{S})$ the total angular momentum operator. Then both M_z and $\boldsymbol{M}^2$ (but *not* S_z or k_z) commute with H_3 and H_5. The eigenvalues of $\boldsymbol{M}^2$ are $J(J+1)$ with $J=|l-S)|$, $|l-S|+1, \ldots, l+S$ and J is a good quantum number. The expectation values of H_3 and H_5 will depend on the quantum numbers S and J, as well as on n and l.

For an S-state, $l=0$ and hence S equals J and is either zero or one, and the eigenvalue of $\mathbf{s}_1\cdot\mathbf{s}_2$ is $-\frac{3}{4}$ or $+\frac{1}{4}$, respectively. With $\overline{\boldsymbol{k}^2}=\overline{\boldsymbol{k}}=l=0$, the expectation value of H_3 and of the term involving $1/r^3$ in H_5' is zero. From the δ-function term in (23.3) we then get for the expectation value W of H_3+H_5',

$$W=\frac{8}{3}\mu_0^2\,\mathbf{s}_1\cdot\mathbf{s}_2\,R_{n0}^2(0)=\frac{\alpha^2}{6n^3}\,\mathrm{Ry}\left\{\begin{array}{rl}-3 & \text{for}\quad S=0\\ 1 & \text{for}\quad S=1,\end{array}\right\} \tag{23.4}$$

where $R_{n0}(r)$ is the normalized nonrelativistic radial wave function (for reduced mass $\frac{1}{2}m$). The expectation values of H_3 and H_5' can also be evaluated for states with $l\neq 0$, following the procedures given in Sect. 40.

We have to consider next a term H_{pair} to be added to the HAMILTONian, which has no analogue in the theory of other hydrogen-like atoms, nor of helium. This term, specific to positronium (and DIRAC pair theory coupled with quantum electrodynamics), arises from the possibility of *virtual* pair annihilation. One finds a non-zero matrix element for a transition (which does *not* necessarily conserve energy) in which an electron-positron pair of total momentum $\boldsymbol{P}$ is converted into a *single* photon of the same momentum (or vice versa), if the pair is in a triplet state ($S=1$). Using second order perturbation theory one gets an additional matrix element for the scattering of an electron from a positron: In the first step the initial pair is converted into a virtual photon and this photon is then converted into another pair (with the same total, but not the same relative, momentum). The energy denominator in this matrix element is of order $2mc^2$ and if the kinetic energies are all small compared with mc^2 the additional matrix element for a real scattering between electron and positron with momentum transfer $\boldsymbol{q}$ is almost independent of $\boldsymbol{q}$ and is of order $e^2/(mc)^2$, compared with e^2/q^2 for scattering by a COULOMB potential. The FOURIER transform of this scattering matrix element corresponds to a spatial interaction potential H_{pair}. To lowest order in α one finds

$$H_{\text{pair}}=2\pi\left(\frac{e\hbar}{mc}\right)^2\delta_{S1}\,\delta^{(3)}(\boldsymbol{r}),\qquad \overline{H}_{\text{pair}}=\frac{\alpha^2}{2n^3}\,\mathrm{Ry}\,\delta_{S1}\,\delta_{l0}, \tag{23.5}$$

where $\overline{H}$ is the expectation value for a positronium state with quantum numbers n, l, S and J.

The expectation value $\overline{H}_{\text{pair}}$, which is non-zero only for triplet S-states ($l=0$, $S=J=1$), has to be added to the expectation values of H_1 to H_5, defined in (42.1). The total energy separation between the triplet and singlet S-states with the same value of n is, from (23.4) and (23.5),

$$\Delta W=\frac{7}{6}\frac{\alpha^2}{n^3}\,\mathrm{Ry}=\frac{1}{n^3}\,2.044\times 10^5\ \mathrm{Mc/sec}. \tag{23.6}$$

For a positronium state with arbitrary n, l, S and J the deviation (to order α^2 Ry) from the nonrelativistic value $-\mathrm{Ry}/2n^2$ is[1]

$$\left.\begin{aligned} W_{nlSJ} &= \left[\frac{11}{32n^4} + \left(\varepsilon_{lSJ} - \frac{1}{2l+1}\right)\frac{1}{n^3}\right]\alpha^2\,\mathrm{Ry};\\ \varepsilon_{l,S=0,J} = 0,\quad \varepsilon_{l,S=1,J} &= \frac{7}{6}\delta_{l0} + \frac{1-\delta_{l0}}{2(2l+1)}\begin{cases} \dfrac{3l+4}{(l+1)(2l+3)} & \text{if } J=l+1\\ -\dfrac{1}{l(l+1)} & \text{if } J=l\\ -\dfrac{3l-1}{l(2l-1)} & \text{if } J=l-1.\end{cases}\end{aligned}\right\}\quad (23.7)$$

The relativistic splitting of the energy level for any value of n, given by (23.7), is different from that either of hydrogen or helium. Unlike hydrogen, no degeneracy with respect to J remains to order α^2 Ry. The "good quantum numbers" are the same as for helium, but in *non*relativistic approximation the l- and S-degeneracy is not yet removed. A picture of the level splitting for $n=2$ is given in Fig. 14 (to be compared with that of H in Fig. 13). The level splitting of excited states in positronium has not yet been investigated experimentally, but we discuss very accurate experiments for the ground state below.

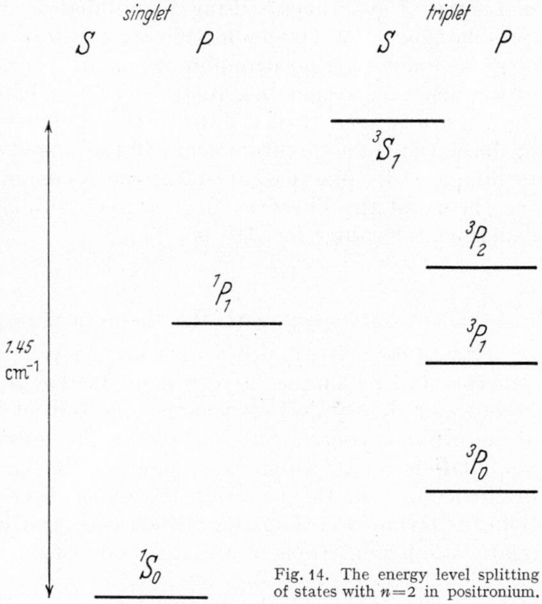

Fig. 14. The energy level splitting of states with $n=2$ in positronium.

β) The ground state. The ground state of positronium ($n=1, l=0$) is split into a singlet ($S=0$) and a triplet ($S=1$) state. The splitting energy ΔW to lowest order (α^2 Ry) is given by (23.6), but there are a number of radiative correction terms of order α^3 Ry. In addition to the (lowest order) LAMB shift and vacuum polarization terms (see Sect. 18), there are some additional terms of order α^3 Ry, which are either absent in hydrogen or contribute corrections of smaller order there. Some of these terms, for instance those representing the interchange of *two* virtual photons between electron and positron, are equivalent to the correction to hyperfine structure in hydrogen of order $\alpha^3(m/M)^2$ Ry. Other terms are specific to positronium, for instance one which represents the virtual annihilation of the pair with the emission of *two* virtual photons (followed by the creation of another pair). This particular term is present only in the singlet state. Most of these terms of order α^3 Ry cannot be calculated from the BREIT equation, but have all been evaluated using a more fully relativistic treatment of the two-body problem.

[1] All terms of order α^2 Ry were first calculated by J. PIRENNE, Arch. Sci. phys. nat. **29**, 121, 207, 265 (1947); V. BERESTETSKI and L. LANDAU, J. exp. theor. Phys. USSR. **19**, 673, 1130 (1949). Some errors in these papers were corrected by R. A. FERRELL, Phys. Rev. **84**, 858 (1951).

The total theoretical result[1] for these corrections of order α^3 Ry to the hyperfine splitting ΔW of the positronium ground state is

$$\Delta W^{(2)} = \alpha^3 \left[-\frac{1}{\pi} \left(\frac{16}{9} + \log 2 \right) + \frac{1}{2} i \right] \text{Ry}. \tag{23.8}$$

The imaginary term in (23.8) represents a "line width" of the singlet level, *not* an energy shift, i.e. its inverse (times $\frac{1}{2}\hbar$) gives the mean lifetime (23.1) of the singlet state against *real* two-quantum annihilation of the pair. The real part of $\Delta W^{(2)}$ is about 10^3 Mc/sec and, added to the expression (23.6) with $n=1$, gives a total theoretical value of

$$\Delta W_{\text{th}} = 2.0337 \times 10^5 \text{ Mc/sec}. \tag{23.9}$$

The splitting energy (in frequency units) between the singlet and triplet components of the positronium ground state has been measured very accurately in a series of experiments using a combination of microwave and counter techniques, largely by M. DEUTSCH and collaborators. In principle the experiment proceeds as follows: If positronium atoms are placed in an oscillating magnetic field of frequency corresponding to the energy splitting ΔW, transitions are induced from the longlived triplet state to the shortlived singlet states. The quenching of the slower three-quantum decay of the singlet state is then observed by counter techniques. In practice, an additional constant magnetic field is present and the theory of the ZEEMAN effect is used to analyse the experiment. The latest experimental value[2] for ΔW is

$$\Delta W_{\text{exp}} = (2.0338 \pm 0.0004) \times 10^5 \text{ Mc/sec}, \tag{23.10}$$

in excellent agreement with the theoretical result (23.9).

This agreement to such a high accuracy is not only a major achievement of experimental techniques in a difficult field, but a remarkable verification of the DIRAC pair theory and relativistic quantum electrodynamics. Unlike any other atom, a major contribution already to the terms of order α^2 Ry comes from the annihilation term, which is specific to the pair theory[3] and has no analogue in single-electron theory. But the experimental error is even 20 times smaller than the terms of order α^3 Ry, which (for positronium) also test the modern fully relativistic formulations of the two-body problem.

II. The helium atom without external fields.

a) Nonrelativistic theory.

24. The SCHRÖDINGER equation for helium (symmetry). SCHRÖDINGER'S equation for atoms having two electrons is

$$\Delta_1 u + \Delta_2 u + 2\left(E + \frac{Z}{r_1} + \frac{Z}{r_2} - \frac{1}{r_{12}}\right) u = 0. \tag{24.1}$$

r_1 and r_2 are the distances of the first and second electrons from the nucleus, r_{12} their mutual separation; $\Delta_1 = \frac{\partial^2}{\partial x_1^2} + \frac{\partial^2}{\partial y_1^2} + \frac{\partial^2}{\partial z_1^2}$ is the LAPLACian operator in

[1] R. KARPLUS and A. KLEIN: Phys. Rev. **87**, 848 (1952). Terms of the same order for excited states have been calculated by T. FULTON and P. MARTIN, Phys. Rev. **95**, 811 (1954).

[2] R. WEINSTEIN, M. DEUTSCH and S. BROWN: Phys. Rev. **98**, 223 (1955).

[3] A few years ago some doubts existed as to whether the virtual effects of pair creation (or annihilation) should be included in the theory. Since about 40% of the theoretical splitting energy (23.9) is due to the annihilation term, the experimental value (23.10) confirms its presence beyond any doubt.

the space of the first electron; u is a function of the six coordinates x_1, y_1, z_1, x_2, y_2 and z_2.

The differential equation remains unchanged when the coordinates of the first electron are interchanged with those of the second electron. Thus, $u(\boldsymbol{r}_1, \boldsymbol{r}_2)$ and $u(\boldsymbol{r}_2, \boldsymbol{r}_1)$ satisfy the same differential equation. [$u(\boldsymbol{r}_2, \boldsymbol{r}_1)$ is obtained from $u(\boldsymbol{r}_1, \boldsymbol{r}_2)$ by replacing $x_1\, y_1\, z_1$ with $x_2\, y_2\, z_2$ and vice versa.] $u(\boldsymbol{r}_2, \boldsymbol{r}_1)$ is, of course, subject to the same requirements as $u(\boldsymbol{r}_1, \boldsymbol{r}_2)$, it must be a bounded, continuous and single valued function. Therefore[1],

$$u(\boldsymbol{r}_2\, \boldsymbol{r}_1) = \varkappa\, u(\boldsymbol{r}_1\, \boldsymbol{r}_2), \tag{24.2}$$

where $\varkappa$ is a constant. Interchanging $\boldsymbol{r}_1$ and $\boldsymbol{r}_2$ once more in $u(\boldsymbol{r}_2\, \boldsymbol{r}_1)$ we obviously get $u(\boldsymbol{r}_1\, \boldsymbol{r}_2)$ again, so that

$$u(\boldsymbol{r}_1\, \boldsymbol{r}_2) = \varkappa^2 u(\boldsymbol{r}_1\, \boldsymbol{r}_2); \quad \varkappa = \pm 1; \quad u(\boldsymbol{r}_2\, \boldsymbol{r}_1) = \pm u(\boldsymbol{r}_1\, \boldsymbol{r}_2). \tag{24.3}$$

Thus, the eigenfunctions of an atom with two electrons either remain unchanged or change sign on interchange of the coordinates of the two electrons, i.e., the eigenfunctions are either symmetric or antisymmetric. States of symmetric eigenfunctions are called para-, those of antisymmetric eigenfunctions ortho-states.

The above does not constitute a complete theory of atoms with two electrons because, as we know, electrons possess spin. As a good approximation for light atoms we may at first neglect both the spin-orbit interaction and the relativistic change in mass (cf. Sect. 12). Then the energy does not depend on the orientation of spin relative to orbital angular momentum, and we only need to specify the components of the spins in a fixed direction z (in addition to specifying the spatial eigenfunction) in order to describe the atom completely. The complete eigenfunction is a product of the spatial eigenfunction satisfying (24.1) and a function depending on the spin coordinates [cf. (12.12)].

The spin wave function is of a particularly simple nature. Let $\mathbf{s}_1$ and $\mathbf{s}_2$ be the spin operators for the two electrons, s_{1z} and s_{2z} the components of these vector operators in a fixed z-direction. The only possible eigenvalues of s_{1z} (or s_{2z}) are $+\frac{1}{2}$ and $-\frac{1}{2}$. We then have four independent spin states, which could be represented as the product of two 2-component spinors. In the notation of (12.12) we write the state with $s_{1z} = s_{2z} = +\frac{1}{2}$ as $\alpha(1)\,\alpha(2)$, the state with $s_{1z} = +\frac{1}{2}$, $s_{2z} = -\frac{1}{2}$ as $\alpha(1)\,\beta(2)$, and so on.

Combining these four spin states with the spatial eigenfunctions, we would expect four times as many eigenstates for an atom with two spin-electrons than for two spin-less particles. In reality the number of possible states is reduced by the requirements of the PAULI exclusion principle. This requires that the *total* wave function change sign if *all* the coordinates (spatial as well as spin coordinates) of the two electrons are interchanged. Hence the spin wave function must change sign if the spatial wave function remains the same after interchanging the two electrons, and vice versa.

Of the four spin wave functions discussed above neither $\alpha(1)\,\beta(2)$ nor $\beta(1)\,\alpha(2)$ is symmetric or antisymmetric, but two simple linear combinations of them have this property. Consider the following four mutually orthogonal spin wave functions

$$\left.\begin{aligned} S_+ &= \alpha(1)\,\alpha(2), \quad S_- = \beta(1)\,\beta(2), \\ S_0 &= \frac{1}{\sqrt{2}}\left[\alpha(1)\,\beta(2) + \beta(1)\,\alpha(2)\right] \end{aligned}\right\} \tag{24.4}$$

[1] Except for degenerate eigenvalues, but in that case the eigenfunctions can always be chosen so that (24.2) holds.

and

$$S_P = \frac{1}{\sqrt{2}} \left[\alpha(1)\,\beta(2) - \beta(1)\,\alpha(2)\right]. \tag{24.5}$$

Each of these wave functions is normalized to unity. The first three, (24.4), are symmetric (remain unchanged) for an interchange of the two electrons, the last one, (24.5), is antisymmetric (changes sign). Let $\boldsymbol{S} = \boldsymbol{s}_1 + \boldsymbol{s}_2$ be the operator for the total spin, $S_z = s_{1z} + s_{2z}$ its component in the z-direction, $\boldsymbol{S}^2$ its square.

The three symmetric states S_+, S_0, S_- are eigenstates of S_z with eigenvalues 1, 0, -1 respectively. Using the explicit representation of the Pauli spin matrices, Sect. 10, one also finds that each of these states is an eigenstate of $\boldsymbol{S}^2$ with eigenvalue $1(1+1) = 2$. For these states, then, the quantum number for the "absolute value of the total spin" is $S = 1$. Similarly the state S_P is a simultaneous eigenstate of $\boldsymbol{S}^2$ and S_z with quantum numbers $S_z = S = 0$.

According to the Pauli principle, an antisymmetric spatial wave function (ortho-state) *must be* multiplied by one of the three symmetric spin wave functions S_+, S_0, S_-. Let $\boldsymbol{j} = \boldsymbol{k} + \boldsymbol{S}$ be the total angular momentum operator, where $\boldsymbol{k} = \boldsymbol{k}_1 + \boldsymbol{k}_2$ is the sum of the two orbital angular momentum operators. The nonrelativistic spatial wave functions can be characterized by a quantum number l (besides other quantum numbers), which corresponds to the "absolute value of $\boldsymbol{k}$". According to the rules of Sect. 11, one can find linear superpositions of the various ortho-states, with a fixed value of l and with $S = 1$, which are eigenstates of $\boldsymbol{j}^2$ with quantum number

$$j = l + 1, \quad l \text{ or } l - 1. \tag{24.6}$$

In a purely nonrelativistic theory, the energy eigenvalues of all the ortho-states (with *fixed* values of l and of other spatial quantum numbers) are degenerate. If the relativistic interaction between spin and orbital angular momentum is taken into account, however, this degeneracy is partially removed. As we shall see later, each nonrelativistic (ortho) level is split into a triplet, the energy being slightly different for the three values (24.6) of the quantum number j.

A symmetric spatial wave function (para-state), on the other hand, *must* be multiplied by the single antisymmetric spin wave function S_P. For a fixed value of l the quantum number j must then be equal to l, since $S_z = S = 0$. Thus, even if the spin-orbit interaction is included, each nonrelativistic energy level of the para-system remains unsplit (singlet system). We shall see, however, that the energy eigenvalues for states of para-helium are quite different from those for ortho-helium (for the same l-value), *even* in the purely nonrelativistic theory.

Until Sect. 38 we shall neglect the spin-orbit interaction entirely and use the nonrelativistic Schrödinger Eq. (24.1). The errors due to this approximation (for the energy eigenvalue, etc.) are of relative order of magnitude α^2, where α is the fine structure constant. In this approximation one finds that transitions from a triplet to a singlet state (or vice versa) of helium with the emission of light are forbidden. This is due to the fact that the operator for the electric dipole moment $(x_1 + x_2)$ and the spatial wave function for a para-state are unchanged if the two electrons are interchanged, whereas the spatial wave function for an ortho-state changes sign. Now the transition matrix element involves an integral over the spatial coordinates of both electrons (see Sect. 59). This integral then vanishes[1] from these symmetry considerations.

[1] Even if the integral were finite, the singlet and triplet spin wave functions are orthogonal and the sum over the spin coordinates would make the matrix element vanish.

To summarize:

The level scheme of helium and of ions with two electrons consists of two system of levels, one containing triplet levels (orthohelium) and the other singlet levels (parahelium), which do not combine optically with each other.

25. Discussion of variation and perturbation methods. The differential equation (24.1) for the two-electron system is not separable. Unlike the solutions for the hydrogen atom, the solutions for the eigenfunctions u and energy eigenvalues E of (24.1) cannot be expressed in closed analytic form. We shall have to use various approximation methods, including the RITZ variational method, the perturbation method and some modifications of these methods. We first give a general discussion of these methods without explicit reference to (24.1). To apply the variational method we merely note that (24.1) is a HAMILTONian equation of form

$$H u = E u, \tag{25.1}$$

where the HAMILTONian H is a differential operator which does not involve the energy eigenvalue E explicitly. To apply the perturbation method we split this HAMILTONian into two parts $(H_0 + \lambda H_1)$ where

$$\left.\begin{aligned} H_0 &= -\tfrac{1}{2}(\Delta_1 + \Delta_2) + V_0(\boldsymbol{r}_1, \boldsymbol{r}_2), \\ \lambda H_1 &= -\frac{Z}{r_1} - \frac{Z}{r_2} + \frac{1}{r_{12}} - V_0. \end{aligned}\right\} \tag{25.2}$$

In later sections we discuss various choices of V_0 which attempt to keep H_0 a simple enough operator, yet make the contribution of λH_1 relatively small.

α) RITZ variation method. Consider an equation of type (25.1) which has a discrete spectrum of eigenvalues E of H. Let U be an *arbitrary* function (of the same number of dimensions as the eigenfunctions of H) and consider the expression

$$E[U] = \frac{\int d\tau\, U^* H U}{\int d\tau\, U^* U}. \tag{25.3}$$

If the function U is identical with any one of the exact eigenfunctions u, then $E[U]$ is identical with the corresponding exact eigenvalue E. Further, if U differs from any of the eigenfunctions u by an infinitesimally small function of first order, then $E[U]$ differs from the exact E by a quantity which is small of second order. In other words, SCHRÖDINGER'S variational principle states that any function U for which the functional $E[U]$ has a stationary value is a solution of (25.1).

Now consider the special case of a function U which is fairly close to the eigenfunction u_g belonging to the *lowest* eigenvalue E_g of H. We can consider U written in the form

$$U = N_g u_g + \sum_{n \neq g} \delta_n u_n,$$

where u_n is any normalized eigenfunction of H and δ_n is a small expansion coefficient. (25.3) then becomes

$$E[U] = E_g + \frac{\sum\limits_n |\delta_n|^2 (E_n - E_g)}{|N_g|^2 + \sum\limits_n |\delta_n|^2} \geq E_g. \tag{25.4}$$

Thus any function U other than the exact u_g will give a value for $E[U]$ *larger* than E_g, the discrepancy being smaller the smaller the difference between U and u_g is. The RITZ variation method then starts by choosing some suitable analytic form for U, involving some arbitrary parameters. The expression $E[U]$ of (25.3) is then evaluated as a function of these parameters and the minimum value with respect to all parameters found. This *minimum* value of $E[U]$ then gives an *upper* limit for E_g. If a large enough number of suitable parameters is used and minimized against, then this upper bound for E_g should be very close to the exact value.

This variation method does *not*, without modification, give good approximations for the higher eigenvalues. However, consider trial wave functions U which are orthogonal to all eigenstates of H which belong to eigenvalues lower than a certain eigenvalue E_e. For such functions U, N_g and δ_n in (25.4) will be zero for all states for which $(E_n - E_g)$ is negative. In this case $E[U]$ will again be an upper limit for E_e.

β) Variation perturbation theory. Consider a general HAMILTONian equation

$$(H_0 + \lambda H_1 - E)\,u = 0, \tag{25.5}$$

where H_0 and H_1 are any two HERMITian operators and λ is considered as a small parameter. We consider the eigenfunction u and eigenvalue E expanded in powers of this parameter,

$$E = \sum_{n=0}^{\infty} \lambda^n E_n, \qquad u = \sum_{n=0}^{\infty} \lambda^n U_n. \tag{25.6}$$

If we substitute these expansions into (25.5) and equate the coefficient of each power of λ to zero, we get an infinite set of coupled linear equations,

$$H_0 U_0 - E_0 U_0 = 0, \tag{25.7}$$

$$H_0 U_1 + H_1 U_0 - E_0 U_1 - E_1 U_0 = 0, \tag{25.8}$$

$$H_0 U_2 + H_1 U_1 - E_0 U_2 - E_1 U_1 - E_2 U_0 = 0, \tag{25.9}$$

$$\cdots\cdots\cdots\cdots\cdots\cdots\cdots\cdots\cdots$$

$$H_0 U_n + H_1 U_{n-1} - \sum_{m=0}^{n} E_m U_{n-m} = 0.$$

We call (25.7) the unperturbed (or zero order) HAMILTONian equation. This equation, like the full Eq. (25.5), has a whole spectrum of solutions. We consider one *particular* solution and consider U_0 and E_0 as known completely and U_0 normalized. Multiply (25.7) by U_1, (25.8) by U_0, substract the two equations and integrate over all space[1]. One then obtains the well-known expression for E_1, the first order perturbation energy,

$$E_1 = \int U_0 H_1 U_0 \, d\tau. \tag{25.10}$$

A knowledge of the zero-order wave function U_0, for one particular state alone, thus yields both E_0 and E_1 for this state.

In Eq. (25.8) for the particular state we are considering, the constants E_0 and E_1 and the function U_0 are now known. (25.8) is then an inhomogeneous differential equation for U_1, which does not contain any unknown eigenvalue. Since U_1 must satisfy some definite boundary conditions (conditions of "good behavior"), the Eq. (25.8) determines the function U_1 for the particular state *uniquely*[2], at least *in principle*. We shall discuss practical methods of solving for

[1] We restrict ourselves to the case of real functions U_0, U_1, U_2, etc. for the sake of simplicity.

[2] Except for an additive multiple of U_0. The normalization, etc., can be so arranged that U_1 (and U_2, etc.) is orthogonal to U_0.

U_1 in a moment. Once U_1 has been found, both E_2 and E_3 can be evaluated as follows. Multiplying (25.7) by U_2, (25.9) by U_0, subtracting the equations and integrating, we get

$$E_2 = \int U_0 H_1 U_1 d\tau, \tag{25.11}$$

where we have assumed the normalization such that U_0 and U_1 are orthogonal. Next multiply (25.7) by $-U_3$, (25.8) by $-U_2$, (25.9) by $+U_1$ and the next equation by $+U_0$. Adding these equations and integrating gives

$$E_3 = \int (U_1 H_1 U_1 - E_1 U_1^2)\, d\tau. \tag{25.12}$$

After E_2 and U_1 have been found, the Eq. (25.9) determines the function U_2 (in principle), and so on. In general, after each additional wave function (e.g. U_2) has been found, *two* additional eigenvalues (e.g. E_4 and E_5) can be evaluated.

We turn now to possible methods of solving (25.8) for the function U_1 (given U_0, E_0 and E_1). Solving this inhomogeneous differential equation *directly* is usually impractical, (but there are situations where this is not only possible but in fact the simplest method). The conventional SCHRÖDINGER perturbation method proceeds as follows. The zero order Eq. (25.7) is first solved for *all* the possible eigenfunctions and eigenvalues. After this complete set of eigenfunctions of H_0 has been found, the matrix elements of H_1 are evaluated between *any* function of this set and the eigenfunction U_0 which corresponds to the *particular* state we are considering. The unknown function U_1 is considered expanded in terms of the complete set of eigenfunctions of H_0. The expansion coefficients of U_1, and also the eigenvalue E_2, are then given in terms of the matrix elements of H_1. These expressions for U_1 and E_2 do not involve any explicit solution of the differential equation (25.8). But in many practical cases the evaluation of all the required matrix elements of H_1 is much too involved. In such cases one can still find *approximations* for U_1 and E_2 by the following method.

Consider U_0, E_0 and E_1 to be known exactly, for one *particular* state only, and let U_1 be an arbitrary trial wave function. We start from the following expression

$$E_2[U_1'] = \int (2U_1' H_1 U_0 + U_1' H_0 U_1' - E_0 U_1'^2 - 2E_1 U_0 U_1')\, d\tau. \tag{25.13}$$

The condition that this expression have a stationary value with respect to any variation of U_1' reduces exactly to the Eq. (25.8). Comparison of (25.8), (25.11) and (25.13) shows further that $E_2[U_1']$ equals the correct value of E_2, if U_1' equals the unique solution U_1 of (25.8). Let us consider now that particular state for which E_0 is the *lowest* of all the eigenvalues of H_0. For this state one can easily show that $E_2[U_1']$ is *larger* than E_2, unless U_1' equals U_1. We can then proceed as in the usual RITZ variation method. We again choose for the trial wave function U_1' a suitable analytic function with some parameters left arbitrary. We form the expression (25.13) and minimize it with respect to all the parameters. This minimum value of $E_2[U_1']$ then gives directly an *upper* limit for E_2. If enough suitable parameters are included, this bound should give a good approximation for E_2 and the corresponding function U_1' should be close to the correct U_1 .This method can be extended to give approximations for E_3, U_2, E_4, etc.

γ) Unsymmetric perturbation theory. We finally discuss another modification of first order perturbation theory, which we shall find useful in the next few sections. Consider a HAMILTONian H which can be split into a zero order HAMILTONian and a small perturbation part in two different ways,

$$H = H_{0a} + \lambda H_{1a} = H_{0b} + \lambda H_{1b}. \tag{25.14}$$

All four HAMILTONians are HERMITian, λ is a small parameter and hence the two zero order HAMILTONians H_{0a} and H_{0b} differ from each other only by a term of first order in λ. Let U_{0a} and U_{0b} be particular normalized eigenfunctions of H_{0a} and H_{0b}, respectively,

$$(H_{0a} - E_{0a})\, U_{0a} = (H_{0b} - E_{0b})\, U_{0b} = 0. \tag{25.15}$$

We restrict ourselves to cases where $E_{0a} = E_{0b} \equiv E_0$, say. Further, let U_{0a} and U_{0b} be orthogonal to each other to *zero* order in λ (since H_{0a} and H_{0b} are identical to zero order in λ, their eigenfunction spectrum is identical to the same order[1]). We are interested in that eigenfunction u of the total HAMILTONian which reduces to ($2^{-\frac{1}{2}}$ times) the sum of U_{0a} and U_{0b} in zero order. We put

$$(H - E)\, u = 0, \quad E = E_0 + \lambda E_1, \quad u = \frac{1}{\sqrt{2}} (U_{0a} + U_{0b}) + \lambda U_1. \tag{25.16}$$

From (25.14), (25.15) and (25.16) we find

$$\sqrt{2}\, (H - E)\, U_1 + (H_{1a} U_{0a} + H_{1b} U_{0b}) - E_1 (U_{0a} + U_{0b}) = 0. \tag{25.17}$$

We next multiply (25.17) by $(U_{0a} + U_{0b})$ and integrate over all space. We only wish to keep terms of zero order in λ in the resulting equation. To this order, $(H - E)$ $(U_{0a} + U_{0b})$ is zero and U_{0a} orthogonal to U_{0b}. We then get the following approximation for E_1,

$$E_1 = \tfrac{1}{2} \int (U_{0a} + U_{0b})\, (H_{1a} U_{0a} + H_{1b} U_{0b})\, d\tau. \tag{25.18}$$

(25.18) is the required generalization of expression (25.10) for the first order perturbation energy. Since U_{0a} and U_{0b} are only approximately orthogonal, it would however be difficult to extend the present scheme to include the higher order approximations in a systematic and simple way.

26. Level scheme of helium. As mentioned before, the SCHRÖDINGER equation for helium-like atoms cannot be solved exactly. Before discussing approximation methods in detail, we give a qualitative survey of the eigenvalue spectrum and eigenfunctions.

Consider the exact HAMILTONian (24.1) split into two parts as in (25.2). We take the zero order HAMILTONian H_0 of form

$$\left.\begin{aligned} H_0 &= -\frac{1}{2} (\Delta_1 + \Delta_2) + V(r_1) + V(r_2), \\ W \equiv \lambda H_1 &= -\frac{Z_1}{r_1} - V(r_1) - \frac{Z}{r_2} - V(r_2) + \frac{1}{r_{12}}, \end{aligned}\right\} \tag{26.1}$$

where V is a central potential (arbitrary, as yet). The zero-order wave equation

$$(H_0 - E_0)\, U_0 = 0 \tag{26.2}$$

is then separable with this choice for H_0. Let u_1 and u_2 be any two of the solutions u_n of the single-particle wave equation

$$\left[\tfrac{1}{2}\Delta + \varepsilon_n - V(r)\right] u_n(\boldsymbol{r}) = 0. \tag{26.3}$$

(26.2) is then solved by the substitution

$$E_0 = \varepsilon_1 + \varepsilon_2, \qquad U_0 = u_1(r_1)\, u_2(r_2). \tag{26.4}$$

[1] We assume the system has a degenerate eigenvalue spectrum, so that two orthogonal states U_{0a} and U_{0b} of the same energy exist.

Since the potential $V(r)$ is central, the single-particle Eq. (26.3) is separable in spherical polar coordinates. A solution of (26.3) can then be characterized by three quantum numbers[1] n, l, and m,

$$u_{n l m}(\boldsymbol{r}) = R_{n l}(r)\, Y_{l m}(\vartheta, \varphi).$$

We shall not specify the potential $V(r)$ any further in this section, but consider it chosen so that the effect of the perturbation potential W in (26.1) is fairly small. If we choose a simple COULOMB form for V, the energy eigenvalue ε_n of (26.3) would be given by

$$V(r) = -\frac{(Z-s)}{r}, \qquad \varepsilon_n = -\frac{1}{2}\frac{(Z-s)^2}{n^2} \tag{26.5}$$

and be independent of the quantum numbers l and m. We shall see later that some value between zero and one would be the best choice for the "screening constant" s (see also Sect. 17). In Sects. 27 and 31 we shall see that a better choice for $V(r)$ consists of replacing the constant s in (26.5) by a monotonically increasing function of r, which is zero at the origin and unity at infinity (HARTREE potential). For such a potential the l-degeneracy is removed and the energy eigenvalue $\varepsilon_{n l}$ of (26.3) increases (at least slightly) with increasing orbital quantum number l (for fixed n).

We return now to the spectrum of eigenstates of the zero-order, two-particle Eq. (26.2). Leaving aside for the moment the question of symmetrization, each wave function (26.4) is characterized by six quantum numbers, the values of n, l and m for each of the two electrons. For fixed values of n_1, l_1, n_2 and l_2, the states with different values of m_1 and m_2 are still degenerate. By taking linear superpositions of these degenerate eigenfunctions one can then form simultaneous eigenstates of the square and the z-component of the operator for the sum of the orbital angular momenta, $\boldsymbol{k} = \boldsymbol{k}_1 + \boldsymbol{k}_2$. The corresponding *total* orbital quantum number can take the values $l = |l_1 - l_2|, \ldots, l_1 + l_2$ and the eigenvalues of k_z are $m_l = -l, -l+1, \ldots, l$. In the zero-order approximation (26.2) these states with different l and m_l values (but same l_1 and l_2) are still degenerate. However, if the interaction $1/r_{12}$ between the two electrons (contained in the perturbation HAMILTONian W) is considered, the l-degeneracy (but not the m_l-degeneracy) is in general removed. The number and complexity of the states to be considered is reduced greatly if we restrict ourselves to states for which one of the two electrons is in the ground state, $n_1 = 1$, $l_1 = m_1 = 0$. In this case, the values of l and m_l for the atom as a whole are simply equal to the corresponding values for the second electron.

For helium the only states of practical importance are in fact those for which at least one electron is in the ground state, for the following reason. One finds that the energy of any state in He, for which both electrons are excited, is higher than the ground state energy of a He^+-ion (H-like ion with $Z=2$) plus a *free* electron. These states then lie in the continuum and the same holds for all other He-like ions. One can show further that, for such a doubly excited state in He, dissociation into He^+ plus a free electron (AUGER effect) is much more probable than a radiative transition to a bound state of He. Spectral lines involving such doubly excited He-states are very rare in practice and we shall *not* consider them any further[2].

[1] For a general central potential the principal quantum number n is defined as $(l+1)$ plus the number of nodes of the radial wave function.

[2] For a discussion of doubly excited states see T. Y. WU, Phys. Rev. **66**, 291 (1944)

For the genuinely discrete states of He, to which we restrict ourselves from now on, one of the two electrons is in the ground state. These states are then characterized by merely *three* quantum numbers, n, l and m of the other electron, just as for a single-electron atom. However, besides the m-degeneracy we have also another type of degeneracy, namely the zero-order energy (26.2) is the same for the two states

$$U_0' = u_{100}(\boldsymbol{r}_1)\, u_{nlm}(\boldsymbol{r}_2), \qquad U_0'' = u_{nlm}(\boldsymbol{r}_1)\, u_{100}(\boldsymbol{r}_2). \tag{26.6}$$

As discussed in Sect. 24, the exact spatial wave function must be either symmetric or antisymmetric to the interchange of spatial coordinates of the two electrons. We shall require the same symmetry properties of our zero-order wave functions and use instead of the two functions (26.6) the two linear combinations

$$U_\pm = \frac{1}{\sqrt{2}}\left[u_{100}(1)\, u_{nlm}(2) \pm u_{nlm}(1)\, u_{100}(2)\right]. \tag{26.7}$$

In (26.7) the symbols (1) and (2) denote the coordinates of the first and second electron and the plus sign refers to the spatially symmetric *para*-states, the minus to *ortho*-states. We consider u_{100} and u_{nlm} orthogonal and normalized to unity. The factor $1/\sqrt{2}$ then ensures that U_+ and U_- are also normalized.

In our zero order Eq. (26.2), the two states U_+ and U_- are still degenerate of course (for *any* choice of the potential V). We shall see, however, (Sect. 28) that the "perturbation" caused by the electron-electron interaction $1/r_{12}$ removes this degeneracy and the exact energy for a para-state U_+ lies slightly higher than for the corresponding ortho-state U_-.

The ground state of helium, in which *both* electrons are in the $n=1$ state, forms an exception to (26.7). Since the two single-particle wave functions are identical, the wave function U_- for the ortho-state vanishes. We can then *only* have a para-state, whose normalized zero-order wave function is simply given by

$$U_{+g} = u_{100}(1)\, u_{100}(2). \tag{26.8}$$

The absence of an ortho-state for the He-ground state is also in line with the original formulation of the PAULI principle: "Two electrons cannot be in *exactly* the same state." If the spatial quantum numbers are the same, then the two electrons must have "opposite spin". This is the case for the spin wave function S_p, Eq. (24.5), which corresponds to para-states. The symmetric spin functions (24.4) for ortho-states represent "parallel spin" and thus at least one of the three "spatial" quantum numbers of the two electrons must be different.

We can now summarize the qualitative features of the helium spectrum (disregarding all doubly excited states): (1) As for the hydrogen spectrum, the states are characterized by three quantum numbers n, l, m and the energy is degenerate with respect to the value of m. The ground state is non-degenerate as in hydrogen. (2) The l-degeneracy is removed and the energy (for fixed n) decreases with decreasing l. (3) For each value of n, l, m (except for the ground state) we have both an ortho- and a para-state, the energy of the para-state being the higher. Thus for each hydrogen energy level with principal quantum number n we have $2n$ levels in helium ($l=0, 1, \ldots, n-1$ for ortho and para).

We finally give a preview of the quantitative positions of the various energy levels. Consider first states with fairly high values of both n and l. The wave function of the excited electron is then concentrated at appreciably larger radial distances than the inner electron. One then finds that the potential (26.5) with $s=0$ (no screening) describes the motion of the inner electron quite well; and (26.5) with $s=1$ (full screening) describes that of the outer electron. The total energy of the helium-like atom is then given approximately by

$$E_{nlm} \approx -\frac{1}{2} Z^2 - \frac{1}{2} \frac{(Z-1)^2}{n^2}. \tag{26.9}$$

For *large* n and l, then, the energies (except for the additive constant $\frac{1}{2}Z^2$) for He are very close to those for H, the energies for Li^+ close to those for He^+, and so on. For small values of n and l (especially for S-states) the wave functions of

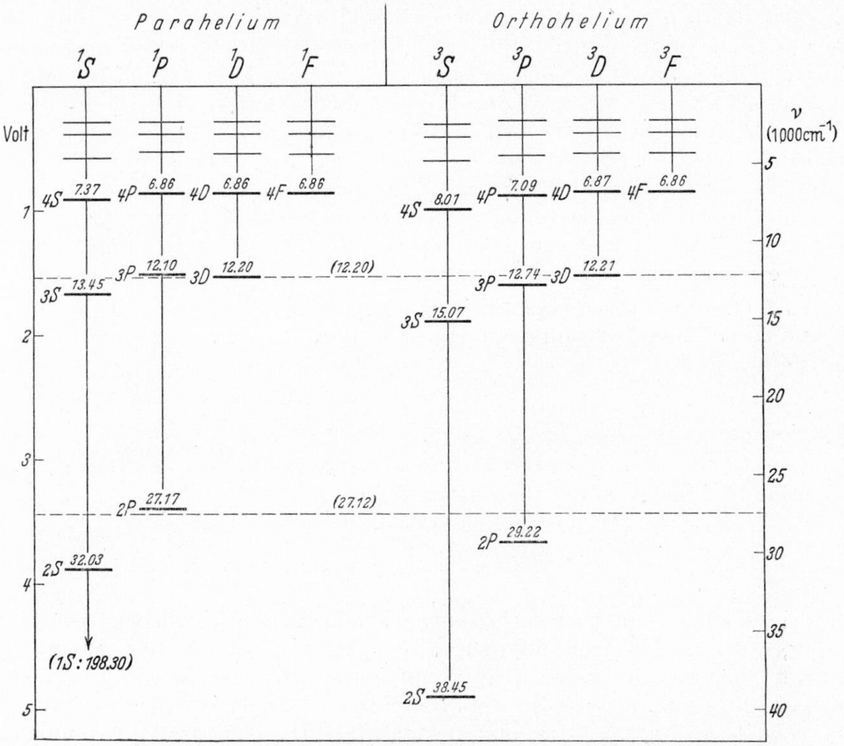

Fig. 15. The experimental energy levels of helium. The scale on the left represents ionization potential in electron volts. The numbers next to the levels are the wave numbers corresponding to the ionization potential, expressed in units of 10^3 cm^{-1}. The dotted lines represent the energy levels of hydrogen (nuclear charge $= Z-1=1$).

the two electrons overlap to an appreciable extent. The deviation of the energy eigenvalue from (26.9) is then quite considerable: it is different for ortho- and para-helium and it depends on the l-value. For He-like ions of larger charge Z (Li^+, Be^{++}, etc.) the situation is qualitatively similar, but the deviations of the correct energies from (26.9) are smaller fractions of (26.9) for larger values of Z.

In Fig. 15 we give the experimental[1] scheme of the energy levels of He.

27. Survey of approximations to be used. Approximation methods have to be used to solve the wave equation (24.1) for He-like atoms. It is convenient to use different approximation methods under different circumstances, depending on whether the quantum number n or l is large or small, whether Z is large or small, whether an accurate energy eigenvalue or a relatively simple wave function is more important, and so on. We give first a brief survey of the various approximation methods to be used in the following sections.

[1] Experimental energy levels in helium and helium-like ions (up to $Z=9$) are given by C. E. MOORE, Atomic Energy Levels, Vol. 1, N.B.S. Circular 467, Washington 1949.

Most (but not all) of the approximation methods are based on perturbation theory. More specifically, one chooses the zero-order HAMILTONian H_0 of form similar to (26.1),

$$H_0 = -\tfrac{1}{2}(\Delta_1 + \Delta_2) + V_1(r_1) + V_2(r_2),$$
$$W = -\left(\frac{Z}{r_1} + V_1(r_1)\right) - \left(\frac{Z}{r_2} + V_2(r_2)\right) + \frac{1}{r_{12}}. \tag{27.1}$$

The great advantage of this choice, with V_1 and V_2 central and *single-particle* potentials, lies in the fact that the zero-order wave equation (26.2) is now separable. The zero-order wave functions and energy eigenvalues have already been discussed in Sect. 26 for cases where V_1 and V_2 are chosen identical. For the ground state of He-like atoms (where the two electrons are in identical states) we shall always make this choice. For excited states, however, the wave functions of the two electrons are radically different and it is sometimes convenient to use one potential V_1 for the inner electron and a *different* potential V_2 for the excited electron. In Sect. 25γ we have shown how perturbation theory can be carried up to *first* order even in such cases.

α) Expansion in powers of 1/Z (large Z). The simplest choice of the potentials V_1 and V_2 is obtained by simply omitting the interaction $1/r_{12}$ between the electrons altogether in H_0,

$$V_1(r) = V_2(r) = -\frac{Z}{r}, \quad W = \frac{1}{r_{12}}. \tag{27.2}$$

The zero-order wave functions are then simply products of hydrogen-like wave functions for charge Z and the zero-order energy is

$$E_0 = -\frac{Z^2}{2} - \frac{Z^2}{2n^2}. \tag{27.3}$$

In principle one could then carry conventional perturbation theory to any desired order, with the electron interaction $1/r_{12}$ as the perturbation HAMILTONian. This method has the great advantage that the successive orders of perturbation theory form a power series in negative powers of Z. If one can carry this series far enough, one then obtains solutions for *all* the He-like ions of different charge Z simultaneously.

Unfortunately the calculations of the orders of perturbation theory after the first order get harder very rapidly. Even the rigorous calculation of the second order is extremely tedious. Only for the ground state have the first few terms in this series been calculated by HYLLERAAS[1], using the combined perturbation-variation method outlined in Sect. 25β. This method gives excellent results for the ground state of two-electron ions of *large* Z and will be discussed in Sect. 32. It is not suitable for low Z, such as for He itself.

β) Constant screening factor (ground state). The next simplest choice of the potentials for the ground state is to take V_1 and V_2 equal and of the form of (26.5). Unlike the choice (27.2), the use of the screening constant s takes some account of the COULOMB repulsion between the two electrons. In fact one may choose the screening constant s such that the *first* order perturbation energy vanishes. This value turns out to be (see Sect. 32β) $s = \frac{5}{16}$ for the ground state, for any value of Z. The ground-state energy is then, to zero and first order [see Eq. (26.5)],

$$E_0 + E_1 = E_0 = -(Z - \tfrac{5}{16})^2. \tag{27.4}$$

[1] E. HYLLERAAS: Z. Physik **65**, 209 (1930).

The zero-order wave function is then the product of two hydrogen-like ground state wave functions of nuclear charge $(Z - \frac{5}{16})$. This very simple wave function is convenient if very high accuracy is not desired and is also a useful approximation for the two K-shell $(1s)$ electrons in complex atoms. This approximation is nevertheless very crude. Particularly in the ground state do the wave functions of the two electrons interpenetrate considerably. The "effective screening" thus varies appreciably as a function of radial distance and polarization is also quite important.

γ) HEISENBERG'S *choice (excited states).* If the electron 1 is in the ground state and electron 2 in a highly excited state, then most of the charge cloud of electron 1 lies appreciably closer to the nucleus than the bulk of the charge cloud of electron 2. This is the case especially when electron 2 has a large value of l (as well as n), since its wave function is then extremely small at small radial distances. Since $r_1 \ll r_2$ for the most important part of the wave function, a good approximation to the inter-electron interaction $1/r_{12}$ should be the simple function $1/r_2$. We are thus led to the *unsymmetric* choice of the potentials

$$V_1(r_1) = -\frac{Z}{r_1}, \quad V_2(r_2) = -\frac{Z-1}{r_2}, \quad W = \frac{1}{r_{12}} - \frac{1}{r_2}. \tag{27.5}$$

In other words, we consider the screening of the inner on the outer electron as "complete" (screening constant $s = 1$) and neglect screening of the outer on the inner one. The zero-order wave function is again hydrogen-like for each of the two electrons, but with a *different* charge. The zero order energy is then given by (26.9).

To obtain the small, but finite, dependence of energy on l and on the symmetry of the wave function (ortho *vs.* para) we have to proceed at least to first order perturbation theory. This will be discussed in Sect. 28. As discussed in Sect. 25 γ, the lack of symmetry between V_1 and V_2 in (27.5) makes an entirely systematic treatment of perturbation theory impossible. To overcome this formal difficulty, HEISENBERG[1] made the following *symmetric* choice of potentials

$$V_1(r) = V_2(r) = \begin{cases} -\dfrac{Z-1}{r} & \text{if} \quad r > r_0, \\[2ex] -\dfrac{Z}{r} + \dfrac{1}{r_0} & \text{if} \quad r < r_0. \end{cases} \tag{27.6}$$

r_0 is chosen to lie between the "characteristic radii" of the wave functions of the inner and outer electron. The rigorous zero-order eigenfunctions of (27.6) are very complicated, but a method, based on (27.5), can be used to justify the less systematic treatment of our Sect. 28.

It is practically impossible to carry out an *exact* second order perturbation calculation based on (27.5) or (27.6). The effect of "polarization" by the outer on the inner electron can, nevertheless be obtained in a semi-quantitative manner. This will be discussed in Sect. 29. For S-states ($l = 0$ for the outer electron) the interpenetration of the two electron clouds is fairly large and HEISENBERG'S method does not give very satisfactory results.

δ) HARTREE'S[2] *method* is the most far-reaching of the attempts to approximate the true potential by means of the unperturbed potential. The potential energy acting on the first electron is taken to be the COULOMB field of the nucleus plus

[1] W. HEISENBERG: Z. Physik **39**, 499 (1927).
[2] D. R. HARTREE: Proc. Cambridge Phil. Soc. **26**, 89 (1928).

the potential of the charge distribution of the second electron, viz.,

$$V_1(r_1) = -\frac{Z_1}{r_1} + \int d\tau_2\, u_2^2(2) \cdot \frac{1}{r_{12}}. \tag{27.7}$$

The true potential energy is thus averaged over all possible positions of the second electron. The potential energy on the second electron $V_2(r_2)$ is obtained in the same way.

HARTREE'S method contrasts with the procedures described above in this sense: The eigenfunctions in zeroth, and the eigenvalues in first, approximation evidently represent very good approximations. On the other hand, a systematic perturbation treatment cannot be carried out because the potentials V_1 and V_2 differ, and consequently the eigenfunctions U do not form an orthogonal system. Thus, unlike the procedure of expanding in powers of $1/Z$, HARTREE'S method does not enable one to obtain, even in principle, the exact eigenvalue by continuing the procedure to higher approximations. From the practical viewpoint HARTREE'S method has the disadvantage of requiring rather lengthy numerical integrations; furthermore, eigenfunctions and potentials satisfying (26.3) and (27.7) can be obtained only through a procedure of successive approximations.

The energy of the ground state is given much more accurately by the variation method than by HARTREE'S method. But for many applications it is useful to have as good a wave function as possible, which is still of the form of a product of two single-particle wave functions. HARTREE'S method gives the best wave function of this type and will be discussed in Sect. 31.

ε) FOCK'S method[1]. This method is similar to HARTREE'S, but uses fully symmetrized wave functions of product form. FOCK'S method thus takes exchange effects into account, but the numerical calculations are considerably more involved than even for HARTREE'S method. This method will be discussed only for highly excited S-states (Sect. 30), where HEISENBERG'S method is too crude and exchange effects are important.

ζ) The variation method[2] (cf. Sects. 32 through 34). The most exact results for eigenvalues and eigenfunctions may be obtained by means of RITZ'S variation method. A plausible form for the eigenfunction is set up from simple physical considerations, in which several numerical constants such as screening constants, coefficients in power series expansions, etc., are left arbitrary. These parameters are then determined by the condition that SCHRÖDINGER'S variational integral, i.e., the total energy, be a minimum. SCHRÖDINGER'S variational problem is thus reduced to an ordinary minimum problem. By including a sufficient number of arbitrary constants in the general form of the eigenfunction, to be determined by the minimizing condition, one can approximate the eigenfunction and eigenvalue as closely as one pleases. An adroit choice of the form of the eigenfunction will make the procedure converge rapidly. In this connection a choice of suitable independent variables is particularly important.

The procedure, unfortunately, is applicable only to low levels because the eigenfunction of an excited state must always be orthogonal to the eigenfunctions of all lower levels. This imposes a large number of subsidiary conditions on the excited state eigenfunctions which make the variational procedure unwieldy and eventually useless (cf. Sect. 35).

---

[1] V. FOCK: Z. Physik **61**, 126 (1930).

[2] E.g., E. A. HYLLERAAS: Z. Physik **54**, 347 (1929). — G. KELLNER: Z. Physik **44**, 91 (1927).

28. First order HEISENBERG's method (excited states). We discuss now HEISENBERG's method in detail, which is especially suitable if one of the two electrons is in a fairly highly excited state of non-zero angular momentum. We now apply the method, discussed at the end of Sect. 25γ, to the choice of potentials of (27.5). In the notation of (25.14) we have

$$\left.\begin{aligned} H_{0a} &= -\frac{1}{2}(\Delta_1 + \Delta_2) - \frac{Z}{r_1} - \frac{Z-1}{r_2}, \\ W_a &\equiv \lambda H_{1a} = \frac{1}{r_{12}} - \frac{1}{r_2}. \end{aligned}\right\} \tag{28.1}$$

Let u_1 denote the normalized ground state wave function for a hydrogen-like atom of charge Z, u_{nlm} the normalized hydrogen-like wave function for an excited state with charge $(Z-1)$. Then $u_1(1)\, u_{nlm}(2)$ is an eigenstate of the zero-order HAMILTONian H_{0a} with energy eigenvalue E_0 given by (26.9). Define H_{0b} and W_b as in (28.1), but with the roles of r_1 and r_2 interchanged. Then $u_{nlm}(1)\, u_1(2)$ is an eigenstate of H_{0b} with the *same* eigenvalue E_0.

We now take as our zero-order wave functions, following (26.7),

$$U_{\pm}(1,2) = \frac{1}{\sqrt{2}}\left[u_1(1)\, u_{nlm}(2) \pm u_{nlm}(1)\, u_1(2)\right], \tag{28.2}$$

where the plus sign refers to para-states, the minus sign to ortho-states[1]. We now apply Eq. (25.18) for E_1, the first order perturbation energy. Putting the perturbation parameter λ equal to unity, we have

$$E_1 = \frac{1}{\sqrt{2}}\int d\tau_1\, d\tau_2\, U_{\pm}^* \left[\left(\frac{1}{r_{12}} - \frac{1}{r_2}\right) u_1(1)\, u_{nlm}(2) \pm \left(\frac{1}{r_{12}} - \frac{1}{r_1}\right) u_{nlm}(1)\, u_1(2)\right], \tag{28.3}$$

where $d\tau_1$, $d\tau_2$ are the volume elements for the first and second electron, respectively. Consider now the integrals involving $1/r_2$. In keeping with the philosophy of the method of Sect. 25β we *assume*[2] that u_1 and u_{nlm} are orthogonal to zero-order. We thus make the replacement

$$\int d\tau_1\, u_1(1)\, u_{nlm}^*(1) \int d\tau_2\, u_{nlm}^*(2)\, u_1(2) = 0$$

with a similar equation for some terms involving $1/r_1$. (28.3) then reduces to

$$E_1 = \frac{1}{2}\int d\tau_1\, d\tau_2 \left[2\,|U_{\pm}|^2 \frac{1}{r_{12}} - |u_1(1)|^2\, |u_{nlm}(2)|^2 \frac{1}{r_2} - |u_{nlm}(1)|^2 |u_1(2)|^2 \frac{1}{r_1}\right]. \tag{28.4}$$

We next expand out the expression $|U_{\pm}|^2$ and collect integrals which are identical. Adding E_1 to the zero-order energy E_0, Eq. (26.9), we get finally for the total energy, up to and including first order,

$$E_{(1)} \equiv E_0 + E_1 = -\frac{1}{2} Z^2 - \frac{1}{2}\frac{(Z-1)^2}{n^2} + J \pm K, \tag{28.5}$$

where

$$J = \int d\tau_1\, d\tau_2 \left(\frac{1}{r_{12}} - \frac{1}{r_2}\right) u_1^2(1)\, |u_{nlm}(2)|^2, \tag{28.6}$$

$$K = \int d\tau_1\, d\tau_2\, u_1(1)\, u_{nlm}^*(1) \frac{1}{r_{12}}\, u_1(2)\, u_{nlm}(2). \tag{28.7}$$

---

[1] The choice of the linear combinations U_+ and U_- is not only *convenient* for the consideration of the PAULI principle, etc., but is *necessary* from the point of view of perturbation theory. This choice, and no other, ensures that the perturbation HAMILTONian W has zero matrix element $\langle U_{\pm}^* W U_{\mp}\rangle$ between these two degenerate zero-order eigenstates.

[2] For the special case of $l = 0$ these two wave functions are not exactly orthogonal, since they correspond to different nuclear charges. A more systematic derivation of (28.4) will be found in ref. [*10*], Sect. 14, based on our Eq. (27.6).

α) Physical meaning of the integrals. J and K have a very simple physical meaning: J is the COULOMB interaction between the charge distributions of the two electrons plus the interaction between the outer electron and one unit of positive charge concentrated at the nucleus.

The latter interaction appears in the perturbation theory because in zeroth approximation we regarded the outer electron to be under the influence of an effective nuclear charge $Z-1$ rather than the actual nuclear charge Z. Since the charge cloud of the inner electron lies almost entirely inside that of the outer electron, the COULOMB effect on the outer electron is almost the same as if the cloud of the inner electron were concentrated at the nucleus. Hence, the two COULOMB interactions of which J is composed almost cancel each other. This is a welcome indication of the usefulness of our unperturbed potential and zeroth order eigenfunctions. The COULOMB integral J does not vanish altogether, only because a small fraction of the charge cloud of the inner electron is farther from the nucleus than the charge cloud of the outer electron. J has a small negative value because the unscreened remainder of the nuclear charge exercises an attractive force on the outer electron.

K is the so-called exchange integral. It is a measure of the frequency with which the two electrons exchange their quantum states. To make this clear, let us assume that we *know*[1] that at time $t=0$ electron 1 is in the ground state and electron 2 is in an excited state. We may, for example, assume that electron 2 has just been bound to a He^+ ion. Then the wave function at $t=0$ would be

$$\Psi(0) = u_1(1)\,u_n(2) = \frac{1}{\sqrt{2}}\,(U_+ + U_-).$$

Including the time factors in the eigenfunctions we obtain as the wave function at time t:

$$\left.\begin{aligned}\Psi(t) &= \frac{1}{\sqrt{2}}\,(\Psi_+(t) + \Psi_-(t)) = \frac{1}{\sqrt{2}}\,(U_+\,e^{-i(E+K)t} + U_-\,e^{-i(E-K)t})\\ &= e^{-iEt}\cdot\left[u_1(1)\,u_n(2)\cos Kt - i\,u_n(1)\,u_1(2)\sin Kt\right]\end{aligned}\right\} \tag{28.8}$$

[E is the arithmetic mean between the energies of ortho and para state as given by (28.5)]. When the time interval $\pi/2K$ has elapsed, the two electrons have interchanged their respective roles; electron 1 is now excited and electron 2 is in the ground state. At time π/K they are back in their original orbits. Time is, of course, measured in the atomic unit $(1/4\pi\,\mathrm{Ry})$ (Ry = RYDBERG frequency). In c.g.s. units the period of the exchange is $\frac{\pi}{K}\cdot\frac{1}{4\pi\,\mathrm{Ry}} = \frac{1}{4K\,\mathrm{Ry}} = \frac{0.75\times10^{-16}\,\mathrm{sec}}{K}$. The more the eigenfunctions of the two electrons overlap (i.e., the smaller the principal and orbital quantum numbers of the outer electron are), the larger will be K and the more frequently will the electron exchange take place. If, for example, the outer electron is in the $2p$ state then (Sect. 28γ) $K=0.00382$ and an exchange (there and back) takes 10^{-14} sec. If, on the other hand, the outer electron has quantum numbers $n=10$, $l=9$, an exchange of electrons takes place only once every 0.5×10^{11} sec $=1600$ years, although the "diameter" of the outer electron orbit amounts to only 100 atomic units (0.5×10^{-6} cm).

The separation between the ortho and the corresponding para term, when measured in units of frequency, is precisely equal to the frequency of the electron exchange. The para term lies always somewhat higher then the ortho term

---

[1] This assumption violates the principle of the indistinguishability of electrons and the following argument should not be taken too seriously.

because K, being the potential due to the effect of the charge distribution $u_1 u_{nlm}$ on itself, is always positive.

β) Evaluation of the direct COULOMB *interaction integral.* We would like to evaluate the integrals J and K and shall do so, considering J first. Let us recall that the eigenfunction u_{nlm} is the product of a radially dependent function and a spherical harmonic:

$$u_{nlm} = R_{nl}(r)\, Y_{lm}(\vartheta, \varphi).$$

Substituting this into (28.6) we obtain

$$J = \int_0^\infty \int_0^\infty r_1^2\, d r_1\, r_2^2\, d r_2\, R_{10}^2(r_1)\, R_{nl}^2(r_2)\, J(r_1 r_2), \tag{28.9}$$

where

$$J(r_1 r_2) = \int_0^\pi \sin\vartheta_1\, d\vartheta_1 \int_0^{2\pi} d\varphi_1 \int_0^\pi \sin\vartheta_2\, d\vartheta_2 \int_0^{2\pi} d\varphi_2 \left(\frac{1}{r_{12}} - \frac{1}{r_2}\right) Y_{00}^2(\vartheta_1, \varphi_1)\, |Y_{lm}(\vartheta_2, \varphi_2)|^2. \tag{28.10}$$

The integrations over angles in $J(r_1 r_2)$ can easily be carried out by expanding $1/r_{12}$ in terms of spherical harmonics. Paying attention to the normalization of the spherical harmonics, one obtains

$$J(r_1 r_2) = \left\{\begin{matrix} 1/r_1 - 1/r_2, & \text{if } r_1 > r_2, \\ 0, & \text{if } r_1 < r_2. \end{matrix}\right\} \tag{28.11}$$

$u_{10}(r_1)$ is the eigenfunction of the ground state of an atom having nuclear charge Z and a single electron [cf. Eq. (3.18)], hence,

$$R_{10}(r) = 2 Z^{\frac{3}{2}} e^{-Zr}, \tag{28.12}$$

so that

$$\left.\begin{aligned} \int_0^\infty R_{10}^2(r_1)\, J(r_1 r_2)\, r_1^2\, d r_1 &= \int_{r_2}^\infty \left(\frac{1}{r_1} - \frac{1}{r_2}\right) r_1^2\, d r_1 \cdot 4 Z^3 e^{-2Z r_1} \\ &= -\left(Z + \frac{1}{r_2}\right) e^{-2Z r_2}. \end{aligned}\right\} \tag{28.13}$$

The eigenfunction of the excited electron $R_{nl}(r_2)$, as we have seen, is also a hydrogenic eigenfunction, but the nuclear charge must be taken to be $Z-1$. Accordingly, from (3.16) we obtain:

$$\left.\begin{aligned} R_{nl}(r_2) &= \frac{(n-l-1)!^{\frac{1}{2}}}{(n+l)!^{\frac{3}{2}}\,(2n)^{\frac{1}{2}}} \cdot \left[\frac{2(Z-1)}{n}\right]^{\frac{3}{2}} \varrho^l e^{-\frac{1}{2}\varrho} L_{n+l}^{2l+1}(\varrho), \\ \varrho &= \frac{2(Z-1)}{n}\, r_2. \end{aligned}\right\} \tag{28.14}$$

Substituting (28.13) and (28.14) into (28.9) and replacing the integration variable r_2 by ϱ throughout, we obtain

$$J = -\frac{(n-l-1)!}{(n+l)!^3\, 2n} \cdot Z \cdot \int_0^\infty e^{-\varrho - \frac{Zn}{Z-1}\varrho}\, \varrho^{2l+2} \left(L_{n+l}^{2l+1}(\varrho)\right)^2 \left[1 + \frac{2(Z-1)}{n Z \varrho}\right] d\varrho. \tag{28.15}$$

The integration over ϱ is straightforward for the case $n = l+1$ (corresponding to the circular orbits of BOHR's theory) because the LAGUERRE function reduces to a constant, viz.,

$$L_{2l+1}^{2l+1} = -(2l+1)!,$$

as may be seen by inspection of (3.7). The COULOMB integral (28.15) can be carried out by elementary means and amounts to

$$J = -Z \cdot \frac{(Z-1)^{2n+1}}{[Z(n+1)-1]^{2n+1}} \left[1 + \frac{Z(n+1)-1}{Z n^2}\right]. \tag{28.16}$$

This formula made its first appearance in HEISENBERG'S classic work on the helium spectrum[1]. The integration of (28.15) also presents no particular difficulty[2] for $n = l+2$ for which the LAGUERRE function consists of two terms. For larger n (and fixed l) however, the evaluation of, and the final formula for, J become rather complicated. For very large n, on the other hand, it is possible to obtain a relatively simple asymptotic formula which may be derived by making use of the generating function for the associated LAGUERRE function which is given at the end of Sect. 3. One obtains[3]

$$\left.\begin{aligned} J = -\frac{1}{n^3} \frac{(Z-1)^{2l+3}}{Z^{2l+2}} e^{-2\frac{Z-1}{Z}} \sum_{k=0}^{\infty} \left(\frac{Z-1}{Z}\right)^{2k} \times \\ \times \frac{1}{k!\,(2l+k+1)!} \left[1 + \frac{2l+k+2}{2}\left(1 - \frac{Z-1}{Z\cdot(2l+k+2)}\right)^2\right]. \end{aligned}\right\} \tag{28.17}$$

The summation over k introduces no complications because the sum converges extremely rapidly. The following conclusions may be drawn from (28.17) without further calculations:

1. For large principal quantum number, the COULOMB integral J is inversely proportional to $1/n^3$ and does not otherwise depend on n. It is therefore possible to sum up the unperturbed energy of the outer electron in the field of the nuclear charge $Z-1$ and the COULOMB energy J in a formula of the RYDBERG type:

$$-\frac{(Z-1)^2}{2n^2} + J = -\frac{(Z-1)^2}{2(n+\delta_C)^2}. \tag{28.18}$$

The RYDBERG correction δ_c is given by

$$\delta_c = \frac{n^3 J}{(Z-1)^2} = \frac{1}{Z} \cdot \left(\frac{Z-1}{Z}\right)^{2l+1} e^{-2\frac{Z-1}{Z}} \cdot \sum_k \ldots, \tag{28.19}$$

(28.19) is the most convenient expression for the deviation of the helium spectrum from the hydrogen spectrum since it is (for large n) independent of the principal quantum number n[4]. (The index c stands for COULOMB interaction).

2. The RYDBERG correction δ_c falls off rapidly with increasing orbital quantum number on account of both the factor $\left(\frac{Z-1}{Z}\right)^{2l+1}$ and the denominators $(2l+1+k)!$. This comes about in this way: J is the larger, the more frequently electron 2 penetrates the charge cloud of the inner electron 1. After all, according to (28.11), only the regions $r_1 > r_2$ contribute to J (see also the above discussion about the meaning of the COULOMB integral). Electrons with small orbital quantum number (moving in eccentric BOHR orbits) are more likely to penetrate than those with large l (the probability of finding an electron in the neighborhood of the nucleus is proportional to r^{2l}).

[1] W. HEISENBERG: Z. Physik **39**, 499 (1926).

[2] Cf. W. HEISENBERG: loc. cit. Eq. (16).

[3] E. HYLLERAAS: Z. Physik **66**, 453 (1930).

[4] For small n, δ_c, defined by (28.18) and computed by evaluating the appropriate J, e.g. (28.16), naturally differs somewhat from its value for large n. The relative difference is so very small however (cf. Table 4), that the value of δ_c for any n may be found very accurately by interpolating between its values at three values of n, such as $n = l+1$, $l+2$, ∞.

3. The dependence of the RYDBERG correction δ_c on the nuclear charge Z comes about from the presence of two mutually opposing effects. On the one hand, there is the factor $1/Z$ in (28.19) which has its origin in that δ_c essentially represents the ratio of the interaction J between the two electrons to the interaction between the outer electron and the nucleus (unperturbed energy of the outer electron). On the other hand, there is the factor $\left(\frac{Z-1}{Z}\right)^{2l+1} \exp\left(-2\frac{Z-1}{Z}\right)$ which increases rapidly with increasing Z. Its presence is consistent with the fact that the ratio between the radii of inner and outer electronic orbits is proportional to $Z/Z-1$. The larger Z is, the more contracted is the orbit of the outer electron relative to that of the inner electron, and, thus, the more frequently does the outer electron penetrate the K shell (cf. Sect. 2). For small nuclear charge this increase in $|\delta_c|$ with increasing Z outweighs the decrease due to $1/Z$ (cf. Table 4, He and Li^+).

γ) Evaluation of the exchange integral. The integral over the angles

$$K(r_1 r_2) = \iiiint \sin\vartheta_1\, d\vartheta_1\, d\varphi_1 \sin\vartheta_2\, d\vartheta_2\, d\varphi_2\, Y_{00}(\vartheta_1\varphi_1)\, Y_{lm}^*(\vartheta_1\varphi_1)\, Y_{00}(\vartheta_2\varphi_2)\, Y_{lm}(\vartheta_2\varphi_2)\, \frac{1}{r_{12}}$$

is most easily carried out by expanding $1/r_{12}$ again in terms of spherical harmonics. The result is

$$K(r_1 r_2) = \frac{1}{2l+1}\frac{r_1^l}{r_2^{l+1}}, \quad \text{if} \quad r_1 < r_2; \qquad \frac{1}{2l+1}\frac{r_2^l}{r_1^{l+1}}, \quad \text{if} \quad r_1 > r_2. \tag{28.20}$$

Substituting this into (28.7) gives

$$K = \frac{2}{2l+1}\int_0^\infty r_2^{l+2}\, dr_2\, R_{10}(r_2)\, R_{nl}(r_2) \int_{r_2}^\infty r_1^{-l+1}\, dr_1\, R_{10}(r_1)\, R_{nl}(r_1). \tag{28.21}$$

The factor of 2 comes from indicating an integration over the region $r_1 > r_2$ only, the region $r_1 < r_2$ contributes an exactly equal amount. Substituting the radial eigenfunctions (28.12) and (28.14) we obtain, for $n = l+1$ [1],

$$K = \frac{4Z^3(Z-1)^{2n+1}\, n^2}{[Z(n+1)-1]^{2n+3}}\,\frac{2n+3}{2n-1}. \tag{28.22}$$

We shall at once write down the RYDBERG correction for large n which must be applied to the principal quantum number of the outer electron because of electron exchange, viz.,

$$\left.\begin{aligned} \delta_A &= \frac{n^3}{(Z-1)^2} K \\ &= \frac{2}{Z(2l+1)}\left(\frac{Z-1}{Z}\right)^{2l+1} e^{-2\frac{Z-1}{Z}} \sum_{k=0}^\infty \frac{2l+k+2}{k!\,(2l+k+1)!}\left(\frac{Z-1}{Z}\right)^{2k} \Phi_{2l+k+2}\left(\frac{Z-1}{Z}\right) \end{aligned}\right\} \tag{28.23}$$

where the index A stands for exchange and

$$\begin{aligned} \Phi_\lambda(x) = {} & 2\left(1-\frac{x}{\lambda}\right)\left[1-\frac{x}{\lambda}+4x\left(2-\frac{1}{\lambda}\right)F(1,\lambda+1,-x) - 8xF(1,\lambda,-x)\right] + \\ & + (\lambda+1)\left(1-2\frac{x}{\lambda}+\frac{x^2}{\lambda(\lambda+1)}\right)\left[1+4\frac{x}{\lambda}-\frac{x^2}{\lambda(\lambda+1)}-8\frac{x}{\lambda}F(1,\lambda+1,-x)\right]. \end{aligned}$$

---

[1] Cf. W. HEISENBERG: loc. cit. There may be found the somewhat more complicated formula for $n = l+2$ (Eq. 22).

F is the confluent hypergeometric function

$$F(1, \lambda, -x) = \sum_{\varrho=0}^{\infty} \frac{(-x)^{\varrho}}{\lambda(\lambda+1)\cdots(\lambda+\varrho-1)} . \tag{28.24}$$

In spite of its complicated appearance, formula (28.23) is easily managed since all series (both over ϱ and k) converge very rapidly. They are considerably simpler than those of HYLLERAAS[1].

The qualitative behavior of the RYDBERG correction δ_A is evidently the same as that of $\delta_c \cdot \delta_A$ is constant for large n (otherwise there would be no sense to introducing it); changes very little when passing to small n (with l fixed); falls off rapidly with increasing l and contains two factors which are respectively increasing and decreasing functions of Z. The qualitative justification for this is also quite analogous to that for the COULOMB integral. It is true that K, unlike J, does not depend on the penetration of the charge cloud of the inner electron by the outer electron, but it does depend on the extent of overlap of the two charge clouds and this amounts to the same thing as far as the l and Z dependences are concerned.

δ) Result of the first approximation. The total energy in first approximation of the outer electron of an atom having two electrons thus amounts to [cf. Eq. (28.5)]

$$E_1 + \frac{1}{2} Z^2 = -\frac{1}{2} \frac{(Z-1)^2}{(n+\delta_c \pm \delta_A)^2} . \tag{28.25}$$

The positive sign in front of δ_A belongs to parahelium, the negative sign to orthohelium. Table 4 shows a comparison between observed and calculated values of the RYDBERG correction $\delta_c \pm \delta_A$ of the helium terms. As empirical value of δ_c we must, of course, take the arithmetic mean between the RYDBERG corrections of ortho and parahelium, as δ_A half the difference of the two RYDBERG corrections[2].

Table 4. RYDBERG *corrections for He and Li⁺.*

δ_0, δ_P are observed ortho and para corrections; δ_c and δ_π are the theoretical first order and polarization COULOMB corrections and δ_A the exchange correction.

	$-\delta_c$	$-(\delta_c+\delta_\pi)$	$-\frac{1}{2}(\delta_0+\delta_P)$ Observed	δ_A	$\frac{1}{2}(\delta_0-\delta_P)$ Observed
		He			
∞S	0.168	0.216	0.218	0.376	0.078
$2P$	0.0083	0.0232	0.0265	0.0305	0.0358
				(0.0339)	
$3P$	0.009	0.0242	0.0273	0.0332	0.0384
∞P	0.0104	0.0248	0.027_9	0.0351	0.039_8
$3D$	0.00010	0.00203	0.00198	0.00034	0.00020
				(0.00029)	
∞D	0.00018	0.00262	0.0025_2	0.00066	0.0003_5
$4F$	$< 10^{-5}$	0.00008	0.00013	$< 10^{-5}$	0.00008
		Li⁺			
∞S	0.112	0.127	0.127	0.145	0.052
$2P$	0.009	0.017	0.020	0.030	0.033
∞P	0.011	0.019	0.021	0.033	0.034
$3D$	0.0002	0.0016	0.0015	0.0006	0.0005

[1] E. A. HYLLERAAS: Z. Physik **66**, 453 (1930).

[2] The experimental results are taken from C. E. MOORE, Atomic Energy Levels, Vol. I, NBS Circular No. 467. 1949.

As the Table 4 shows, both the experimental and theoretical RYDBERG corrections increase very slowly with increasing principal quantum n and decrease very rapidly with increasing orbital quantum number l. For $l \neq 0$ the theoretical exchange correction δ_A is at least in semi-quantitative agreement[1] with the ortho-para separation, $\frac{1}{2}(\delta_0 - \delta_P)$. The theoretical COULOMB correction, δ_c, on the other hand, is much too small compared with the experimental $\frac{1}{2}(\delta_0 + \delta_P)$, especially for the larger values of l. The agreement with $\frac{1}{2}(\delta_0 + \delta_P)$ is much improved if δ_π, a correction due to polarization of the inner electron by the outer, is added to δ_c. A method for calculating δ_π is outlined in Sect. 29. For S-states the present method gives unsatisfactory results for δ_A. The S-states with large n are discussed in Sect. 30, those with $n=2$ in Sect. 35.

29. Polarization for excited states. In Sect. 28 we merely treated HEISENBERG'S choice of potential (28.1) in first order perturbation theory. This consisted of taking the expectation value of the HAMILTONian over the zero-order wave function, which consists of the product of two independent single-particle wave functions. In reality, the correct He wave functions cannot be exactly of this simple form, since the presence of one electron at a particular position affects the wave function of the other. The COULOMB repulsion due to one electron polarizes the charge distribution of the other such as to increase their mutual separation. Conventional second order perturbation theory would take account of the perturbation of the zero-order wave function, and hence of polarization. A rigorous second-order treatment is, however, much too tedious. We shall merely outline[2] a cruder but relatively simple approximation method, applicable to excited states.

We shall only evaluate the effect of polarization on the COULOMB correction δ_c, *not* its effect on the exchange term, δ_A. For this purpose it is sufficient to take an *unsymmetrized* wave function. We consider electron 1 to be in the ground state, electron 2 in the excited state. The zero-order energy is still given by (26.9), but the zero-order wave function U_0 and first-order energy E_1 (putting $\lambda = 1$ again) by

$$U_0 = u_1(1)\, u_{nlm}(2), \qquad E_1 = \int d\tau_1\, d\tau_2\, W\, |U_0|^2 = J. \tag{29.1}$$

In (29.1) the perturbation potential W is given by (28.1),

$$W(\boldsymbol{r}_1, \boldsymbol{r}_2) = \frac{1}{r_{12}} - \frac{1}{r_2}, \tag{29.2}$$

and J by (28.6). The first order perturbation U_1 to the wave function is then determined by the differential Eq. (25.8), which takes the form

$$\left[\frac{1}{2}(\Delta_1 + \Delta_2) + \frac{Z}{r_1} + \frac{Z-1}{r_2} - \frac{Z^2}{2} - \frac{(Z-1)^2}{2n^2}\right] U_1 = (W - J)\, U_0. \tag{29.3}$$

Once U_1 has been determined, the second order perturbation E_2 to the energy is then given by the integral (25.11),

$$E_2 = \int d\tau_1\, d\tau_2\, W(\boldsymbol{r}_1, \boldsymbol{r}_2)\, U_0\, U_1. \tag{29.4}$$

We discuss only an approximate method for solving (29.3). We make use of the fact that the "average velocity" of the outer electron 2 is small compared with that of the inner electron 1. This follows from the fact that for a state of larger principal quantum number (electron 2) the binding energy and hence (from the virial theorem) the average *kinetic energy* is smaller than for $n=1$.

---

[1] The values in parentheses in the δ_A-column of Table 4 (for $2P$ and $3D$) are discussed at the end of Sect. 29.

[2] A detailed account of this method will be found in ref. [*10*], Sect. 15.

We can then apply an approximation method, somewhat equivalent to the FRANCK CONDON principle used in the treatment of molecules. Physically speaking, we consider the slow-moving electron 2 as "temporarily at rest" at some position $\boldsymbol{r}_2$. The inner electron 1 then "sees", in addition to the zero order potential, the potential W, Eq. (29.2), for this *fixed* value of $\boldsymbol{r}_2$. For each value of $\boldsymbol{r}_2$ we then have a polarized wave function for the inner electron, somewhat like in the quadratic STARK effect (Sect. 52). The outer electron 2 at position $\boldsymbol{r}_2$, on the other hand, "sees" only the average charge distribution of the fast-moving inner electron 1. Electron 2 then "sees", in addition to the zero order potentials only an extra potential $\varepsilon_1(\boldsymbol{r}_2)+\varepsilon_2(\boldsymbol{r}_2)$, due to the charge cloud of the inner electron 1, but *integrated* over the coordinates of electron 1. The potential ε_1 is due to the zero order, unpolarized, distribution of electron 1 and simply leads to the first order energy $E_1=J$. The potential ε_2 is due to the polarization of electron 1. ε_1 and ε_2 are fairly small and do not affect the wave function of the outer electron greatly. The expectation value of ε_2, averaged over the unperturbed wave function of electron 2, should then give the desired approximation for the effect of polarization on the total energy.

Mathematically speaking, we write the first order wave function in the form

$$U_1 = u_{\boldsymbol{r}_2}(\boldsymbol{r}_1)\, u_{n l m}(\boldsymbol{r}_2), \tag{29.5}$$

where $u_{\boldsymbol{r}_2}$ is an (as yet arbitrary) function of $\boldsymbol{r}_1$, which also depends on $\boldsymbol{r}_2$, and u_{nlm} is the unperturbed wave function of the outer electron. By substituting (29.5) into (29.3), we can still get an exact equation for $u_{\boldsymbol{r}_2}(\boldsymbol{r}_1)$. Our physical approximation consists of dropping all derivatives with respect to $\boldsymbol{r}_2$ in this equation. In this case this six-dimensional equation reduces to an infinite uncoupled set of three-dimensional equations, one for each value of $\boldsymbol{r}_2$,

$$\left(\frac{1}{2}\Delta_1+\frac{Z}{r_1}-\frac{Z^2}{2}\right) u_{\boldsymbol{r}_2}(\boldsymbol{r}_1)=\left(\frac{1}{r_{12}}-\frac{1}{r_2}-J\right) u_{100}(\boldsymbol{r}_1), \tag{29.6}$$

where u_{100} is the zero order wave function for electron 1. After solving (29.6) for $u_{\boldsymbol{r}_2}$, we then get an approximation for the second order energy E_2 from (29.4),

$$E_2=\int d\tau_2\, |u_{nlm}(2)|^2\, \varepsilon_2(\boldsymbol{r}_2), \tag{29.7}$$

where

$$\varepsilon_2(\boldsymbol{r}_2)=\int d\tau_1\, u_{\boldsymbol{r}_2}(\boldsymbol{r}_1)\left(\frac{1}{r_{12}}-\frac{1}{r_2}\right) u_{100}(r_1). \tag{29.8}$$

We approximate the Eq. (29.6) further before solving it. The term involving J is fairly small and would give an even smaller contribution to E_2 and we omit it. Next we expand $\left(\frac{1}{r_{12}}-\frac{1}{r_2}\right)$ in spherical harmonics and keep only the first nonzero term,

$$\frac{1}{r_{12}}-\frac{1}{r_2}=\frac{1}{r_1}-\frac{1}{r_<}+\frac{r_<}{r_>^2}\cos\vartheta_{12}+\cdots,$$

where ϑ_{12} is the angle between $\boldsymbol{r}_1$ and $\boldsymbol{r}_2$, $r_<$ and $r_>$ are the smaller and larger, respectively, of r_1 and r_2. Since r_2 is "mostly" much larger than r_1, the higher terms are not very important and, since $\frac{1}{r_1}-\frac{1}{r_<}$ is "mostly" zero, we drop this term also. (29.6) then reduces to the simpler equation

$$\left.\begin{aligned} u_{\boldsymbol{r}_2}(\boldsymbol{r}_1) &\equiv w_{\boldsymbol{r}_2}(r_1)\cos\vartheta_{12}, \\ \left(\frac{d^2}{dr_1^2}+\frac{2}{r_1}\frac{d}{dr_1}-\frac{2}{r_1^2}-Z^2+\frac{2Z}{r_1}\right) w_{\boldsymbol{r}_2}(r_1) &= 2\frac{r_<}{r_>^2}\, u_{100}(r_1). \end{aligned}\right\} \tag{29.9}$$

This equation, finally, can be solved fairly simply[1] for $w_{r_2}(r_1)$, using the explicit form (3.18) for u_{100} and the fact that w must be finite for $r_1 = 0$ and ∞. The integral (29.8) can then be evaluated explicitly and the resulting expression for $\varepsilon_2(r_2)$ is an elementary but lengthy expression[2] involving exponentials and polynomials in the quantity $(Z r_2)$.

For $Z r_2$ approaching infinity the "exact" expression[3] for $\varepsilon_2(r_2)$ reduces to the simple expression

$$\varepsilon_2(r_2) = -\frac{9}{4Z^4}\frac{1}{r_2^4}. \tag{29.10}$$

This *limiting* expression could have been obtained much more simply by replacing the electric field due to the very distant electron 2 by the *constant* electric field $F = 1/r_2^2$. The ordinary formula (52.3) for the STARK effect then immediately yields (29.10). Clearly, this approximation is valid only if r_2 is much larger than the BOHR radius of the inner electron, i.e. if $Z r_2 \gg 1$. For smaller values of r_2 the exact expression for ε_2 has to be used. For $Z r_2 \ll 1$, for instance, ε_2 reduces to $-\frac{2}{3}(Z r_2)^2$.

Finally, the second order correction E_2 is obtained by substituting the exact expression for $\varepsilon_2(r_2)$ into the integral (29.7), using the explicit hydrogen-like wave functions u_{nlm}. This integral can be evaluated explicitly (the rather lengthy results are given in ref. [*10*], p. 344). For large principal quantum number n, E_2 (as well as E_1) is proportional to n^{-3}. In analogy with (28.25) we define a "polarization correction" δ_π by the relation

$$E_0 + E_1 + E_2 + \frac{Z^2}{2} = -\frac{1}{2}\frac{(Z-1)^2}{n^2} + J \pm K + E_2 \equiv -\frac{1}{2}\frac{(Z-1)^2}{(n+\delta_C+\delta_\pi\pm\delta_A)^2}. \tag{29.11}$$

The term δ_π, as well as δ_c and δ_A, is then a slowly varying function of n.

For large orbital quantum number l, the wave function of the outer electron is extremely small at "small" radial distances ($Z r_2 \lesssim 1$). If the approximation (29.10) is used for ε_2 in (29.7), then E_2 is simply $-9/4Z^4$ times the expectation[4] value $\overline{r^{-4}}$ in (3.27). If, in addition, n is large, we have

$$\delta_\pi = \frac{n^3}{(Z-1)^2} E_2 \approx -\frac{27}{8}\frac{(Z-1)^2}{Z^4 l^5}\prod_{s=1}^{3}\left(1+\frac{s}{2l}\right)^{-1}. \tag{29.12}$$

For lower values of l, however, the wave function of the outer electron penetrates to an appreciable extent to radial distances smaller than the BOHR radius of the inner electron. For such small values of r_2, (29.10) is a bad overestimate for ε_2. For the $2P$, ∞P and $3D$ states in He, for instance, the ratio of the exact expression for δ_π to the approximation obtained from (29.10) is 0.32, 0.26 and 0.93, respectively. For S-states the expectation value of ε_2 as given by (29.10) would diverge altogether.

In the second column of Table 4, Sect. 28, we have added to the first order COULOMB correction δ_c the polarization correction δ_π, calculated from the "exact" expression for E_2. The table shows that δ_π decreases with increasing values of l, but not as rapidly as δ_c. For larger l, then, δ_π dominates δ_c and the theoretical expression $(\delta_c + \delta_\pi)$ is in fairly good agreement with the experimental value $\frac{1}{2}(\delta_0 + \delta_P)$, even for S-states.

[1] This is an example in which direct solution of a perturbation equation is simpler than expansion in a series of eigenfunctions of the unperturbed equation, cf. remarks after (25.12).

[2] The functions w and ε_2 are given explicitly in ref. [*10*], pp. 342 and 343.

[3] I.e. making no approximations *after* those leading to (29.9).

[4] In this expectation value, Z is replaced by $(Z-1)$.

The methods discussed in this section can also be extended to evaluate the effect of polarization on the exchange correction δ_A. These calculations are very tedious and the effect is small. It has nevertheless been calculated approximately by LUDWIG[1] for the $2P$ and $3D$ terms in He. The theoretical values for δ_A including LUDWIG's corrections for these two states are given in Table 4 in brackets. This correction improves the agreement with experiment slightly.

30. FOCK's method[2] (excited S-states). In Sects. 28 and 29 we have found theoretical expressions for the "average quantum defect" $\frac{1}{2}(\delta_0+\delta_P)$ (COULOMB or screening effects) and for the difference of the ortho-para defects, $\delta_0-\delta_P$ (exchange effects). For excited S-states, the theoretical expression for $\delta_0+\delta_P$ agrees reasonably well with the observed value, but the expression for $\delta_0-\delta_P$ does not agree at all. For S-states, the effect of polarization on $\delta_0+\delta_P$ is fairly small and one can show that its effect on $\delta_0-\delta_P$ is even smaller. The failure of HEISENBERG's method in calculating the exchange effect for S-states is thus due not to the use of product wave functions as such, but due to a poor choice for these wave functions.

The exchange integral K, Eq. (28.7), depends on the "overlap charge density" $\chi\equiv u_{100}(\boldsymbol{r})\,u_{nlm}(\boldsymbol{r})$. For large l, u_{nlm} is extremely small for small radial distances r and the overlap density χ has its maximum value for r appreciably larger than the BOHR radius a_0 for the inner electron. For S-states, on the other hand, u_{nlm} is appreciable even for small values of r and χ has its maximum for r of the order of a_0. Most of the contribution to the exchange integral K then comes from radial distances of the second electron which are partly *inside* the charge distribution of the inner electron. Now, HEISENBERG's method is based on the assumption that the outer electron "sees" only the COULOMB potential due to a "fully screened" effective charge $(Z-1)$. Although this is still a good approximation for the bulk of the wave function of the excited electron (at $r\sim n\,a_0\gg a_0$), it is *not* good at the smaller distances ($r\sim a_0$) from which most of the contribution to the exchange integral comes. We shall, therefore, attempt to find a wave function which is still of product form (polarization neglected), but with correct symmetrization and of *better* form than the simple hydrogenic wave functions of HEISENBERG's method.

FOCK's method restricts itself to wave functions of this type,

$$U(\boldsymbol{r}_1,\boldsymbol{r}_2)=\frac{1}{\sqrt{2}}\left[u_1(1)\,u_2(2)\pm u_2(1)\,u_1(2)\right], \qquad (30.1)$$

but finds the *most accurate* form possible for the two functions $u_1(\boldsymbol{r})$ and $u_2(\boldsymbol{r})$. One starts from the general variational principle which states that the expression (25.3) has a stationary value with respect to any infinitesimal variation of the trial wave function U, if U coincides with a correct eigenfunction of the total HAMILTONian H. We next substitute the form (30.1) for U into the expression (25.3) and require it to have a stationary value for any infinitesimal change $\delta u_1(\boldsymbol{r})$ and $\delta u_2(\boldsymbol{r})$ of the functions u_1 and u_2. Since $u_1(1)$ and $u_1(2)$ are identical functions, $\delta u_1(\boldsymbol{r}_1)$ and $\delta u_1(\boldsymbol{r}_2)$ are also identical and we have only two (not four) independent variations δu_1 and δu_2. Collecting together the terms involving δu_1 and δu_2, the variational principle takes the form

$$\sum_{i=1}^{2}\int d\tau_1\,\delta u_i(1)\left\{\int d\tau_2\,u_j(2)\,(H-E)\left[u_j(2)\,u_i(1)\pm u_i(2)\,u_j(1)\right]\right\}=0, \qquad (30.2)$$

---

[1] G. LUDWIG: Helv. phys. Acta **7**, 273 (1934).
[2] V. FOCK: Z. Physik **61**, 126 (1930).

where $j=2$ if $i=1$ and vice versa. Now $\delta u_1(1)$ and $\delta u_2(1)$ are independent of each other and arbitrary for *each* value of $\boldsymbol{r}_1$. For (30.2) to hold, the coefficients of $\delta u_1(1)$ and $\delta u_2(1)$ for each value of $\boldsymbol{r}_1$ (the two expressions in curly brackets in (30.2) with $i=1$ and 2) must vanish separately. This results in two coupled differential equations for the two unknown functions $u_1(\boldsymbol{r})$ and $u_2(\boldsymbol{r})$, which involve the eigenvalue E. These two equations, together with the boundary conditions of "good behavior", determine (in *principle*) the best approximations to the set of eigenfunctions and eigenvalues which are compatible with the restriction (30.1).

We introduce the following abbreviations (u_1 and u_2 are normalized to unity),

$$\left.\begin{aligned} H_0(r) &= -\frac{1}{2}\Delta - \frac{2}{r}, \\ I_{12} &= I_{21} = \int d\tau\, u_1 u_2, \\ H_{ik} &= H_{ki} = \int d\tau\, u_i H_0 u_k, \\ G_{ik}(r_1) &= G_{ki}(r_1) = \int d\tau_2\, u_i(2)\, u_k(2)\, \frac{1}{r_{12}}. \end{aligned}\right\} \tag{30.3}$$

Using the explicit form (24.1) for the HAMILTONian for He the two equations for u_1 and u_2 become[1]

$$\left.\begin{aligned} [H_0(\boldsymbol{r})-E+H_{22}+G_{22}(\boldsymbol{r})]\,u_1(\boldsymbol{r}) &= \mp[I_{12}(H_0-E)+H_{12}+G_{12}(\boldsymbol{r})]\,u_2(\boldsymbol{r}), \\ [H_0(\boldsymbol{r})-E+H_{11}+G_{11}(\boldsymbol{r})]\,u_2(\boldsymbol{r}) &= \mp[I_{12}(H_0-E)+H_{12}+G_{12}(\boldsymbol{r})]\,u_1(\boldsymbol{r}), \end{aligned}\right\} \tag{30.4}$$

where the minus-sign refers to para-, the plus-sign to ortho-He. The two Eqs. (30.4) have to be solved simultaneously and the "constants" I_{12} and H_{ik} and the function $G_{ik}(r)$ themselves depend on the form of the wave functions u_1 and u_2. As in HARTREE's method (see Sect. 31), these equations have to be solved by a method of successive approximation. The general solution of (30.4) would be much more laborious still than of the HARTREE equation, due to the presence of the terms on the right hand side of these equations (which stem from our requirement of symmetrization). We shall only discuss an approximate method of solving (30.4) for S-states.

We restrict ourselves to highly-excited S-states[2], i.e. outer electrons with $l=0$ and very large principal quantum number n. As n tends to infinity, $n^{\frac{3}{2}} u_2(r)$ becomes independent of n for finite values of r (see Sect. 3 δ). From our previous discussion of the HEISENBERG method we know that the total energy E of the helium atom will be of form

$$E = E_1 + E_2, \quad E_1 = -2, \quad E_2 = -\frac{1}{2(n+\delta)^2}, \tag{30.5}$$

where δ approaches a constant limit as n tends to infinity. We wish to determine these limits of δ and of $n^{\frac{3}{2}} u_2(\boldsymbol{r})$.

Consider the first equation in (30.4) for "finite" values of r (r of order unity, rather than n), where the wave function u_1 is appreciable (and of order unity). On the right side of this equation I_{12}, H_{12} and G_{12}, as well as u_2, are of order $n^{-\frac{3}{2}}$. The whole right hand side is then of order n^{-3} and can be dropped. On

[1] Since we are mainly interested in S-states, (30.2) to (30.4) are written for real wave functions only. The extension for complex u_1, u_2 is trivial.

[2] The ground state with $n=1$ and the states with $n=2$ are treated most accurately by the variation method (see Sects. 32 and 35). Since the RYDBERG corrections δ_0 and δ_P are slowly varying functions of n, a discussion of $n=1$, 2 and ∞ should suffice. For a separate discussion of S-states with intermediate values of n, see also E. HYLLERAAS, Z. Physik **83**, 739 (1933).

the left side H_{22}, G_{22} and $-E_2$ are of order n^{-2} and their sum can be shown to be of order n^{-3}, which we again neglect. With an error of order n^{-3} only, the differential equation for u_1 is then identical with that for the ground state wave function of He^+,

$$(H_0 - E_1)\, u_1 = 0, \qquad u_1 = 2^{\frac{5}{2}} e^{-2r}. \tag{30.6}$$

Physically speaking, only a fraction of order n^{-3} of the charge cloud of the outer electron penetrates inside the BOHR radius of the inner electron, whose wave function is then almost unscreened. Using (30.6), H_{11} reduces to E_1, H_{12} to $E_1 I_{12}$ and the second equation in (30.4) reduces to

$$[H_0 - E_2 + G_{11}(\boldsymbol{r})]\, u_2(\boldsymbol{r}) = \mp [E_1 I_{12} + G_{12}(\boldsymbol{r})]\, u_1(\boldsymbol{r}). \tag{30.7}$$

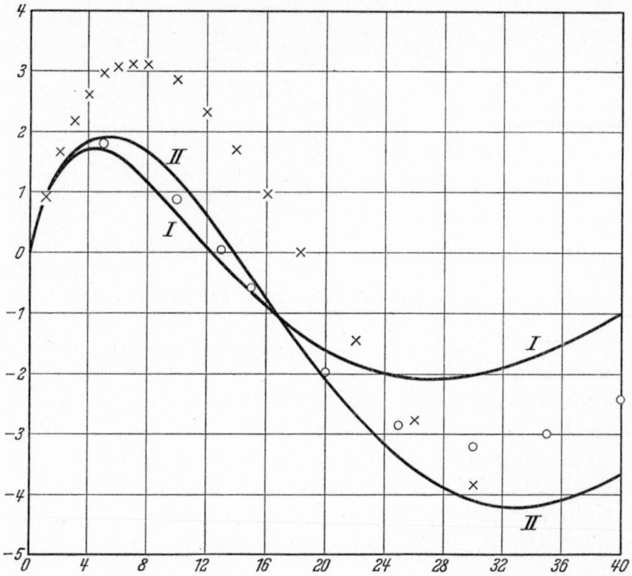

Fig. 16. The radial wave function $r\,R(r)$ for highly excited s-electrons in helium, according to FOCK's method (calculated by L. P. SMITH), plotted against radial distance r. Curve I is for orthohelium, curve II for parahelium, the circles denote the HARTREE wave function (exchange neglected) and the crosses denote the hydrogenic wave function (for zero energy).

For S-states, u_2 is spherically symmetric and (30.7) reduces to

$$\left[\frac{1}{2}\frac{d^2}{dr^2} + \frac{2}{r} - G_{11}(r) + E_2\right] v(r) = \pm [E_1 I_{12} + G_{12}(r)]\, r\, u_1(r), \tag{30.8}$$

where $v(r) = r u_2(r)$. Since u_1 is given by (30.6) and E_1 by (30.5), (30.8) is an nhomogeneous integral-differential equation for a single unknown function v of one variable r with one eigenvalue E_2. This equation was solved by SMITH[1], using a semi-numerical method. He treated the regions of $r < r_0$ and $r > r_0$ separately, where $1 \ll r_0 \ll n$. In the inner region both v and G_{12} are of order $n^{-\frac{3}{2}}$ and one can drop the term in E_2, which is smaller by two powers of n than the leading terms. The resulting equation, independent of n, can then be solved numerically, using the boundary condition $v(0) = 0$. This solution gives the logarithmic derivative of $v(r)$ at $r = r_0$ (which is appreciably different from that of a hydrogen wave function). In the outer region $r > r_0$ (r much larger than first BOHR radius), the term involving u_1 is very small and can be dropped and $G_{11}(r)$

[1] L. P. SMITH: Phys. Rev. 42, 176 (1932).

replaced by $1/r$. The term involving $E_2 = -\frac{1}{2}(n+\delta)^{-2}$ on the other hand, is retained. The general solution in the outer region for very large n can be found, using the WKB method (see Sects. 3δ and 53), and is required to match the solution for the inner region at $r = r_0$. The outer solution remains regular at infinity only for values of $(n+\delta)$ which differ from an integer by a constant amount and the RYDBERG correction δ is thus found (separately for ortho- and para-helium).

The values calculated by SMITH for the RYDBERG correction δ for highly excited S-states are -0.289 and -0.160 for ortho- and para-helium, respectively, in quite good agreement with the experimental values of -0.298 and -0.140. In Fig. 16 we give the calculated $v(r)$, which is r times the wave function of the excited electron for ortho- and para-He. The HARTREE wave function, obtained by omitting the right side (the exchange effects) of (30.4), and the hydrogen wave function (used in HEISENBERG's method) are also shown.

31. HARTREE's method[1]. The HARTREE method (see Sect. 27δ) has been very successful for the treatment of even very complex atoms. An outline of the procedure is as follows. The wave function of a particular atom is written in the form of a product of single particle wave functions $u_i(\boldsymbol{r}_i)$, one for each of the electrons. A guess is made of the wave function u_i of each electron and the electrostatic potential throughout space, $V_i(\boldsymbol{r})$, due to the charge distribution $|u_i(\boldsymbol{r}_i)|^2$ is calculated. These potentials V_i are summed over all values of i, except a particular one, k, and averaged over angles. This central potential (plus the nuclear one) is substituted into the SCHRÖDINGER equation for the k-th electron and the equation solved numerically for the wave function $u'_k(\boldsymbol{r}_k)$. This procedure is carried out for all values of k. In general the initial (guessed) wave functions u_i do not agree with the final ones u'_i. The whole procedure is then repeated, using now as *initial* wave functions u'_i (or some compromise between u_i and u'_i). New final wave functions u''_i are then calculated and used again as initial ones. This procedure is repeated until the initial and final wave functions agree to the desired accuracy. The field in which the electrons are assumed to move is then "self-consistent", i.e. identical with the field produced by the charge distribution of the electrons.

For two-electron atoms the HARTREE method is relatively simple. The wave function U of the atom is taken of the form $u_1(1)\,u_2(2)$. This is of similar form to the choice (30.1) of the FOCK method, but *without* symmetrization; hence HARTREE's method gives the same wave functions and energies for ortho- and para-states (exchange effects are neglected). Two equations for u_1 and u_2 can then be derived from the SCHRÖDINGER variational principle in analogy with the derivation of (30.4) in Sect. 30. The resulting equations are identical with (30.4), except that the right side of each equation in (30.4) is replaced by zero. Various states (including even doubly-excited ones) in He, Li^+, etc. have been investigated by HARTREE, WILSON and LINDSAY[2] and others.

We consider here only the ground state of He. Since the two electrons are in identical states we consider the two functions u_1 and u_2 as identical,

$$U = u(r_1)\,u(r_2)\,. \tag{31.1}$$

(31.1) already has the right symmetry properties and HARTREE's and FOCK's methods are identical. The expression $E(U)$, Eq. (25.3), is then required to have

[1] D. R. HARTREE: Proc. Cambridge Phil. Soc. **24**, 89 (1928).

[2] For a list of earlier references see W. S. WILSON and R. B. LINDSAY, Phys. Rev. **47**, 681 (1935). For a discussion of K-shell electrons in heavier atoms see R. E. MEYEROTT, Phys. Rev. **95**, 72 (1954).

a stationary value with respect to a variation in the *single* function u. This requirement leads to a single differential-integral equation, instead of (30.4). This differential-integral equation can be written in the form of two coupled equations,

$$\left[\frac{1}{2}\Delta + E_1 + \frac{2}{r} - G(r)\right] u(r) = 0, \tag{31.2}$$

together with

$$G(r_1) = \int d\tau_2 u^2(r_2) \frac{1}{r_{12}}, \tag{31.3}$$

and the function $u(r)$ is normalized to unity. The Eqs. (31.2) and (31.3) are then solved simultaneously, by the method of successive approximation outlined above, which yields the wave function $u(r)$ and eigenvalue E_1.

The solution of (31.2) and (31.3) yields the HARTREE wave function $u(r)$, which gives the best total wave function of form (31.1), and the corresponding eigenvalue parameter E_1 of (31.2). We now have to find the corresponding approximation for the total energy E of the actual atom, which is *not* simply twice E_1. This approximation to E is defined as the expectation value (25.3) of the total HAMILTONian H over the HARTREE wave function $u(r_1)\,u(r_2)$. Since we are considering the *ground* state of the atom, the arguments of Sect. 25α show that this value for E is an *upper* limit for the correct expression and the best (i.e. lowest) value obtainable with a wave function of product form (31.1).

To evaluate the energy expectation value we write the total HAMILTONian H in the form

$$H = H_1 + H_2 + \left[\frac{1}{r_{12}} - G(r_1) - G(r_2)\right], \quad H_i = -\frac{1}{2}\Delta_i - \frac{2}{r_i} + G(r_i), \tag{31.4}$$

where G is defined by (31.3). The expectation value of H_1 and H_2 is simply E_1 each and the expectation value E of H is then

$$E = 2E_1 - \overline{G}, \tag{31.5}$$

where

$$\overline{G} = \int d\tau\, u^2(r)\, G(r) = \iint d\tau_1\, d\tau_2\, u^2(r_1) \frac{1}{r_{12}} u^2(r_2) \tag{31.6}$$

and $u(r)$ is the normalized HARTREE wave function. The function $G(r)$ is the potential due to the charge distribution of one electron and $\overline{G}$ is the electrostatic interaction energy between the two electrons. The physical reason for the expression (31.5) is the fact that in evaluating the energy $2E_1$ we have included this interaction *twice*, once each in the wave equation (31.2) for each electron.

The ionization potential J of the helium ground state is the difference in energy of the ground states of the singly ionized helium ion He^+ (energy $E_0 = -2$ a.u.) and of the helium atom [E given by (31.5)]. Thus

$$J = E_0 - E = -2E_1 + \overline{G} + E_0. \tag{31.7}$$

The best value of J obtainable from the HARTREE wave function is given by (31.7), but one can show that J is at least fairly close to $-E_1$, as follows.

The normalized wave function u_0 of the He^+ ground state satisfies the equation

$$\left(\frac{1}{2}\Delta + E_0 + \frac{2}{r}\right) u_0(r) = 0. \tag{31.8}$$

Multiply (31.2) by u_0, (31.8) by $-u$, add the two equations and integrate over all space. In the resulting equation we call $\delta u \equiv u - u_0$, *assume* that δu is reasonably small and neglect terms quadratic in δu. In this approximation, comparison with (31.7) gives the following relation

$$J + E_1 \approx \int d\tau\, u\, \delta u\, [G(r) - \overline{G}]. \qquad (31.9)$$

Since $G(r)$ is a fairly slowly varying function of r (it is finite at the origin), the difference $G - \overline{G}$ will be fairly small. If, in addition, δu is fairly small, as we have assumed, then the right hand side of (31.9) will be quite small. These arguments can be generalized to complex atoms, where HARTREE's single-electron eigenvalue E_1 for a particular electron is often used as a simple approximation for (minus) the electron's ionization potential.

Eqs. (31.2) and (31.3) were solved first by HARTREE and, more accurately, by WILSON and LINDSAY[1]. A shortened version of their results is given in Table 5. The function $P(r)$ is r times the wave function, normalized such that

$$\int_0^\infty dr\, P^2(r) = 1,$$

with r in atomic units. Instead of $G(r)$, Eq. (31.3), a function $Z_p(r)$ is tabulated which is defined by

$$\frac{Z_p(r)}{r} = \frac{2}{r} - G(r). \qquad (31.10)$$

The total charge (including the nucleus) inside radius r is given by

$$Z_{\text{eff}}(r) = 2 - 2\int_0^r dr'\, P^2(r') = 2\int_r^\infty dr'\, P^2(r'). \qquad (31.11)$$

The calculations also give (in atomic units)

$$2E_1 = -1.836, \quad G(0) = +1.687, \quad \left(\frac{P}{r}\right)_{r=0} = 4.75_5. \qquad (31.12)$$

Using the tabulated values of $P(r)$ and $G(r)$, the constant $\overline{G}$, Eq. (31.6), can be evaluated by numerical integration. The result is $\overline{G} = 1.027$. Using (31.7) one finds for the ionization potential, $J = 1.726$ Ry (which is indeed not very different from $-E_1 = 1.836$ Ry as predicted above). The experimental value is $J = 1.807$ Ry. The much simpler hydrogenic wave function discussed in Sect. 27β would give [see Eq. (27.4)] $J = 1.695$ Ry. The energy eigenvalue obtained by

Table 5. *The ground state of the neutral helium atom; self-consistent field, potential and charge distribution.*

r	$P(r)$	$Z_p(r)$	$Z_{\text{eff}}(r)$	r	$P(r)$	$Z_p(r)$	$Z_{\text{eff}}(r)$
0	0.000	2.000	2.000	1.6	0.489	1.024	0.239
0.05	0.215	1.916	1.998	1.8	0.405	1.014	0.158
0.1	0.390	1.834	1.989	2.0	0.333	1.009	0.105
0.2	0.643	1.683	1.932	2.2	0.272	1.005	0.068
0.3	0.798	1.552	1.826	2.4	0.221	1.003	0.044
0.4	0.885	1.442	1.683	2.6	0.178	1.0018	0.028
0.5	0.924	1.352	1.518	2.8	0.143	1.0011	0.018
0.6	0.930	1.279	1.345	3.0	0.115	1.0006	0.012
				3.2	0.092	1.0004	0.007
0.8	0.880	1.173	1.014				
1.0	0.789	1.106	0.734	3.6	0.058	1.0001	0.0028
1.2	0.686	1.065	0.516	4.0	0.036	1.0000	0.0012
1.4	0.584	1.039	0.355	4.8	0.014	1.0000	0.0002

[1] W. S. WILSON and R. B. LINDSAY: Phys. Rev. **47**, 681 (1935).

the HARTREE method is thus not much better than the (simpler) approximation (27.4) and is much worse than the value given by the (more complicated) variation method (see Sect. 32). For helium-like atoms the main advantage of the HARTREE method lies in furnishing the most accurate wave functions obtainable in product form (31.1). For many applications the HARTREE wave function is much easier to handle than the more accurate, but much more complicated, variational one. Correlation effects between the two electrons are, of course, not included but the *overall* charge distribution of the two electron given by the HARTREE method agrees very well[1] with the variational one (see Fig. 17, Sect. 32).

32. RITZ variation method (helium ground state). Historically, an accurate quantum mechanical treatment of the ground state of He was of great interest since the "old quantum theory" had failed completely in such problems. It was therefore gratifying that even the earliest wave mechanical calculations[2] gave a reasonably good value for the ground state energy E of He. Today the wave mechanical value for this energy is one of the most accurate of all quantum mechanical results which have to be obtained by *approximation* methods. An accurate knowledge of the ground state *wave function* is also required for calculating many macroscopic quantities, such as the diamagnetic (Sect. 50) and dielectric (Sect. 58) susceptibility, VAN DER WAALS' constant, boiling point, etc. Helium is especially suitable for the comparison of the experimental and theoretical values for such constants, since it is the simplest monatomic gas.

The most suitable method for the treatment of the He ground state is the RITZ procedure which was first applied to the He problem by KELLNER[3] and then with even greater success by HYLLERAAS[4]. The starting point of the procedure is SCHRÖDINGER's variational principle

$$E[U] \equiv \frac{\int UHU\,d\tau}{\int U^2\,d\tau} = \text{Min.} \tag{32.1}$$

(H is the HAMILTONian operator). The general form of the eigenfunction U is assumed, but, to begin with, a number of parameters, such as the effective nuclear charge or the coefficients of a power series expansion, are left arbitrary. Then the integrals in (32.1) are carried out, and E is a function of the parameters which have been introduced. By finding the absolute minimum of this function, the parameters, thereby the eigenfunction, and above all, the energy of the atom are determined.

We use as our three distance coordinates the two "elliptic coordinates" plus the interparticle distance,

$$s = r_1 + r_2, \quad t = r_1 - r_2, \quad u = r_{12}. \tag{32.2}$$

The variables s and u are positive, by definition, while t can take both positive and negative values. The exact symmetry requirement (24.3) then takes the simple form that U be an even function of t for parahelium, an odd function of t for ortho-helium. Since the HAMILTONian H is an even function of t and since the integrals in (32.1) contain two factors, the contribution to the integral from $-t$ is identical with that from $+t$. We therefore restrict ourselves to positive

[1] H. A. BETHE: Z. Physik **55**, 431 (1929).

[2] For instance A. UNSÖLD, Ann. d. Phys. **82**, 355 (1927).

[3] G. W. KELLNER: Z. Physik **44**, 91 (1927).

[4] E. A. HYLLERAAS: Z. Physik **48**, 469 (1928) and particularly **54**, 347 (1929). See also E. A. HYLLERAAS, Die Grundlagen der Quantenmechanik mit Anwendungen auf atomtheoretische Ein- und Mehrelektronenprobleme, Oslo 1932 (Norske Vidensk. Akad. Skrift., Mat.-naturv. Kl. **1932**, No. 6).

values of t in the integrals and multiply the volume element by a factor of 2. Since the Hamiltonian H and also the wave function U (for S-states) do not depend on the Euler angles, we can integrate over them immediately. The resulting volume element is then found to be[1]

$$d\tau = 2\pi^2 (s^2 - t^2)\, u\, ds\, dt\, du \tag{32.3}$$

and the limits of integration are

$$0 \leqq t \leqq u \leqq s \leqq \infty . \tag{32.4}$$

We now have to rewrite the Hamiltonian H,

$$H = -\tfrac{1}{2}\Delta_1 - \tfrac{1}{2}\Delta_2 + V, \tag{32.5}$$

in terms of the variables s, t and u. The potential energy V is

$$V = -\frac{Z}{r_1} - \frac{Z}{r_2} + \frac{1}{r_{12}} = -\frac{4Zs}{s^2 - t^2} + \frac{1}{u}. \tag{32.6}$$

The integrals involving the Laplace operators Δ can be rewritten, using Green's theorem,

$$\overline{p_1^2} = -\int d\tau\, U \Delta_1 U = +\int d\tau\, (\mathrm{grad}_1 U)^2, \tag{32.7}$$

and expressing grad_1 in terms of differentiation with respect to s, t, u. The variational principle (32.1) finally takes the form

$$\left.\begin{aligned} &\frac{1}{N}\int_0^\infty ds \int_0^s du \int_0^u dt \Big\{u(s^2-t^2)\left[\left(\frac{\partial U}{\partial s}\right)^2 + \left(\frac{\partial U}{\partial t}\right)^2 + \left(\frac{\partial U}{\partial u}\right)^2\right] + 2\frac{\partial U}{\partial u} \times \\ &\times \left[s(u^2-t^2)\frac{\partial U}{\partial s} + t(s^2-u^2)\frac{\partial U}{\partial t}\right] - U^2\left[4Zsu - s^2 + t^2\right]\Big\} = E = \min, \end{aligned}\right\} \tag{32.8}$$

where

$$N = \int_0^\infty ds \int_0^s du \int_0^u dt\, u(s^2 - t^2)\, U^2 .$$

α) First order. In Sect 27β we have discussed a simple wave function for the ground state of form

$$U = e^{-(Z-\sigma)r_1} e^{-(Z-\sigma)r_2} = e^{-(Z-\sigma)s} \tag{32.9}$$

where the screening factor σ represents, in a crude way, the partial screening of each electron by the other. As a first step in our variation method let us choose a trial wave function U, which is an *arbitrary* function of the variable s but, like (32.9), is independent of t and u. We can then integrate (32.8) over t and u, which gives

$$\delta \int_0^\infty ds \left\{\frac{4}{15} s^5 \left(\frac{dU}{ds}\right)^2 - \left(\frac{4}{3}Z - \frac{5}{12}\right) s^4 U^2 - E\cdot\frac{4}{15} s^5 U^2\right\} = 0. \tag{32.10}$$

This variational principle then reduces to the differential equation

$$\frac{d^2 U}{ds^2} + \frac{5}{s}\frac{dU}{ds} + \left(E + 5\frac{Z}{s} - \frac{25}{16s}\right) U = 0. \tag{32.11}$$

The lowest eigenvalue E of this equation is $-(Z - \frac{5}{16})^2$ and the corresponding eigenfunction is *exactly* (32.9) with $\sigma = 5/16$.

[1] For a derivation see ref. [*10*], p. 354.

The experimentally measured quantity is not the *total* energy E of a helium-like atom, but its ionization potential J. J equals $E_0 - E$, where E_0 is the ground state energy of the singly ionized (hydrogen-like) atom, $E_0 = -Z^2/2$. The simple wave function (32.9) then gives the following approximation for the ionization potential[1] for nuclear charge Z

$$J_Z = \left[\left(Z - \frac{5}{16}\right)^2 - \frac{1}{2} Z^2\right] \text{a.u.} = \left(Z^2 - \frac{5}{4} Z + \frac{25}{128}\right). \qquad (32.12)$$

The comparison of this expression with the experimental values in Rydberg[2] is as follows

	H^-	He	Li^+	Be^{++}
Theoretical	−0.055	+1.695	+5.445	+11.195
Experimental	+0.055	+1.807	+5.560	+11.312
Difference	0.110	0.112	0.115	0.117

The agreement is gratifying, considering the simplicity of the derivation. Note also that the difference between the approximation (32.12) and the experimental value is almost independent of Z [see also Eq. (33.12)].

The same result (32.12) could also have been obtained as follows. Following the discussion of partial screening in Sect. 27β, we choose a trial wave function of form (32.9) with σ an arbitrary parameter. Substituting this wave function into (32.8), we obtain E as a function of σ. One finds that $E(\sigma)$ has its minimum value exactly for $\sigma = \frac{5}{16}$, which leads to (32.12). The introduction of the screening constant σ into the unscreened hydrogenic wave function e^{-Zs} is equivalent to a simple change of scale of radial distance r_1 and r_2 (and hence of s). This scale factor in the wave function is important, for obtaining good values for the energy. If we had, for instance, substituted the unscreened wave function e^{-Zs} for He instead of (32.9) into (32.8), the discrepancy between the experimental and theoretical values for the energy would have been about three times larger.

β) Higher approximations. We may except, therefore, that the convergence of higher approximations will also be considerably improved if we let the "effective nuclear charge" (or unit of length) be arbitrary in the eigenfunction, i.e., let

$$U(s, t, u) = \varphi(ks, kt, ku). \qquad (32.13)$$

The "effective charge" k is to be fixed by the condition that E be a minimum. Thus $\varphi(s, t, u)$ will not depend on k. In arriving at a more detailed statement about the form of φ, we are guided by the fact that the eigenfunction in first approximation (32.9) is an exponential function of s and independent of t and u. Therefore, a suitable assumption is

$$\varphi(s, t, u) = e^{-\frac{1}{2}s} P(s, t, u). \qquad (32.14)$$

$P = 1$ corresponds to the first approximation. For higher approximations we expand P in a power series which may be expected to converge rapidly for medium-sized values of s, t, and u:

$$P = \sum_{l,n,m=0}^{\infty} c_{n,2l,m}\, s^n t^{2l} u^m. \qquad (32.15)$$

[1] 1 a.u. of energy = 2 Ry (see Introduction).

[2] Actually in terms of R_{He}, R_{Li}, etc., the RYDBERG for the appropriate reduced mass (see Sect. 5). The "experimental" value for H^- is actually an accurate theoretical one (Sect. 34).

Of course, the series contains only even powers of t [cf. remark following (32.2)]. The exponential factor in (32.14) assures convergence of the integrals (32.8). If (32.13) and (32.14) are substituted into (32.8), one obtains

$$E = \frac{k^2 M - k L}{N}, \tag{32.16}$$

with the abbreviations

$$\left.\begin{aligned} L &= \int_0^\infty ds \int_0^s du \int_0^u dt\,(4 Z s u - s^2 + t^2)\,\varphi^2(s, t, u),\\ M &= \int_0^\infty ds \int_0^s du \int_0^u dt \Big\{u(s^2 - t^2)\left[\left(\frac{\partial\varphi}{\partial s}\right)^2 + \left(\frac{\partial\varphi}{\partial t}\right)^2 + \left(\frac{\partial\varphi}{\partial u}\right)^2\right] + \\ &\qquad + 2s(u^2 - t^2)\frac{\partial\varphi}{\partial s}\frac{\partial\varphi}{\partial u} + 2t(s^2 - u^2)\frac{\partial\varphi}{\partial t}\frac{\partial\varphi}{\partial u}\Big\},\\ N &= \int_0^\infty ds \int_0^s du \int_0^u dt\, u(s^2 - t^2)\,\varphi^2. \end{aligned}\right\} \tag{32.17}$$

The expressions L, M, and N are quadratic in the coefficients $c_{n,2l,m}$ only; however, E depends also on k, as per (32.16). We must make E a minimum as a function of the variables $c_{n,2l,m}$ and k. The coefficients c, the "effective nuclear charge" k, and E are to be determined by the minimizing conditions

$$\frac{\partial E}{\partial c_{n,2l,m}} = 0, \qquad \frac{\partial E}{\partial k} = 0. \tag{32.18}$$

In view of (32.16), the last condition can be satisfied immediately by taking

$$k = \frac{L}{2M}. \tag{32.19}$$

Thus, if the $c_{n,2l,m}$ are fixed, the minimum E has the value

$$E = -\frac{L^2}{4MN}. \tag{32.20}$$

Now (32.17) is, of course, a function of the coefficients c only. The more coefficients one has at one's disposal, i.e., the more terms of the power series expansion (32.15) of the eigenfunction are taken, the more accurate, naturally, will be the eigenvalue and eigenfunction; but the more complicated also will be the calculation.

To proceed from (32.20), in carrying out an actual calculation, is hardly the thing to do, because both L^2 and MN are fourth degree expressions in the coefficients c, and, consequently, the Eq. (32.18) would be of third degree in the c's. A better procedure is to substitute an approximate value for k in (32.16). We then obtain the system of equations

$$k^2 \frac{\partial M}{\partial c_{n,2l,m}} - k\frac{\partial L}{\partial c_{n,2l,m}} - E\frac{\partial N}{\partial c_{n,2l,m}} = 0 \quad \text{for all} \quad n, l, m. \tag{32.21}$$

The unknowns in the Eq. (32.21) are the coefficients $c_{n,2l,m}$. The equations are linear and homogeneous in these unknowns since L, M, and N are quadratic functions of the $c_{n,2l,m}$. The system of equations (32.21) will have solutions if the determinant of its coefficients vanishes:

$$\left| k^2 \frac{\partial^2 M}{\partial c_{n,2l,m}\,\partial c_{n',2l',m'}} - k\frac{\partial^2 L}{\partial c_{n,2l,m}\,\partial c_{n',2l',m'}} - E\frac{\partial^2 N}{\partial c_{n,2l,m}\,\partial c_{n',2l',m'}}\right| = 0. \tag{32.22}$$

From this, an equation determining E is obtained in the usual fashion, the degree of the equation being equal to the number of terms of the power series expansion (32.15). The lowest root of this equation is the eigenvalue E. Once it is determined (32.21) may be solved for the $c_{n,2l,m}$. If the values of the c's found in this manner are now substituted into (32.19) and (32.20), even better values for E and k are obtained. At the same time the procedure enables us to keep track of our calculations by permitting a comparison with the values previously obtained[1].

More recently KINOSHITA[2] has used variational wave functions of a more general type than the HYLLERAAS functions (32.15). Besides the terms occurring in (32.15), he also includes terms of the form

$$c_{hij}\, s^{h+1} \left(\frac{u}{s}\right)^i \left(\frac{t}{u}\right)^{2j}. \tag{32.23}$$

Because of the inequality (32.4), such terms have no singularity in the region of integration for h, i, j all positive (or zero).

γ) Results. For the ground state of helium itself ($Z=2$) such variational calculations have by now been carried out with wave functions containing up to thirty-eight[3,4] parameters. In Table 6 we give the parameters used and their coefficients [$c_{n,2l,m}$ in (32.15), normalized such that $c_{0,0,0}$ is unity], as well as the scale factor k, for HYLLERAAS' three and six parameter and KINOSHITA's ten parameter wave functions.

The results for the total energy E and the ionization potential J from these more accurate calculations are as follows. Writing

$$E = -(2.90 + 0.001\,x)\ \text{a.u.}, \qquad J = (1.80 + 0.002\,x)\ \text{a.u.} \tag{32.24}$$

the results are

	HYLLERAAS		CHANDRASEKHAR *et al.*			KINOSHITA
	3	6	10	14	18	38
x	2.44	3.24_0	3.603	3.701	3.715	3.723

compared with $x=-52$ for the one-parameter expression (32.12). The thirty-eight parameter value for E,

$$E = -2.903\,722_5\ \text{a.u.}\ (J = 1.807445\ \text{Ry}) \tag{32.25}$$

is still a *rigorous upper limit* to the exact value. The convergence of the values for E in the table above is seen to be quite good. From Table 10, Sect. 36, another expectation value, $(\overline{H^2} - E^2)/E$, can be evaluated for each wave function. From the convergence of this quantity one can estimate that the inclusion of infinitely

[1] Nowadays the minimization for a wave function with many parameters can be carried out on electronic computing machines by a method of successive approximation. In this case it may be practical to minimize directly the quartic expression (32.20) for E. After minimization, k is then given by (32.19).

[2] T. KINOSHITA: Unpublished work. See also H. M. SCHWARTZ, Phys. Rev. **103**, 110 (1956), for other wave functions.

[3] E. A. HYLLERAAS: Z. Physik **54**, 347 (1929).

[4] CHANDRASEKHAR, HERZBERG and ELBERT: Phys. Rev. **91**, 1172 (1953); **98**, 1050 (1955). Also T. KINOSHITA (unpublished) and E. A. HYLLERAAS (unpublished). KINOSHITA's thirty-eight parameter wave function is not yet fully minimized with respect to energy.

many parameters would probably[1] lower the energy E by not much more than 10^{-6} a.u. below the value in (32.25). Although the value of J in (32.25) is a lower limit to the nonrelativistic expression for an infinitely heavy nucleus, it is actually *higher* than the experimental value of $J = 1.80739\, R_{\mathrm{He}^4}$. This is due to some corrections for nuclear motion (the mass-polarization, Sect. 37) and to some relativistic and radiative corrections (Sect. 41). These corrections (see Table 12, Sect. 41) add $(-6.5_5 \pm 0.4)$ cm^{-1} to the ionization potential J. Using the thirty-eight parameter value in (32.25) for the uncorrected J (and $R_{\mathrm{He}^4} = 109722.27\,\mathrm{cm}^{-1}$) to evaluate the total theoretical ionization potential, we find

$$J_{\mathrm{theor}}^{\mathrm{tot}} = 198310.4_1\ \mathrm{cm}^{-1}, \quad J_{\mathrm{exp}} = (198310.5 \pm 1)\ \mathrm{cm}^{-1}, \tag{32.26}$$

where the experimental value is taken from unpublished work by HERZBERG and ZBINDEN. The phenomenal agreement in (32.26) supports the estimate that (32.25) is not in error by much more than 10^{-6} a.u. ≈ 0.2 cm^{-1}.

Table 6. *Variational wave functions for the helium ground state.*

Term	$10c(u)$	$10c(s)$	$100c(t^2)$	$100c(u^2)$	$100c(s^2)$	$100c(us)$	$10c\left(\frac{u^2}{s}\right)$	$10c\left(\frac{t^2}{u}\right)$	$10c\left(\frac{t^2}{s}\right)$	$100c\left(\frac{st^2}{u}\right)$	k
3 param.	0.81		1.0								3.63
6 param.	0.972	−0.277	0.97	−0.24	0.25						3.636
10 param.	1.2128	−0.5210	0.5486		0.2271	−0.3145	−0.2377	0.0575	0.0743	0.1189	3.4592

Since the war, completely analogous accurate calculations for $Z = 1, 3, 4$ and 8 have been carried out by HENRICH[2] (H^-), ERIKSSON[3] (Li^+), CHANDRASEKHAR and HERZBERG[4] (Li^+ and $O^{(6+)}$) and HYLLERAAS[5] (H^-, Li^+ and Be^{++}). The best (i.e. lowest) values for E in atomic units are: $-0.527\,72_5$ for[5] H^-, $-7.279\,90_9$ for[5] Li^+, $-13.655\,56_3$ for[5] Be^{++} and $-59.156\,59$ for[5] $O^{(6+)}$. The absolute accuracy of these values should be almost as good as that of (32.25) for He. The rapidity of convergence of E as a function of the number of parameters becomes somewhat better with increasing Z. Comparisons of these values of E for He and heavier ions with experiment are given in Sect. 33, a discussion of the H^--ion in Sect. 34.

A simple 4-parameter variational wave function of form (32.13), (32.14) for Li^+ is[6]

$$\varphi(s, t, u) = e^{-\frac{1}{2}s}\left(1 + 0.587 \times 10^{-1} u + 0.510 \times 10^{-2} t^2 - 0.103 \times 10^{-2} u^2\right). \tag{32.27}$$

with $k = 5.660$.

33. Ground state of helium-like ions with arbitrary Z. The variation procedure discussed in Sect. 32, which includes as a parameter the "effective charge" or scale parameter k, gives very accurate results but has to be carried through

[1] The value of $E_{(n)}$ must decrease monotonically as the degree n of the polynomial in the wave function increases, but cannot fall below the correct value E. $E_{(n)}$ is therefore bounded, but the question remains whether $E_{(n)}$ converges towards E or towards some higher constant. This question, first raised by J. BARTLETT, J. GIBBONS and C. DUNN: Phys. Rev. **47**, 679 (1935), has not yet been answered with complete mathematical rigor but it now seems likely that $E_{(n)}$ *does* converge towards E; see, for instance V. A. FOCK, Izv. Acad. Nauk. SSSR., Ser. Fiz. **18** (2), 161 (1954) and T. KATO, Trans. Amer. Math. Soc. **70**, 212 (1951).

[2] L. R. HENRICH: Astrophys. J. **99**, 59 (1944).

[3] H. A. ERIKSSON: Ark. Mat. Astron. Fysik, B **30**, No. 6 (1944).

[4] S. CHANDRASEKHAR and G. HERZBERG: Phys. Rev. **98**, 1050 (1955).

[5] E. A. HYLLERAAS and J. MIDTDAL: Phys. Rev. **103**, 829 (1956). These authors use 24 parameters including terms of the type of (32.23) and some terms involving log s. These are the best results to date for $Z = 1$, 3, 4 and 8.

[6] H. A. ERIKSSON: Z. Physik **109**, 762 (1938).

separately for each value of Z. For the ions with large Z it is more convenient to use a procedure which does not include the scale parameter k but gives results as a function of Z in one calculation. Such a method, based on the variation-perturbation method discussed in Sect. 25β, was devised by HYLLERAAS[1].

In our SCHRÖDINGER equation (24.1), let us change the unit of length to $(1/2Z)$ a.u. and of energy to $2Z^2$ a.u. $= 4Z^2$ Ry, i.e.

$$\varrho = 2Zr; \quad \sigma = 2Zs, \quad \tau = 2Zt, \quad v = 2Zu; \quad \varepsilon = \frac{E}{2Z^2}. \tag{33.1}$$

In these units the SCHRÖDINGER equation is then of the form of (25.5),

$$(H_0 + \lambda H_1 - \varepsilon)\, u = 0, \tag{33.2}$$

where

$$H_0 = -\left(\Delta_1 + \Delta_2 + \frac{1}{\varrho_1} + \frac{1}{\varrho_2}\right); \quad H_1 = +\frac{1}{\varrho_{12}}, \quad \lambda = \frac{1}{Z}. \tag{33.3}$$

We can then expand the energy eigenvalue ε in inverse powers of Z,

$$\varepsilon = \varepsilon_0 + \varepsilon_1 \frac{1}{Z} + \varepsilon_2 \frac{1}{Z^2} + \varepsilon_3 \frac{1}{Z^3} + \cdots, \tag{33.4}$$

with a similar expansion for the wave function u.

The zero order wave equation (25.7), with H_0 given by (33.3), has the simple and exact normalized solution

$$U_0 = \tfrac{1}{2}\, e^{-\frac{1}{2}\sigma}, \quad \varepsilon_0 = -\tfrac{1}{2} \tag{33.5}$$

for the ground state. With H_1 given by (33.3), the expression (25.10) for the first order energy ε_1 can then be easily integrated, using (29.11), and the result is

$$\varepsilon_1 = 2 \times \tfrac{1}{4} \int_0^\infty d\varrho_1\, \varrho_1^2 \int_{\varrho_1}^\infty d\varrho_2\, \varrho_2\, e^{-(\varrho_1+\varrho_2)} = \tfrac{5}{16}. \tag{33.6}$$

It is interesting to compare the results so far with the results of Sect. 32β, using the simple wave function (32.9) *with* the scale parameter $(Z-\sigma)$. In our present units, (32.12) would give $-\frac{1}{2}(1 - 5/16Z)^2$ as an approximation for ε. The values for ε_0 and ε_1 would be the same as (33.5) and (33.6) and the value $-25/512 = -0.0488$ would be obtained as a (very crude) approximation for ε_2.

To obtain an accurate expression for ε_2 one has to minimize the expression (25.13) with respect to the first order trial wave function U_1. It is convenient to write

$$U_1 = U_0\, \varphi. \tag{33.7}$$

After using (25.7) and (33.7) and the explicit form of H_0 and H_1, carrying out an integration by parts and simplifying the expressions, one can finally rewrite (25.13) in the form

$$\varepsilon_2 = 2 \int d\tau\, U_0^2 \left[(H_1 - E_1)\, \varphi + \tfrac{1}{2} (\mathrm{grad}_1 \varphi)^2 + \tfrac{1}{2} (\mathrm{grad}_2 \varphi)^2\right] = \min. \tag{33.8}$$

In analogy with (32.15), HYLLERAAS takes the trial wave function φ of form

$$\varphi = \sum c_{nlm}\, \sigma^n \tau^{2l} v^m \tag{33.9}$$

and minimizes ε_2 with respect to all the parameters which are included. Using eight parameters he found

$$\left.\begin{aligned} U_1 = e^{-\frac{1}{2}\sigma} (&0.05737\,\sigma + 0.18797\, v + 0.01539\, \tau^2 + 0.00118\, \sigma^2 - 0.01495\, v^2 \\ &+ 0.00472\, \sigma v - 0.00076\, \tau^2 v + 0.00041\, v^3). \end{aligned}\right\} \tag{33.10}$$

[1] E. A. HYLLERAAS: Z. Physik 65, 209 (1930).

and $\varepsilon_2 = -0.07865$. The inclusion of 12 parameters gave $\varepsilon_2 = -0.07872$ and finally a more recent calculation[1], using 24 carefully selected combinations of the 50 terms up to $(n+2l+m)=6$, gave

$$\varepsilon_2 = -0.078827_8. \tag{33.11}$$

The convergence of ε_2 with the number of parameters is quite rapid and (33.11) should be an excellent approximation (and is a rigorous upper limit) to ε_2.

In principle, the same variation method could also be used to calculate the higher coefficients ε_3, ε_4, etc. Unfortunately this procedure converges extremely slowly already for ε_3 and is impractical for higher terms. Nevertheless, we now have exact values for ε_0 and ε_1, and a very accurate approximation for ε_2. One can then get an excellent semi-empirical expansion for ε by using these values of ε_0 to ε_2 and by fitting ε_3 to ε_6 to the values of ε determined *directly* for $Z=1, 2, 3$ and 8 (see Sect. 32). The actual energy E in Rydberg for any Z is $4Z^2\varepsilon$ and the ionization potential $J = E_0 - E = -Z^2(4\varepsilon+1)$ Ry, where E_0 is the ground state energy of the hydrogenic atom with charge Z. The expansion for J (in Rydberg) is then

$$\left.\begin{aligned} J = Z^2 - \tfrac{5}{4} Z + 0.315\,311 - 0.01707\frac{1}{Z} + 0.00068\frac{1}{Z^2} + \\ + 0.00164\frac{1}{Z^3} + 0.00489\frac{1}{Z^4}. \end{aligned}\right\} \tag{33.12}$$

It is interesting to note how small the coefficients of negative powers in (33.12) are. The constant term in (33.12) and the individual expressions for $Z=1$ to 3 and for 8, from which this polynomial for J was derived, are all rigorous lower limits. For other values of Z the interpolation formula (33.12) is not *rigorously* a lower limit (but probably is in practice) and should be an excellent approximation. For Be^{++} ($Z=4$) this formula gives $J = 11.311131$ Ry, the direct evaluation gave 11.311125 Ry.

The theoretical values for the ionization potentials J for $Z=2$ to 8 are given in Table 7. The experimental values are, of course, measured in units of cm^{-1}. We have so far restricted ourselves to the ideal case of infinitely heavy nuclei. In Sect. 37 we shall discuss in detail the effect of nuclear motion. We shall see, however, that most of this effect is accounted for if in the theoretical expressions the energy unit Ry $= R_\infty$ is replaced by R_A, the appropriate unit for a nucleus of atomic mass A (see Sect. 5). With A in physical atomic mass units, we have

$$R_A \approx R_\infty\left(1 - \frac{m}{M_A}\right) = \left(109\,737.31 - \frac{60.22}{A}\right)\text{cm}^{-1}. \tag{33.13}$$

In Table 7 we also give the experimental[2] ionization potentials, in units of R_A. The agreement between theory and experiment is seen to be excellent. The remaining (very small) discrepancies are largely due to further corrections for nuclear motion (see Sect. 37) and especially to relativistic effects (see Sect. 41).

A simple variational wave function U for arbitrary Z is given by Eriksson[3] as

$$\left.\begin{aligned} U(\sigma,\tau,v) = \frac{1}{2}e^{-\frac{1}{2}\sigma}\Big[\Big(1 - \frac{1.0694}{Z} - \frac{0.174}{Z^2}\Big) + \Big(\frac{0.1220}{Z} - \frac{0.022}{Z^2}\Big)v + \\ + \Big(\frac{0.0800}{Z} + \frac{0.018}{Z^2}\Big)\sigma + \Big(\frac{0.00927}{Z} + \frac{0.0070}{Z^2}\Big)\tau^2\Big]. \end{aligned}\right\} \tag{33.14}$$

[1] E. A. Hylleraas and J. Midtdal: Phys. Rev. **103**, 829 (1956). Some terms of the type of (32.23) and logarithmic terms were also included.

[2] G. Herzberg and R. Zbinden (unpublished) for $Z=1$; C. E. Moore, Atomic Energy Levels, I, NBS Circular 467 (1949) for $Z \gtrless 2$.

[3] H. A. Eriksson: Z. Physik **109**, 762 (1938).

Table 7. *Nonrelativistic theoretical ionization potentials in Ry (= ½ atomic units) and experimental values in units of R_A.*

	He	Li^+	Be^{++}	$B^{(3+)}$	$C^{(4+)}$	$N^{(5+)}$	$O^{(6+)}$
J_{obs}	1.80739	5.5599	11.3116	19.0643	28.820	40.578	54.340
J_{theor}	1.80744	5.55982	11.31113	19.06194	28.8125	40.5629	54.3132

34. The negative hydrogen ion. The H^--ion is an interesting special case of He-like ions ($Z=1$). It is "only just" stable against dissociation into a neutral hydrogen atom plus a free electron. The dissociation energy J of the H^- ground state is only about 0.75 eV and this ion possesses *no* other bound states. This ion therefore has no discrete spectrum and its continuous spectrum is difficult to observe under laboratory conditions[1] and its dissociation energy has not yet been measured directly.

The structure of the negative hydrogen ion has been of interest almost since the advent of quantum mechanics in connection with the theory of alkali hydrides. These structures can be thought of as a combination of a positive alkali ion (closed shell) and the negative H^- ion. Lithium hydride is particularly simple theoretically, since both Li^+ and H^- are helium-like ions. Some time ago already HYLLERAAS[2] succeeded in calculating the attractive COULOMB force and repulsive exchange force between these two ions. This calculation gave values for the lattice spacing and binding energy of the LiH crystal in good agreement with experiment.

More recently, the negative hydrogen ion has been found to be of great importance for the opacity of the atmosphere of the sun and of similar stars. The ionization potential of H^-, $J \approx 0.75$ eV, equals k (BOLTZMANN's constant) times about 8700 °K, which is slightly higher than the temperature in the solar atmosphere. Some free electrons are released by the ionization of the metals present in the gas and, since neutral hydrogen is the main constituent by far of the gas, many of these electrons will be captured to form H^-. Conversely, the flux of radiation coming from the sun's interior will tend to be absorbed by the H^- ions accompanied by dissociation of these ions (photoeffect, Sect. 74). The electrons released will again be captured by H-atoms with the emission of radiation (recombination, Sect. 75), and so on. This process is the main source of opacity in the solar atmosphere and the continuous absorption coefficient of H^- has been studied extensively and used in the theory of the solar atmosphere. In fact, discrepancies between early calculations and observational evidence on the sun's radiation pointed out the inaccuracies of the wave functions for H^- which were available then[3].

Calculations of the wave function and energy of H^- are also of purely methodological interest, since this most loosely bound of all He-like ions provides the most severe test of the approximation methods used in the preceding sections. The simple hydrogen-like wave function U with screening constant $\frac{5}{16}$, for instance, would give a *negative* value (32.12) for the ionization potential J, i.e. no binding at all,

$$U = e^{-0.688(r_1+r_2)}, \qquad J = -\frac{7}{128}\,\text{Ry}. \tag{34.1}$$

[1] R. FUCHS: Z. Physik **130**, 69 (1951).
[2] E. A. HYLLERAAS: Z. Physik **63**, 771 (1930).
[3] For a discussion of these astrophysical topics see L. H. ALLER, Astrophysics, The Atmospheres of the Sun and Stars, New York: Ronald Press 1953 and R. WOOLLEY and D. STIBBS, The Outer Layers of A Star. Oxford: Clarendon Press 1953.

The variation method of Sect. 32 has been applied to the H^- ion by BETHE[1], HYLLERAAS[2], and HENRICH[3], using wave functions with 3, 6 and 11 parameters, respectively. The corresponding values for the ionization potential J (in Ry) were 0.0506, 0.0529 and 0.05512, respectively. Comparison with the equivalent values for He (Sect. 32) shows that the convergence of J with the number of parameters is slower for H^-. The best value is the 24-parameter result[4] of $J = 0.055451_1$.

Table 8. *Coefficients of the three-parameter wave functions for the ground states of H^-, He and Li^+.*

	c_1	c_2	k
H^-	0.20	0.05	1.535
He	0.08	0.010	3.63
Li^+	0.08	0.004	5.792

The wave function of the negative hydrogen ion is also of interest, since it shows up many features of He-like wave functions most drastically. The three-parameter wave function of form

$$\left.\begin{aligned} U(s,u,t) &= \varphi(ks, ku, kt), \\ \varphi(s,u,t) &= e^{-\frac{1}{2}s}(1 + c_1 u + c_2 t^2) \end{aligned}\right\} \quad (34.2)$$

is compared with the analogous functions for He and Li^+ in Table 8. For this (as well as the more accurate) wave functions the coefficients of u, t^2, etc. are

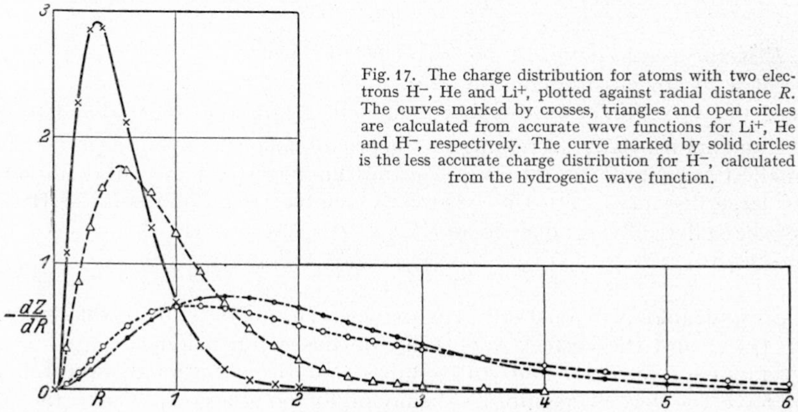

Fig. 17. The charge distribution for atoms with two electrons H^-, He and Li^+, plotted against radial distance R. The curves marked by crosses, triangles and open circles are calculated from accurate wave functions for Li^+, He and H^-, respectively. The curve marked by solid circles is the less accurate charge distribution for H^-, calculated from the hydrogenic wave function.

considerably larger for H^- than for He (and smaller still for Li^+, etc.). The smaller the nuclear charge Z, the stronger is the effect of the electrons on each other. The charge distribution, obtained by integrating the square of the variational wave function over the coordinates of one electron, is compared in Fig. 17 with that obtained from the simple hydrogen-like approximation (34.1). Note that the hydrogenic charge distribution is too small both at very small and at very large radial distances.

The behavior of the wave function for large values of r_1 is also illustrated by considering the simpler expression obtained by setting r_2 equal to zero. For the 11-parameter wave function this gives

$$U(r_1, 0) = e^{-0.708\, r_1}\left[1 + 1.19\frac{r_1}{10} + 6.1\left(\frac{r_1}{10}\right)^2 + 4.7\left(\frac{r_1}{10}\right)^4 + 1.8\left(\frac{r_1}{10}\right)^6\right] \quad (34.3)$$

compared with the hydrogen-like one-parameter expression

$$U(r_1, 0) = e^{-0.688\, r_1} = e^{-0.708\, r_1}\left[1 + 0.20\frac{r_1}{10} + 0.020\left(\frac{r_1}{10}\right)^2 + \cdots\right].$$

[1] H. A. BETHE: Z. Physik **57**, 815 (1929).
[2] E. A. HYLLERAAS: Z. Physik **63**, 291 (1930).
[3] L. R. HENRICH: Astrophys. J. **99**, 59 (1944).
[4] E. HYLLERAAS and J. MIDTDAL: Phys. Rev. **103**, 829 (1956).

The series (34.3) should be a fairly good approximation for $r_1 \gtrsim 5$ and in this range is larger than the hydrogen-like expression above. The same qualitative features are found for He, Li^+, etc., but to a much smaller extent.

The hydrogen-like wave function is too small at small distances, since the actual screening is much smaller near the nucleus than the assumed constant $\frac{5}{16}$. The behavior at large distances can be seen as follows. The exact wave function for the negative hydrogen ion can (in principle) be written in the form

$$U(\boldsymbol{r}_1, \boldsymbol{r}_2) = \sum_{nlm} f_{nlm}(\boldsymbol{r}_1)\, u_{nlm}(\boldsymbol{r}_2). \tag{34.4}$$

In (34.4), u_{nlm} are the normalized, mutually orthogonal hydrogen wave functions for $Z=1$ (which form a complete set) and f_{nlm} are arbitrary functions (of a single coordinate) which have to be determined from the wave equation. Consider now values of r_1 very large compared with the radial distances for which $u_{nlm}(r_2)$ is appreciable. Multiply the full wave equation by $u^*_{nlm}(\boldsymbol{r}_2)$ and integrate over $\boldsymbol{r}_2$. We can then neglect the terms involving $(r_1^{-1} - r_{12}^{-1})$ and the remaining equation reduces to an asymptotic equation for f,

$$(\Delta_1 + 2E - 2E_n)\, f_{nlm}(\boldsymbol{r}_1) = 0, \tag{34.5}$$

where E is the total energy of the two-electron atom and $E_n = -1/2n^2$ is the energy of a hydrogen atom in the state u_{nlm}.

Since the wave function must be bounded at infinity, the radial part of f must be an exponentially decreasing factor proportional to $\exp(-\sqrt{2E_n - 2E}\, r_1)$. The smallest exponent comes from $n=1$ and this term (in 34.4) will predominate at very large distances. For the spherically symmetric ground state of H^-, f_{100} will also be spherically symmetric and $E = -0.52756$ a.u. In this case we have asymptotically

$$f_{100}(r) = a_1 e^{-\sqrt{2J}\, r} = a_1 e^{-0.235\, r}, \tag{34.6}$$

where a_1 is an unknown constant. The exponent in (34.6) is much smaller[1] than that in (34.1) and the correct wave function has a much longer "tail".

A comparison of (34.3) and (34.6) shows that the variational wave function cannot have the correct asymptotic behavior for *very* large r_1, where the polynomial in square brackets in (34.3) is a poor approximation (and an *under*estimate) for $e^{+0.473\, r_1}$. This large difference in the exponents of (34.3) and (34.6) suggests the use of trial wave functions for H^- of a form slightly different from the standard HYLLERAAS wave function (32.15). CHANDRASEKHAR[2] has investigated a function of the form

$$U = (e^{-ar_1 - br_2} + e^{-br_1 - ar_2})(1 + cr_{12}). \tag{34.7}$$

Even with the polarization term in r_{12} omitted ($c=0$), the variation method gave $a=1.039$, $b=0.283$ and $J=0.027$ Ry. Although this value of J is quite poor, it is much better than the *negative* value obtained from (34.1). Note how close a is to unity and b to the exponent of (34.6); this wave function "almost" represents an unscreened hydrogen atom plus a very loosely bound outer electron. Including also the term in cr_{12}, CHANDRASEKHAR found $a=1.075$, $b=0.478$, $c=0.312$ and $J=0.0518$ Ry (better than the 3-parameter HYLLERAAS value, worse than the 6-parameter value).

Attempts have been made to use trial wave functions of form similar to (34.7), but with more parameters, for the H^- ground state. When the number of parameters is large, a wave function of this type does not seem to give a better energy value than the standard HYLLERAAS wave function with as many parameters.

[1] Due to the fact that the ionization potential J of H^- is so small.

[2] S. CHANDRASEKHAR: Astrophys. J. **100**, 176 (1944).

It should be remembered that, although (34.6) is the *asymptotic* form of the correct wave function, the constant a_1 may be quite small and the function may approach (34.6) only for *very* large values of r_1. For He, Li^+, etc. the variational wave functions also decrease more rapidly than the correct ones for very large radial distances, but the discrepancy is much smaller for the larger values of Z.

35. Variation method for excited states. *α) General remarks.* The calculation of excited states is rendered more difficult, compared to that of the ground state, by the appearance of the subsidiary condition that the eigenfunction of every excited state must be orthogonal to the eigenfunctions of all lower states[1]. This subsidiary condition reduces considerably the number of available trial functions which may be chosen to approximate the eigenfunction and inserted in the variation integral; as a result, the convergence of the procedure is not nearly as good as before.

However, cases do exist in which the subsidiary condition is satisfied automatically if the form of the trial function is taken as prescribed by the character of the term to be calculated. A case in point is the $2S$ term of orthohelium. Every function designed to approximate the eigenfunction of this term must, of course, be chosen to be antisymmetric in the coordinates of the two electrons, and this in itself is sufficient to assure orthogonality to the symmetric eigenfunction of the ground state. The subsidiary condition is satisfied automatically also for the two $2P$ terms. The eigenfunction of every P term has an explicit, characteristic dependence on the orientation of the atom in space, while the eigenfunctions of S terms depend only on the mutual separations of the electrons and on their distances from the nucleus. As a result, the product of an S and P eigenfunction vanishes on integration over the Eulerian angles; however, S states are the only states which are lower than the two $2P$ states. Furthermore, the eigenfunctions belonging to the $2\,^1P$ and the $2\,^3P$ terms are also orthogonal to each other since they are of different symmetries in the two electrons and, thus, the subsidiary condition is satisfied for both $2P$ states. In general, the eigenfunctions belonging to two states of an atom are automatically orthogonal if either the total orbital angular momentum L or the total spin S (or both) have different values for the two states. Hence, the calculation by the Ritz method of the lowest state belonging to a given L and S is always straigtforward; it does not matter if there exist lower terms, as long as they have some other value for L or/and S. According to this rule, the $2\,^3S$, $2\,^1P$, and $2\,^3P$ (also $3\,^1D$, $3\,^3D$, etc.) states of helium can be treated by the Ritz procedure without additional complications, i.e., any function which has the appropriate symmetry and angular dependence may be adopted as trial function. In the calculation of the $2\,^1S$ term, on the other hand, one must specifically provide for the orthogonality of the eigenfunction to that of the ground state $1\,^1S$.

β) The $2\,^3S$-state. We start with the lowest state of ortho-helium, which contains a $1s$-electron and a $2s$-electron. Let us consider as a simple trial wave function the antisymmetrized product of two hydrogen-like wave functions with nuclear charge Z_i and Z_a for the inner and outer electron. This wave function is

$$\left.\begin{aligned} U &= e^{-Z_i r_1} e^{-\frac{1}{2} Z_a r_2} \left(\tfrac{1}{2} Z_a r_2 - 1\right) - e^{-Z_i r_2} e^{-\frac{1}{2} Z_a r_1} \left(\tfrac{1}{2} Z_a r_1 - 1\right) \\ &= e^{-ks} \left[\left(-\tfrac{1}{2} Z_a s + 2\right) \operatorname{Sin} ct - \tfrac{1}{2} Z_a t \operatorname{Cos} ct\right], \end{aligned}\right\} \tag{35.1}$$

[1] If the subsidiary condition is disregarded and the Ritz procedure is carried out to sufficiently high approximation, one always obtains a (bad) approximation to the ground state rather than the desired (good) approximation to the excited state. This will happen even if the initial form of the trial function is a good choice for the eigenfunction of the excited level.

where

$$2k = Z_i + \tfrac{1}{2} Z_a, \quad 2c = Z_i - \tfrac{1}{2} Z_a. \tag{35.2}$$

One can then substitute (35.1) into the variational integral (32.8), consider k and c (i.e. Z_i and Z_a) as parameters to be varied and find the energy minimum E. Such calculations were carried out by ECKART[1] both for He and Li^+. His results are given in Table 9, where J is again the ionization potential of the state, i.e. minus the total energy E minus Z^2 Ry.

Table 9. ECKART'S *results for the $n=2$ states in He and Li^+. (Energy in Ry.)*

	He				Li^+			
	Z_i	Z_a	J_{theor}	J_{exp}	Z_i	Z_a	J_{theor}	J_{exp}
$2\,^3S$	2.01	1.53	0.334	0.350	3.03	2.56	1.21	1.21
$2\,^3P$	1.99	1.09	0.262	0.266	2.98	2.16	1.04	1.05
$2\,^1P$	2.00	0.97	0.245	0.247	3.01	1.94	0.99	1.00

It is interesting to note that, both for He and Li^+ ($Z=2$ and 3), the value of Z_a lies between the two limiting values $(Z-1)$ and $(Z-\frac{5}{16})$. The lower limit is appropriate for highly excited states, where the outer electron is totally screened by the inner one[2], and the upper limit for the ground state. Z_i is slightly larger than Z, i.e. the outer electron "pushes in" the charge cloud of the inner one towards the nucleus to a small extent.

For He, a trial wave function similar to (35.1), but containing more parameters (c_1 to c_6) has been used by HYLLERAAS and UNDHEIM[3]. This wave function, odd in t, is

$$U = e^{-ks}\left[(c_1 + c_2 s + c_4 u + c_5 u s)\,\mathrm{Sin}\,ct + t(c_3 + c_6 u)\,\mathrm{Cos}\,ct\right]. \tag{35.3}$$

Minimizing the energy with respect to all parameters[4], they find $J=0.35044$ Ry, in excellent agreement with the experimental value of $0.35047\,R_{\text{He}}$. A similar calculation, but with fewer parameters, for Li^+ was carried out by BREIT and collaborators. Their value[5] for J is lower than the experimental one, $J=1.2215\,R_{\text{Li}}$, by about 0.3%.

γ) The 2P terms. In dealing with P terms there appear a number of features which distinguish them from S terms, the only type we have treated so far[6]. In the first place, the P terms are degenerate. The magnetic quantum number m, i.e., the angular momentum about a distinguished z-axis in units of $\hbar$, can assume the values 1, 0, and -1, and to each value of m belongs an eigenfunction. Secondly, the eigenfunctions depend explicitly on the orientation of the atom in space relative to a distinguished z-axis. To be specific, if ϑ_1, φ_1 are the polar coordinates of the first electron and ϑ_2, φ_2 those of the second electron (z is the

[1] C. ECKART: Phys. Rev. **36**, 878 (1930).

[2] The energy value for He obtained from the variational integral by simply substituting $Z_i=2$, $Z_a=1$ is $J=0.247$ Ry, considerably worse than ECKART's value.

[3] E. HYLLERAAS and B. UNDHEIM: Z. Physik **65**, 759 (1930). See also S. HUANG: Astrophys. J. **108**, 354 (1948).

[4] They find $k=1.32$ and $c=0.725$ and (35.2) then gives $Z_i=2.05$ and $Z_a=1.19$.

[5] G. BREIT and F. DOERMANN: Phys. Rev. **36**, 1732 (1930). More recently, a much more accurate wave function for the $2\,^3S$-state in Li^+ has been obtained by LUKE, MEYEROTT and CLENDENIN, Phys. Rev. **85**, 401 (1952). Their method is outlined in Sect. 36β and gives a value of J in almost exact agreement with experiment.

[6] Cf. G. BREIT: Phys. Rev. **35**, 569 (1930).

polar axis), the eigenfunctions may be written in the following form:

$$\left.\begin{aligned} U_1 &= \frac{\sqrt{3}}{4\pi}\left(F \sin\vartheta_1 e^{i\varphi_1} \mp \tilde{F} \sin\vartheta_2 e^{i\varphi_2}\right) \qquad (m=1), \\ U_0 &= \frac{\sqrt{6}}{4\pi}\left(F \cos\vartheta_1 \mp \tilde{F} \cos\vartheta_2\right) \qquad (m=0), \\ U_{-1} &= \frac{\sqrt{3}}{4\pi}\left(F \sin\vartheta_1 e^{-i\varphi_1} \mp \tilde{F} \sin\vartheta_2 e^{-i\varphi_2}\right) \qquad (m=-1). \end{aligned}\right\} \tag{35.4}$$

In the above, F depends only on the distances r_1, r_2 of the electrons from the nucleus and their mutual separation r_{12}; or, what amounts to the same thing, F depends only on r_1, r_2 and Θ, the angle between the radius vectors $\boldsymbol{r}_1$ and $\boldsymbol{r}_2$. $\tilde{F}$ arises from F by interchanging the two electrons:

$$\tilde{F}(r_1, r_2, \Theta) = F(r_2, r_1, \Theta). \tag{35.5}$$

In (35.4) the minus sign refers to the ortho-state $2\,^3P$, the plus sign to the para-state $2\,^1P$.

For the radial trial wave function F, ECKART again chose a product of a $1s$ and a $2p$ hydrogenlike radial function with nuclear charge Z_i and Z_a, respectively,

$$F = r_1 e^{-\frac{1}{2}Z_a r_1} e^{-Z_i r_2}. \tag{35.6}$$

Substituting the wave function (35.4) with (35.6) into the variational integral, he evaluated the energy minimum for variations of the parameters Z_i and Z_a. His results for the $2\,^3P$ and $2\,^1P$ states[1] of He and Li^+ are given in Table 9. Note that Z_a is much closer to $(Z-1)$ (complete screening) than for the $2S$ states.

One could improve the calculation by using instead of (35.6) a trial wave function with more parameters, which give an account of polarization effects. So far only a wave function with one extra parameter c has been used for the $2\,^3P$ state in He by BREIT[2],

$$F = r_1 e^{-\frac{1}{2}Z_a r_1} e^{-Z_i r_2}(1 + c\cos\Theta). \tag{35.7}$$

He finds $c = -0.0089$ and almost the same values for J, Z_i and Z_a as ECKART. (35.7), unlike (35.6), gives an approximate, but simple, account of polarization (the term in c), which is seen to be small. The first order HEISENBERG method of Sect. 28 ($Z_i = 2$, $Z_a = 1$) gives $J = 0.260$ Ry, the second order calculation (polarization) of Sect. 29 gives $J = 0.264$ Ry. This second value is better (but involves lengthier calculations) than BREIT's and ECKART's $J = 0.262$ Ry. The experimental value is $J = 0.266$ Ry.

δ) The $2\,^1S$-state. One is tempted to treat the $2\,^1S$-state of para-helium in an analogous manner to $2\,^3S$ but with a symmetric, instead of antisymmetric, trial wave function. As mentioned before, such a wave function is not necessarily orthogonal to the wave function of the ground state (with lower energy) and the standard variation method cannot be applied. HYLLERAAS and UNDHEIM[3] have, nevertheless, developed a modification of the variation method which can be used.

---

[1] He also performed similar calculations for the $3\,^3D$ and $3\,^1D$ states.

[2] G. BREIT: Phys. Rev. **36**, 383 (1930).

[3] E. HYLLERAAS and B. UNDHEIM: Z. Physik **65**, 759 (1930). For a similar calculation for the $3\,^3P$ and $3\,^1P$ states in He see L. GOLDBERGER and A. CLOGSTON, Phys. Rev. **56**, 696 (1939).

They choose a trial wave function with a number of parameters and substitute it into the variational integral, as in the conventional variation method. They require the energy integral E to be stationary for variations of the parameters and again obtain the determinantal equation (32.22). However, they solve not for the lowest root $E_{(1)}$ (which would correspond to the ground state), but for the *second* lowest root $E_{(2)}$ of this equation. The corresponding wave function $U_{(2)}$ is then at least orthogonal to the *trial* wave function $U_{(1)}$ corresponding to the lowest root. Although $U_{(1)}$ is only an approximation to the ground state wave function, they show that the second root $E_{(2)}$ is *rigorously* an *upper limit* to the total energy of the second state of the para-system (the $2\,^1S$-state). The remaining procedure is then identical with the standard variation method.

They used a trial wave function identical with (35.3), except for an interchange of the Cos and Sin terms so that the wave function is symmetric. They found $k=1.34$, $c=0.73$ [$Z_i=2.08$, $Z_a=1.21$ in (35.2)] and for the ionization potential $J=0.2898$ Ry, compared with the experimental value of $J=0.2920$ Ry. The convergence of J with the number of parameters is much slower for the $2\,^1S$ state than for $2\,^3S$ (whose trial wave function is automatically orthogonal to the ground state).

COOLIDGE and JAMES[1] have obtained a much improved theoretical value of $J=0.2916$ Ry, using essentially the same method but a better trial wave function. The improvement is due largely to the inclusion of terms with two different exponential factors for the outer electron [compare the discussion of (34.7)]. They also give an illuminating comparison of the HEISENBERG, HARTREE, FOCK and variation methods as applied to the $2\,^1S$ state.

36. Miscellaneous calculations. We have discussed in detail some of the more commonly used methods of approximation in the treatment of He-like atoms. We shall merely mention some other methods and some properties of the wave functions (mainly for the ground state).

α) The "local energy". Let U be some approximation to some exact eigenfunction of the total HAMILTONian operator H, given by (24.1) in our case. We can then define a function of position, called the "local energy", by

$$E_{\text{loc}}(\boldsymbol{r}_1, \boldsymbol{r}_2) = \frac{1}{U(\boldsymbol{r}_1, \boldsymbol{r}_2)} H\, U(\boldsymbol{r}_1, \boldsymbol{r}_2). \tag{36.1}$$

If the wave function U were the exact eigenfunction, E_{loc} would of course be a constant equal to the exact energy eigenvalue. In the first order perturbation method and in the variation method one first finds some approximate function U and uses, as an approximation to the correct energy eigenvalue, the expectation value of E_{loc} (or the HAMILTONian) over this function,

$$E \equiv \overline{H} = \int d\tau\, U^* H\, U = \int d\tau\, |U|^2 E_{\text{loc}}. \tag{36.2}$$

The variation method chooses a function U such that the error in this expectation value is minimized. The *overall* form of the function U will then be excellent (if enough parameters are used) in the regions where the wave function is appreciable. But the variational function U will *not* be good at extremely large values of r_1 or r_2 (where U is extremely small). One can also show that the second and higher derivatives of any variational wave function (with a finite number of parameters) are poor approximations if r_1, r_2 or r_{12} are very small. In fact, when these wave functions are used, E_{loc} tends to $-\infty$ as r_1 or r_2 approach zero and tends to $+\infty$ as r_{12} approaches zero.

[1] A. COOLIDGE and M. JAMES: Phys. Rev. **49**, 676 (1936).

BARTLETT[1] recently obtained an approximate wave function for the ground state of helium in numerical form. This wave function, obtained by a numerical iteration procedure on an electronic computing machine, was designed to give as small fluctuations of E_{loc} as possible. For this wave function, E_{loc} is finite even at r_1, r_2 or r_{12} equal to zero and lies between -2.88 and -2.92 (a.u.) for all values of r_1 and r_2 up to about 4 a.u. But the energy eigenvalue E cannot be determined from this wave function to very much better than $-2.90 \pm 0.01_5$. The HYLLERAAS six-parameter wave function, on the other hand, gives $E = -2.9032$ (in error by only 0.0005) but has large fluctuations of E_{loc} around this value (apart from infinite values of E_{loc} if r_1, r_2 or r_{12} is zero). Nevertheless the normalized HYLLERAAS (6-parameter) and BARTLETT wave functions do not differ by more than $\pm 3\%$ from each other for all values of r_1 and r_2 up to about 4 a.u.

A variational method can also be devised which minimizes not E itself but the fluctuations of the function E_{loc}. One again chooses a trial wave function U with some arbitrary parameters and finds the minimum with respect to the parameters of

$$\overline{(E_{\text{loc}} - E)^2} = \int d\tau \, |(H - E)\, U|^2. \tag{36.3}$$

This method has not been used extensively in practice[2].

β) Expansion in LEGENDRE *polynomials.* For S-states of helium-like atoms, the exact wave function U depends only on the shape and size of the triangle formed by the coordinates of the two electrons, $\boldsymbol{r}_1$ and $\boldsymbol{r}_2$, and the line joining them. We can choose for the three variables describing this triangle the radial distances r_1 and r_2 and the angle ϑ_{12} between the vectors $\boldsymbol{r}_1$ and $\boldsymbol{r}_2$. The full normalized wave function U can then be expressed as an expansion in the normalized LEGENDRE polynomials $\mathscr{P}_{l0}$,

$$U(\boldsymbol{r}_1, \boldsymbol{r}_2) = \sum_{l=0}^{\infty} c_l \, \Phi_l(r_1, r_2) \, \mathscr{P}_{l0}(\cos\vartheta_{12}), \tag{36.4}$$

where Φ_l is some normalized function of two variables and c_l is a constant. Substituting (36.4) into the full wave equation for U, one then obtains an infinite set of coupled differential equations in r_1 and r_2 for the functions $c_l \Phi_l$. For all S-states in He-like atoms (except possibly for H^-) the constant c_0 is almost unity and c_1, c_2, etc. are small and decrease rapidly. These equations can then be solved by an iteration method, starting from the homogeneous equation for Φ_0.

A very accurate wave function for the $2\,{}^3S$ state in Li^+ has been obtained by this method[3]. The constant c_1 is only about 0.014, c_2 about 0.003. This method has not yet been applied to the ground state of He, but the HYLLERAAS six-parameter wave function has been expanded[4] in the form of (36.4). The first few coefficients c_l for the He ground state are

$$c_0 = 0.998, \quad c_1 = 0.063, \quad c_2 = 0.012, \quad c_3 = 0.004. \tag{36.5}$$

Each function Φ_l could in turn be written as an infinite sum of products of single particle wave functions. Actually Φ_0 is fairly close[5] to the HARTREE wave

[1] J. H. BARTLETT: Phys. Rev. **98**, 1076 (1955).

[2] H. JAMES and F. YOST: Phys. Rev. **54**, 646 (1938).

[3] LUKE, MEYEROTT and CLENDENIN: Phys. Rev. **85**, 401 (1952).

[4] L. C. GREEN *et al.*: Phys. Rev. **91**, 35 (1953); **96**, 319 (1954).

[5] See also H. MITLER: Phys. Rev. **99**, 1835 (1955). MITLER uses the HARTREE wave function and energy as a starting point and calculates the correlation energy (the effect of the correlation between the positions of the two electrons) by a perturbation method.

function (Sect. 31) and Φ_1, is approximated (very roughly) by

$$\Phi_1(r_1, r_2) = N r_1 r_2 e^{-2.3(r_1+r_2)}, \tag{36.6}$$

where N is a normalization constant.

γ) Wave functions in momentum space. In analogy with the discussions of Sect. 8, the SCHRÖDINGER equation for a He-like atom can be written in the form of an integral equation in momentum space. The momentum space wave function $\psi(\boldsymbol{p}_1, \boldsymbol{p}_2)$ is the six-dimensional FOURIER transform of the spatial wave function $U(\boldsymbol{r}_1, \boldsymbol{r}_2)$. Taking the FOURIER transform of the SCHRÖDINGER equation (24.1) gives the desired integral equation in momentum space. Replacing for the moment the nuclear potential $-Z/r$ by a general potential $V(\boldsymbol{r})$, we get

$$\left.\begin{aligned}(E - \tfrac{1}{2}p_1^2 - \tfrac{1}{2}p_2^2)\,\psi(\boldsymbol{p}_1, \boldsymbol{p}_2) = \int d^3k\, V'(-\boldsymbol{k})\,[\psi(\boldsymbol{p}_1+\boldsymbol{k}, \boldsymbol{p}_2) + {}\\ + \psi(\boldsymbol{p}_1, \boldsymbol{p}_2+\boldsymbol{k})] + \int d^3k\, \frac{1}{2\pi^2 k^2}\,\psi(\boldsymbol{p}_1-\boldsymbol{k}, \boldsymbol{p}_2+\boldsymbol{k}),\end{aligned}\right\} \tag{36.7}$$

where

$$\psi(\boldsymbol{p}_1, \boldsymbol{p}_2) = \frac{1}{(2\pi)^3}\iint d^3r_1\, d^3r_2\, e^{-i(\boldsymbol{r}_1\cdot\boldsymbol{p}_1+\boldsymbol{r}_2\cdot\boldsymbol{p}_2)}\, U(\boldsymbol{r}_1, \boldsymbol{r}_2)$$

and $V'(\boldsymbol{k})$ is $(2\pi)^{-\frac{3}{2}}$ times the FOURIER transform of $V(\boldsymbol{r})$. If $V(\boldsymbol{r})$ is the nuclear potential $-Z/r$, then $V'(\boldsymbol{k}) = -Z(2\pi^2k^2)^{-1}$. The last term on the right side of (36.7) represents the interaction of the two electrons.

For an S-state, $\psi(\boldsymbol{p}_1, \boldsymbol{p}_2)$ only depends on the absolute values p_1 and p_2 of the two vectors $\boldsymbol{p}_1$ and $\boldsymbol{p}_2$ and on the angle ϑ_{12} between them. Another quantity of interest for S-states is the momentum distribution function $P(p)$, which gives the probability that either electron has momentum p (regardless of its direction or of the value of the momentum of the other electron). If ψ is normalized we have

$$P(p_1) = 4\pi p_1^2 \int d^3p_2\, \psi^2(p_1, p_2, \vartheta_{12}), \qquad \int_0^\infty dp\, P(p) = 1.$$

For the ground state of He-like atoms with nuclear charge Z, the simplest approximate wave function is again the hydrogen-like one with $z = Z - \frac{5}{16}$. Using (8.10) we find

$$\psi = \frac{8}{\pi^2}\,\frac{z^5}{(p_1^2+z^2)^2\,(p_2^2+z^2)^2}, \qquad P(p) = \frac{32 z^5 p^2}{\pi(p^2+z^2)^4}. \tag{36.8}$$

As discussed in Sect. 8, better wave functions could be obtained by successive iterations of (36.7), using as the initial function occurring in the integrals the approximation (36.8). One such iteration has been carried out[1] and the corresponding approximation for $P(p)$ evaluated. Further iterations would be extremely tedious and no very accurate wave functions in momentum space are as yet available for helium.

δ) Some expectation values. We shall discuss now the ground state expectation values (denoted by bars) of a few operators, evaluated by using various wave functions. These expectation values will be needed in evaluating some relativistic corrections (Sect. 41) and also throw some light on the various types of wave functions.

Consider first the three-dimensional DIRAC delta-functions $\delta^{(3)}(\boldsymbol{r}_1)$ and $\delta^{(3)}(\boldsymbol{r}_{12})$. Their expectation values are

$$\left.\begin{aligned}\overline{\delta^{(3)}(\boldsymbol{r}_1)} &= \int d\tau_1\, U^2(\boldsymbol{r}_1, 0),\\ \overline{\delta^{(3)}(\boldsymbol{r}_{12})} &= \int d\tau_1\, U^2(\boldsymbol{r}_1, \boldsymbol{r}_1).\end{aligned}\right\} \tag{36.9}$$

[1] R. McWEENEY and C. COULSON: Proc. Phys. Soc. Lond. A **62**, 509 (1949).

If we use either the Hartree or hydrogen-like wave functions for the ground state of a He-like atom, U is of form $u(r_1)\,u(r_2)$. If $u(r)$ is normalized we then have

$$\overline{\delta^{(3)}(\boldsymbol{r}_1)} = u^2(0), \qquad \overline{\delta^{(3)}(\boldsymbol{r}_{12})} = \int d\tau\, u^4(r). \tag{36.10}$$

For the hydrogen-like wave function for nuclear charge $(Z-\frac{5}{16})$, in particular, this gives

$$\overline{\delta^{(3)}(\boldsymbol{r}_1)} = \frac{1}{\pi}\left(Z-\frac{5}{16}\right)^3, \qquad \overline{\delta^{(3)}(\boldsymbol{r}_{12})} = \frac{1}{8\pi}\left(Z-\frac{5}{16}\right)^3. \tag{36.11}$$

If the Hylleraas variational wave functions are used, the integrals (36.9) can be expressed in terms of the usual variables u, s, t and evaluated analytically.

We consider next the operator for (twice) the kinetic energy of one electron, $p_1^2 = -\Delta_1$. For a wave function of product form (hydrogenic or Hartree) the single particle wave function $u(r_1)$ satisfies an equation of form

$$p^2 u = -\Delta u = 2\,[\varepsilon - V(r)]\,u(r). \tag{36.12}$$

For such a wave function the expectation value of p^2 is then

$$\overline{p^2} = 2\int d\tau\, u^2(r)\,[\varepsilon - V(r)]. \tag{36.13}$$

For the hydrogenic wave function, $\overline{p^2}$ is simply $(Z-\frac{5}{16})^2$ a.u. For the Hartree wave function (Sect. 31) the integral in (36.13) can be evaluated numerically. For the variational wave functions, $\overline{p_1^2}$ is simply equal to minus E, the expression for the total energy (see Sect. 36ε).

We finally consider the square of the kinetic energy operator for electron 1, or $p_1^4 = \nabla_1^4 \equiv \Delta_1^2$. We first note that

$$\mathrm{div}_1\,[U\,\mathrm{grad}_1(\Delta_1 U) - (\Delta_1 U)\,\mathrm{grad}_1 U] = U(\Delta_1^2 U) - (\Delta_1 U)^2. \tag{36.14}$$

For any analytic function U which falls off exponentially at large distances, the integral of the left side of this equation over the *whole* $\mathbf{r}_1$-space must vanish (from Gauss' theorem). We then have two alternative forms for the expectation value of p^4,

$$\overline{p_1^4} = \int d\tau_1\, d\tau_2\, U\,\Delta_1^2 U = d\tau_1\, d\tau_2 (\Delta_1 U)^2. \tag{36.15}$$

Great care must be taken if the first form in (36.15) is used: For the exact wave function, $\Delta_1 U$ behaves like Z/r_1 or like $1/r_{12}$ if r_1 or r_{12} approaches zero, just like the potential energy in the total Hamiltonian. $\Delta_1^2 U$ then has a delta-function type of singularity at $r_1 = 0$ and $r_{12} = 0$ and a *wrong* answer would be obtained if the first integral in (36.15) were evaluated by a limiting process which excludes an infinitesimal region around the origin and around $r_{12} = 0$. The second form of (36.15) is free from these difficulties and is, in any case, easier to evaluate in practice.

For a normalized product wave function, this second form of (36.15) becomes, using (36.12),

$$\overline{p^4} = 4\int d\tau\, u^2(r)\,[\varepsilon - V(r)]^2. \tag{36.16}$$

For the hydrogen-like wave function we find, using (3.25),

$$\overline{p^4} = 5\,(Z - \tfrac{5}{16})^4 \text{ a.u.} \tag{36.17}$$

For the Hartree wave function, (36.16) can be integrated numerically. For the variational wave functions, $(\Delta_1 U)$ can be expressed in terms of the variables u, s and t and the analytic evaluation of the second integral in (36.15) is elementary but tedious.

Table 10. *Expectation values in atomic units of various operators for the ground state of Helium.*

Wave function[2]	H-like	HARTREE	3	6	18	38
$-E=-\overline{H}$	2.8438	2.8670	2.9024	2.90324	2.903715	2.903723
$-\overline{H^2}/\overline{H}$	3.160		2.9188	2.9091	2.90403	2.90376
$\overline{\delta^{(3)}(\boldsymbol{r}_1)}$	1.530	1.798	1.7984	1.8167	1.8102	1.8106
$\overline{\delta^{(3)}(\boldsymbol{r}_{12})}$	0.191	0.188	0.1162	0.1114	0.1072	0.1065
$\overline{p_1^4}$	40.54	52.46	53.42	54.50	54.072	54.092
$\overline{\boldsymbol{p}_1\cdot\boldsymbol{p}_2}$	0	0	-0.178	-0.164	-0.1591	-0.1591

The results[1] obtained with different wave functions for these expectation values for He ($Z=2$) are given in Table 10. The most reliable value in each case is probably (but *not* necessarily) the one for the variational wave function with the most parameters. Note that the HARTREE wave function (as well as the hydrogenic one) overestimates $\overline{\delta^{(3)}(\boldsymbol{r}_{12})}$ badly, since the polarization depresses the wave function appreciably when the two electrons are close (or coincide). For the other expectation values the HARTREE wave function gives much better results than the hydrogenic one and the polarization effects are not very strong.

It can also be seen from Table 10 that, for the variational wave functions, the fractional accuracy of the expectation value of most other operators is much poorer than that of the HAMILTONian H itself. For instance, the fractional differences between the expectation values for the 3 and 38 parameter functions are about 0.6×10^{-2} for $\delta^{(3)}(\boldsymbol{r}_1)$ and 9×10^{-2} for $\delta^{(3)}(\boldsymbol{r}_{12})$, but only 4×10^{-4} for H. Imagine a normalized variational wave function U_{var} expanded in terms of the *exact* normalized eigenfunctions U_n of the HAMILTONian H for helium,

$$U_{\text{var}} = \sqrt{1-\sum_{n=1}^{\infty}|c_n|^2}\; U_0 + \sum_{n=1}^{\infty} c_n U_n, \tag{36.18}$$

where U_0, E_0 are the true wave function and energy of the ground state. We then have

$$\overline{H} - E_0 = \sum_n |c_n|^2 (E_n - E_0), \qquad \overline{H^2} - E_0^2 = \sum_n |c_n|^2 (E_n - E_0)^2. \tag{36.19}$$

If the coefficients c_n are small, then the error in the expectation value of an operator Q which does not commute with H will (in general) involve terms like $\sum c_n Q_{0n}$ which are linear in the c_n, whereas the error in $\overline{H}$ only contains terms quadratic in the c_n.

The error in $\overline{H^2}$ is also quadratic in the c_n, but with large coefficients: The quantity $(E_n+E_0)_{\text{av}}$ defined by

$$(E_n+E_0)_{\text{av}} \equiv \frac{\sum|c_n|^2(E_n^2-E_0^2)}{\sum|c_n|^2(E_n-E_0)} = \frac{\overline{H^2}-E_0^2}{\overline{H}-E_0} \tag{36.20}$$

measures, in a certain sense, the average energy of the most important higher terms in the expansion (36.18). The values of $\overline{H^2}$ and $\overline{H}$ for the three-parameter

[1] These results were obtained by T. KINOSHITA, D. BOWERS, J. F. BIRD and P. KABIR (unpublished). The expression $\overline{p_1^4}$ in the Table denotes the *second* integral in (36.15).

[2] "H-like" denotes the one-parameter hydrogenic wave function, the last four wave functions are the variational 3- and 6-parameter ones of HYLLERAAS', KINOSHITA'S 38-parameter and HERZBERG and CHANDRASEKHAR'S 18-parameter functions. Actually, a slightly improved version of the 18-parameter function was used, i.e. the function was minimized (for energy) more accurately by KINOSHITA by a method of successive approximation. The 38-parameter function is not yet fully minimized.

function, for instance, give a value[1] of about 30 a.u. or 60 Ry for $(E_n + E_0)_{\text{av}}$, which is very large compared with the ionization potential.

ε) The virial theorem. In Sect. 32γ we have discussed variational wave functions for the ground state of a helium-like atom. The expectation value of the total kinetic energy T and of the total potential energy V is then $k^2 M/N$ and $-k\,L/N$, respectively [M, L, N defined by Eq. (32.17)]. Using (32.19) we then find that

$$\tfrac{1}{2}\overline{V} = -\overline{T} = \overline{H}, \tag{36.21}$$

where the bar denotes expectation values. This relation, which is an outcome of the virial theorem[2], can be generalized to apply to *any* bound and stationary state of an *arbitrary* atom, as follows.

Consider a nonrelativistic system of n charged particles which interact with each other only by means of COULOMB interactions. The total HAMILTONian H, kinetic energy T and potential energy V are then of the form

$$H = T + V, \quad T = \sum_i \frac{p_i^2}{2m_i}, \quad V = \sum_{i \neq j} \frac{a_{ij}}{r_{ij}}, \tag{36.22}$$

where m_i and a_{ij} are constants. Let φ be any bounded, quadratically integrable function of $\boldsymbol{r}_1, \boldsymbol{r}_2, \ldots, \boldsymbol{r}_n$ and call

$$L = -\int d\tau\, \varphi^* V \varphi, \quad M = \int d\tau\, \varphi^* T \varphi, \quad N = \int d\tau\, \varphi^* \varphi,$$

where the integral is extended over all values of the coordinates $\boldsymbol{r}_1$ to $\boldsymbol{r}_n$. Now let k be an arbitrary (as yet) parameter and form the following expectation value

$$\overline{H} = \frac{\int d\tau\, U^* H U}{\int d\tau\, U^* U} = \frac{k^2 M - k L}{N}, \tag{36.23}$$

where

$$U(\boldsymbol{r}_1, \ldots, \boldsymbol{r}_n) = \varphi(k\boldsymbol{r}_1, \ldots, k\boldsymbol{r}_n).$$

The factors k^2 and $-k$ stem from the fact that the operator T only contains second derivatives with respect to position and the operator V (for a COULOMB potential) only contains terms of the minus first power of distance.

For any correct eigenfunction of H, the expectation value (36.23) must have a stationary value with respect to any infinitesimal variation of the wave function, including a variation of the scale parameter k. We thus have, for any correct eigenfunction

$$\frac{\partial \overline{H}}{\partial k} = 0, \quad k = \frac{L}{2M}, \quad 2\overline{T} = -\overline{V} = -2\overline{H},$$

which is the required relation. For a more general potential of form $V = \sum_{i,j} a_{ij} r_{ij}^{\nu}$, one can similarly prove the relation

$$2\overline{T} = \nu \overline{V} = \frac{2\nu}{2+\nu} \overline{H}. \tag{36.24}$$

---

[1] The very accurate 38-parameter value of $\overline{H}$ can be used as an approximation for E_0 when evaluating the expression (36.20) for *less* accurate wave functions. The numerical value of $(E_n + E_0)_{\text{av}}$ fluctuates somewhat from one variational wave function to another but, as a general trend, increases with increasing accuracy of the wave function (from about 10 a.u. for the 1-parameter to about 80 a.u. for a 14-parameter function). Rigorous upper bounds to the discrepancy between $\overline{H}$ for any function and the true energy E_0 can be calculated, if $\overline{H^2}$ is known [L. WILETS and I. CHERRY, Phys. Rev. **103**, 112 (1953)]. These upper bounds grossly overestimate the actual error in $\overline{H}$ (this is connected with the fact that $(E_n + E_0)_{\text{av}}$ is so large for these functions). If we *assume* that $(E_n + E_0)_{\text{av}}$ is of the same order of magnitude (or larger) for 38 as for, say, 14 parameters and use the value of $(\overline{H} - \overline{H^2}/\overline{H})$ in Table 10 for the 38 parameter function, we find that the error in $\overline{H}$ for this function is only of the order of magnitude of 10^{-6} a.u.

[2] See also ref. [4], p. 140.

37. Motion of the nucleus. Next, we shall study the influence of the motion of the nucleus having mass M and coordinates $\xi_0\,\eta_0\,\zeta_0$. Let us consider an atom with n electrons having mass m and coordinates $\xi_1\,\eta_1\,\zeta_1\ldots\xi_n\,\eta_n\,\zeta_n$. We introduce the coordinates of the center of mass

$$X=\frac{1}{M+n\,m}\,(M\,\xi_0+m\,\xi_1+\cdots+m\,\xi_n)\qquad\text{(similarly for } Y, Z) \tag{37.1}$$

and the relative coordinates

$$x_i=\xi_i-\xi_0\;(i=1,2,\ldots,n)\qquad\text{(similarly for } y_i, z_i). \tag{37.2}$$

Then we obtain

$$\frac{\partial}{\partial\xi_i}=\frac{\partial}{\partial X}\cdot\frac{m}{M+n\,m}+\frac{\partial}{\partial x_i}\qquad(i=1,\ldots,n),$$
$$\frac{\partial}{\partial\xi_0}=\frac{\partial}{\partial X}\cdot\frac{M}{M+n\,m}-\frac{\partial}{\partial x_1}-\cdots-\frac{\partial}{\partial x_n}.$$

The following expression, twice the kinetic energy, appears in the SCHRÖDINGER equation:

$$\frac{1}{M}\frac{\partial^2}{\partial\xi_0^2}+\frac{1}{m}\left(\frac{\partial^2}{\partial\xi_1^2}+\cdots+\frac{\partial^2}{\partial\xi_n^2}\right)=\frac{1}{M+n\,m}\frac{\partial^2}{\partial X^2}+\frac{1}{m}\sum_i\frac{\partial^2}{\partial x_i^2}+\frac{1}{M}\sum_{ik}\frac{\partial^2}{\partial x_i\,\partial x_k}. \tag{37.3}$$

Separating out the motion of the center of mass of the atomic system, i.e., the dependence of the eigenfunction on XYZ, we obtain the SCHRÖDINGER equation in c.g.s. units:

$$\left[\frac{\hbar^2}{2m}\sum_{i=0}^{n}\Delta_i+\frac{\hbar^2}{2M}\sum_{i=1}^{n}\sum_{k=1}^{n}\left(\frac{\partial^2}{\partial x_i\,\partial x_k}+\frac{\partial^2}{\partial y_i\,\partial y_k}+\frac{\partial^2}{\partial z_i\,\partial z_k}\right)+E-V\right]U=0. \tag{37.4}$$

The second term is the effect of the motion of the nucleus which we sought; it results in a correction of the eigenvalue which is proportional to the ratio of the electron mass to the nuclear mass, m/M. It is expedient to divide that term into two parts, one containing terms with $i=k$, and the other terms with $i\neq k$. Introducing the reduced mass of the electron,

$$\mu=\frac{m\,M}{M+m}, \tag{37.5}$$

(37.4) becomes

$$\left[\frac{\hbar^2}{2\mu}\sum_i\Delta_i+\frac{\hbar^2}{M}\sum_{i<k}\left(\frac{\partial^2}{\partial x_i\,\partial x_k}+\frac{\partial^2}{\partial y_i\,\partial y_k}+\frac{\partial^2}{\partial z_i\,\partial z_k}\right)+E-V\right]U=0. \tag{37.6}$$

Thus, the motion of the nucleus modifies the SCHRÖDINGER equation in two ways. In the first place, the effective mass of the electron μ replaces the actual mass of the electron m. Secondly, to the SCHRÖDINGER equation in which the motion of the nucleus is not considered, is added a perturbing term which changes the energy of the atom by the amount

$$\varepsilon_2=-\frac{\hbar^2}{M}\sum_{i<k}\int U\left(\frac{\partial^2}{\partial x_i\,\partial x_k}+\frac{\partial^2}{\partial y_i\,\partial y_k}+\frac{\partial^2}{\partial z_i\,\partial z_k}\right)U\,d\tau.$$

Introducing atomic units and integrating by parts, the above is seen to be equal to

$$\varepsilon_2=+\frac{m}{M}\sum_{i<k}\int(\mathrm{grad}_i\,U\cdot\mathrm{grad}_k\,U)\,d\tau. \tag{37.7}$$

α) *Elementary mass correction.* We are familiar with the first modification of the SCHRÖDINGER equation, from the theory of the atoms which contain but a single electron. It can be dealt with simply by introducing a new atomic unit for the energy which differs from the usual energy unit by the factor

$$\frac{\mu}{M} = \frac{M}{M+m} \approx 1 - \frac{m}{M}.$$

Thus, if we solve the SCHRÖDINGER equation and express the energy of an atomic state in RYDBERG units, then, instead of taking the RYDBERG corresponding to infinite nuclear mass

$$R_\infty = \frac{m\, e^4}{2\pi\, c\, \hbar^3} = 109737.32 \text{ cm}^{-1}, \tag{37.8}$$

we must take the RYDBERG corresponding to the mass of the atom in question, viz.,

$$R_M = R_\infty \frac{M}{M+m} \approx R_\infty \left(1 - \frac{m}{M}\right). \tag{37.9}$$

We may also put it this way: First, we calculate the energy levels for infinite nuclear mass, and then we apply the correction $\varepsilon_1 = -\frac{m}{M} E_\infty$ in which E_∞ is the term value for $M = \infty$. This part of the mass correction affects all the levels of the atom in the same way, and is also independent of the state of ionization of the atom. The frequencies of the spectral lines of the atom are all reduced in the same ratio $1 - \frac{m}{M}$.

β) *Mass correction due to electron exchange*[1]. On the other hand, the second part of the mass correction (37.7) differs for the various states of the atom. If the electrons in the atom moved entirely independently of each other, i.e., if the eigenfunction of the atom were a simple product of the eigenfunctions of the individual electrons,

$$U = \prod_{i=1}^{n} u_i(i),$$

then the second part of the mass correction would vanish, viz.,

$$\varepsilon_2 = \frac{m}{M} \sum_{i<k} \int d\tau_i\, u_i \operatorname{grad} u_i \int d\tau_k\, u_k \operatorname{grad} u_k = 0.$$

This follows from the fact that for a bound electron the expectation value of the momentum in any direction x,

$$\int u \frac{\partial u}{\partial x}\, d\tau,$$

is necessarily equal to zero. Thus the mass correction ε_2 is essentially determined by the extent to which the electrons affect one another's motion, i.e., insofar as definite phase relationships exist between the orbital motions of the electrons. The importance of these phase relationships for the mass correction is easily understood. If, for example, the electrons tend to move in the same direction, then the nucleus, in order to balance the motion of the electrons, will move about much more than if the motions of the individual electrons move independently of one another or even tend to be predominantly opposed to each other.

[1] Cf. D. S. HUGHES and C. ECKART: Phys. Rev. **36**, 694 (1930).

There are two reasons why the individual electrons affect one another's motion, the Pauli principle and the electrostatic interaction (polarization effect). We shall pursue both of these influences more closely in the example of an atom with two electrons. We consider first the exchange effects and approximate the eigenfunction by a sum of products of the eigenfunctions belonging to the two individual electrons; i.e., we neglect the polarization effect resulting from the electronic interaction:

$$U = \frac{1}{\sqrt{2}} \left(u(1)\, v(2) \pm v(1)\, u(2)\right). \tag{37.10}$$

The plus sign belongs to parahelium and the minus sign to orthohelium. Substituting (37.10) into (37.7) we obtain

$$\varepsilon_2 = \frac{m}{M} \int \operatorname{grad} u^*(1)\, v^*(2) \left[u(1) \operatorname{grad} v(2) \pm v(1) \operatorname{grad} u(2)\right] d\tau_1\, d\tau_2. \tag{37.11}$$

The first term inside the brackets yields zero, because

$$\int u \operatorname{grad} u^*\, d\tau = 0$$

vanishes, since it is the expectation value of the momentum of a bound electron. The second term yields

$$\varepsilon_2 = \pm \frac{m}{M} \left| \int \operatorname{grad} u^* \cdot v\, d\tau \right|^2. \tag{37.12}$$

The above integral is essentially the optical transition probability for going from the one occupied electronic state to the other. Thus, the mass correction (37.12) is applicable only if the two electronic states combine optically. Since, in the case of atoms with two electrons, one of the electrons is always in the ground state, which is a $1s$ state, it follows that only p states are affected by the additional mass correction. In that case, the energy of the para levels is raised, i.e., for those terms the correction acts in the same direction as the elementary mass correction; the energy of the ortho terms is lowered. Physically, this means that in para states the two electrons move mostly in the same direction, and in ortho states more frequently in opposite directions.

γ) Polarization-mass correction (He-ground state). We now consider the second type of correlation effect, produced by the electrostatic repulsion between the electrons. Due to this polarization effect, the exact wave function cannot be of the simple product form (37.10), but depends also on the distance between the electrons. Hence the integral (37.7) will not be exactly zero even for states with $l \neq 1$. But for excited states the polarization of the wave function is fairly small and decreases rapidly with increasing orbital quantum number l (see Sect. 29). For the He-ground state, however, the two electrons are close and the polarization effect is by no means negligible, especially in view of the high accuracy of the variational calculations (Sect. 32).

For the ground state of He-like atoms the variational wave functions (Sects. 32 and 33) should be accurate enough to give a good account of polarization. We again introduce the coordinates s, t and u, Eq. (32.2). The integral (37.7) then takes the form

$$\left.\begin{aligned} \varepsilon_M = \frac{m}{MN} \int_0^\infty ds \int_0^s du \int_0^u dt \Big\{ (s^2 + t^2 - 2u^2) \left[\left(\frac{\partial U}{\partial s}\right)^2 - \left(\frac{\partial U}{\partial t}\right)^2\right] u - \\ - (s^2 - t^2)\, u \left(\frac{\partial U}{\partial u}\right)^2 - 2 \frac{\partial U}{\partial u} \left[s \frac{\partial U}{\partial s} (u^2 - t^2) + t \frac{\partial U}{\partial t} (s^2 - u^2)\right]\Big\}, \end{aligned}\right\} \tag{37.13}$$

where M is the nuclear mass and N a normalization factor, given in (32.8).

The expression (37.13) has now been evaluated both for HYLLERAAS' and CHANDRASEKHAR[1] *et al.*'s functions and for KINOSHITA'S[2] 38-parameter wave function. The 38-parameter results for He^4 are (see Table 10, Sect. 36 for $\boldsymbol{p}_1 \cdot \boldsymbol{p}_2$)

$$\varepsilon_M = + \frac{0.1591\, m}{M} = + 2.18 \times 10^{-5} \text{ a.u.} = + 4.79 \text{ cm}^{-1}. \qquad (37.14)$$

HYLLERAAS' (presumably less accurate) six-parameter wave function[3] gave $+4.95 \text{ cm}^{-1}$. Using CHANDRASEKHAR *et al.*'s wave functions for Li^+ and $O^{(+6)}$, WILETS and CHERRY find

$$\varepsilon_M = + 0.271\, m/M = + 4.7 \text{ cm}^{-1} \quad (Li^+, \; Z = 3, \; A = 7),$$
$$\varepsilon_M = + 1.00\, m/M = + 7.5 \text{ cm}^{-1} \quad (O^{(6+)}, \; Z = 8, \; A = 16).$$

The expression (37.13) for ε_M has also been evaluated[4] for helium-like ions of arbitrary Z, using a variational wave function similar to (33.14), but involving more terms. Results from this expression for $Z = 3$ and 8 disagree with the (presumably much more accurate) ones of WILETS and CHERRY, but ε_M is at any rate less than the experimental error in J for Li^+ and all heavier ions.

The mass-polarization term ε_M is additional to the main effect ε_1 of the nuclear mass on the energy of the helium ground state. This main effect we have already taken into account by using the "reduced mass RYDBERG", Eq. (37.9), which reduces the ionization potential J of helium by $J m/M$ or about 27 cm^{-1} from the value obtained by using R_∞. The correction term ε_M raises the ground state energy and thus also lowers the ionization potential J.

δ) Comparison with experiment. For excited states of He-like atoms the largest mass effect (apart from the elementary one, ε_1) should be the exchange effect, which is present for P-states only. For P-states we neglect the polarization effects and use a wave function of form (37.10) which leads to (37.12). Using for u and v the simple hydrogenic wave functions of ECKART (Sect. 35γ), (37.12) reduces to

$$\varepsilon_2 = \pm \frac{128}{3} \frac{m}{M} (Z_i Z_a)^5 \frac{(Z_i n - Z_a)^{2n-4}}{(Z_i n + Z_a)^{2n+4}} n^3 (n^2 - 1) \text{ Ry}. \qquad (37.15)$$

Using ECKART's values for the charge parameters Z_i and Z_a (Table 9, Sect. 35) we find for the $n = 2$ states of He^4

$$\varepsilon_2 = -1.72 \text{ cm}^{-1} \, (2\,^3P), \qquad \varepsilon_2 = +1.13 \text{ cm}^{-1} \, (2\,^1P). \qquad (37.16)$$

The polarization effect for the $2S$ states, calculated[5] from the variational wave functions of Sect. 35, is only -0.22 cm^{-1} for 2^3S and -0.48 for 2^1S. For $n = 3$ in He^4, (37.15) gives about -0.52 cm^{-1} for 3^3P and $+0.35 \text{ cm}^{-1}$ for 3^1P. The polarization effects for $3\,S$ should again be smaller and the effects for $3\,D$ negligible. The total mass corrections for P-states have not yet been calculated using very accurate wave functions which also take polarization into account, but (37.15) should be a fairly good approximation.

Two isotopes of the helium atom exist with physical atomic mass units 4.0039 and 3.0170, respectively. The small frequency difference of a large number of equivalent spectral lines for these two isotopes have been measured very accurately[6].

---

[1] L. WILETS and I. CHERRY: Phys. Rev. **103**, 112 (1956).

[2] T. KINOSHITA: Phys. Rev. (1957, in print).

[3] Previously quoted values of 5.2 cm^{-1} and 4.1 cm^{-1} for the six-parameter function are wrong.

[4] H. A. ROBINSON: Phys. Rev. **51**, 14 (1937).

[5] A. P. STONE: Proc. Phys. Soc. Lond. A **68**, 1152 (1955).

[6] FRED, TOMPKINS, BRODY and HAMERMESH: Phys. Rev. **82**, 406 (1951). — L. BRADLEY and H. KUHN: Proc. Roy. Soc. Lond., Ser. A **209**, 325 (1951).

Their spectra differ in part by the presence of hyperfine structure effects for He^3, but not for He^4. These effects have been analyzed in detail, are fairly small and reasonably well understood (Sect. 44). After applying corrections for these hyperfine structure effects to the experimental frequencies, the remaining frequency shifts between He^4 and He^3 should be largely due to the various mass effects discussed above. These mass effects are larger in He^3 than in He^4 by a factor 4.004/3.017. From these experiments one can then deduce the total mass-effect in He^4, say, for each spectral line. This, in turn, gives the difference in the mass-effects for the lower and upper states of the transition.

The experiments of FRED *et al.*, and BRADLEY and KUHN[1] certainly confirm the theoretical order of magnitude of the exchange mass effect for P-states and the smallness of the polarization effects for S and D states, etc. (in addition to the much larger elementary mass correction ε_1). Quantitatively, however, the agreement with theoretical predictions for ε_2 is rather poor. The cause of these discrepancies is not yet known.

b. Relativistic Theory.

38. Discussion of the BREIT equation. We consider in the next few sections relativistic corrections to the energy eigenvalues of helium-like atoms. At present the exact relativistic theory for the two-electron system cannot be written in closed form. However, methods are available for obtaining (at least in principle) energy eigenvalues to any accuracy in the form of an expansion in powers of α, the fine structure constant. We shall discuss mainly the case of small nuclear charge Z, where one can also expand in powers of $Z\alpha$. We shall carry explicitly only corrections to the nonrelativistic energy up to relative order $(Z\alpha)^2$ and only indicate possible methods for calculating higher order corrections. The $(Z\alpha)^2$ corrections give the energy to the same order of accuracy as the PAULI approximation (Sects. 12 and 13) for hydrogenic atoms. For large values of Z other approximation methods are available, which involve expansions in powers of $1/Z$ as well as of α (but not of $Z\alpha$). These will be discussed briefly in Sect. 43.

One possible starting point for such calculations, if Z is small, is the BREIT equation[2], which has been used extensively in the past. It is a differential equation for a relativistic wave function U for two electrons, interacting with each other and with an external electromagnetic field. The BREIT equation is akin to the DIRAC equation for a single electron, but—unlike the DIRAC equation—is *not* fully LORENTZ invariant and is only an approximation. It reads (for a stationary state)

$$\left(E - H_{(1)} - H_{(2)} - \frac{e^2}{r_{12}}\right) U = -\frac{e^2}{2r_{12}}\left[\boldsymbol{\alpha}_1\cdot\boldsymbol{\alpha}_2 + \frac{(\boldsymbol{\alpha}_1\cdot\boldsymbol{r}_{12})(\boldsymbol{\alpha}_2\cdot\boldsymbol{r}_{12})}{r_{12}^2}\right] U, \qquad (38.1)$$

where

$$H_{(1)} = -e\varphi(\boldsymbol{r}_1) + \beta_1 mc^2 + \boldsymbol{\alpha}_1\cdot\left(c\boldsymbol{p}_1 + e\boldsymbol{A}(\boldsymbol{r}_1)\right). \qquad (38.2)$$

The wave function U depends on the positions $\boldsymbol{r}_1$ and $\boldsymbol{r}_2$ of the two electrons and has sixteen spinor components, four each for electrons 1 and 2. The operator $H_{(1)}$ is identical with the DIRAC HAMILTONian, Eq. (10.1), and the DIRAC matrices $\boldsymbol{\alpha}_1$ and β_1 operate on the spinor components of U (for electron 1) in the usual way. The momentum operator $\boldsymbol{p}_1$ is again $-i\hbar\,\mathrm{grad}_1$, φ and $\boldsymbol{A}$ are the scalar and vector potentials of the external electromagnetic field (including the nuclear COULOMB potential), $\boldsymbol{r}_{12}$ the distance between the two electrons and E the total energy.

[1] See footnote 6, previous page.

[2] G. BREIT: Phys. Rev. **34**, 553 (1929); **36**, 383 (1930); **39** 616 (1932). See also J. R. OPPENHEIMER, Phys. Rev. **35**, 461 (1930).

The BREIT equation is based on two, essentially distinct, types of approximations. First, the term on the right side of (38.1) is only an approximation to the relativistic interaction between the two electrons (in addition to the "instantaneous" COULOMB interaction e^2/r_{12}), which is prescribed by quantum electrodynamics. But even if quantum electrodynamic effects were absent altogether, the remaining BREIT equation would still not be exact. More precisely, this equation would be compatible with DIRAC single-electron theory, but not with DIRAC pair ("hole") theory (see Sect. 15γ). In a correct field-theoretic treatment of pair theory, processes involving the creation of virtual electron-positron pairs occur, which are not treated exactly by (38.1). We shall discuss the two types of approximations separately.

α) Single-electron theory. We treat the electrons at first not according to field theory, but simple single-electron theory (negative energy states treated on the same footing as positive ones). If we were also to neglect quantum electrodynamic effects, the obvious semi-relativistic wave equation [1] for the two electrons would be (38.1) with the right hand side replaced by zero,

$$\left(E - H_{(1)} - H_{(2)} - \frac{e^2}{r_{12}}\right) U = 0. \tag{38.3}$$

The Eq. (38.3) would satisfy two requirements. First, if we take the nonrelativistic limit it would reduce to the SCHRÖDINGER equation for the two-electron system, (24.1). Second, if we neglect the COULOMB interaction e^2/r_{12}, the solutions are

$$\left.\begin{aligned} U &= U_1(\boldsymbol{r}_1)\, U_2(\boldsymbol{r}_2), & E &= E_1 + E_2; \\ (E_i - H_{(i)})\, U_i(\boldsymbol{r}_i) &= 0; & i &= 1, 2. \end{aligned}\right\} \tag{38.4}$$

U_1 and U_2 are thus solutions of the LORENTZ-invariant DIRAC equation and (38.4) would be fully relativistic. The COULOMB term in (38.3), however, is not even approximately LORENTZ invariant and relativistic corrections to the interaction between the two electrons are furnished by quantum electrodynamics. A number of methods are available for treating these interactions via the quantized transverse electromagnetic field. All these methods make use of the fact that the coupling of each electron with this field involves the small fine structure constant $\alpha = e^2/\hbar c$. We shall only consider the lowest order non-zero terms in an expansion in powers of α. We shall use "old-fashioned" perturbation theory, which is the least elegant of the various methods but, to this order, the simplest.

We assume that all the eigenstates U_n and energy eigenvalues E_n of (38.3) have been found (in principle) and let U_0, E_0 refer to a particular such eigenstate. We treat the quantized electromagnetic field just as in Sect. 19β and evaluate the energy change ΔW, due to the perturbation H', Eq. (19.5) [2], in second order perturbation theory only. Following the discussion of Sect. 19β, we find two types of terms. One type involves the emission of a virtual photon by one electron, which is then absorbed by the *other* electron. This term, which requires the presence of two electrons, is the interaction term we wish to calculate and will lead to an energy change of order $\alpha(Z\alpha)(Z^2\,\text{Ry})$. The other type involves the emission and absorption of the photon by the *same* electron. Although these terms would actually diverge individually if no cut-off were used, their sum—including mass renormalization terms—is finite and small. In fact, this sum leads to the LAMB

[1] For a formal justification see Sect. 38β.

[2] Except that the momentum $\boldsymbol{p}$ is replaced by the DIRAC matrix $mc\boldsymbol{\alpha}$. For details see refs. [5], [6] and [13] of the bibliography.

shift for a two-electron atom which is only of order $\alpha(Z\alpha)^2(Z^2\,\mathrm{Ry})$: This is smaller than the desired terms by one order[1] of $Z\alpha$ and we shall omit it (see, however, Sect. 41β).

The second order energy ΔW, due to the exchange of a photon between the two electrons, can be calculated in a similar manner to the derivation of (19.6). However, we replace the nonrelativistic expression $\boldsymbol{p}$ by $mc\,\boldsymbol{\alpha}$, do not neglect retardation and do not introduce a cut-off in the integration over k. We again use units such that $\hbar=1$ and $e^2=\alpha c$. Before summing over polarization directions and integrating over the directions of $\boldsymbol{k}$, we obtain

$$\Delta W = -\frac{e^2\,c}{4\pi^2}\sum_{\pi}\int\frac{d^3k}{k}\sum_{n}\frac{\langle 0|\alpha_{1\pi}\,e^{i\boldsymbol{k}\cdot\boldsymbol{r}_1}|\,n\rangle\langle n|\,e^{-i\boldsymbol{k}\cdot\boldsymbol{r}_2}\alpha_{2\pi}|\,0\rangle}{k\,c+E_n-E_0} \tag{38.5}$$

plus a similar term with the subscripts 1 and 2 interchanged. $\alpha_{1\pi}$ is the component of the DIRAC matrix $\boldsymbol{\alpha}_1$ in the direction of polarization $\boldsymbol{\pi}$. $\boldsymbol{\pi}$ is summed over two directions perpendicular to each other and to the vector $\boldsymbol{k}$. $\langle 0|A|n\rangle$ denotes the matrix element of an operator A for a transition between the initial state 0 and another atomic state n. The n-summation extends over all eigenstates (discrete and continuous spectrum) of (38.3). The term shown in (38.5) corresponds to the photon going from electron 1 to electron 2, the other term to the inverse process.

It would be very difficult to evaluate the expression (38.5) exactly. It is simplified considerably, however, if we neglect (E_n-E_0) compared with kc in the denominator of (38.5). This approximation will lead to the BREIT interaction. It can be justified as follows, for a bound state in a "weak" external field. By "weak" we mean that the binding energies of all bound states are small compared with mc^2 and that $\bar{p}$, the "average" momentum in these states is small compared with mc. If the external field is a COULOMB potential with nuclear charge Z, then $\bar{p}$ and a^{-1} (a is the "atomic radius") are of order $(Z\alpha)mc$. The important values of k in the integral in (38.5) are of the same order of magnitude ($ka\sim 1$). One then finds that the important values of $|E_n-E_0|$ in the sum over n in (38.5) are of the order of $\bar{p}^2/m\sim k^2/m\sim Z^2\,\mathrm{Ry}\sim(Z\alpha)^2\,mc^2$, which is one order of $Z\alpha$ smaller than the important values of kc. Omitting E_n-E_0 in (38.5) is then a good approximation if the atomic states are essentially nonrelativistic, i.e. if $Z\alpha\ll 1$ or $Z\ll 137$. Actually, the omission is also justified (at least in some cases) if $Z\gg 1$, for a different reason. This will be discussed in Sect. 43β. For the moment we restrict ourselves to the case of weak potentials (Z small).

If E_n-E_0 is omitted in the denominator of (38.5), the summation over n can be carried out immediately by means of a sum rule. Also carrying out the summation over the two directions of polarization π, we get[2]

$$\left.\begin{aligned} \Delta W &= \langle 0|B|0\rangle,\\ B &= -\frac{e^2}{2\pi^2}\int\frac{d^3k}{k^2}\,e^{i\boldsymbol{k}\cdot\boldsymbol{r}_{12}}\left[\boldsymbol{\alpha}_1\cdot\boldsymbol{\alpha}_2-\frac{(\boldsymbol{\alpha}_1\cdot\boldsymbol{k})\,(\boldsymbol{\alpha}_2\cdot\boldsymbol{k})}{k^2}\right], \end{aligned}\right\} \tag{38.6}$$

where the expectation value of the operator B is to be evaluated over the wave function of the particular eigenstate of (38.3). The DIRAC matrices $\boldsymbol{\alpha}_1$ and $\boldsymbol{\alpha}_2$ commute with $\boldsymbol{k}$ and $\boldsymbol{r}_{12}$ and the integral in (38.6) can be evaluated as shown in

[1] The LAMB shift involves one interaction with the nuclear COULOMB potential, in addition to one virtual photon. Actually it is smaller by one order of $Z\alpha\log\alpha$.

[2] Adding the term not explicitly shown in (38.5), which is identical with (38.5) in this approximation.

Sect. 39β. Using (39.8) and (39.7) we get

$$B = -\frac{e^2}{2r_{12}}\left[\boldsymbol{\alpha}_1 \cdot \boldsymbol{\alpha}_2 + \frac{(\boldsymbol{\alpha}_1 \cdot \boldsymbol{r}_{12})(\boldsymbol{\alpha}_2 \cdot \boldsymbol{r}_{12})}{r_{12}^2}\right]. \tag{38.7}$$

This expression, called the BREIT operator, is identical with the operator occuring on the right hand side of (38.1).

The BREIT equation (38.1) is thus a good approximation (for a weak external field) as long as the small BREIT operator B on the right hand side is only treated by first order perturbation theory for a particular atomic state. In this case one simply evaluates its expectation value over an eigenfunction of (38.3) to obtain the perturbation energy ΔW [see Eq. (38.6)]. However, one would get quite wrong results if one solved (38.1) exactly or treated B in higher order perturbation theory. This can be seen as follows. The Eq. (38.3) also has eigenstates l in which both electrons are in negative energy states. If 0 denotes an ordinary positive energy eigenstate and l one particular such negative energy state, perturbation theory applied to (38.1) would give a matrix element $\langle 0|B|l\rangle$ for a transition between these states. If we use quantum electrodynamics, as we should, we get, instead, an expression similar to (38.5) but with $\langle n|\boldsymbol{\alpha}_2|0\rangle$ replaced by $\langle n|\boldsymbol{\alpha}_2|l\rangle$. Consider again a weak potential, so that $\bar{p} \ll mc$. The properties of the DIRAC matrix $\boldsymbol{\alpha}$ are such that the main contribution comes from terms where electron 1 is in a negative energy state in the intermediate state n. Thus $E_n - E_0$ is of order $-2mc^2$, which is *not* small, but in fact *large* compared with kc. We could replace $(kc + E_n - E_0)$ by $-2mc^2$ and again apply a sum rule. The quantum electrodynamic matrix element would then be of form $\langle 0|B'|l\rangle$, but the operator B' would be given approximately by

$$B' = +\frac{e^2}{4\pi^2 m c}\int \frac{d^3k}{k} e^{i\boldsymbol{k}\cdot\boldsymbol{r}_{12}}\left[\boldsymbol{\alpha}_1 \cdot \boldsymbol{\alpha}_2 - \frac{(\boldsymbol{\alpha}_1 \cdot \boldsymbol{k})(\boldsymbol{\alpha}_2 \cdot \boldsymbol{k})}{k^2}\right]. \tag{38.8}$$

This operator is of quite a different order of magnitude (smaller by an order of $1/mcr_{12}$) than the BREIT operator B, Eq. (38.6).

Also, if in (38.1) we treated the BREIT operator B by second order perturbation theory, the corresponding energy change would be

$$\Delta W_2 = \sum_l \frac{\langle 0|B|l\rangle\langle l|B|0\rangle}{E_0 - E_l}. \tag{38.9}$$

The DIRAC matrices contained in B ensure that the main contribution to this sum comes from states l in which both electrons are in negative energy states. For such transitions the operator B should be replaced by B', Eq. (38.8). Thus, even for a positive energy state 0 in a weak potential, the expression (38.9) would be of quite the wrong order of magnitude (and too large).

To summarize the situation for single-electron theory in a weak external potential: The BREIT equation (38.1) gives the leading term for the relativistic corrections to the interaction between the two electrons, if the BREIT operator on the right hand side is treated by first order perturbation theory. This term is of order $\alpha(Z\alpha)(Z^2\,\text{Ry})$. The BREIT equation cannot, without modification, be used consistently to evaluate higher order corrections. The higher corrections could, however, be calculated, for instance by starting from (38.3) and using higher order perturbation theory for the electron's interaction with the virtual radiation field. We merely outline how the next highest terms could be obtained (see also Sect. 41β).

Transitions involving the emission and absorption of a single virtual photon by the *same* electron, plus renormalization terms, lead to the LAMB shift. The calculation[1] proceeds in a similar manner to the discussion of Sect. 19β and the result is again of order $\alpha(Z\alpha)^2(Z^2\,\mathrm{Ry})\log\alpha$. Consider next the exchange of a single photon between the two electrons. The leading term for this process is already contained in (38.6). One can then evaluate (at least approximately) the difference between (38.6) and the exact expression (38.5). The calculation for this difference is similar to that of the LAMB shift and the result is of order $\alpha^2(Z\alpha)\log\alpha\,(Z^2\,\mathrm{Ry})$.

One would consider next terms corresponding to the exchange of *two* photons, by means of fourth order perturbation theory. The expression (38.9) with B replaced by B', Eq. (38.8), represents one such term. This term corresponds to the absorption of the first photon *before* the emission of the second one. Other terms of the same order of magnitude also occur, for instance a term representing the emission of two successive photons by one electron, followed by their absorption by the second electron. These processes would give energy shifts of order $\alpha^2(Z\alpha)(Z^2\,\mathrm{Ry})$.

β) Pair theory. For a discussion of the modifications introduced by DIRAC pair theory, it is convenient to work in momentum space. We first FOURIER transform the BREIT equation (38.1) into an integral equation in momentum space. Following the notation of (16.1), this equation is

$$\left.\begin{aligned}(E-H_{01}-H_{02})\,\psi(\boldsymbol{p}_1,\boldsymbol{p}_2) = -e\int d^3k\,\{[\varphi(-\boldsymbol{k})-\boldsymbol{\alpha}_1\cdot\boldsymbol{A}(-\boldsymbol{k})]\,\psi(\boldsymbol{p}_1+\boldsymbol{k},\boldsymbol{p}_2)+{}&\\ +[\varphi(-\boldsymbol{k})-\boldsymbol{\alpha}_2\cdot\boldsymbol{A}(-\boldsymbol{k})]\,\psi(\boldsymbol{p}_1,\boldsymbol{p}_2+\boldsymbol{k})\}+{}&\\ +\frac{e^2}{2\pi^2}\int\frac{d^3k}{k^2}\,(1-\mathscr{B})\,\psi(\boldsymbol{p}_1-\boldsymbol{k},\boldsymbol{p}_2+\boldsymbol{k}),&\end{aligned}\right\}\tag{38.10}$$

where

$$\left.\begin{aligned}H_{01}&=mc^2\beta_1+c\,\boldsymbol{\alpha}_1\cdot\boldsymbol{p}_1,\\ \mathscr{B}&=\boldsymbol{\alpha}_1\cdot\boldsymbol{\alpha}_2-\frac{(\boldsymbol{\alpha}_1\cdot\boldsymbol{k})\,(\boldsymbol{\alpha}_2\cdot\boldsymbol{k})}{k^2}.\end{aligned}\right\}\tag{38.11}$$

The momentum space wave function ψ is, like U, a 16-component spinor on which the DIRAC matrices for the two electrons operate.

It is convenient to rewrite (38.10) in the mixed representation defined and discussed in Sect. 16α. There we split the DIRAC wave function (16.8) into two parts. These two parts were eigenstates of H_0 with positive and negative eigenvalues, respectively, and involved a PAULI spinor, ψ_+ and ψ_-, respectively. We were then able to write the DIRAC equation as two coupled integral equations, (16.13), involving only PAULI (not DIRAC) operators and the two PAULI spinors ψ_+ and ψ_-. Similarly we can split the 16-component two-electron wave function $\psi(\boldsymbol{p}_1,\boldsymbol{p}_2)$ into four parts. One part is a simultaneous eigenstate of $H_{01}(\boldsymbol{p}_1)$ and $H_{02}(\boldsymbol{p}_2)$ with *positive* eigenvalues $E(p_1)$ and $E(p_2)$, where

$$E(p)=+\sqrt{(mc^2)^2+(pc)^2}.\tag{38.12}$$

This part of the wave function involves known DIRAC operators and a PAULI-type spinor $\psi_{++}(\boldsymbol{p}_1,\boldsymbol{p}_2)$ which has four components ("spin up" and "spin down" for each of the two electrons). Similarly a second part is an eigenstate of H_{01} and H_{02} with eigenvalues $+E(\boldsymbol{p}_1)$ and $-E(\boldsymbol{p}_2)$, respectively, and involves a PAULI spinor ψ_{+-}, and so on. By methods analogous to those of Sect. 16α one

[1] For further discussion and references see Sect. 41β.

can then rewrite (38.10) in the form of four coupled integral equations involving only the PAULI spinors $\psi_{++}, \psi_{+-}, \psi_{-+}$ and ψ_{--}. We shall not write out this set of equations explicitly, but only discuss an approximation to them.

In Sect. 16β we discussed approximate forms for the equivalent set of Eq. (16.13), valid for an electron in a weak potential with total energy close to the rest mass energy mc^2. We showed that the fine structure effects could be obtained, to a good approximation, by merely considering the equation for ψ_+ and putting ψ_- equal to zero in this equation. We can get an equally good approximation in our present case for two electrons in a weak potential in a state of total energy close to $2mc^2$. Of the four coupled equations we consider only the one which involves ψ_{++} on the left hand side. In the integrals on the right hand side of this equation we simply replace ψ_{+-}, ψ_{-+} and ψ_{--} by zero, retaining only the term in ψ_{++}. We are then left with an equation which only involves ψ_{++},

$$\left.\begin{aligned}
&[E-E(p_1)-E(p_2)]\,\psi_{++}(\boldsymbol{p}_1,\boldsymbol{p}_2)\\
&\quad=-e\int d^3k\{[\varphi(-\boldsymbol{k})I^{(1)}_{++}(\boldsymbol{p}_1,\boldsymbol{p}_1+\boldsymbol{k})-\boldsymbol{A}(-\boldsymbol{k})\cdot\boldsymbol{\alpha}^{(1)}_{++}(\boldsymbol{p}_1,\boldsymbol{p}_1+\boldsymbol{k})]\,\psi_{++}(\boldsymbol{p}_1+\boldsymbol{k},\boldsymbol{p}_2)+\\
&\qquad+[\varphi(-\boldsymbol{k})\,I^{(2)}_{++}(\boldsymbol{p}_2,\boldsymbol{p}_2+\boldsymbol{k})-\boldsymbol{A}(-\boldsymbol{k})\cdot\boldsymbol{\alpha}^{(2)}_{++}(\boldsymbol{p}_2,\boldsymbol{p}_2+\boldsymbol{k})]\,\psi_{++}(\boldsymbol{p}_1,\boldsymbol{p}_2+\boldsymbol{k})\}+\\
&\qquad+\frac{e^2}{2\pi^2}\int\frac{d^3k}{k^2}\,[I^{(1)}_{++}(\boldsymbol{p}_1,\boldsymbol{p}_1-\boldsymbol{k})\,I^{(2)}_{++}(\boldsymbol{p}_2,\boldsymbol{p}_2+\boldsymbol{k})-\mathscr{B}']\,\psi_{++}(\boldsymbol{p}_1-\boldsymbol{k},\boldsymbol{p}_2+\boldsymbol{k}),
\end{aligned}\right\}\quad(38.13)$$

where

$$\mathscr{B}'=\boldsymbol{\alpha}^{(1)}_{++}(\boldsymbol{p}_1,\boldsymbol{p}_1-\boldsymbol{k})\cdot\boldsymbol{\alpha}^{(2)}_{++}(\boldsymbol{p}_2,\boldsymbol{p}_2+\boldsymbol{k})-\frac{(\boldsymbol{\alpha}^{(1)}_{++}\cdot\boldsymbol{k})\,(\boldsymbol{\alpha}^{(2)}_{++}\cdot\boldsymbol{k})}{k^2}. \qquad (38.14)$$

In (38.13), $E(p)$ is the function defined in (38.12) and $I^{(1)}_{++}, \boldsymbol{\alpha}^{(1)}_{++}$ are the expressions defined in (16.12) with the PAULI spin matrix σ replaced by σ_1, the matrix which operates on those spin components of ψ_{++} which refer to the first electron.

The Eq. (38.13) is only an approximation to the set of four equations which is identical with the BREIT equation, but has one formal advantage. The difficulties encountered in Sect. 38α by treating the BREIT operator exactly, or at least to higher order than the first, were all connected with negative energy states. In (38.13) all reference to negative energy states has been eliminated and no inconsistencies would be encountered in an attempt to solve this equation exactly or to treat $\mathscr{B}'$, Eq. (38.14), in higher order perturbation theory. Of course, higher order corrections involving more than one virtual photon or any virtual pairs are not contained in (38.13). We shall merely outline a method for calculating higher order corrections in a manner consistent with DIRAC's pair theory which involves (38.13) as a first step.

One technique for treating the two-electron system to any required order, according to DIRAC pair (hole) theory, is the TAMM-DANCOFF method[1]. One starts from a symbolic equation of form

$$(E-H_0)\,\Psi=H'\Psi. \qquad (38.15)$$

The symbolic operator H' represents the interaction of charged particles with photons, the COULOMB interaction between particles and the interaction of particles with external fields. If $H'=0$ (no interactions at all, e.g. if the electronic charge is replaced by zero), the eigenstates of the "unperturbed" HAMILTONIAN H_0 are states containing *any* number of "bare" (i.e. non-interacting) particles and photons. One considers the state function Ψ expanded as an infinite sum

[1] I. TAMM: J. Phys. USSR. **9**, 449 (1945). — S. M. DANCOFF: Phys. Rev. **78**, 382 (1950).

of eigenstates of H_0, each term corresponding to some definite number of "bare" particles and photons ("FOCK space" expansion),

$$\Psi = \Phi_0 \psi_0 + \Phi_{1,0} \psi_{1,0}(\boldsymbol{p}) + \Phi_{2,0} \psi_{2,0}(\boldsymbol{p}_1, \boldsymbol{p}_2) + \Phi_{1,1} \psi_{1,1}(\boldsymbol{p}; \boldsymbol{k}) + \cdots. \quad (38.16)$$

Φ_0 is a symbolic state vector representing no bare particles or photons at all (the "bare vacuum"), ψ_0 its probability amplitude for the actual state Ψ. Similarly $\Phi_{1,0}$ is a state vector representing one bare particle and no bare photons, $\psi_{1,0}(\boldsymbol{p})$ the probability amplitude for finding one such particle with momentum $\boldsymbol{p}$ (and a certain spin, etc.) in state Ψ. Similarly for the higher terms.

The matrix elements of H' for transitions between such states containing different numbers of bare particles and photons, $\Phi_{n,m}$ and $\Phi_{n',m'}$ are given by standard rules of field theory[1], in terms of operators which create and destroy individual "bare" particles and photons with known commutation rules for these operators. With Ψ expanded in terms of bare particle states $\Phi_{n,m}$, one can then write out $H'\Psi$ in terms of a similar expansion. One can then isolate from (38.15) the terms involving a particular number of bare particles (n) and photons (m) i.e. the terms involving $\Phi_{n,m}$. Formally this is done by operating on both sides of (38.15) with n particle and m photon absorption operators and taking the scalar product of this resulting equation with the bare vacuum state vector Φ_0. In this manner one finally obtains an infinite set of coupled integral equations in momentum space involving the various probability amplitudes $\psi_{n,m}(\boldsymbol{p}_1, \ldots)$. This set of "TAMM-DANCOFF equations" no longer involves creation or annihilation operators nor any symbolic state vector Φ.

Consider now an eigenstate Ψ of (38.15) which represents a two-electron system. The leading term in (38.16) is then $\Phi_{2,0} \psi_{2,0}(\boldsymbol{p}_1, \boldsymbol{p}_2)$. Let us omit for the moment the coupling between electrons and photons in (38.15). If, further, we were using single-electron theory, then negative energy states of an electron are treated on an equal footing with positive energy ones. In this case one finds that H' in (38.15) only has non-zero matrix elements for transitions between states of the same number of electrons (but not necessarily the same numbers in positive and negative energy states) and photons. In this case the TAMM-DANCOFF equations are uncoupled and we simply get a *single* equation for $\psi_{2,0}(\boldsymbol{p}_1, \boldsymbol{p}_2)$ for our two-electron state. This equation is identical with (38.10), with the term in $\mathcal{B}$ omitted, and is exactly the FOURIER transform of (38.3).

According to pair theory, however, no electrons are supposed to exist in negative energy states. Instead of these negative energy states we now have states involving positrons (also of positive energy). In this formalism, the operator H' also couples states which contain a *different* number of positron-electron pairs. For our two-electron state the leading term is still $\psi_{2,0}$. But only those parts of $\psi_{2,0}$ are present which correspond to both electrons in positive energy states, ψ_{++} in the notation of our mixed representation, Eq. (38.13). But other probability amplitudes, e.g. for three electrons plus one positron, also occur and we have an infinite set of coupled equations. However, as a first approximation, we can omit all probability amplitudes except $\psi_{2,0}$. Then only one equation remains, which is *identical* with (38.13), except for the absence of $\mathcal{B}'$. Thus, in the present approximation, single-electron and pair theory give identical results.

We still have to include in H' the interaction of the electrons with the radiation field. Instead of using perturbation theory on these terms, as in Sect. 38α, they can also be treated in the framework of the TAMM-DANCOFF method. $\psi_{2.0}$ is then coupled to $\psi_{2,1}$, the probability amplitude for two (positive energy)

[1] See refs. [*11*], [*12*] and [*13*].

electrons plus a photon. In the pair theory treatment, $\psi_{2,0}$ is also coupled to $\psi_{2,(1),1}$, the symbol (1) referring to one electron-positron pair. The equation for $\psi_{2,1}$, in turn, is coupled back to $\psi_{2,0}$ and also to $\psi_{2,(1),0}$, $\psi_{2,(1),2}$ and $\psi_{2,2}$; and so on. If one puts all probability amplitudes except $\psi_{2,0}$ and $\psi_{2,1}$ equal to zero, one can then express $\psi_{2,1}$ explicitly in terms of $\psi_{2,0}$ and finally get an equation involving $\psi_{2,0}$ alone. This approximate equation is found to be identical[1] with (38.13), *including* the term $\mathscr{B}'$, except that $\mathscr{B}'$ is multiplied by the factor

$$\frac{1}{2}\,\frac{k c}{k c+E(p_1)+E(|\boldsymbol{p}_2+\boldsymbol{k}|)-E}+\frac{1}{2}\,\frac{k c}{k c+E(|\boldsymbol{p}_1-\boldsymbol{k}|)+E(p_2)-E}, \qquad (38.17)$$

where $E(p)$ is again given by (38.12).

For a weak potential the effect of replacing the factor (38.17) by unity is found to be small. To within the accuracy of the PAULI approximation, the TAMM-DANCOFF method (based on pair theory) gives the same results as single-electron theory [from which (38.13) was derived]. In principle at least, higher order corrections could then be calculated by successive approximation by including more and more of the terms $\psi_{2,2}$, $\psi_{2,(1),1}$, etc. of the full TAMM-DANCOFF equations.

A very similar set of equations was derived by BROWN and RAVENHALL[2] by a slightly different method (using successive contact transformations). They showed explicitly that all relativistic correction terms of order $(Z\alpha)^2(Z^2\,\mathrm{Ry})$ and $\alpha(Z\alpha)(Z^2\,\mathrm{Ry})$ are contained in (38.13). These terms will be derived from (38.13) in the next three sections. They also showed that, except for the LAMB shift and vacuum polarization terms of order $\alpha(Z\alpha)^2(Z^2\,\mathrm{Ry})$ which we have encountered in Sect. 38α, all terms omitted in (38.13) are of order $\alpha^2(Z\alpha)(Z^2\,\mathrm{Ry})$ or smaller.

Other methods for evaluating higher order corrections are also available (in principle). One example is the socalled "New TAMM-DANCOFF Method"[3]. Like the TAMM-DANCOFF method it involves an infinite set of coupled integral equations; but it also involves probability amplitudes for negative energy states. Formally these equations are obtained by operating on (38.15) with creation *and* annihilation operators and then taking the scalar product of this equation with a certain state vector Ψ_0. This state vector Ψ_0 is *not* Φ_0, the "bare vacuum" term. Instead, Ψ_0 is the eigenstate of (38.15) with the lowest eigenvalue, which represents the "real vacuum" in the presence of the external field and the electron-photon interaction. The "New TAMM-DANCOFF" equations have the conceptual advantage that negative energy states also appear and the lowest order equation is of form similar to (but not identical with) the BREIT Eq. (38.10) or (38.1). In particular, if the interaction between the electrons is neglected altogether these equations automatically reduce to the DIRAC equation for two non-interacting electrons. This method, however, has not yet been used in any explicit calculations for the two-electron system.

The methods outlined above are not formulated in a manner which exhibits the LORENTZ invariance of the theory automatically. For the simpler case of two electrons (or any two FERMI-DIRAC particles) interacting with each other in the *absence* of any external field, fully relativistic methods have been developed in detail. These methods will be discussed in Sect. 42γ. They can be[4] generalized

[1] After dropping self-energy and mass renormalization terms, which lead to the LAMB shift and are thus small.

[2] G. E. BROWN and G. RAVENHALL: Proc. Roy. Soc. Lond., Ser. A **208**, 552 (1951).

[3] F. J. DYSON: Phys. Rev. **90**, 994 (1953).

[4] G. WENTZEL: Phys. Rev. **89**, 684 (1952). — A. O. ROBINSON: Canad. J. Phys. **33**, 369, 707 (1955).

to the case of two electrons interacting with the COULOMB field of a nucleus, but no detailed calculations of higher relativistic corrections for the helium atom have yet been performed with these methods. In fact, only some but *not all* the corrections of order $\alpha^2 (Z\alpha)(Z^2 \mathrm{Ry})$ have been calculated so far (by *any* method).

39. The PAULI approximation (low *Z*). α) *Momentum space.* We use the approximate form (38.13) of the BREIT equation as our starting point for the treatment of the two-electron system in a weak external electromagnetic field. For the case of helium-like atoms, "weak" means low nuclear charge, $Z \ll 137$. No inconsistencies would be encountered in an attempt to solve (38.13) exactly. However, some correction terms of order $\alpha (Z\alpha)^2 (Z^2 \mathrm{Ry})$ are missing from (38.13) and we shall only use this equation to evaluate the energy eigenvalue up to (and including) order $(Z\alpha)^2 (Z^2 \mathrm{Ry})$ and $Z\alpha^2 (Z^2 \mathrm{Ry})$. To this accuracy it is sufficient to expand the integrand of (38.13) in powers of p/mc and k/mc and drop all terms higher than $1/c^2$. This treatment will be equivalent to the PAULI approximation to the DIRAC theory for a single electron, as derived in Sect. 16β.

We write for the nonrelativistic energy $W = E - 2mc^2$ and expand the expression (38.12) for $E(p)$ in powers of p/mc. For the PAULI operators I_{++} and $\boldsymbol{\alpha}_{++}$ we use, instead of the exact expressions (16.12), the approximations (16.14). We further rewrite I_{++}, using the operator identity (16.11), use the vector identity

$$(\boldsymbol{a} \times \boldsymbol{k}) \cdot (\boldsymbol{b} \times \boldsymbol{k}) = k^2 (\boldsymbol{a} \cdot \boldsymbol{b}) - (\boldsymbol{a} \cdot \boldsymbol{k})(\boldsymbol{b} \cdot \boldsymbol{k})$$

and note that $\boldsymbol{k} \cdot \boldsymbol{A}(\boldsymbol{k}) = 0$, since $\operatorname{div} \boldsymbol{A}(\boldsymbol{r}) = 0$. The PAULI approximation for the two-electron system is then (dropping the subscript $++$ from ψ)

$$\left.\begin{aligned}
&\left[W - \frac{1}{2m}(p_1^2 + p_2^2) + \frac{1}{8m^3c^2}(p_1^4 + p_2^4)\right]\psi(\boldsymbol{p}_1, \boldsymbol{p}_2) = \\
&-e\int d^3k\,\varphi(-\boldsymbol{k})\left\{\left[1 + \frac{\boldsymbol{p}_1\cdot\boldsymbol{k} + i\,\boldsymbol{\sigma}_1\cdot(\boldsymbol{p}_1\times\boldsymbol{k})}{(2mc)^2}\right]\psi(\boldsymbol{p}_1 + \boldsymbol{k}, \boldsymbol{p}_2) + \right. \\
&\qquad\qquad \left. + \left[1 + \frac{\boldsymbol{p}_2\cdot\boldsymbol{k} + i\,\boldsymbol{\sigma}_2\cdot(\boldsymbol{p}_2\times\boldsymbol{k})}{(2mc)^2}\right]\psi(\boldsymbol{p}_1, \boldsymbol{p}_2 + \boldsymbol{k})\right\} + \\
&+\frac{e^2}{2\pi^2}\int\frac{d^3k}{k^2}\left\{1 + \frac{(\boldsymbol{p}_2 - \boldsymbol{p}_1)\cdot\boldsymbol{k} - i\,\boldsymbol{\sigma}_1\cdot(\boldsymbol{p}_1\times\boldsymbol{k}) + i\,\boldsymbol{\sigma}_2\cdot(\boldsymbol{p}_2\times\boldsymbol{k})}{(2mc)^2}\right\}\psi(\boldsymbol{p}_1 - \boldsymbol{k}, \boldsymbol{p}_2 + \boldsymbol{k}) - \\
&-\frac{e^2}{2\pi^2(2mc)^2}\int\frac{d^3k}{k^2}\left\{4\left[\boldsymbol{p}_1\cdot\boldsymbol{p}_2 - \frac{(\boldsymbol{p}_1\cdot\boldsymbol{k})(\boldsymbol{p}_2\cdot\boldsymbol{k})}{k^2}\right] + 2i\left[\boldsymbol{\sigma}_2\cdot(\boldsymbol{p}_1\times\boldsymbol{k}) - \boldsymbol{\sigma}_1\cdot(\boldsymbol{p}_2\times\boldsymbol{k})\right] + \right. \\
&\qquad\qquad \left. + \left[k^2\,\boldsymbol{\sigma}_1\cdot\boldsymbol{\sigma}_2 - (\boldsymbol{\sigma}_1\cdot\boldsymbol{k})(\boldsymbol{\sigma}_2\cdot\boldsymbol{k})\right]\right\}\psi(\boldsymbol{p}_1 - \boldsymbol{k}, \boldsymbol{p}_2 + \boldsymbol{k}) + \\
&+\frac{e}{2mc}\int d^3k\,\boldsymbol{A}(-\boldsymbol{k})\cdot\left\{(2\boldsymbol{p}_1 + i\,\boldsymbol{k}\times\boldsymbol{\sigma}_1)\,\psi(\boldsymbol{p}_1 + \boldsymbol{k}, \boldsymbol{p}_2) + \right. \\
&\qquad\qquad \left. + (2\boldsymbol{p}_2 + i\,\boldsymbol{k}\times\boldsymbol{\sigma}_2)\,\psi(\boldsymbol{p}_1, \boldsymbol{p}_2 + \boldsymbol{k})\right\}.
\end{aligned}\right\} \quad (39.1)$$

In (39.1), as in (38.13), the wave function ψ is a PAULI (*not* DIRAC) spinor with four components, two for the spin variable of the first electron on which the PAULI matrix $\boldsymbol{\sigma}_1$ operates and two for electron 2. On the right hand side of (39.1), the first term in parentheses represents the interaction with the external electric field (including relativistic corrections). The second term represents the COULOMB interaction between the two electrons, the third term the interaction between the two electrons via the quantized radiation field (the BREIT operator), and the fourth term the interaction with the external magnetic field.

If we dropped all terms in (39.1) which contain negative powers of c (and hence should be small), this equation would reduce to

$$\left.\begin{aligned}\left[W_0-\frac{1}{2m}(p_1^2+p_2^2)\right]\psi_0(\boldsymbol{p}_1,\boldsymbol{p}_2)=-e\int d^3k\,\varphi(-\boldsymbol{k})\,[\psi_0(\boldsymbol{p}_1+\boldsymbol{k},\boldsymbol{p}_2)+\\+\psi_0(\boldsymbol{p}_1,\boldsymbol{p}_2+\boldsymbol{k})]\\+\frac{e^2}{2\pi^2}\int\frac{d^3k}{k^2}\psi_0(\boldsymbol{p}_1-\boldsymbol{k},\boldsymbol{p}_2+\boldsymbol{k}).\end{aligned}\right\}\quad(39.2)$$

(39.2) is identical with the nonrelativistic SCHRÖDINGER equation (36.7) for the twoelectron system, written in momentum space. In the next two sections we shall find an approximation to the eigenvalue W of (39.1), as follows. We first solve (39.2) for the nonrelativistic energy W_0 and eigenfunction ψ_0. We then merely take the expectation values over ψ_0 of the other operators occuring in (39.1), to find a correction to the energy W_0 according to first order perturbation theory.

It should be remembered that the operators occuring in (39.1) are good approximations to those in (38.13) *only* for $p\ll mc$, $k\ll mc$. For $p\gg mc$, the operators in (39.1) are quite wrong, for instance $E(p)-mc^2$ is proportional to p for very large momenta, not to p^2 or p^4. Similarly, the eigenfunctions ψ_0 of (39.2) are good approximations to those of (38.13) only for $p\ll mc$. For $p_1, p_2\gg mc$, ψ_0 decreases more rapidly with increasing momentum than the correct eigenfunction ψ of (38.13) (cf. Table 2). For a "weak" external potential (like the COULOMB potential for low charge Z), the characteristic momenta are of order $\bar{p}\ll mc$. In momentum space, the expectation value of an operator consists of an integral over the momenta $\boldsymbol{p}_1$ and $\boldsymbol{p}_2$, which involves a wave function $\psi(\boldsymbol{p}_1,\boldsymbol{p}_2)$. One can show that the main contribution to these integrals comes from momenta of order $\bar{p}$, if (a) the operators occuring in (38.13) and the *correct* eigenfunctions ψ of (38.13) are used, or if (b) the operators occuring in (39.1) and the *nonrelativistic* eigenfunctions ψ_0 of (39.2) are used. It therefore does not matter that, for case (b), in the relativistic region $p\gg mc$, both the operators and wave functions are quite wrong (operators too large, wave functions too small). However, (39.1), unlike (38.13), is *not* a completely self-consistent equation. For instance, spurious divergences in the integrals are encountered if (39.1) is treated in higher order perturbation theory.

β) Position space. For many practical applications it is more convenient to work in ordinary position space, instead of momentum space. In particular, the FOURIER transforms of the eigenfunctions ψ_0 of (39.2) are simply the nonrelativistic wave functions in position space, which were discussed at great length in Sects. 24 to 37. We therefore carry out the FOURIER transformation of Eq. (39.1).

We shall make use of some general properties of FOURIER transforms, which can be derived as follows. Let $(2\pi)^{\frac{3}{2}}V'(\boldsymbol{p})$ and $\psi(\boldsymbol{p})$ be the FOURIER transforms of $V(\boldsymbol{r})$ and $U(\boldsymbol{r})$, respectively. We then have

$$\left.\begin{aligned}&(2\pi)^{-\frac{3}{2}}\int d^3p\,e^{i\boldsymbol{r}\cdot\boldsymbol{p}}\int d^3k\,V'(\boldsymbol{k})\,\psi(\boldsymbol{p}-\boldsymbol{k})\\&\quad=\int d^3k\,V'(\boldsymbol{k})\,e^{i\boldsymbol{r}\cdot\boldsymbol{k}}\int d^3q\,(2\pi)^{-\frac{3}{2}}\psi(\boldsymbol{q})\,e^{i\boldsymbol{r}\cdot\boldsymbol{q}}=V(\boldsymbol{r})\,U(\boldsymbol{r}).\end{aligned}\right\}\quad(39.3)$$

We denote this relation simply by

$$V'(\boldsymbol{k})\,\psi(\boldsymbol{p}-\boldsymbol{k})\to V(\boldsymbol{r})\,U(\boldsymbol{r}).\quad(39.4)$$

By differentiating the integrands of the various integrals in (39.3) with respect to $\boldsymbol{r}$, we can verify the following general relations

$$\boldsymbol{p}\,V'(\boldsymbol{k})\,\psi(\boldsymbol{p}-\boldsymbol{k})\to -i\,\mathrm{grad}\,[V(\boldsymbol{r})\,U(\boldsymbol{r})]=\boldsymbol{p}\,V\,U,\quad(39.5)$$

$$\boldsymbol{k}\,V'(\boldsymbol{k})\,\psi(\boldsymbol{p}-\boldsymbol{k})\to -i\,[\mathrm{grad}\,V(\boldsymbol{r})]\,U(\boldsymbol{r})=[\boldsymbol{p}\,V-V\boldsymbol{p}]\,U.\quad(39.6)$$

We also shall make use of the following relations $\left(\frac{\partial}{\partial \boldsymbol{r}}\right.$ stands for $\left.\mathrm{grad}_{\boldsymbol{r}}\right)$

$$\frac{1}{2\pi^2}\int \frac{d^3k}{k^2}\, e^{i\boldsymbol{k}\cdot\boldsymbol{r}} = \frac{1}{r}\,, \tag{39.7}$$

$$\left.\begin{aligned} \frac{1}{2\pi^2}\int \frac{d^3k}{k^2}\, e^{i\boldsymbol{k}\cdot\boldsymbol{r}}\, \frac{(\boldsymbol{a}\cdot\boldsymbol{k})\,(\boldsymbol{b}\cdot\boldsymbol{k})}{k^2} &= \frac{i}{2}\left(\boldsymbol{a}\cdot\frac{\partial}{\partial\boldsymbol{r}}\right)\int d^3k\, e^{i\boldsymbol{k}\cdot\boldsymbol{r}}\left(\boldsymbol{b}\cdot\frac{\partial}{\partial\boldsymbol{k}}\right)\frac{1}{k^2} \\ &= \frac{1}{2}\left(\boldsymbol{a}\cdot\frac{\partial}{\partial\boldsymbol{r}}\right)\left[\boldsymbol{b}\cdot\boldsymbol{r}\,\frac{1}{r}\right] = \frac{1}{2r}\left[\boldsymbol{a}\cdot\boldsymbol{b} - \frac{(\boldsymbol{a}\cdot\boldsymbol{r})\,(\boldsymbol{b}\cdot\boldsymbol{r})}{r^2}\right], \end{aligned}\right\} \tag{39.8}$$

$$\frac{1}{2\pi^2}\int \frac{d^3k}{k^2}\, e^{i\boldsymbol{k}\cdot\boldsymbol{r}}\,\boldsymbol{k} = i\,\frac{\boldsymbol{r}}{r^3}\,. \tag{39.9}$$

We now have to deal with some operators which exhibit a singularity in position space of the type of a DIRAC delta-function. Generally, a momentum space potential $V'(\boldsymbol{k})$ which does not decrease with increasing k (for very large k), may lead to a position space potential $V(\boldsymbol{r})$ whose volume integral over an *infinitesimal* volume around the origin is non-zero. A constant $V'(\boldsymbol{k})$ gives simply a three-dimensional DIRAC delta-function,

$$\frac{1}{2\pi^2}\int \frac{d^3k}{k^2}\, e^{i\boldsymbol{k}\cdot\boldsymbol{r}}\, k^2 = -\Delta\left(\frac{1}{r}\right) = +4\pi\,\delta^{(3)}(\boldsymbol{r})\,. \tag{39.10}$$

We consider next a particular $V'(\boldsymbol{k})$ which depends on the direction but not the magnitude of $\boldsymbol{k}$, namely $(\boldsymbol{a}\cdot\boldsymbol{k})\,(\boldsymbol{b}\cdot\boldsymbol{k})/2\pi^2k^2$. Carrying out the FOURIER transformation directly, we get

$$\left.\begin{aligned} V(\boldsymbol{r}) &\equiv \frac{1}{2\pi^2}\int \frac{d^3k}{k^2}\, e^{i\boldsymbol{k}\cdot\boldsymbol{r}}\,(\boldsymbol{a}\cdot\boldsymbol{k})\,(\boldsymbol{b}\cdot\boldsymbol{k}) \\ &= -\left(\boldsymbol{a}\cdot\frac{\partial}{\partial\boldsymbol{r}}\right)\left(\boldsymbol{b}\cdot\frac{\partial}{\partial\boldsymbol{r}}\right)\frac{1}{r} = \frac{1}{r^3}\left[\boldsymbol{a}\cdot\boldsymbol{b} - 3\,\frac{(\boldsymbol{a}\cdot\boldsymbol{r})\,(\boldsymbol{b}\cdot\boldsymbol{r})}{r^2}\right]. \end{aligned}\right\} \tag{39.11}$$

The last expression on the right hand side of (39.11) is unique only for *non-zero* values of r and has a strong singularity at the origin. We want to consider next the volume integral of $V(\boldsymbol{r})$, multiplied by a function $f(\boldsymbol{r})$, over a sphere around the origin with infinitesimally small radius ε. We assume that $f(\boldsymbol{r})$ is finite and continuous at the origin and use for $V(\boldsymbol{r})$ the first form on the right hand side of (39.11). Keeping only terms which remain finite when ε tends to zero, we find

$$\int_\varepsilon d\tau\, V(\boldsymbol{r})\, f(\boldsymbol{r}) = -f(0)\int_\varepsilon d\tau\left(a_x b_x \frac{\partial^2}{\partial x^2} + a_y b_y \frac{\partial^2}{\partial y^2} + a_z b_z \frac{\partial^2}{\partial z^2}\right)\frac{1}{r}\,.$$

Now, from symmetry requirements, the value of the integral can depend only on the relative but *not* the absolute orientation in space of the two vectors $\boldsymbol{a}$ and $\boldsymbol{b}$. We can then replace $a_x b_x$ (as well as $a_y b_y$ and $a_z b_z$) by the average value $\frac{1}{3}\,\boldsymbol{a}\cdot\boldsymbol{b}$ and get, using the fact that $\Delta r^{-1} = -4\pi\delta^{(3)}(\boldsymbol{r})$,

$$\int_\varepsilon d\tau\, V(\boldsymbol{r})\, f(r) = \frac{4\pi}{3}\,(\boldsymbol{a}\cdot\boldsymbol{b})\int d\tau\,\delta^{(3)}(\boldsymbol{r})\, f(\boldsymbol{r}) = \frac{4\pi}{3}\,(\boldsymbol{a}\cdot\boldsymbol{b})\, f(0)\,. \tag{39.12}$$

Using (39.10) and (39.12), we can express the behavior near the origin of the function $V(\boldsymbol{r})$, defined in (39.11) in the following way

$$\left.\begin{aligned} V(\boldsymbol{r}) - \frac{4\pi}{3}\,(\boldsymbol{a}\cdot\boldsymbol{b})\,\delta^{(3)}(\boldsymbol{r}) &\equiv \frac{1}{2\pi^2}\int \frac{d^3k}{k^2}\, e^{i\boldsymbol{k}\cdot\boldsymbol{r}}\left[(\boldsymbol{a}\cdot\boldsymbol{k})\,(\boldsymbol{b}\cdot\boldsymbol{k}) - \frac{1}{3}\,(\boldsymbol{a}\cdot\boldsymbol{b})\,k^2\right] \\ &= \left[\frac{\boldsymbol{a}\cdot\boldsymbol{b}}{r^3} - 3\,\frac{(\boldsymbol{a}\cdot\boldsymbol{r})\,(\boldsymbol{b}\cdot\boldsymbol{r})}{r^5}\right]'. \end{aligned}\right\} \tag{39.13}$$

The prime $[\,]'$ on the right hand side of (39.13) indicates the following prescription: When $[\,]'$ occurs in any integral over position space, replace $[\,]'$ by zero for $r<\varepsilon$, evaluate the integral and then take the limit of $\varepsilon\to 0$. With this prescription, the integral over all space of any *spherically symmetric* function $f(r)$ times the right hand side of (39.13) is zero[1].

Using the relations given above we can finally carry out the FOURIER transformation of (39.1). This gives the BREIT equation in PAULI approximation in position space. This equation takes the form of the differential equation

$$\left.\begin{aligned}
&W\,U=(H_0+H_1+H_2+\cdots+H_6)\,U;\\
&H_0=-eV+\frac{1}{2m}(p_1^2+p_2^2),\\
&H_1=-\frac{1}{8m^3c^2}(p_1^4+p_2^4),\\
&H_2=-\frac{e^2}{2(mc)^2}\frac{1}{r_{12}}\left[\boldsymbol{p}_1\cdot\boldsymbol{p}_2+\frac{\boldsymbol{r}_{12}\cdot(\boldsymbol{r}_{12}\cdot\boldsymbol{p}_1)\,\boldsymbol{p}_2}{r_{12}^2}\right],\\
&H_3=\frac{\mu}{mc}\left\{\left[\mathcal{E}_1\times\boldsymbol{p}_1+\frac{2e}{r_{12}^3}\boldsymbol{r}_{12}\times\boldsymbol{p}_2\right]\cdot\boldsymbol{s}_1+\left[\mathcal{E}_2\times\boldsymbol{p}_2+\frac{2e}{r_{12}^3}\boldsymbol{r}_{21}\times\boldsymbol{p}_1\right]\cdot\boldsymbol{s}_2\right\},\\
&H_4=\frac{ie\hbar}{(2mc)^2}(\boldsymbol{p}_1\cdot\mathcal{E}_1+\boldsymbol{p}_2\cdot\mathcal{E}_2),\\
&H_5=4\mu^2\left\{-\frac{8\pi}{3}(\boldsymbol{s}_1\cdot\boldsymbol{s}_2)\,\delta^{(3)}(\boldsymbol{r}_{12})+\frac{1}{r_{12}^3}\left[\boldsymbol{s}_1\cdot\boldsymbol{s}_2-\frac{3(\boldsymbol{s}_1\cdot\boldsymbol{r}_{12})(\boldsymbol{s}_2\cdot\boldsymbol{r}_{12})}{r_{12}^2}\right]'\right\},\\
&H_6=2\mu\,[\mathcal{H}_1\cdot\boldsymbol{s}_1+\mathcal{H}_2\cdot\boldsymbol{s}_2]+\frac{e}{mc}[\boldsymbol{A}_1\cdot\boldsymbol{p}_1+\boldsymbol{A}_2\cdot\boldsymbol{p}_2],
\end{aligned}\right\}\qquad(39.14)$$

where

$$V=\frac{Ze}{r_1}+\frac{Ze}{r_2}-\frac{e}{r_{12}}+\varphi(r_1)+\varphi(r_2),\qquad \mu=\frac{e\hbar}{2mc}.$$

In (39.14), V in H_0, all of H_4 and the part of H_3 which[2] involves $\mathcal{E}$ correspond to the first two curly brackets in (39.1). H_2, the part of H_3 involving r_{12} and H_5 correspond to the three parts of the third curly bracket (the BREIT operator) in (39.1). Finally, H_6 corresponds to the last curly bracket in (39.1). It should be remembered that the momentum operator $\boldsymbol{p}_1=-i\,\mathrm{grad}_1$, does not in general commute with functions of position. Nevertheless, using the fact that curl $\mathcal{E}_1$ and div $\boldsymbol{A}$ are zero and some symmetry properties, one can shown that the order of the momentum operators and functions of position is immaterial in all terms in (39.14) *except*[3] in H_2 and H_4.

The physical significance of the various terms in (39.14) is as follows:

H_0 is the ordinary nonrelativistic HAMILTONian.

H_1 is the relativistic correction due to the "variation of mass with velocity" (which does not depend on electron spin).

---

[1] The relation (39.13) could be derived more rigorously along the following lines: Multiply the integral over $\boldsymbol{k}$ on the left hand side of (39.13) by any function $f(\boldsymbol{r})$, for which the radius of convergence of its TAYLOR expansion around the origin is non-zero. Integrate this product over a sphere of radius ε around the origin in position space, carrying out the $\boldsymbol{r}$-integration before the $\boldsymbol{k}$-integration. One can then show that this double integral tends to zero when ε approaches zero. See also J. SUCHER and H. FOLEY, Phys. Rev. **95**, 966 (1955).

[2] $\mathcal{E}_1=-\mathrm{grad}_1 V$ is the COULOMB field due to the nucleus *plus* electron 2 plus any external field (potential φ).

[3] For non-commuting vector operators, $\boldsymbol{a}\cdot(\boldsymbol{a}\cdot\boldsymbol{b})\,\boldsymbol{c}$ means $\sum_{i,j=1}^{3} a_i\,a_j\,b_j\,c_i$.

H_2 corresponds to the classical relativistic correction to the interaction between the electrons. This correction is due to the retardation of the electromagnetic field produced by an electron.

H_3 is the interaction between the spin magnetic moment and the orbital magnetic moment of the electrons (spin-orbit coupling).

H_4 is a term characteristic of the DIRAC theory, which is also present in the HAMILTONian for a single electron in an electric field (see Sect. 12).

H_5 represents the interaction between the spin magnetic dipole moments of the two electrons.

H_6 is the interaction with an external magnetic field.

It is sometimes found convenient to rewrite the terms (H_1+H_4) in a different form, as follows. As discussed earlier, we shall not solve (39.14) exactly but use eigenfunctions U_0 of

$$(W-H_0)\,U_0=0$$

to evaluate the expectation values of the operators H_1 to H_6. We then have the relation

$$\frac{1}{2m}(p_1^2+p_2^2)\,U_0=f\,U_0, \qquad f\equiv W+eV.$$

Using (16.16) we then find that

$$\frac{1}{2m}(p_1^2+p_2^2)^2\,U_0=f\,(p_1^2+p_2^2)\,U_0+i\,e\,[\boldsymbol{p}_1\cdot\mathcal{E}_1+\mathcal{E}_1\cdot\boldsymbol{p}_1+\boldsymbol{p}_2\cdot\mathcal{E}_2+\mathcal{E}_2\cdot\boldsymbol{p}_2]\,U_0. \tag{39.15}$$

With the help of (39.15) we can then rewrite H_1+H_4 in the form

$$\left.\begin{aligned} H_1+H_4&=H_1'+H_4',\\ H_1'&=-\frac{1}{(2mc)^2}\left[f\,(p_1^2+p_2^2)-\frac{1}{m}\,p_1^2p_2^2\right],\\ H_4'&=-\frac{i e\hbar}{(2mc)^2}\,[\mathcal{E}_1\cdot\boldsymbol{p}_1+\mathcal{E}_2\cdot\boldsymbol{p}_2].\end{aligned}\right\} \tag{39.16}$$

One can then also show that the expectation value of H_1' can be rewritten as

$$\int d\tau\,U_0^*\,H_1'\,U_0=-\frac{1}{8m^3c^2}\int d\tau\,[|p_1^2U_0|^2+|p_2^2U_0|^2]. \tag{39.17}$$

As we discussed in Sect. 16β and 36δ, the expectation value $\overline{H}_1$ of H_1 equals that of H_1' *if* care is taken to extend the integrals over all of space (or if the evaluations are carried out in momentum space). However, $p_1^4U_0$ has a delta-function singularity at $r_1=0$ and $r_{12}=0$ and it is more convenient to use the form (39.17), where an infinitesimal region around $r_1=0$ and $r_{12}=0$ can be excluded without making an error. It should also be remembered that, in evaluating the expectation value of the second part of H_5, an infinitesimal region around $r_{12}=0$ has to be excluded from the integral.

From (39.16) and the fact that the expectation values of H_1 and H_1' are equal it also follows that the expectation values of H_4 and H_4' are equal[1]. We can then

[1] In the footnote below (16.16) we showed that the expectation value of $\boldsymbol{p}\cdot\mathcal{E}+\mathcal{E}\cdot\boldsymbol{p}$ over a *real* and bounded position space wave function is zero for *any* real vector function $\mathcal{E}(\boldsymbol{r})$. This expectation value is also zero for any wave function of form $R(r)\,Y_{lm}(\vartheta,\varphi)$, with R real, if $\mathcal{E}(\boldsymbol{r})$ is any real and *central* field. In our present discussion of the two-particle system, the wave functions U_0 and $\mathcal{E}_1$ are more complicated. The expectation values of H_4 and H_4' are equal only if $\mathcal{E}_1$ is the *special* function $-\text{grad}_1 V$, where V is the potential which occurs in the HAMILTONian H_0 of which U_0 is an eigenfunction.

write these expectation values (denoted by a bar) as

$$\left.\begin{aligned}\overline{H}_4=\overline{H}'_4&=\frac{1}{2}\frac{ie\hbar}{(2mc)^2}\left(\overline{\boldsymbol{p}_1\cdot\mathcal{E}_1}-\overline{\mathcal{E}_1\cdot\boldsymbol{p}_1}+\overline{\boldsymbol{p}_2\cdot\mathcal{E}_2}-\overline{\mathcal{E}_2\cdot\boldsymbol{p}_2}\right)\\&=\frac{1}{2}\frac{e\hbar}{(2mc)^2}\left(\overline{\operatorname{div}_1\mathcal{E}_1}+\overline{\operatorname{div}_2\mathcal{E}_2}\right).\end{aligned}\right\}\qquad(39.18)$$

The differential equation (39.14) can also be derived directly in position space from the BREIT equation (38.1). The method[1] of derivation is very similar to that used in Sect. 12 for the case of the DIRAC equation. By this method one also gets a small term H'_6 to be added to H_6 in (39.14), which is quadratic in the vector potential,

$$H'_6=\frac{e^2}{2mc^2}\left(A_1^2+A_2^2\right).\qquad(39.19)$$

However, in such a position space derivation it is easy to miss some terms which involve delta-function types of singularities. In particular, the first part of H_5 was missed in older derivations[2]. Recently, another method for the reduction of equations of the BREIT form to equations of the PAULI form has been developed[3], which is a generalization of the FOLDY-WOUTHUYSEN method (see Sect. 16γ). This method can also be applied[4] to relativistic two-body equations (discussed in Sect. 42γ).

40. Fine structure splitting[5] of helium. Using the differential equation (39.14), we shall now calculate the relativistic energy levels of atoms with two electrons in the absence of external fields ($\mathcal{H}=0$). Because of the small magnitude of the fine structure constant it is sufficient to determine the eigenfunction in zeroth and the eigenvalues in first approximation[6]. The zeroth approximation is given by the solutions of the nonrelativistic SCHRÖDINGER equation

$$E_0U_0=H_0U_0$$

with which we have dealt extensively in Sects. 24 to 36. Thus, the unperturbed eigenfunctions (cf. Sect. 24) are products of a spatial and a spin eigenfunction; in the case of orthohelium the three spin eigenfunctions S_+, S_0, S_- [cf. Eqs. (24.4) and (24.5)] are possible, for parahelium only the one spin function S_p (24.6). The unperturbed eigenfunctions may be characterized by the magnetic quantum numbers of spin and orbit, i.e., by m_l and m_s[7]. The energy in zeroth approximation does not depend on these two quantum numbers, it depends only on the principal, orbital and spin quantum numbers, n, l and S[8].

[1] See ref. [*10*], Sect. 22.

[2] This term was omitted in ref. [*10*] and also by H. A. ERIKSSON, Z. Physik **109**, 762 (1938). ERIKSSON also omitted a part of the expectation value of H_1. More specifically, he evaluated the integral of $U_0^*(p_1^4U_0)$ not over all space (as one should) but over a region excluding spheres of infinitesimal radius about the points $r_1=0$ and $r_{12}=0$. The delta-function part of H_5 has been derived by V. BERESTETSKI and L. LANDAU, J. exp. theor. Phys. USSR. **19**, 673 (1949); A. SESSLER and H. FOLEY, Phys. Rev. **92**, 1321 (1953); J. SUCHER and H. FOLEY, Phys. Rev. **95**, 966 (1954).

[3] Z. V. CHRAPLYVY: Phys. Rev. **91**, 388; **92**, 1310 (1953).

[4] W. BARKER and F. GLOVER: Phys. Rev. **99**, 317 (1955).

[5] Cf. G. BREIT: Phys. Rev. **36**, 483 (1930); also W. HEISENBERG, Z. Physik **39**, 499 (1926); Y. SUGIURA, Z. Physik **44**, 190 (1927); L. GAUNT, Proc. Roy. Soc. Lond. **122**, 153 (1929); Phil. Trans. **228**, 151 (1929).

[6] The eigenvalues will then be given correctly to within order α^2. As a matter of fact, a greater accuracy is not possible in view of the manner of derivation of (39.14).

[7] $m_s=1, 0, -1$ for S_+, S_0, S_-. m_l is the second index of the spherical harmonic $Y_{lm_l}(\vartheta,\varphi)$ which specifies the angular dependence of the spatial eigenfunction.

[8] S is determined by the term system, it equals 1 for ortho and 0 for parahelium.

Of the relativistic perturbations three of them, namely H_1, H_2, H_4, do not remove the degeneracy of the eigenvalues with respect to m_l and m_s [1]. Their only effect is to shift the eigenvalue by a small amount, which is of no interest to us, since the shift is negligibly small compared to the errors committed in our previous calculation of the nonrelativistic eigenvalue [2]. On the other hand, the perturbations H_3 and H_5 split each term of orthohelium [3] into three fine structure levels having inner quantum numbers $j = l+1$, l and $l-1$, where $j(j+1)$ is equal to the square of the magnitude of the total angular momentum $\boldsymbol{M} = \boldsymbol{k} + \boldsymbol{S}$. In view of this splitting, the above mentioned products of a space and spin function are actually not the correct zeroth order eigenfunctions; instead, one must form appropriate linear combinations of them. We shall save ourselves the trouble of explicitly forming these linear combinations by using the matrix method in our calculations.

In order to obtain the greatest possible accuracy in the evaluation of the fine structure, the calculations must, of course, be based on the exact spatial eigenfunction of the level in question. BREIT has carried out an accurate calculation for the 2^3P state of He, in which he determined the eigenfunction by means of the variation method [4]. We shall discuss his results below.

In Sect. 41 we shall discuss the expectation values of all the operators occuring in (39.14) for the ground state of helium-like atoms. In this section we discuss only the fine structure *splitting*, which can only be produced by the operators H_3 and H_5. It follows from the symmetry arguments given above, that even these terms can give splitting only for states in which both l and S are non-zero, i.e. for ortho-helium states other than S-states. We shall also verify this explicitly. We shall make some general remarks about the expectation values of H_3 and H_5, which hold for any wave functions with the correct symmetry properties (and hence also for the exact one). We shall carry out explicit calculations only using simple approximate wave functions. We first of all neglect polarization effects, but should nevertheless take a product form spatial wave function,

$$U = \frac{1}{\sqrt{2}} \left[u_1(1)\, u_n(2) - u_n(1)\, u_1(2)\right],$$

of the correct symmetry for ortho-states. Actually we shall only take an unsymmetrized wave function

$$U = u_1(1)\, u_n(2). \tag{40.1}$$

One can show that the error committed in leaving out symmetrization (exchange integrals) is only of the order of the ratio of the "radius" of the orbit of the inner electron to that of the outer. Since the inner electron is in the ground state and the outer electron in an excited state of non-zero l, this ratio is reasonably small. For such states we shall also approximate u_{nlm} by the corresponding hydrogenic wave function for nuclear charge $(Z-1)$, (complete screening). The errors due to all these approximations should become smaller as n and l increase.

[1] This follows from the fact that H_1, H_2 and H_4 depend only on the spatial position of the electron and, thus, are independent of spin. Consequently, these operators commute with S_z; thus k_z is a constant of the motion and therefore S_z is also. [$M_z = k_z + S_z$ is a constant of the motion even for the total HAMILTONian function.]

[2] Except for the ground state; see Sect. 41.

[3] The terms of parahelium, of course, are not split; since there exists only one spin eigenfunction S_p, the quantum states are completely determined by the specification of m_l only. Evidently, the energy must be independent of m_l since no direction in space is distinguished.

[4] However, the eigenfunction used by BREIT does not meet the highest standards of accuracy, as the corresponding eigenvalue is rather bad.

α) Spin-orbit interaction. We evaluate now the spin-orbit interaction, i.e. the expectation value of the operator H_3 in (39.14). We first note that the spin-operator $\boldsymbol{s}_1$ can be written in the form

$$\boldsymbol{s}_1 = \tfrac{1}{2}\boldsymbol{S} + \tfrac{1}{2}(\boldsymbol{s}_1 - \boldsymbol{s}_2); \quad \boldsymbol{S} = \boldsymbol{s}_1 + \boldsymbol{s}_2, \tag{40.2}$$

with a similar relation for $\boldsymbol{s}_2$. For any of the four (symmetric or antisymmetric) spin wave functions, the expectation value of the odd operator $(\boldsymbol{s}_1 - \boldsymbol{s}_2)$ is identically zero. Since $\boldsymbol{s}_1$ and $\boldsymbol{s}_2$ occur linearly in H_3, the expectation value of H_3 remains unchanged if we replace $\boldsymbol{s}_1$ (as well as $\boldsymbol{s}_2$) by $\frac{1}{2}\boldsymbol{S}$. Making this replacement and substituting $\mathscr{E}_1 = (Z\boldsymbol{r}_1/r_1^3 - \boldsymbol{r}_{12}/r_{12}^3)$ we have, in atomic units,

$$H_3 = \frac{1}{4}\alpha^2\left[\frac{Z}{r_1^3}\boldsymbol{r}_1\times\boldsymbol{p}_1 + \frac{Z}{r_2^3}\boldsymbol{r}_2\times\boldsymbol{p}_2 + \frac{3}{r_{12}^3}(\boldsymbol{r}_1-\boldsymbol{r}_2)\times(\boldsymbol{p}_2-\boldsymbol{p}_1)\right]\cdot\boldsymbol{S}. \tag{40.3}$$

For singlet states (parahelium), the total spin $\boldsymbol{S}$ is zero and the expectation value of H_3 vanishes identically (for *any* wave function, including the exact one).

For triplet states (orthohelium) we note that $\boldsymbol{r}_1\times\boldsymbol{p}_1 = \boldsymbol{k}_1$ and $\boldsymbol{r}_2\times\boldsymbol{p}_2 = \boldsymbol{k}_2$, where $\boldsymbol{k}_1$ and $\boldsymbol{k}_2$ are the operators of orbital angular momentum for the inner and outer electron. For the inner $(1s)$ electron, $\boldsymbol{k}_1 = 0$ and the first term in (40.3) vanishes[1]. If the outer electron is also in an s-state, then $\boldsymbol{k}_2$ and l are zero and the expectation values of the second and third terms in (40.3) also vanish[2]. Thus, for $l = 0$, the expectation value of H_3 is exactly zero (for *any* wave function).

For $l \neq 0$ we then have, using the fact that $\boldsymbol{k}_1 = 0$,

$$H_3 = \frac{1}{4}\alpha^2\left\{\frac{Z}{r_2^3}\boldsymbol{k}_2 + \frac{3}{r_{12}^3}[(\boldsymbol{r}_1\times\boldsymbol{p}_2 - \boldsymbol{k}_2) + \boldsymbol{r}_2\times\boldsymbol{p}_1]\cdot\boldsymbol{S}. \tag{40.4}$$

We now restrict ourselves to the approximate wave function (40.1) and note further that the important contributions to the wave function[3] come from $r_1 \ll r_2$ (at least if the outer electron is in a *highly* excited state). We therefore neglect r_1 compared with r_2 and replace r_{12} by r_2. For our product wave function (no polarization) the expectation value of $\boldsymbol{r}_2\times\boldsymbol{p}_1$ vanishes from symmetry arguments (with $\boldsymbol{k}_1 = 0$). With these approximations, H_3 reduces to

$$H_3 = \frac{1}{4}\alpha^2(Z-3)\frac{1}{r_2^3}\boldsymbol{S}\cdot\boldsymbol{k},$$

where $\boldsymbol{k} = \boldsymbol{k}_2$ is the total orbital angular momentum, since $\boldsymbol{k}_1 = 0$.

We now have to evaluate the expectation value of $\boldsymbol{S}\cdot\boldsymbol{k}$ for ortho-states. The nonrelativistic eigenfunctions are eigenstates of $\boldsymbol{S}^2$ with eigenvalue $S(S+1)$, where $S = 1$, and of $\boldsymbol{k}^2$ with eigenvalue $l(l+1)$. In the nonrelativistic theory the eigenstates with the same $S = 1$ and l, but different values of m_l and m_s,

[1] The expectation value of r_1^{-3} itself diverges for an s-state electron. However, the operators occuring in (39.14) are only approximations, which break down where the potentials are very large. The correct operator, to which r_1^{-3} is an approximation, is less singular for very small r_1 and its expectation value is finite (although large). Since $\boldsymbol{k}_1$ is exactly zero, dropping the first term in (40.3) is justified.

[2] The third term vanishes for the following reason: Any S-state spatial wave function is invariant to the simultaneous rotation of the vectors $\boldsymbol{r}_1$ and $\boldsymbol{r}_2$ through the same angle. The expectation value of the component of the (pseudo) vector $\boldsymbol{r}_{12}\times(\boldsymbol{p}_2 - \boldsymbol{p}_1)$ in any direction is then independent of the direction and hence zero.

[3] Actually, the expectation values of some of the terms in (40.4) diverge *individually* as r_{12} approaches zero. An inspection of the term in square brackets in (40.3) shows that the *total* operator behaves only like r_{12}^{-2} as $r_{12}\to 0$ and the contribution to the expectation value integral from small r_{12} is finite and even *small* compared with the contribution from $r_1 \ll r_{12}$, which we are retaining.

are degenerate. Rewriting $\boldsymbol{k}\cdot\boldsymbol{S}$ in terms of the total angular momentum operator $\boldsymbol{M}=\boldsymbol{k}+\boldsymbol{S}$ [with the help of (13.4)], we see that H_3 removes this degeneracy. The correct stationary states are those linear combinations of the nonrelativistic wave functions which are eigenstates of $\boldsymbol{M}^2$ with quantum number j equal to $l-1$ or l or $l+1$. If we call X the expectation value of $2\boldsymbol{k}\cdot\boldsymbol{S}$, as in (13.5), we have

$$\tfrac{1}{2}X=\tfrac{1}{2}[j(j+1)-l(l+1)-S(S+1)]=\left\{\begin{array}{ll} l & \text{for } j=l+1 \\ -1 & \text{for } j=l \\ -(l+1) & \text{for } j=l-1. \end{array}\right\} \quad (40.5)$$

We finally use a hydrogenic wave function for charge $(Z-1)$ for u_{nlm} and obtain the expectation value of r_2^{-3} from (3.26). In our approximation, then, the final expression for the expectation value E_3 of H_3 is

$$\left.\begin{aligned} E_3 &= \tfrac{1}{4}\alpha^2(Z-3)\,\overline{r_2^{-3}}\,(\tfrac{1}{2}X), \\ \overline{r_2^{-3}} &= \frac{2(Z-1)^3}{n^3(2l+1)(l+1)\,l}. \end{aligned}\right\} \quad (40.6)$$

Generally speaking, the energy level in *any* atom (with given values of S and l) will be split into the components with different j-values, running from $|l-S|$ to $l+S$. If the splitting energy of each component is proportional to the expectation value X of $2\boldsymbol{k}\cdot\boldsymbol{S}$, we speak of a "regular multiplet" (LANDÉ interval rule). This was the case in hydrogen (see Sect. 13). If H_3 were the only operator contributing to the splitting in orthohelium, according to (40.6) we would have "regular triplets". For He itself $(Z-3)$, and hence the multiplying factor of X, is negative and we speak of an "inverted regular triplet" (and for Li^+ this factor is zero). The effect of the inner electron, so to speak, overcompensates that of the nucleus. The observed level splitting in He and Li^+ is quite different, due to the spin-spin interaction, which we discuss next.

β) Spin-spin interaction. We consider next the expectation value E_5 of the operator H_5 in (39.14). This term, derived from the BREIT operator, represents the magnetic interaction between the spins of the two electrons. The expectation value of the part of H_5 involving the delta function depends on the value of S, but not on the inner quantum number j. Hence it contributes to the level shift (cf. Sect. 41), but not to the level *splitting* and we omit it. The expectation value of the second part of H_5 vanishes for S-states from symmetry considerations. For non-zero l we again approximate r_{12} by r_2 in this part of H_5 and note that $\boldsymbol{k}=\boldsymbol{k}_2\,(\boldsymbol{k}_1=0)$. We further rewrite the expectation value of this approximate operator, using the relation (A.33), derived in the Appendix,

$$\left.\begin{aligned} E_5 &\equiv \alpha^2\,\overline{\left[\frac{\boldsymbol{s}_1\cdot\boldsymbol{s}_2}{r_2^3}-3\,\frac{(\boldsymbol{s}_1\cdot\boldsymbol{r}_2)(\boldsymbol{s}_2\cdot\boldsymbol{r}_2)}{r_2^5}\right]} = -\frac{\alpha^2\,\overline{r_2^{-3}}}{(2l+3)(2l-1)}\,Y, \\ Y &= 2(\boldsymbol{s}_1\cdot\boldsymbol{s}_2)\,\boldsymbol{k}^2-3(\boldsymbol{s}_1\cdot\boldsymbol{k})(\boldsymbol{s}_2\cdot\boldsymbol{k})-3(\boldsymbol{s}_2\cdot\boldsymbol{k})(\boldsymbol{s}_1\cdot\boldsymbol{k}). \end{aligned}\right\} \quad (40.7)$$

We first rewrite

$$(\boldsymbol{s}_1\cdot\boldsymbol{k})(\boldsymbol{s}_2\cdot\boldsymbol{k})+(\boldsymbol{s}_2\cdot\boldsymbol{k})(\boldsymbol{s}_1\cdot\boldsymbol{k})=(\boldsymbol{S}\cdot\boldsymbol{k})^2-(\boldsymbol{s}_1\cdot\boldsymbol{k})^2-(\boldsymbol{s}_2\cdot\boldsymbol{k})^2.$$

Further, making use of the commutation rules of $\boldsymbol{k}$ and of the spin operator $\boldsymbol{s}$ for an individual electron (see Sect. 11),

$$\boldsymbol{k}\times\boldsymbol{k}=i\,\boldsymbol{k}, \qquad \boldsymbol{s}\times\boldsymbol{s}=i\,\boldsymbol{s}, \qquad s_i s_j+s_j s_i=\tfrac{1}{2}\delta_{ij},$$

we can write further

$$(\boldsymbol{s}_1\cdot\boldsymbol{k})^2=\tfrac{1}{4}\boldsymbol{k}^2-\tfrac{1}{2}\boldsymbol{s}_1\cdot\boldsymbol{k}.$$

We therefore get the following expression for the operator Y in (40.7),

$$Y=(2\boldsymbol{s}_1\cdot\boldsymbol{s}_2+\tfrac{3}{2})\,\boldsymbol{k}^2-\tfrac{3}{2}(\boldsymbol{S}\cdot\boldsymbol{k})-3\,(\boldsymbol{S}\cdot\boldsymbol{k})^2. \tag{40.8}$$

Each term in (40.8) commutes with $\boldsymbol{k}^2$, $\boldsymbol{S}^2$ and $\boldsymbol{M}^2$ and hence the operator Y is diagonal in a representation in terms of the quantum numbers l, S and j. If $l=0$ (S-state), the eigenvalue of Y is zero for any value of the "total spin" quantum number S. We also have

$$2\boldsymbol{s}_1\cdot\boldsymbol{s}_2=S(S+1)-s_1(s_1+1)-s_2(s_2+1)=S(S+1)-\tfrac{3}{2}. \tag{40.9}$$

For para-states the quantum number S is zero and Y again vanishes, for any value of l. For ortho-states with non-zero l, we have $S=1$, $\boldsymbol{k}^2=l(l+1)$, $2\boldsymbol{s}_1\cdot\boldsymbol{s}_2=\frac{1}{2}$ and $\boldsymbol{S}\cdot\boldsymbol{k}$ is given by (40.5). For ortho-states we get finally

$$Y=-\tfrac{1}{2}\begin{cases} l(2l-1) & \text{for } j=l+1,\\ -(2l+3)(2l-1) & \text{for } j=l,\\ (2l+3)(l+1) & \text{for } j=l-1.\end{cases} \tag{40.10}$$

γ) More accurate calculations. The expectation values of the operators H_3 and H_5 in (39.14) have been calculated more accurately by BREIT[1]. He used the variational wave functions for the $2\,^3P$ states of He, which were discussed in Sect. 35. These wave functions are antisymmetrized correctly and take polariza tion into account at least approximately. BREIT evaluated the expectation values of the operators for these wave functions without neglecting r_1 compared with r_2.

We have so far considered only the *expectation* values of the operators H_3 and H_5 for states of fixed quantum numbers l and S. Actually, H_3 and H_5 also have matrix elements for transitions between states of *different* values for l and S, as long as the inner quantum number j is the same for both states. For instance, in H_3 the odd operator $(\boldsymbol{s}_1-\boldsymbol{s}_2)$ occurs, whose expectation values vanish but which has matrix elements for transitions between orthostates ($S=1$) and para-states ($S=0$). Thus, in the relativistic theory, l and S are no longer strictly "good" quantum numbers, but j is. The correct eigenfunctions of the total HAMILTONian are no longer pure $^3P_1$, $^1P_1$, etc. wave functions, but have a small admixture of wave functions belonging to other states with the same value of j. Since H_3 and H_5 are very small compared with H_0, the amount of mixing should be quite small (of order $Z^2\alpha^2$) but could become appreciable if different states with the same j value happened to have very similar energies[2].

This mixture between various wave functions has been investigated by ARAKI[3]. With these admixtures included, the fine structure splitting of the ortho-states is not simply given by the expectation values of H_3 and H_5, but also depends on the non-diagonal matrix elements of these operators. The largest mixing effect for an ortho-state comes from the para-state with the same values of n and l, since their energy difference is rather small (given by the exchange integral K, Sect. 28). Even so the effect of mixing on the fine structure separation is very small (of relative order H_3/K), less than 1% for all states in He.

ARAKI's calculation of the fine structure separations in He is similar to BREIT'S, but he used the type of wave functions mentioned in Sect. 29 (given in detail

[1] G. BREIT: Phys. Rev. **36**, 383 (1930).
[2] The case of $Z\gg 1$ is discussed in Sect. 43α.
[3] G. ARAKI: Proc. Phys. Math. Soc. Japan **19**, 128 (1937).

in [*10*], Sect. 15) instead of the variational ones. Both BREIT's and ARAKI's results should be considerably better than those of our simple approximations, (40.5) and (40.7). But they are still not very accurate, since the results depend fairly strongly on the details of the wave functions used, which in turn are not very accurate.

δ) Results. We discuss first our approximate results (40.5) with (40.6) and (40.7) with (40.10) for E_3 and E_5, respectively. E_3 alone would give rise to regular triplets for $Z \geq 4$, no splitting at all for $Z=3$ (Li^+) and inverted regular triplets for $Z=2$. E_5 alone would give rise to partially inverted triplets, the $j=l-1$ level being highest and $j=l$ lowest. For Li^+ this is indeed the whole effect. For $Z>4$, E_3 becomes more important relative to E_5 with increasing Z and with increasing l. For low values of l and Z, even the qualitative features of the level splitting change from one value of l or Z to another.

For ^3P states ($l=1$) the energy separation between the states of $J=0$ and 1 (or $J=1$ and 2) is given by (in RYDBERG'S)

$$\Delta E = \frac{\alpha^2 (Z-1)^3}{6 n^3} \begin{Bmatrix} 6-(Z-3) & \text{for} \quad j=0\to 1 \\ -\frac{2}{5}-2(Z-2) & \text{for} \quad j=1\to 2. \end{Bmatrix} \tag{40.11}$$

For ^3D states ($l=2$) we have

$$\Delta E = \frac{\alpha^2 (Z-1)^3}{30 n^3} \begin{Bmatrix} 4-2(Z-3) & \text{for} \quad j=1\to 2 \\ \frac{3}{7}-3(Z-2) & \text{for} \quad j=2\to 3. \end{Bmatrix} \tag{40.12}$$

Quite generally the level splitting is independent of the principal quantum number n, according to our simple approximation, except for an overall multiplying factor of n^{-3}. For He the more accurate results of BREIT and ARAKI are only slightly different from ours. Note that, for the ^3P levels in He, the $J=1$ and $J=2$ levels happen to have almost the same energy (for all values of n). In Fig. 18 we give a schematic diagram of the level splitting of ^3P states for $Z=2$ (He), $Z=3$ (Li^+) and large Z ($Z>10$).

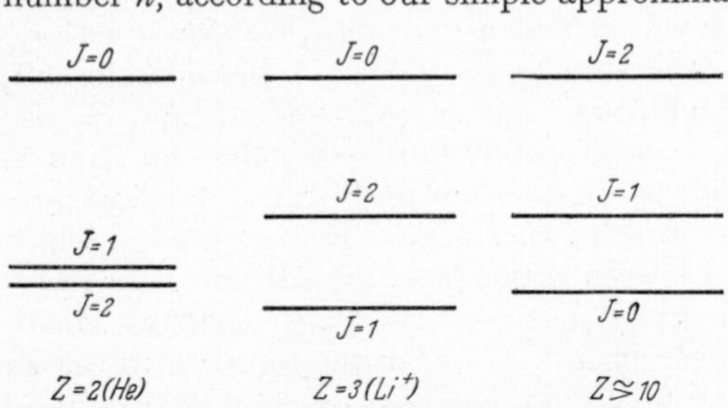

Fgi. 18. Schematic energy level splitting of ^3P states in helium-like ions with nuclear charge $Z=2$, 3 and for large Z.

Measurements of the fine structure splitting of many energy levels in helium-like atoms have been carried out by means of optical spectroscopy, but it is rather difficult to obtain an accuracy of better than ± 0.01 cm^{-1}. Only recently microwave methods have been developed for measuring the energy differences in direct transitions between the components of ^3P-triplets. These methods are capable of an accuracy of much better than ± 0.001 cm^{-1}. In Table 11 we compare the theoretical results, obtained from the approximation (40.11) (labeled Appr.) and from BREIT's and ARAKI's calculations, with experimental measurements[1] of the splitting of a few ^3P-states. The agreement is fairly good, but not excellent, and the discrepancies are most probably due to the inaccuracy of the wave functions used in the theoretical calculations.

[1] FRED, TOMKINS, BRODY and HAMERMESH: Phys. Rev. **82**, 406 (1951) for He $2P$ (optical). H. SCHÜLER: Z. Physik **42**, 487 (1927) for Li^+ $2P$ (optical, using the Li_6 isotope, which has no observable hyperfine structure). T. MAIMAN and W. LAMB: Phys. Rev. **98**, 1194 (1955) for He $3P$ (microwave).

Table 11. *Fine structure splitting of ^3P levels in* He *and* Li^+ *(in cm^{-1}).*

	2 *P* (He)				3 *P* (He)			2 *P* (Li^+)	
	Appr.	BREIT	ARAKI	Expt.	Appr.	ARAKI	Expt.	Appr.	Expt.
$^3P_0 - {}^3P_1$	0.84	0.97	0.94	0.99	0.25	0.22	0.272	5.82	5.1_5
$^3P_1 - {}^3P_2$	−0.05	0.14	0.07	0.08	-0.01_5	0.01_8	0.0220	−2.33	-2.1_0

41. Relativistic corrections for the ground state. For the ground state ($1\,^1S$) of helium-like atoms, l, S and j are all zero and there is no fine structure splitting. Nevertheless, the operators H_1 to H_5 in (39.14) contribute relativistic corrections (or level shifts) to the nonrelativistic energy eigenvalue (Sects. 32 and 33) of relative order $(Z\alpha)^2$ and $Z\alpha^2$. These corrections, derived from the PAULI approximation, are themselves only the leading terms in an expansion in powers of α and $Z\alpha$. The accuracy of the nonrelativistic calculations on the ground state energy and of the measurements of the ionization potential of He warrants the inclusion of the PAULI approximation terms (Sect. 41 α) and even (to some extent) of the higher correction terms (of which the most important is the LAMB shift, Sect. 41 β).

α) PAULI approximations. We consider now the expectation values of the operators H_1 to H_5 in (39.14) for the ground state of a He-like atom with nuclear charge Z. Working in atomic units and denoting expectation values by bars, we get for the expectation value E_1 of H_1

$$E_1 = -\frac{\alpha^2}{8}\left(\overline{p_1^4} + \overline{p_2^4}\right) = -\frac{\alpha^2}{4}\,\overline{p_1^4}. \tag{41.1}$$

As discussed in Sect. 36 δ, great care must be taken in the evaluation of $\overline{p_1^4}$ and it is simplest and safest to use the last form on the right hand side of (36.15) [see also Eq. (39.17)].

It can be shown (after some algebra) that the expectation value E_2 of the operator H_2 vanishes if any wave function of product form $U = u(r_1)\,u(r_2)$ is used, i.e. both for the hydrogen-like and for the HARTREE wave function. If a more accurate wave function, which includes the effects of polarization, is used, then a finite (but numerically small) value is obtained for E_2. As was shown in Sect. 40 α, the expectation value of H_3 vanishes *exactly* (for any wave function) for all S-states and hence for the ground state.

The expectation value E_4 of the operator H_4 is given by (39.18) with $\operatorname{div}\mathcal{E}_1 = -\Delta_1 V$. Using the explicit expression (39.14a) for V (in the absence of an external field) and working in atomic units, we get (using $\Delta r^{-1} = -4\pi\,\delta^{(3)}(\boldsymbol{r})$,

$$E_4 = +\pi\alpha^2\left[Z\,\overline{\delta^{(3)}(\boldsymbol{r}_1)} - \overline{\delta^{(3)}(\boldsymbol{r}_{12})}\right]. \tag{41.2}$$

We finally come to the expectation value E_5 of the operator H_5. The expectation value of the second term in the expression for H_5 in (39.14) vanishes exactly for any S-state. From (40.9), for any singlet state ($S=0$) we have $\overline{\mathbf{s}_1\cdot\mathbf{s}_2} = -\frac{3}{4}$ and the first part of H_5 gives (in atomic units)

$$E_5 = +2\pi\alpha^2\,\overline{\delta^3(\boldsymbol{r}_{12})}. \tag{41.3}$$

The total energy shift for the ground state of the helium-like atom, in the PAULI approximation, is given by the sum of E_1, E_2, E_4 and E_5. The corresponding energy shift for the ion with one of the two electrons removed is, from (13.14), $-(Z^4\alpha^2/8)$ atomic units (in the PAULI approximation). The shift E_J in the ionization potential J of the two-electron atom is then

$$E_J = \alpha^2 \left[-\frac{Z^4}{8} + \frac{1}{4} \overline{p_1^4} - \pi Z \, \delta^{(3)}(\boldsymbol{r}_1) - \pi \, \delta^{(3)}(\boldsymbol{r}_{12}) \right] - E_2. \tag{41.4}$$

Accurate numerical evaluations will be discussed in Sect. 41γ. If we use as a very simple approximation to the wave function of the two-electron atom the hydrogenic form

$$\exp\left[-\tfrac{1}{2}\left(Z - \tfrac{5}{16}\right)(r_1 + r_2)\right],$$

then $E_2 = 0$ and the other expectation values are given by (36.11) and (36.17). The resulting approximation for E_J, carrying only the first three terms in an expansion in powers of $1/Z$, is

$$E_J \approx \tfrac{1}{4} \alpha^2 Z^2 (Z^2 - 6Z + 4.5) \,\mathrm{Ry}. \tag{41.5}$$

In Sect. 41γ we shall give a somewhat more accurate expansion in powers of $1/Z$ for E_J, Eq. (41.11).

β) The LAMB *shift.* We have so far considered only relativistic corrections of relative order $Z^2\alpha^2$ and $Z\alpha^2$ to the nonrelativistic energy of the two-electron atom and the corresponding one-electron ion. There are also radiative corrections (see Sects. 18 to 21) which are smaller by one more power of α. For helium, at least, these radiative corrections are not smaller than the experimental error of the ionization potential.

For the one-electron ion, the radiative corrections to the ground state energy of relative order $Z^2\alpha^3$ are simply the (lowest order) LAMB shift, (21.2), and there are no terms of order $Z\alpha^3$. From (21.2) we have for this shift

$$E_{L,1} = \frac{8\alpha^3 Z}{3} \frac{Z^3}{\pi} \left[2 \log \frac{1}{Z\alpha} - \log \frac{K_0}{Z^2 \,\mathrm{Ry}} + 0.63 \right] \mathrm{Ry}, \tag{41.6}$$

where $K_0 = 19.77 Z^2$ Ry is the average excitation energy defined in (19.10). For the two-electron atom, the only radiative corrections of order $Z^2\alpha^3$ are also LAMB shift terms, which correspond to the emission of a virtual photon by either electron, this electron's interaction with the nuclear COULOMB potential and reabsorption of the photon by the same electron. These terms contribute[1] a shift to the ground state energy of the two-electron atom of

$$E_L = \frac{3}{16} \alpha^3 Z \, \overline{\delta^3(\boldsymbol{r}_1)} \left[\log \frac{mc^2}{K_0} + \frac{19}{30} - \log 2 \right] \mathrm{Ry}, \tag{41.7}$$

where the bar again denotes the expectation value in atomic units. The average excitation energy K_0 in (41.7) is defined in a manner similar to (19.10), but using the wave-functions for the two-electron atom. The evaluation of K_0 is discussed in Sect. 74γ. K_0 approaches $19.77 Z^2$ Ry for large Z and is about 84 Ry for He ($Z = 2$).

For the two-electron atom there are a large number of terms, which contribute corrections of relative order $Z\alpha^3$. One such term corresponds to a LAMB shift type of process, as E_L above, but the electron interacts with the COULOMB potential due to the other electron (instead of that due to the nucleus). Another term comes from a correction to the BREIT operator, which corrects for the neglect of $E_n - E_0$ in the energy denominator of (38.5). A third term corresponds to the exchange of two virtual photons between the two electrons. Some of these terms involve, besides $Z\alpha^3$, also the factor $\log \alpha$ and these terms (to an accuracy

[1] H. E. HAKANSSON: Ark. Fysik 1, 555 (1950). — P. KABIR and E. SALPETER: (unpublished work).

of ± 1 as compared with $\log\alpha$) can be calculated fairly easily using quantum electrodynamics and a perturbation method[1]. The sum of the terms involving $\log\alpha$ is

$$E'_L = \tfrac{28}{3}\alpha^3 \overline{\delta^3(\boldsymbol{r}_{12})} \log\alpha \,\mathrm{Ry}\,. \tag{41.8}$$

The terms of order $Z\alpha^3 (Z^2\,\mathrm{Ry})$ which do not involve $\log\alpha$ have not been calculated, but since E'_L is numerically rather small[2] compared with E_L (even for low Z), their neglect is not expected to introduce very large errors.

The radiative correction to the ionization potential J of the two-electron atom is then

$$\Delta E_J = E_{L,1} - E_L - E'_L\,. \tag{41.9}$$

Numerical values for ΔE_J are given in Sect. 41γ.

γ) Numerical results. We consider first the expression (41.4) for the relativistic correction E_J (in the PAULI approximation) to the ground state energy of He ($Z=2$). This expression involves the expectation values of various operators over the nonrelativistic ground state wave function which is not known exactly. These expectation values have been evaluated using various variational wave functions and the HARTREE functions and some of the results are given in Table 10, Sect. 36. For KINOSHITA's 38-parameter wave function, the values of the five terms in (41.4) are (in units of $\alpha^2\,\mathrm{Ry} = \frac{1}{2}\alpha^2$ at. un. $= 5.844\,\mathrm{cm}^{-1}$),

Term involving	ion	E_2	p^4	$\delta(r_1)$	$\delta(r_{12})$	E_J
Value[3]	-4	$+0.28$	$+27.05$	-22.75	-0.67	-0.10

The values of E_J minus the mass-polarization correction ε_M, defined in (37.13), for various wave functions is (in cm^{-1}).

Number of parameters	1	(HARTREE)	3	18	38
$E_J - \varepsilon_M$	-24.0	-10.1	-7.2	-5.41	-5.35

Note that the various contributions to E_J almost cancel each other for He. As discussed in Sect. 36, the percentage errors in the various expectation values which make up E_J are very much larger than the percentage error in the variational nonrelativistic ionization potential. Nevertheless, the 38-parameter value, $E_J - \varepsilon_M = -5.35\,\mathrm{cm}^{-1}$, should not be in error by more than (plus or minus) a few times $0.1\,\mathrm{cm}^{-1}$.

We turn now to the evaluation of ΔE_J, given by (41.6) to (41.9), for He. We use the value in (74.8) for the average excitation energy K_0 and the values given in Table 10 for the expectation values of $\delta^{(3)}(\boldsymbol{r}_1)$ and $\delta^{(3)}(\boldsymbol{r}_{12})$. The result is (in cm^{-1})

$$E_{L,1} = 3.53\,,\quad -E_L = -4.97\,,\quad -E_{L'} = 0.21\,;\ \Delta E_J = -(1.2_3 \pm 0.2)\,\mathrm{cm}^{-1}. \tag{41.10}$$

The probable error includes an order of magnitude estimate of the radiative correction terms which have not yet been evaluated.

---

[1] P. KABIR and E. SALPETER: (unpublished work).

[2] The smallness of these terms, even for small Z, is due to the fact that the expectation value of $\delta(\boldsymbol{r}_{12})$ is very much smaller than that of $\delta(\boldsymbol{r}_1)$ (by a factor of about 17 for He, see Table 10, Sect. 36).

[3] The numerical values are the expectation values multiplied by the coefficients occuring in (41.4).

We turn finally to an evaluation of E_J and ΔE_J for helium-like ions[1] of $Z>2$. For Li^+ $(Z=3)$, we have evaluated the various expectation values which are involved in E_J, using the simple variational wave function (32.26). The result is $E_J=+14\ \text{cm}^{-1}$. This value may be in error by several cm^{-1}. For larger values of Z, the expectation values were evaluated[2], using a wave function given in ERIKSSON's paper which involves four parameters [instead of three, as in (33.14)] and an expansion in powers of $1/Z$. The result for the first few terms in this expansion is

$$E_J = \tfrac{1}{4}\alpha^2 Z^2 (Z^2 - 4.254 Z + 5.57)\ \text{Ry}. \tag{41.11}$$

The term in Z^4 is exact, but the accuracy of the other two coefficients may not be very good. Finally, we use (74.9) and substitute the expectation values from ERIKSSON's wave function into (41.9) to find the radiative corrections. The result, for the first few terms in the expansion in $1/Z$, is

$$\Delta E_J = -\frac{16 Z^4 \alpha^3}{3\pi}\left[(3.745 - \log Z) + \frac{1}{Z}(1.44 \log Z - 6.46)\right]. \tag{41.12}$$

The theoretical and experimental results for the ionization potentials of He and a few helium-like ions are summarized in Table 12: J_{NR} represents the theoretical result for the nonrelativistic ionization potential. For He we have used the value in (32.25) and for the other ions the expression (33.12). Multiplying these expressions by the appropriate values of the "reduced mass RYDBERG", (33.13), gives J_{NR} in cm^{-1}. The mass polarization corrections ε_M (which are rather unimportant for large Z) are taken from Sect. 37, E_J and ΔE_J from the discussions of this section. As Table 12 shows, the agreement between theory and experiment is excellent in all cases.

Table 12. *Experimental and theoretical ionization potentials for helium-like ions (in cm^{-1}).*

Z ion	2 He	3 Li^+	4 Be^{++}	6 $C^{(4+)}$	8 $O^{(6+)}$
J_{NR}	198316.9_8	610072	1241177	3161660	5959980
$E_J-\varepsilon_M$	-5.3_5	$+9$	$+100$	$+840$	$+3320$
ΔE_J	-1.2_3	-6	-23	-120	-360
J_{theor}	198310.4_0	610075	1241254	3162380	5962940
J_{exp}	198310.5 ± 1	610079 ± 25	1241225 ± 100	3162450 ± 300	5963000 ± 600

42. BREIT equation without external field. We consider now the special case of the BREIT equation for two particles, which interact with each other, but in the absence of any external field. We generalize slightly from the case of two electrons to that of two (not necessarily identical) particles of mass and charge m_1, m_2 and e_1, e_2 respectively. But we still asume, for the moment, that each of the particles is a "FERMI-DIRAC particle", which has spin $\frac{1}{2}$ and obeys (if by itself) the DIRAC equation. One can easily generalize the full BREIT equation (38.1) for this case, but we consider only the PAULI approximation (39.14).

The approximate Eq. (39.14) can easily be modified for the case of unequal masses and charges of the two particles. If no external fields are present, this equation simplifies considerably. First, the terms involving $\boldsymbol{A}(\boldsymbol{r})$ are missing and eV, defined in (39.14a), is simply $e_1 e_2/r_{12}$. Second, the total momentum $\boldsymbol{p}_1+\boldsymbol{p}_2$ is now a constant of the motion. If we work in the center of mass system

[1] J. SUCHER and H. FOLEY: Phys. Rev. **95**, 966 (1954). — M. A. ERIKSSON: Z. Physik **109**, 762 (1938).

[2] J. BIRD, D. BOWERS, and P. KABIR: Unpublished work.

($p_1 + p_2 = 0$), the wave function U only depends on the relative displacement ($r_1 - r_2$), instead of on two variables. We write

$$\boldsymbol{p} = \boldsymbol{p}_1 = -\boldsymbol{p}_2, \quad \boldsymbol{r} = \boldsymbol{r}_{12} = \boldsymbol{r}_1 - \boldsymbol{r}_2.$$

We then have, instead of (39.14),

$$\left.\begin{aligned}
&W U = (H_0 + H_1 + \cdots + H_5)\, U:\\
&H_0 = \frac{e_1 e_2}{r} + \frac{1}{2}\left(\frac{1}{m_1} + \frac{1}{m_2}\right) p^2,\\
&H_1 = -\frac{1}{8 c^2}\left(\frac{1}{m_1^3} + \frac{1}{m_2^3}\right) p^4,\\
&H_2 = \frac{e_1 e_2}{2 m_1 m_2 c^2}\,\frac{1}{r}\,(p^2 + p_r^2),\\
&H_3 = -\frac{\boldsymbol{r}\times\boldsymbol{p}}{r^3}\cdot\left[\frac{\mu_1 e_2}{m_1 c}\,\mathbf{s}_1 + \frac{\mu_2 e_1}{m_2 c}\,\mathbf{s}_2 + \frac{2\mu_1 e_2}{m_2 c}\,\mathbf{s}_1 + \frac{2\mu_2 e_1}{m_1 c}\,\mathbf{s}_2\right],\\
&H_4 = \frac{i e_1 e_2 \hbar}{(2 c^2)}\left(\frac{1}{m_1^2} + \frac{1}{m_2^2}\right)\boldsymbol{p}\cdot \operatorname{grad}\frac{1}{r},\\
&H_5 = 4\mu_1\mu_2\left[-\frac{8\pi}{3}(\mathbf{s}_1\cdot\mathbf{s}_2)\,\delta^{(3)}(\boldsymbol{r}) + \frac{1}{r^3}\,(\mathbf{s}_1\cdot\mathbf{s}_2 - 3 s_{1r} s_{2r})'\right],
\end{aligned}\right\} \quad (42.1)$$

where

$$\mu_1 = \frac{e_1\hbar}{2 m_1 c}, \quad \mu_2 = \frac{e_2\hbar}{2 m_2 c}, \quad s_{1r} = \frac{\mathbf{s}_1\cdot\boldsymbol{r}}{r}, \quad p_r^2 = \frac{1}{r^2}\,\boldsymbol{r}\cdot(\boldsymbol{r}\cdot\boldsymbol{p})\,\boldsymbol{p}.$$

α) One heavy particle. The application of Eq. (42.1) to the positronium system is discussed in Sect. 23. This equation can also be used to calculate the effect of nuclear motion and hyperfine structure on the energy levels of hydrogen-like atoms. We assume at the moment that one of the two particles is an electron and the other a nucleus which is a DIRAC particle of mass much larger than the electron's,

$$e_1 = -e, \quad m_1 = m, \quad e_2 = Z e, \quad m_2 = M \gg m.$$

We expand all the expressions in (42.1) in powers of m/M and retain only the zero and first power. We further rearrange the terms so that the largest ones involve the reduced mass $\mathcal{M}$ (called μ in Sect. 5),

$$\mathcal{M} = \frac{m M}{m + M} \approx m\left(1 - \frac{m}{M}\right).$$

(42.1) then reduces to

$$W U = (H_a + H_b + H_c)\, U, \quad (42.2)$$

where

$$H_a = \left(-\frac{Z e^2}{r} + \frac{p^2}{2\mathcal{M}}\right) - \frac{p^4}{8\mathcal{M}^3 c^2} + \frac{1}{r^3}\,\frac{\mu_{\mathcal{M}} Z e\hbar}{\mathcal{M} c}\,\boldsymbol{k}\cdot\mathbf{s}_1 - \frac{i Z e^2\hbar}{(2\mathcal{M} c)^2}\,\boldsymbol{p}\cdot\operatorname{grad}\frac{1}{r},$$

$$H_b = \frac{1}{M c^2}\left[\frac{3}{8 m^2}\,p^4 - \frac{Z e^2}{2 m}\,\frac{1}{r}\,(p^2 + p_r^2) + \frac{i Z e^2\hbar}{2 m}\,\boldsymbol{p}\cdot\operatorname{grad}\frac{1}{r}\right],$$

$$H_c = H_5 + \frac{2\mu_2}{m c}\,\frac{\hbar e}{r^3}\,\boldsymbol{k}\cdot\mathbf{s}_2,$$

and H_5 is given in (42.1). We have also written $\boldsymbol{k} = \boldsymbol{r}\times\boldsymbol{p}$ for the orbital angular momentum and $\mu_{\mathcal{M}}$ for $e\hbar/2\mathcal{M}c$.

So far we have derived (42.2) only under the assumption that the nucleus has spin $\frac{1}{2}$ and only a magnetic moment given by the DIRAC theory. In reality many nuclei have a spin other than $\frac{1}{2}$ and a magnetic moment which bears no simple relation to the DIRAC theory, in view of the complicated structure of nuclei. Even the simple proton, which has spin $\frac{1}{2}$, has a rather large anomalous magnetic moment (stemming from a coupling of the proton with its virtual meson charge cloud). That (42.2) can also be applied to such nuclei can be seen as follows.

Of the terms involving $1/m$ which occur in (42.1), we have only retained those in (42.2) which are linear in $1/m_2$. By referring back to (39.1), one can show that these terms come only from the nonrelativistic kinetic energy $p^2/2m_2$ and from the BREIT operator. The BREIT operator, in turn, represents the exchange of a photon between the electron and nucleus. Let λ denote the direction of polarization and $\boldsymbol{q}$ the momentum of the photon, $\boldsymbol{p}_2$ the momentum of the nucleus. In deriving the approximate form of the BREIT operator occurring in (39.1), we have used a factor

$$e_2 \alpha_{\lambda++} = \frac{e_2}{m_2 c} p_\lambda + \frac{2i}{\hbar} \mu_2 (\boldsymbol{q} \times \mathbf{s}_2)_\lambda. \tag{42.3}$$

Now, according to quantum electrodynamics, for *any* nonrelativistic particle with charge e_2 and an empirical magnetic moment μ interacting with a photon we get a factor exactly of form (42.3), except that $2\mu_2 \mathbf{s}_2$ is replaced by μ. In other words, the nucleus has been treated in a sufficiently nonrelativistic manner in (42.2), so that no terms characteristic of the DIRAC theory (for the nucleus) remain.

In (42.2) all the terms which involve the spin of the nucleus $\mathbf{s}_2$ are contained in H_c. These terms are responsible for the hyperfine structure in hydrogen-like atoms. For these terms we have already written $e\hbar/2Mc$ in the form μ_2. For any nucleus with empirical magnetic moment μ we simply have to replace $2\mu_2 \mathbf{s}_2$ by μ. The expectation value of H_c is evaluated and discussed in Sect. 22.

β) Nuclear motion. We discuss now the effect of the operator H_b in (42.2). The term H_c depends on the direction of the nuclear spin and is zero if the nuclear magnetic moment is zero. The term H_a is exactly the PAULI HAMILTONian for an "electron" with reduced mass $\mathcal{M}$ (not the real electron mass m), but in a *fixed* COULOMB field. If the HAMILTONian consisted solely of H_a, the effect of the nuclear motion on the fine structure would be exactly the same as the effect on the nonrelativistic energy (to first order in m/M). I.e. all energies are $(1 - m/M)$ times those obtained for an infinitely heavy nucleus (fixed potential) and we merely have to replace R_∞ by R_M, the "reduced mass RYDBERG", in all terms in Sect. 13. However, the operator H_b is also of order (m/M) times the fine structure splitting. This order of magnitude is not much smaller than that of the LAMB shift. But we show now that the expectation value of H_b depends only on the principal quantum number n, *not* on l or j, and thus contributes only to a level *shift* and *not* to the fine structure *splitting*.

We evaluate only the expectation value E_b of the operator H_b using the nonrelativistic wave function U_0. Returning now to atomic units, we have

$$\tfrac{1}{2} p^2 U_0 = (W_0 + Z r^{-1}) U_0,$$

where W_0 is the nonrelativistic energy $(-Z^2/2n^2)$ a.u. For a state of orbital quantum number l it follows further from (1.11) that

$$\frac{1}{2} p_r^2 U_0 = \frac{1}{2} \left(p^2 - \frac{1}{r^2} k^2\right) U_0 = \left[W_0 + \frac{Z}{r} - \frac{l(l+1)}{2r^2} + \frac{1}{r}\frac{\partial}{\partial r}\right] U_0. \tag{42.4}$$

We also use the fact (see Sect. 16) that the expectation value of $2\boldsymbol{p} \cdot (\text{grad } 1/r)$ equals that of $-i\Delta r^{-1} = +4\pi i \delta^{(3)}(\boldsymbol{r})$. Using all these relations to evaluate E_b

from the operator H_b in (42.2), we get

$$E_b = \alpha^2 \frac{m}{M} \left\{ \frac{3}{2} \overline{\left(W_0 + \frac{Z}{r}\right)^2} - \overline{\frac{Z}{r}\left[2\left(W_0 + \frac{Z}{r}\right) - \frac{l(l+1)}{2r^2} + \frac{1}{r}\frac{\partial}{\partial r}\right]} - \pi Z \overline{\delta^{(3)}(\boldsymbol{r})} \right\}. \quad (42.5)$$

E_b is clearly independent of the quantum number j, but many of the individual terms in (42.5) depend on l. One has to evaluate all the terms explicitly to show that their sum is independent of l, if hydrogenic wave functions are used. W_0 is simply given by the BALMER formula and the expectation values of r^{-1}, r^{-2} and r^{-3} (for $l \neq 0$) by Eqs. (3.24), (3.25) and (3.26). For S-states, $\overline{r^{-3}}$ itself diverges, but the expression for which this is an approximation is finite. The term in $l(l+1)r^{-3}$ is thus zero for an S-state. On the other hand, the expectation value of $\delta^{(3)}(\boldsymbol{r})$ is simply the square of the wave function at the origin, which vanishes for $l \neq 0$ and, for an S-state, is given by [see (3.46)]

$$\pi \overline{\delta^{(3)}(\boldsymbol{r})} = \pi U_0^2(0) = Z^2/n^3. \quad (42.6)$$

Substituting these expectation values into (42.5) one finds[1], after some algebra,

$$E_b = -\frac{\alpha^2}{8}\frac{m}{M}\left(\frac{Z}{n}\right)^4 = -\left(\frac{Z\alpha}{2n}\right)^2 \frac{m}{M}|W_0|. \quad (42.7)$$

This energy shift is indeed independent of l and j and thus does not contribute to the fine structure splitting. For all states in H this shift is less than 10^{-8} of the nonrelativistic energy, which is beyond the limits of accuracy of optical spectroscopy.

γ) Fully covariant methods. The Eq. (42.1) is only an approximation to the BREIT equation (38.1) which reads, for two FERMI-DIRAC particles in the absence of external fields,

$$\left.\begin{aligned} &(E - H_1 - H_2)\,U(\boldsymbol{r}) = G_B(\boldsymbol{r})\,U(\boldsymbol{r}), \\ &\text{with} \\ &H_1 = m_1 c^2 \beta_1 + c\,\boldsymbol{p}\cdot\boldsymbol{\alpha}_1, \quad H_2 = m_2 c^2 \beta_2 - c\,\boldsymbol{p}\cdot\boldsymbol{\alpha}_2, \\ &G_B(\boldsymbol{r}) = \frac{e_1 e_2}{r}\left[1 - \frac{1}{2}\boldsymbol{\alpha}_1\cdot\boldsymbol{\alpha}_2 - \frac{1}{2}\frac{(\boldsymbol{\alpha}_1\cdot\boldsymbol{r})(\boldsymbol{\alpha}_2\cdot\boldsymbol{r})}{r^2}\right], \end{aligned}\right\} \quad (42.8)$$

where $\boldsymbol{r}$ is the relative distance and $\boldsymbol{p}$ is the relative momentum. Eq. (42.8) is not only written in a non-covariant notation, but actually is not fully compatible with the special theory of relativity. This is connected with the fact (see Sect. 38α) that (42.8) is itself only an approximation. In Sect 38β some methods (e.g. the TAMM-DANCOFF and the perturbation methods) were outlined for calculating exact expressions (in principle) for the energy, etc., in the form of an expansion in powers of the fine structure constant α. These methods have the disadvantage that individual terms in the expansion are not LORENTZ invariant, although their sum is. The evaluation of a higher order term is also tedious since it involves summations over intermediate states or the solution of a set of coupled integral equations.

Other methods[2] have also been developed for treating the interaction of two FERMI-DIRAC particles with each other (according to pair theory and quantum

[1] For a more detailed derivation of (42.7) see G. BROWN and G. BREIT, Phys. Rev. **74**, 1278 (1948). This equation had also been obtained by K. BECHERT and J. MEIXNER, Ann. d. Physik **22**, 525 (1935).

[2] J. SCHWINGER: Proc. Nat. Acad. Sci. USA. **37**, 452, 455 (1951). — E. SALPETER and H. BETHE: Phys. Rev. **84**, 1232 (1951). — M. GELL-MANN and F. LOW: Phys. Rev. **84**, 350 (1951).

electrodynamics), which exhibit the LORENTZ invariance of the theory automatically. There are various (equivalent) ways of formulating such relativistic methods and we shall outline very briefly the BETHE-SALPETER formulation in terms of a fully covariant wave equation.

This wave equation for a two-body system bears some similarity to the BREIT equation, but is radically different in one respect. The wave function occurring in this covariant equation depends on one more variable than the BREIT wave function. In position space, for instance, the wave function depends on the positions of the two particles (as before), but also depends on one time-variable *each* for the two particles (instead of one common time). This puts time and position on the same footing and enables a LORENTZ-invariant formulation. In the absence of external fields and for a stationary state of the system, the momentum-energy four-vector P_μ for the motion of the center of mass can be eparated out. The covariant BETHE-SALPETER wave equation is then of the form

$$\left[\sum_\mu\left(\frac{m_1}{m_1+m_2}P_\mu+p_\mu\right)\gamma_\mu^{(1)}-i m_1 c\right]\left[\sum_\mu\left(\frac{m_2}{m_1+m_2}P_\mu-p_\mu\right)\gamma_\mu^{(2)}-i m_2 c\right]\psi(x_\nu)=i\bar{G}(x_\nu)\,\psi(x_\nu). \quad (42.9)$$

The wave function ψ is a function of the four-vector $x_\nu=(\boldsymbol{r}, ict)$, where $\boldsymbol{r}=\boldsymbol{r}_1-\boldsymbol{r}_2$ is the relative distance as in (42.8) and t, the "relative time" t_1-t_2, is a variable without analogue in (42.8). In (42.9), p_μ is the operator $-i\hbar\,\partial/\partial x_\mu$ and P_μ is a constant four-vector; the invariant $E=\sqrt{-\sum_\mu P_\mu^2}$ is the total energy in the center of mass system and takes the place of the eigenvalue parameter E in (42.8). The interaction operator $\bar{G}$ consists of an infinite series of terms. *Each* term in this series is a LORENTZ-invariant operator G_n, which can be derived from the FEYNMAN formulation of quantum electrodynamics, multiplied by $(e_1 e_2/\hbar c)^n$ for the n-th term. For the first term in this series, G_1 is simply $\sum_\mu \gamma_\mu^{(1)}\gamma_\mu^{(2)}$ times a function of the invariant $\sum_\mu x_\mu^2$, the higher terms are generally integral operators. The four-dimensional FOURIER transform of (42.9) is a *single* integral equation, but the kernel consists of an infinite series of terms.

Little progress has been made so far in the application of (42.9) to *highly* relativistic systems. But for hydrogenlike atoms of low Z and for positronium the coupling constant $(-e_1 e_2/\hbar c)$ is small ($Z\alpha$ and α, respectively). For bound states of such systems the first few terms in the expansion of the energy eigenvalue E in powers of the coupling constant can be obtained from (42.9). The results of some such calculations[1] are quoted in Sects. 20α and 23β. The smallness of the coupling constant makes it possible to write the operator $\bar{G}$ as an „instantaneous" COULOMB interaction plus smaller correction terms. For an instantaneous interaction alone [a function of $\boldsymbol{r}$ times $\delta(t)$], (42.9) can be reduced to a three-dimensional wave equation for $\psi(\boldsymbol{r}, 0)$, which is somewhat similar to the BREIT equation (42.8), and the dependence of $\psi(\boldsymbol{r}, t)$ on t can be found. With this approximate solution of (42.9) as a starting point, the higher relativistic corrections to the energy are then obtained by perturbation (or iteration) methods.

43. Treatment for large Z. α) *The level scheme.* We consider now the case of helium-like atoms of large nuclear charge Z, for which $Z\alpha$ is not very much smaller than unity[2]. In this case the approximations used in the preceding few sections,

[1] E. E. SALPETER: Phys. Rev. **87**, 328 (1952). — R. KARPLUS and A. KLEIN: Phys. Rev. **87**, 848 (1952). — W. BARKER and F. GLOVER: Phys. Rev. **99**, 317 (1955).

[2] No two-electron ions of Z much larger than about 10 can be studied experimentally with good accuracy. However, the spectra of *complex* atoms with Z up to about 100 can be measured and the methods discussed in this section serve as a starting point for the theoretical treatment of the inner electrons in such atoms (see Sect. 17γ).

which considered relativistic effects as small perturbations and obtained results in the form of power series in $Z\alpha$, are no longer very good. On the other hand, we can make use of the fact that $1/Z$ is small and treat the *whole* interaction between the two electrons (including the COULOMB interaction) as a small perturbation compared with the interaction between either electron and the nucleus. Compared with the nonrelativistic energy $2Z^2$Ry, the effect of the spin-orbit interaction for an individual electron (given by the DIRAC equation for a single electron) is of relative order $(Z\alpha)^2$, whereas the interaction energy between the two electrons is of relative order $1/Z$. Thus, if $1/Z \ll (Z\alpha)^2$, i.e. if $Z \gg 27$, one can use the following approximation method, known as the j-j coupling scheme[1].

We first neglect the interaction between the electrons completely. Let $\psi_a(\boldsymbol{r}_1)$ be one of the exact DIRAC wave functions (a spinor with four components) for a stationary state of a single electron (1) in a static central potential $\varphi(r)$. Let $\boldsymbol{M}_1 = \boldsymbol{k}_1 + \boldsymbol{s}_1$ be the total angular momentum of this electron, then $\boldsymbol{M}_1^2$ and M_{1z} are constants of the motion and the state a is characterized by the principal, inner and magnetic quantum numbers n_1, j_1 and m_1, plus the "parity" π_1 of the state (corresponding to the two possibilities $l_1 = j_1 - \frac{1}{2}$ and $l_1 = j_1 + \frac{1}{2}$). In the absence of interaction, the wave function for a state of the two-electron system is of the form

$$\psi(1, 2) = \frac{1}{\sqrt{2}} \left[\psi_a(1)\, \psi_b(2) - \psi_b(1)\, \psi_a(2)\right], \tag{43.1}$$

where 1 refers to the first electron, 2 to the second. This wave function is a 16-component spinor (4 components for each electron) and is automatically antisymmetric to an interchange of all coordinates (spin as well as spatial) of the two electrons, as required by FERMI-DIRAC quantum statistics (of which the PAULI exclusion principle is a consequence).

The state (43.1) is characterized by the quantum numbers $n_1, n_2, j_1, j_2, m_1, m_2$ and the two possible values each of the parities π_1 and π_2. For any central potential $\varphi(r)$, the energy of the state depends on n_1, n_2, j_1 and j_2 but is independent of the values of m_1 and m_2. We restrict ourselves to nuclear charges $Z \gg 27 = \alpha^{-\frac{2}{3}}$. The part of the energy which depends on j_1 and j_2 is proportional to $(Z\alpha)^2$, which we do *not* assume to be small. For $\varphi(r)$ equal to the nuclear COULOMB potential Ze/r, the energy is also independent of π_1 and π_2 (i.e. independent of l_1 and l_2 for fixed j_1 and j_2).

Consider all the states of a given configuration (n_1, n_2, l_1, l_2) which have also fixed values of j_1 and j_2. In our zero-order approximation (central potential only) the energy is independent of the quantum numbers m_1 and m_2 and any linear superposition of the wave functions (43.1) with different m_1 and m_2 (but all other quantum numbers fixed) is also an eigenfunction. In particular, we can form those linear superpositions which are eigenstates of M_z (with eigenvalue M) and of $\boldsymbol{M}^2$ [with eigenvalue $J(J+1)$], where $\boldsymbol{M} = \boldsymbol{M}_1 + \boldsymbol{M}_2$ is the total angular momentum of the whole atom. The operator representing the interaction between the two electrons (discussed in Sect. 43β) commutes with $\boldsymbol{M}^2$ and M_z, but *not* with m_{1z} and m_{2z}. This operator, although small, removes the degeneracy with respect to m_{1z} and m_{2z} and the correct eigenstates are those of $\boldsymbol{M}^2$ and M_z. The possible values of the quantum numbers J and M are

$$J = |j_1 - j_2|, \ldots, j_1 + j_2; \quad M = -J, \ldots, +J. \tag{43.2}$$

The energy of these states is still independent of M (in the absence of external fields), but depends on J because of the electron-electron interaction (the splitting being of order $1/Z$ relative to Z^2Ry).

[1] For details see ref. [5], Chap. 10.

We thus see that for *all* values of the nuclear charge Z, J and M are good quantum numbers. For $Z \ll \alpha^{-\frac{2}{3}} = 27$ (discussed in Sects. 24 to 40), L and S are also (almost) good quantum numbers and the energies of the various levels of a particular configuration depend largely on L and S. For $Z \gg 27$ we have (instead of L and S) j_1 and j_2 as (almost) good quantum numbers and the energy splittings of a configuration depend largely on j_1 and j_2. We have so far considered only levels of a particular configuration (fixed n_1, n_2 and l_1, l_2). In reality these quantum numbers are *not* exact quantum numbers (for any Z) and mixing between various configurations[1] can occur (see Sect. 36β). If one of the two electrons is in the ground state, the configuration interaction is found to be rather small and we do not discuss it further. In Fig. 19 we give a schematic diagram of the level splitting of the configuration $1s\,2p$ (one electron in the ground state $l_1 = 0$, the other in a state with $l_2 = 1$) both for small Z ($5 < Z \ll 27$) and for large Z ($Z \gg 27$). The numbers above the lines denote the values of J (for this configuration $L = 1$ and $j_1 = \frac{1}{2}$ for all levels).

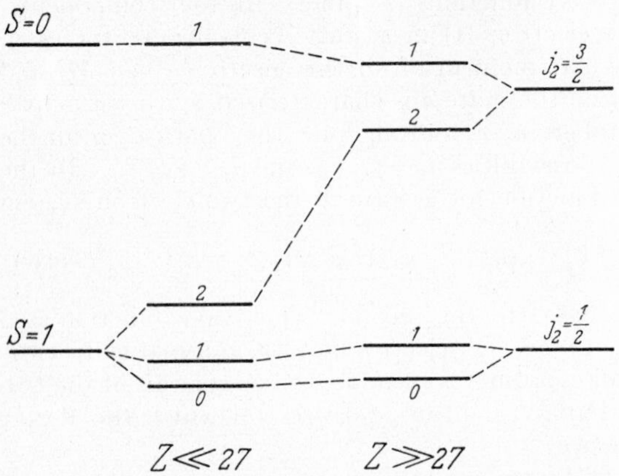

Fig. 19. Schematic energy level diagram for the configuration $1s\,2p$ in helium-like ions, both for small and large nuclear charge Z. The number against each level is the J-value. The levels at the extreme left are those without any spin-orbit coupling, those at the extreme right without any electron-electron interaction.

For very large Z it is most convenient to take as the central potential $\varphi(r)$ simply the nuclear COULOMB potential. In this case the electrostatic as well as the relativistic interaction between the two electrons is treated by a first order perturbation method (see Sect. 43β). The error in such a calculation is of order $1/Z^2$ (relative to Z^2 Ry). If $27 = \alpha^{-\frac{2}{3}} \ll Z \ll 137$ (or for inner electrons in a complex atom) higher accuracy is achieved if one takes the HARTREE potential for $\varphi(r)$ and solves for the DIRAC single-electron eigenfunctions [to be used in (43.1)] numerically[2].

β) *The interaction energy.* We outline briefly[3] how the interaction energy between the two electrons can be obtained from quantum electrodynamics by a perturbation method, if Z is large. We take as our unperturbed HAMILTONian the DIRAC HAMILTONian for two electrons in a central field, but without *any* interaction between the electrons. An unperturbed eigenstate with fixed quantum numbers J and M is given by a linear superposition of wave functions of form (43.1), all from a given configuration and given (j_a, j_b). We denote a term of this wave function of the form $\psi_a(1)\,\psi_b(2)$ by (ab) and $\psi_b(1)\,\psi_a(2)$ by (ba). The symbols a, a' etc. denote the various single-electron states (with fixed n_a, l_a and j_a, but different values of $m_a, m_{a'}$, etc.) which all have the same energy $\varepsilon_a = \varepsilon_{a'}$ etc. Similarly $\varepsilon_b = \varepsilon_{b'}$ etc. (but ε_a and ε_b are generally *not* equal). The expectation value of the operator for the interaction between the two electrons is then a linear superposition of two types of terms: The matrix elements of

[1] See ref. [5], Chap. 15, for details on configuration interaction.
[2] S. COHEN: Ph. D. Thesis, Cornell University, 1955.
[3] For details see G. BREIT, Phys, Rev. **34**, 553 (1929) and G. E. BROWN, Phil. Mag. **43**, 467 (1952).

this operator between wave functions (ab) and $(a'b')$ (direct term) and those between (ab) and $(b'a')$ (exchange term).

The operator for the COULOMB interaction is simply e^2/r_{12}. As discussed in Sect. 38 the two electrons also interact with each other via the quantized electromagnetic field. The lowest order term, corresponding to the exchange of a virtual photon between the electrons, is obtained by second order perturbation theory from quantum electrodynamics and is similar to (38.5). The (exchange) matrix element for a transition between the states (ab) and $(b'a')$, for instance, is given by [the notation is the same as for (38.5)]

$$\langle a\, b\,|B_{tr}|\, b'\, a'\rangle \equiv -\frac{e^2\, c}{4\pi^2}\sum_{\pi}\int\frac{d^3 k}{k}\sum_{n}\frac{\langle a\, b\,|\,\alpha_{1\pi}\, e^{i\boldsymbol{k}\cdot\boldsymbol{r}_1}|\, n\rangle\,\langle n\,|\,\alpha_{2\pi}\, e^{-i\boldsymbol{k}\cdot\boldsymbol{r}_2}|\, b'\, a'\rangle}{k\, c + E_n - \varepsilon_a - \varepsilon_b}, \quad (43.3)$$

plus a similar term with 1 and 2 interchanged. For our complete set of wave functions n we can choose the set $\psi_c(1)\,\psi_d(2)$, where ψ_c, ψ_d are any of the DIRAC single-electron wave functions. Each of the two matrix elements in (43.3) is then the product of two matrix elements involving only single-electron wave functions. In particular, the first part of (43.3) contains the matrix element (for the operator unity, since no operator for electron 2 appears) $\langle b|d\rangle$ and the second part contains $\langle c|b'\rangle$. Since the single-electron wave functions form an orthogonal set, the only non-zero term in the sum over n in (43.3) is the one with $c=b'$ and $d=b$ and with energy $E_n=\varepsilon_b+\varepsilon_{b'}$. We therefore can replace the energy denominator[1] in (43.3) by $(kc+\varepsilon_{b'}-\varepsilon_a)$ and can then eliminate the summation over n by a simple sum rule. This gives

$$\langle a\, b\,|B_{tr}|\, b'\, a'\rangle = -\frac{e^2\, c}{4\pi^2}\int\frac{d^3 k}{k}\sum_{\pi}\frac{\langle a\, b\,|\,\alpha_{1\pi}\,\alpha_{2\pi}\, e^{i\boldsymbol{k}\cdot\boldsymbol{r}_{12}}|\, b'\, a'\rangle}{k\, c + \varepsilon_{b'} - \varepsilon_a} \quad (43.4)$$

plus another term with a and b interchanged and with a' and b' interchanged.

We are only considering states for which $\varepsilon_a=\varepsilon_{a'}$ and $\varepsilon_b=\varepsilon_{b'}$ and we denote $\varepsilon_a-\varepsilon_b$ by $c\Gamma$. The denominators in the term shown explicitly in (43.4) and the other term are then $c(k-\Gamma)$ and $c(k+\Gamma)$, respectively. We add these two terms and use the fact that $\sum_{\pi}$ denotes summation over two directions perpendicular to each other and to $\boldsymbol{k}$. We then find that the matrix element (43.4) is equal to that of the operator

$$B_{tr} = -\frac{e^2}{2\pi^2}\int\frac{d^3 k}{(k^2-\Gamma^2)}\, e^{i\boldsymbol{k}\cdot\boldsymbol{r}_{12}}\left[\boldsymbol{\alpha}_1\cdot\boldsymbol{\alpha}_2 - \frac{(\boldsymbol{\alpha}_1\cdot\boldsymbol{k})\,(\boldsymbol{\alpha}_2\cdot\boldsymbol{k})}{k^2}\right]. \quad (43.5)$$

Note that this "operator" depends on the state (ab) on which it is operating, through the term Γ^2 in the denominator. If we were to neglect Γ^2 compared with k^2, which is justified only if $(Z\alpha)^2 \ll 1$, this operator would reduce to the BREIT operator defined in (38.6). The matrix element (43.3) is an "exchange term", but "direct terms", i.e. matrix elements for transitions from (ab) to $(a'b')$, also occur. A similar analysis can be carried through for these direct terms, resulting in an operator *identical* with (38.6), i.e. with Γ replaced by zero in (43.5).

The integrand in the integral over $\boldsymbol{k}$ in (43.5) has singularities at $|\boldsymbol{k}|=|\Gamma|$. These singularities are connected with the possibility of a spontaneous radiative transition of one of the electrons from the state a to the state b' with the emission of a real photon of energy $\varepsilon_a-\varepsilon_b=\Gamma c$ if $\varepsilon_a>\varepsilon_b$ (a transition from b to a' of the other electron if $\varepsilon_b>\varepsilon_a$). A finite mean lifetime of an atomic state can be represented by a negative imaginary part in the energy of this state. In (43.5), $|\Gamma|$

[1] Note that this replacement involves no nonrelativistic approximation, unlike the replacement by kc, used in Sect. 38.

should then be replaced by $|\Gamma|-i\eta$ where η is positive and small compared with Γ. A good approximation to the integral (43.5) is then obtained by considering η as an infinitesimally small quantity, carrying out the angle integration first and evaluating the integral over k by contour integration. The imaginary part of the result represents a contribution to the "width" [$2\hbar$ times the inverse of the lifetime, see (67.1)] of the initial energy level. For finding the energy shift of a level of fixed J and M we only require the real part of (43.5), which is simply given by the principal part of the integral [see (9.5)].

The integral (43.5) can be evaluated fairly easily, but it is often more convenient to combine this term with the COULOMB interaction

$$\frac{e^2}{r_{12}} = \frac{e^2}{2\pi^2}\int \frac{d^3k}{k^2}\, e^{i\boldsymbol{k}\cdot\boldsymbol{r}_{12}}.$$

The sum of this term and (43.5) can be written as

$$\left.\begin{aligned} B_{\text{tot}} &= \frac{e^2}{2\pi^2}\int \frac{d^3k}{k^2-\Gamma^2}\left[e^{i\boldsymbol{k}\cdot\boldsymbol{r}_{12}}(1-\boldsymbol{\alpha}_1\cdot\boldsymbol{\alpha}_2)+\frac{\mathscr{B}'}{k^2}\right],\\ \mathscr{B}' &= e^{i\boldsymbol{k}\cdot\boldsymbol{r}_{12}}[(\boldsymbol{\alpha}_1\cdot\boldsymbol{k})(\boldsymbol{\alpha}_2\cdot\boldsymbol{k})-\Gamma^2].\end{aligned}\right\} \tag{43.6}$$

We now show that the (exchange) matrix element $\langle a\,b|\mathscr{B}'|\,b'\,a'\rangle$ is zero, as follows. Let $H_1=mc^2\beta_1+c\boldsymbol{p}_1\cdot\boldsymbol{\alpha}_1-e\varphi_1$ be the single-particle HAMILTONIAN of which a, b, etc. are eigenstates. Using the fact that $\Gamma c=\varepsilon_a-\varepsilon_{b'}$ and that (with $\hbar=1$) $[H_1, f(\boldsymbol{r})]=-ic\boldsymbol{\alpha}_1\cdot\operatorname{grad}_1 f(\boldsymbol{r}_1)$, we find

$$\Gamma c\langle a|e^{i\boldsymbol{k}\cdot\boldsymbol{r}}|\,b'\rangle = \langle a|[H_1, e^{i\boldsymbol{k}\cdot\boldsymbol{r}}]|\,b'\rangle = c\langle a|\boldsymbol{\alpha}_1\cdot\boldsymbol{k}\,e^{i\boldsymbol{k}\cdot\boldsymbol{r}_1}|\,b'\rangle.$$

Using a similar relation for $\langle b|e^{-i\boldsymbol{k}\cdot\boldsymbol{r}_2}|\,a'\rangle$ and the fact that $\boldsymbol{r}_{12}=\boldsymbol{r}_1-\boldsymbol{r}_2$, one then finds that

$$\Gamma^2\langle a\,b|e^{i\boldsymbol{k}\cdot\boldsymbol{r}_{12}}|\,b'\,a'\rangle = \langle a\,b|e^{i\boldsymbol{k}\cdot\boldsymbol{r}_{12}}(\boldsymbol{\alpha}_1\cdot\boldsymbol{k})(\boldsymbol{\alpha}_2\cdot\boldsymbol{k})|\,b'\,a'\rangle. \tag{43.7}$$

The matrix element of $\mathscr{B}'$ in (43.6) is then zero. The operator B'_{tot}, obtained by replacing $\mathscr{B}'$ by zero in (43.6) and by evaluating only the principal part of the integral is

$$B'_{\text{tot}} = e^2\,\frac{\cos(\Gamma r_{12})}{r_{12}}\,(1-\boldsymbol{\alpha}_1\cdot\boldsymbol{\alpha}_2). \tag{43.8}$$

The relations (43.7) and (43.8) can also be derived in a more elegant manner from FEYNMAN's[1] covariant formalism. FEYNMAN's papers also contain the justification for an omission we have made in our derivation of (43.4) from (43.3). We have neglected the PAULI exclusion principle in the intermediate states n which forbids, for instance, the state (b, b') if $b'=b$. FEYNMAN shows that these errors are compensated exactly by some changes in the self energy of one of the two electrons, caused by the presence of the other (and the exclusion principle).

For the "direct term" matrix element from (ab) to $(a'b')$, we have already seen that Γ is replaced by zero in the expression equivalent to (43.5). By arguments, equivalent to those leading to (43.7), one can also show that

$$\langle a\,b|e^{i\boldsymbol{k}\cdot\boldsymbol{r}_{12}}(\boldsymbol{\alpha}_1\cdot\boldsymbol{k})(\boldsymbol{\alpha}_2\cdot\boldsymbol{k})|\,a'\,b'\rangle = 0. \tag{43.9}$$

For a "direct term", the total matrix element (including the COULOMB part) is then equal to the matrix element of the operator (43.8) with $\cos(\Gamma r_{12})$ replaced by unity[2].

[1] R. P. FEYNMAN: Phys. Rev. **76**, 749, 769 (1949).

[2] For explicit calculations for inner electrons in heavy atoms, see S. BRENNER and G. E. BROWN, Proc. Roy. Soc. Lond., Ser. A **218**, 422 (1953); S. COHEN, Ph. D. Thesis, Cornell University 1955.

44. Hyperfine structure. We discuss now the hyperfine structure of the energy levels of singly excited states of a helium-like atom with small nuclear charge ($Z \ll 137$). In nonrelativistic approximation the energy (for given principal quantum number $n = n_2$) depends on the orbital quantum number $l = l_2$ ($l_1 = 0$, since one electron is in the ground state) and on the total spin S ($S = 0$ for para— or singlet—states, $S = 1$ for ortho—or triplet—states). Relativistic effects then give a small (fine structure) energy splitting for triplet states (if $l \neq 0$) according to the value of the quantum number J for the total angular momentum of the two electrons, $J = l + 1$, l or $l - 1$. If the nucleus possesses[1] a "spin" I and magnetic moment, a further splitting of the energy levels results, which depends on the quantum number F for the total angular momentum of the whole atom (nucleus plus electrons), where $F = |J - I|, \ldots, J + I$. Since the magnetic moments of nuclei are much smaller than that of the electron, the hyperfine splitting is usually (but not always) small compared with the fine structure splitting and J remains an (almost) good quantum number.

α) Excited states with $l \neq 0$. If one electron is in the ground state (1) and the other in an excited state (n) with non-zero orbital quantum number l, a good approximation to the spatial wave function is (see Sect. 28)

$$U = \frac{1}{\sqrt{2}} \left[u_1(1)\, u_n(2) \pm u_n(1)\, u_1(2) \right]. \tag{44.1}$$

In (44.1) the + sign refers to singlet states, the — sign to triplet states, u_1 is the ground state hydrogenic wave function for nuclear charge Z and u_n the hydrogenic wave function for an excited state for nuclear charge $(Z - 1)$. The magnetic interaction between the nucleus and the electron cloud, which leads to the hyperfine structure splitting, is represented by the sum of two operators, each of form (22.1) with $\boldsymbol{s}$, $\boldsymbol{k}$ and $\boldsymbol{r}$ referring to electron 1 and 2 respectively. If we use a spatial wave function of product form (44.1) to evaluate the expectation value of the sum of these two operators, the spatial integrations can be carried out immediately. Since each operator operates only on the wave function for one of the two electrons and since u_1 and u_n are orthogonal, no "exchange" terms are obtained. The resulting expectation value consists of the sum of two terms. The one term is similar to the hyperfine structure energy shift for a hydrogenic atom (charge Z) in the ground state (see Sect. 22β), the other to the shift for a hydrogenic atom (charge $Z - 1$) in the excited state n. The same angular momentum operators occur in these two terms as in the corresponding terms in Sect. 22β, but their expectation values are of course somewhat different for the two-electron atom.

As discussed in Sect. 22β, the hyperfine structure energy of a single electron decreases rapidly with increasing principal and orbital quantum numbers n and l. We are only considering states with $n \geqq 2$ and $l \geqq 1$ and can, to a good approximation, neglect the interaction of the outer electron with the nuclear moment. In this approximation we find, from (22.10), for the energy shift E due to the nuclear moment

$$E = \tfrac{4}{3}\, \mu_0 \mu_N g\, R_{10}^2(0)\, \overline{\boldsymbol{i} \cdot \boldsymbol{s}_1} \text{ at. un.}, \tag{44.2}$$

where $\boldsymbol{s}_1$ is the spin operator for one (the inner) electron and the bar denotes the expectation value [μ_N and g defined in (22.6)].

In our present approximation we neglect the direct effect on the interaction energy of the outer electron. The hyperfine structure is nevertheless radically

[1] The vector operator for the nuclear angular momentum is denoted by $\boldsymbol{i}$ and the eigenvalue of $\boldsymbol{i}^2$ is $I(I+1)$.

different for two-electron and for one-electron atoms, because the expectation values of the operator $(\boldsymbol{i}\cdot\boldsymbol{s}_1)$ in (44.2) are different. The energy separation between the singlet and triplet states is a nonrelativistic effect and very large compared with both the fine structure and hyperfine structure splitting. We therefore neglect any mixing between singlet and triplet states and only consider the expectation value of $\boldsymbol{i}\cdot\boldsymbol{s}_1$ for states of fixed total spin S. Following the discussion of (40.2) in Sect. 40α, we can then replace $\boldsymbol{s}_1$ by $\frac{1}{2}(\boldsymbol{s}_1+\boldsymbol{s}_2)=\frac{1}{2}\boldsymbol{S}$. The energy E, given by (44.2), is then zero for singlet states ($S=0$). For triplet states we have to evaluate the expectation value of $\frac{1}{2}(\boldsymbol{i}\cdot\boldsymbol{S})$.

In the absence of a nuclear magnetic field, the operator $\boldsymbol{M}^2$, where $\boldsymbol{M}=\boldsymbol{k}+\boldsymbol{S}$, is a constant of the motion with eigenvalue $J(J+1)$. In the presence of the nuclear magnetic field, $\boldsymbol{F}^2$, where $\boldsymbol{F}=\boldsymbol{M}+\boldsymbol{i}$, is an exact constant of the motion with eigenvalue $F(F+1)$. The operator $\boldsymbol{i}\cdot\boldsymbol{S}$ does not commute with $\boldsymbol{M}^2$, so J is no longer exactly a good quantum number. However, if the factor in (44.2) which multiplies $\boldsymbol{i}\cdot\boldsymbol{S}$ is small compared with the energy separation between states of different values of J, we can neglect the mixing of states of different J. Since the nuclear magnetic moment is much smaller than the BOHR magneton, this is usually the case (with some important exceptions, see below). For transitions between states of the *same* J we can use the following replacement [see Eq. (22.8) and also Eq. (46.3)],

$$\boldsymbol{S}\rightarrow\frac{\overline{\boldsymbol{S}\cdot\boldsymbol{M}}}{\overline{\boldsymbol{M}^2}}\boldsymbol{M}=\frac{\overline{\boldsymbol{M}^2}+\overline{\boldsymbol{S}^2}-\overline{\boldsymbol{k}^2}}{2\,\overline{\boldsymbol{M}^2}}\boldsymbol{M}, \tag{44.3}$$

if $J\neq 0$. (If J is zero, $\boldsymbol{S}$ is replaced by zero.) Finally the expectation value of the operator $\boldsymbol{i}\cdot\boldsymbol{M}$ is

$$\tfrac{1}{2}(\overline{\boldsymbol{F}^2}-\overline{\boldsymbol{i}^2}-\overline{\boldsymbol{M}^2})=\tfrac{1}{2}[F(F+1)-I(I+1)-J(J+1)].$$

We thus have for Y_F, the expectation value of $\boldsymbol{i}\cdot\boldsymbol{s}_1$ for a state with fixed quantum numbers $S=1$, l, $J\neq 0$ and F,

$$Y_F=\frac{1}{2}\frac{\overline{(\boldsymbol{S}\cdot\boldsymbol{M})}\,\overline{(\boldsymbol{i}\cdot\boldsymbol{M})}}{\overline{\boldsymbol{M}^2}}=\frac{[J(J+1)+S(S+1)-l(l+1)]\,[F(F+1)-I(I+1)-J(J+1)]}{8J(J+1)}. \tag{44.4}$$

Substituting (44.4) and the explicit expression $4Z^3$ a.u. for $R_{10}^2(0)$ into (44.2) we have for the energy shift (using $\mu_0=\frac{1}{2}\alpha$ a.u., Ry $=\frac{1}{2}$ a.u.)

$$E=\frac{8}{3}Z^3\alpha^2 g\frac{m}{M_p}Y_F\,\mathrm{Ry}, \tag{44.5}$$

if $S=1$, $J\neq 0$. The energy shift is zero for all singlet states $S=0$ and for all states with $J=0$, in the present approximation. Note also that the shift is independent of the principal quantum number n of the excited electron. Consider, for example, the P-states ($l=1$) for any value of n. The $^1P_1$ and the $^3P_0$ states are unsplit. If the nuclear spin I is $\frac{1}{2}$, the $^3P_1$ and $^3P_2$ states each split into a doublet with $F=J\pm\frac{1}{2}$ and the splitting energy ΔE, given by (44.4) and (44.5), is

$$\Delta E=\frac{1}{3}Z^3\alpha^2 g\frac{m}{M_p}\mathrm{Ry}\begin{Bmatrix}\times 5 & \text{for} & ^3P_2,\\ \times 3 & \text{for} & ^3P_1.\end{Bmatrix} \tag{44.6}$$

In Fig. 20 we give the splitting of the 2^3P_1 and 2^3P_2 levels for $Z=2$ and a hypothetical nucleus with $I=\frac{1}{2}$ and $|g|\gtrsim 1$, calculated from (44.4) and (44.5).

The expression (44.4) breaks down if the hyperfine structure is *not* small compared with the fine structure splitting. In spite of the small factor m/M_p in (44.5), this does happen in many practical cases for the following reasons. (1) The fine structure splitting decreases with increasing principal quantum number n, whereas (44.5) does not. (2) For some states of helium-like atoms with small Z (especially for $Z=2$ and to some extent for $Z=3$ and 4, see Sect. 40) fortuitous cancellations make the energy separation of some fine structure components with different J values very small. (3) For many nuclei the numerical value of the g-factor is rather large.

More exact calculations of hyperfine structure splitting have been carried out for[1] Li^+ and for[2] He without assuming this splitting to be smaller than the fine structure. In this case F is still an exact quantum number, but J is not. The exact wave functions for the various states of fixed F are then linear superpositions of the states with different J values. The matrix elements of the operator $\boldsymbol{i}\cdot\boldsymbol{S}$ for transitions between states of *different* J values are required to calculate the amount of mixing of the different states and the energy shifts. In Fig. 20 we show (schematically) the hyperfine splitting of the $2\,^3P_1$ and $2\,^3P_2$ levels for He^3 (the numbers above the lines denote the value of F). The nucleus of this atom has $Z=2$, spin $I=\frac{1}{2}$ and g about -4.26. There is only one level each with $F=\frac{1}{2}$ and $F=\frac{5}{2}$ and their exact theoretical energy shifts are close to the values given by (44.4) and (44.5) (the $^3P_0$ level also has $F=\frac{1}{2}$, but lies about 1 cm^{-1}higher and hardly affects the other $F=\frac{1}{2}$ level). However, there are two levels with $F=\frac{3}{2}$ and their exact energy shifts approximate those given by (44.4) and (44.5) only for $|g|\lesssim 1$, but *not* for the actual value of $g\approx -4.26$.

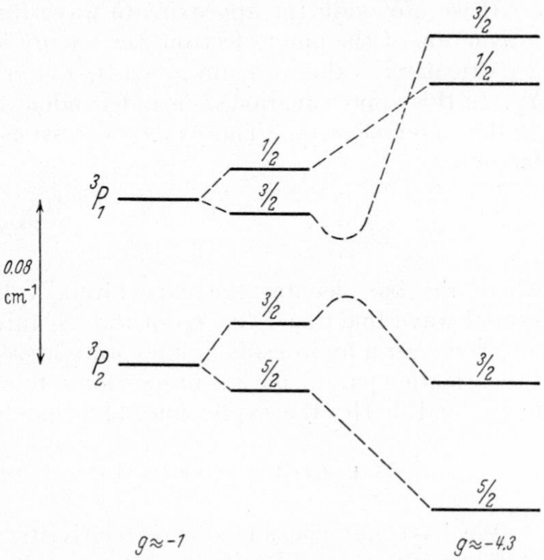

Fig. 20. The schematic hyperfine structure splitting of the $2\,^3P_1$ and $2\,^3P_2$ states in He^3, both for a (hypothetical) value of $g\approx -1$ and for the actual value of g. Each level is marked with its quantum number F.

We have neglected the direct effect of the magnetic interaction of the outer electron with the nuclear moment. For triplet states with $l\gtrless 1$ this effect is very small, especially for large n. For singlet states with $l\gtrless 1$ this interaction results in some hyperfine splitting, but the splitting energy is very small compared with that of triplet states. Singlet S-states have $S=l=J=0$ and $F=I$ and exhibit no splitting at all. The hyperfine splitting of triplet states in He^3 and in the Li^7-positive ion have been measured by optical spectroscopy. The agreement with the theory outlined above (with the interaction of the outer electron neglected) is good[3] for $l\gtrless 1$, although the experimental accuracy is not very great. The splitting of triplet S-states is discussed below.

β) The triplet S-states. Singlet S-states (including the ground state of helium-like atoms) show no fine or hyperfine structure splitting at all. Triplet S-states

[1] P. GÜTTINGER and W. PAULI: Z. Physik **67**, 743 (1931).
[2] FRED, TOMKINS, BRODY and HAMERMESH: Phys. Rev. **82**, 406 (1951).
[3] P. GÜTTINGER: Z. Physik **63**, 749 (1930). — FRED *et al.*, (loc. cit.) and ref. [*10*], p. 389.

have $l=0$ and $S=J=1$ and show no fine structure splitting. They do show hyperfine splitting however, the energy depending on the value of $F(|J-I|$ to $J+I)$. For $I=\frac{1}{2}$ the splitting results in doublets with $F=\frac{1}{2}$ and $\frac{3}{2}$, for $I \geqq 1$ triplets result with $F=I-1$, I and $I+1$. Since the hyperfine splitting energy is extremely small compared with the energy separation of a ^3S-state from states with other values of S or l (the nonrelativistic COULOMB and exchange energies), we need only the expectation value of the interaction operator for fixed $S=J=1$. For such states the expectation value Y_F of $\boldsymbol{i}\cdot\boldsymbol{s}_1$ is [see Eq. (44.4)]

$$Y_F = \tfrac{1}{2}\overline{\boldsymbol{i}\cdot\boldsymbol{S}} = \tfrac{1}{4}\left[F(F+1) - I(I+1) - S(S+1)\right] \tag{44.7}$$

with $S=1$.

If we use again the approximate wave function (44.1) and neglect the direct interaction of the outer electron, the energy shift E of the level component with a particular F value is again given by (44.5), but with the expression (44.7) for Y_F. In this approximation, E is independent of the principal quantum number n of the outer electron. The exact expression for E is (44.5) times a correction factor

$$1+\varepsilon = \frac{\overline{\delta^{(3)}(\boldsymbol{r}_1)} + \overline{\delta^{(3)}(\boldsymbol{r}_2)}}{Z^3/\pi}, \tag{44.8}$$

where the bar denotes the expectation value over the exact nonrelativistic spatial wave function $U(\boldsymbol{r}_1, \boldsymbol{r}_2)$ of the ^3S-state and Z^3/π is the expectation value of $\delta^{(3)}(\boldsymbol{r})$ over a hydrogenic ground state wave function for charge Z. For large n, the correction parameter ε is proportional to n^{-3} and is small. For the $2\,^3S$-states in Li^+ and in He, the expression (44.8) has been evaluated[1] and gives for $1+\varepsilon$

$$1.06191 \pm 0.00003\ (\mathrm{Li}^+)\,; \qquad 1.0363 \pm 0.0007\ (\mathrm{He})\,. \tag{44.9}$$

We have not considered any relativistic or radiative corrections or effects of the nucleus' structure and motion so far. The two largest of these corrections are the "reduced mass" factor (22.16) and the effect of the lowest order anomalous magnetic moment $\alpha/2\pi$ of the electron (see Sect. 22γ). Including these corrections we find for the hyperfine splitting energy ΔE between the components of the doublet $F=\frac{1}{2}, \frac{3}{2}$

$$\Delta E = 2Z^3\alpha^2 \frac{g\,m}{M_p}\left(1+\varepsilon - 3\frac{m}{M} + \frac{\alpha}{2\pi}\right) R_\infty \tag{44.10}$$

for a nucleus with spin $I=\frac{1}{2}$ and mass M. The He^3 nucleus has spin $\frac{1}{2}$ and the ratio gm/M_p is very accurately known (see Sect. 49γ), $\frac{1}{2}g$ being about -2.1276. For the metastable 2^3S-state of He^3 the frequency $\Delta\nu = \Delta E/h$, corresponding to the hyperfine splitting energy, has been measured very accurately by microwave techniques[2]. This experimental value and the theoretical one, using (44.9) and (44.10), are

$$\Delta\nu_{\mathrm{exp}} = (6739.71 \pm 0.05)\ \mathrm{Mc/sec}, \qquad \Delta\nu_{\mathrm{th}} = (6736 \pm 5)\ \mathrm{Mc/sec}, \tag{44.11}$$

[1] For He, W. TEUTSCH and V. HUGHES, Phys. Rev. **95**, 1461 (1954) used the six-parameter wave function discussed in Sect. 35β. For Li^+, P. LUKE, R. MEYEROTT and W. CLENDENIN, Phys. Rev. **85**, 401 (1952) used a very accurate wave function expanded in terms of LEGENDRE polynomials (Sect. 36β). See also G. BREIT and F. DOERMANN, Phys. Rev. **36**, 1732 (1930).

[2] G. WEINREICH and V. HUGHES: Phys. Rev. **95**, 1451 (1954).

corresponding to about 0.225 cm^{-1}. Higher order relativistic and radiative corrections and the effect of the internal structure of the He^3 nucleus have also been calculated[1], but these corrections are smaller than the present uncertainty in $\Delta\nu_{\text{th}}$ due to the poor wave function used in evaluating ε, Eq. (44.9).

III. Atoms in external fields.

a) ZEEMAN effect.

45. ZEEMAN effect for a single-electron atom. We consider now the effect of an external magnetic field on single-electron atoms (with a *central* potential). We use, at the moment, CGS units instead of atomic units. We shall see that part of the effect of the magnetic field depends on the intrinsic spin, another part, connected with the orbital angular momentum, is independent of spin.

α) Spinless electron. We consider first the quantum theory for a spinless (KLEIN-GORDON) particle in an external electromagnetic field. The relativistic wave equation for such a spinless "electron" is not the DIRAC equation but the KLEIN-GORDON (or "relativistic SCHRÖDINGER") equation,

$$\left[\sum_{\mu=1}^{4}\left(p_\mu + \frac{e}{c}A_\mu\right)^2 + (m\,c)^2\right]\psi = 0. \tag{45.1}$$

In (45.1) we have used the covariant notation of Sect. 10,

$$p_\mu = -i\hbar\frac{\partial}{\partial x_\mu}, \qquad x_4 = i\,c\,t, \qquad A_\mu = (\boldsymbol{A}, i\,\varphi),$$

where $\boldsymbol{A}$ is the vector potential and $-iA_4 = \varphi$ the scalar potential of the external electromagnetic field (the charge of the "electron" is $-e$ and the potential energy is $V = -e\varphi$). We restrict ourselves to time-independent fields (we use the LORENTZ gauge for A_μ) and a stationary state of (nonrelativistic) energy E. The time dependence of the wave function ψ is then

$$\psi(\boldsymbol{r}, t) = e^{-\frac{i}{\hbar}(E+mc^2)\,t}\,u(\boldsymbol{r}),$$

where u satisfies the equation

$$\left\{\left[\frac{\hbar^2}{2m}\Delta + E - V\right] - \frac{e}{mc}\boldsymbol{A}\cdot\boldsymbol{p} + \frac{1}{2mc^2}\left[(E-V)^2 - e^2A^2\right]\right\}u = 0. \tag{45.2}$$

The last expression in square brackets is a small relativistic correction. The part quadratic in $(E-V)$ represents the relativistic "variation of mass" and is independent of the magnetic field. The part quadratic in $\boldsymbol{A}$ leads to diamagnetism (see Sect. 50) and is otherwise important only for states of large orbital angular momentum in strong magnetic fields (Sect. 47δ). We omit both these relativistic correction terms at the moment and consider only the effect of the term[2] in $\boldsymbol{A}\cdot\boldsymbol{p}$.

We restrict ourselves now to the special case of a uniform[3] magnetic field $\mathcal{H}$ and a central potential V. We can then take for the vector potential

$$\boldsymbol{A}(\boldsymbol{r}) = \frac{1}{2}\mathcal{H}\times\boldsymbol{r}. \tag{45.3}$$

[1] A. SESSLER and H. FOLEY: Phys. Rev. **98**, 6 (1955).

[2] This term can also be obtained from the *non*relativistic SCHRÖDINGER equation by replacing $\boldsymbol{p}$ by $(\boldsymbol{p} + e\boldsymbol{A}/c)$.

[3] If $\mathcal{H}$ is uniform over distances of the order of many atomic radii, the results are almost the same as for an exactly uniform $\mathcal{H}$.

We then have

$$\frac{1}{\hbar}\boldsymbol{A}\cdot\boldsymbol{p}=\frac{1}{2\hbar}(\mathcal{H}\times\boldsymbol{r})\cdot\boldsymbol{p}=\frac{1}{2\hbar}\mathcal{H}\cdot(\boldsymbol{r}\times\boldsymbol{p})=\frac{1}{2}\mathcal{H}\cdot\boldsymbol{k},$$

where $\hbar\boldsymbol{k}$ is the orbital angular momentum operator (see Sect. 11). If we take our z-axis in the direction of the field $\mathcal{H}$, we have

$$\Delta u+\frac{2m}{\hbar^2}[E-V-\hbar\omega k_z]\,u=0, \tag{45.4}$$

$$\omega=\frac{e\mathcal{H}}{2mc}, \tag{45.5}$$

where ω is the *circular* frequency of the LARMOR precession. The solution of the SCHRÖDINGER equation without a magnetic field,

$$u=R_{nl}(r)\,P_{lm_l}(\vartheta)\,e^{im_l\varphi},$$

is an eigenstate of k_z with eigenvalue m_l. This wave function is thus also a solution of the Eq. (45.4) *with* field and the energy eigenvalue is

$$E=E_0+\hbar\omega m_l, \tag{45.6}$$

where E_0 is the energy without magnetic field.

The interaction energy $\hbar\omega m_l$ is proportional to the strength of the magnetic field and to the magnetic quantum number m_l. It does *not* depend on the quantum numbers n and l, nor on the electrostatic potential V. This result can be interpreted as follows: The orbital angular momentum of the electron gives rise to a magnetic moment $\boldsymbol{\mu}$,

$$\boldsymbol{\mu}=-\frac{e}{2mc}\boldsymbol{r}\times\boldsymbol{p}=-\mu_0\boldsymbol{k},\qquad \mu_0=\frac{e\hbar}{2mc}, \tag{45.7}$$

where $\boldsymbol{r}\times\boldsymbol{p}$ and $\boldsymbol{k}$ are the orbital angular momentum in CGS and atomic units, respectively. The energy of this magnetic moment in the field $\mathcal{H}$ is

$$W_1=-\mathcal{H}\cdot\boldsymbol{\mu}=\mathcal{H}\mu_0 k_z, \tag{45.8}$$

which agrees with (45.4) and (45.6).

The proportionality factor μ_0 in (45.7) is the well-known BOHR magneton. In atomic units μ_0 equals $\frac{1}{2}\alpha$. The equivalent proportionality factor between $\boldsymbol{\mu}$ and $\boldsymbol{r}\times\boldsymbol{p}$, expressed in CGS units, is $e/2mc$ and is thus *independent* of PLANCK'S constant h. In fact, the relation (45.7) (in CGS units) can also be derived from classical electrodynamics.

The result (45.6) which we have derived for the ZEEMAN effect of the hydrogen atom is in complete agreement with the result of the classical theory of the ZEEMAN effect and does not supersede the classical result in any way. In order to appreciate this, we must look at the splitting of the spectral lines in a magnetic field as obtained from (45.6), instead of the splitting of the eigenvalues. As is well known, the magnetic quantum number m of the atom remains unchanged in the emission of light which is linearly polarized parallel to the magnetic field. In this case the frequency of the spectral line is given by

$$\nu_{mm}=\frac{1}{h}(E-E')=\frac{1}{h}(E_0-\hbar\omega m-E_0'+\hbar\omega m)=\nu_0,$$

i.e., it is equal to the frequency of the line without magnetic field. On the other hand, if the light is linearly polarized in a direction perpendicular to the field, then m must change by ± 1 and the line frequencies are given by

$$\nu_{m,m\pm 1} = \frac{1}{h}\left[E_0 - \hbar\,\omega\, m - E_0' + \hbar\,\omega\,(m\pm 1)\right] = \nu_0 \pm \frac{\omega}{2\pi},$$

i.e., the frequency is equal to the frequency of the unperturbed line plus or minus the frequency of the LARMOR precession. Thus, when the light is observed in a direction perpendicular to the magnetic field, in place of every line of the atom without field, there appears a triplet of three equidistant lines, with the two outer components of the triplet polarized in a direction perpendicular to the field and the middle component parallel to the field. On the other hand if the line is observed in a direction parallel to the field, only the outer components appear, the polarization of which is circular[1] about the axis of the magnetic field. This agrees exactly with the old LORENTZ theory. The separation between the outer components of the LORENTZ triplet amounts to

$$\frac{\omega}{\pi c} = \frac{e}{2\pi\, m\, c^2}\,\mathscr{H} = \frac{4.80\times 10^{-10}}{6.28\times 9.11\times 10^{-28}\times 8.99\times 10^{20}}\,\mathscr{H} = 9.34\times 10^{-5}\,\mathscr{H} = \frac{\mathscr{H}}{10710}\ \mathrm{cm}^{-1},$$

in which $\mathscr{H}$ is measured in Gauss. For magnetic field strengths which are ordinarily available, say 30000 Gauss, one obtains ZEEMAN splittings of the order of 3 wave-numbers ≈ 1 Å for visible light.

β) Electron with spin. We turn now to the theory of real electrons which possess spin and obey the DIRAC equation. In Sects. 10 and 12 we have derived from the DIRAC equation an exact quadratic Eq. (10.14) or (12.9), which is of similar form to (45.1) or (45.2) but which contains additional "DIRAC moment" terms. We thus add to (45.2) the expression

$$-\tfrac{1}{2}\, g_s \mu_0 (\boldsymbol{\sigma}\cdot\boldsymbol{\mathcal{H}} - i\,\boldsymbol{\alpha}\cdot\boldsymbol{\mathcal{E}})\, u.$$

According to (12.9) and the DIRAC theory, the factor $\frac{1}{2}g_s$ is exactly unity, but we leave it arbitrary at the moment. The interaction energy W with the magnetic field $\boldsymbol{\mathcal{H}}$ is then not simply given by W_1, Eq. (45.8), but contains an additional term of the same order of magnitude as W_1. We again put $\frac{1}{2}\boldsymbol{\sigma} = \boldsymbol{s}$ for the spin-operator, $\boldsymbol{M}$ for the *total* angular momentum operator $(\boldsymbol{k}+\boldsymbol{s})$, in atomic units, and take our z-axis along the magnetic field. We then have

$$W = \mu_0 \boldsymbol{\mathcal{H}}\cdot(\boldsymbol{k} + g_s\,\boldsymbol{s}) = \mu_0 \mathscr{H}[M_z + (g_s - 1)\, s_z]. \tag{45.9}$$

The atomic DIRAC eigenfunctions for no magnetic field are eigenstates of M_z, but *not* eigenstates of (45.9) and the effect of this interaction energy operator W is more complicated than for spinless particles. We shall use the PAULI approximation to the exact DIRAC theory. The wave functions are then two-component PAULI spinors and in (45.9) the spin operator $\boldsymbol{s}$ is now represented by two-by-two PAULI matrices (not DIRAC matrices). The spin-dependent parts of the total HAMILTONian are then W, Eq. (45.9), plus the spin-orbit coupling term which is independent of the magnetic field [see the last term in (13.2)]. If the central potential is a COULOMB one, this term is

$$\Sigma = \tfrac{1}{2}\,\alpha^2 Z\, \overline{r^{-3}}\, \boldsymbol{k}\cdot\boldsymbol{s}. \tag{45.10}$$

We have to consider the operator $(W+\Sigma)$ as a perturbation on the nonrelativistic HAMILTONian and to find the perturbed eigenfunctions and eigenvalues. This will be discussed in the next section.

[1] The electric field of the light corresponding to the short wave-length component rotates in the same sense as the current which produces the magnetic field; the long wave-length component rotates in the opposite sense.

46. Dependence on magnetic field strength. Let us consider first the unperturbed nonrelativistic HAMILTONian and PAULI-type eigenfunctions, i.e., SCHRÖDINGER spatial wave functions multiplied by two-component spin wave functions. Consider all the possible eigenstates with fixed values of the quantum numbers n and l [the eigenvalue of the square $\boldsymbol{k}^2$ of the orbital angular momentum is $l(l+1)$]. There are $2(2l+1)$ such states with m_l (eigenvalue of k_z) equal to $-l, -l+1, \ldots, l$ and with m_s (eigenvalue of s_z) equal to $+\frac{1}{2}$ or $-\frac{1}{2}$. Using the unperturbed HAMILTONian, these states are all degenerate and any linear superposition of them is also an eigenstate. Our problem is now to find those superpositions which are also eigenstates of the perturbation HAMILTONIAN $(W+\Sigma)$, where the operators W and Σ are defined in (45.9) and (45.10).

We first note that $\boldsymbol{k}^2$, $\mathbf{s}^2$ and $M_z = k_z + s_z$ all commute both with W and with Σ. Hence l, $s=\frac{1}{2}$ [the eigenvalue of $\mathbf{s}^2$ is $s(s+1)$] and $m = m_l + m_s$ are still good quantum numbers. We therefore consider states with fixed values of n, l and also of m, the z-component of the total angular momentum (eigenvalue of M_z). On the other hand, s_z (and k_z) does not commute with Σ and $\boldsymbol{M}^2$ does not commute with W. For the HAMILTONian containing $(W+\Sigma)$, neither s_z (and k_z) nor $\boldsymbol{M}^2$ are in general constants of the motion and the eigenstates and eigenvalues of $(W+\Sigma)$ depend in a rather complicated way on the relative strength of W and Σ, i.e., on the magnetic field strength $\mathscr{H}$. Before discussing the general case, we consider two simple limiting cases: (a) "Weak" magnetic field, so that the expectation values of W are small compared with those of Σ; (b) "Strong" field, so that Σ is small compared with W.

α) Weak magnetic field (anomalous ZEEMAN *effect).* In this case we consider W as a small perturbation to Σ. We use as wave functions the eigenstates of Σ and merely add the expectation value of W (first order perturbation theory), for such a wave function, to the eigenvalue of Σ. For fixed values of n, l, m, the operator Σ has two eigenstates which are eigenstates of $\boldsymbol{M}^2$ with quantum number $j=l+\frac{1}{2}$ and $l-\frac{1}{2}$, respectively (see Sect. 13). The two eigenvalues Σ_j of Σ are given in (13.13). They depend on j (and are responsible for the ordinary fine structure splitting for fixed l), but do *not* depend on m.

We now evaluate the expectation value of

$$W = \mu_0 \mathscr{H}[M_z + (g_s - 1)\, s_z], \tag{46.1}$$

for a simultaneous eigenstate of $\boldsymbol{k}^2$, $\mathbf{s}^2$, $\boldsymbol{M}^2$ and M_z. We shall show in Sect. 48 that similar relations hold for a many-electron atom, with the angular momentum operators mentioned above summed over all electrons. We therefore evaluate the expectation value of W by a general method, based only on commutation rules which also hold in a many-electron atom, and keep the quantum number s [eigenvalue of $\mathbf{s}^2$ is $s(s+1)$] general. We make use of an operator identity, derived from the commutation rules in [5], p. 60,

$$\tfrac{1}{4}\,[\boldsymbol{M}^2, [\boldsymbol{M}^2, \mathbf{s}]] = \tfrac{1}{2}(\boldsymbol{M}^2 \mathbf{s} + \mathbf{s}\,\boldsymbol{M}^2) - \boldsymbol{M}(\boldsymbol{M}\cdot\mathbf{s}). \tag{46.2}$$

We now take the expectation values of both sides of (46.2) over a simultaneous eigenstate of $\boldsymbol{k}^2$, $\mathbf{s}^2$ and $\boldsymbol{M}^2$. The left hand side then vanishes and on the right hand side $\boldsymbol{M}^2$ and $2\boldsymbol{M}\cdot\mathbf{s} = \boldsymbol{M}^2 + \mathbf{s}^2 - \boldsymbol{k}^2$ are replaced by their eigenvalues. Thus[1]

$$\overline{\mathbf{s}} = \left[\frac{\overline{\boldsymbol{M}\cdot\mathbf{s}}}{\boldsymbol{M}^2}\right]_{lsj} \overline{\boldsymbol{M}} = \frac{j(j+1) + s(s+1) - l(l+1)}{2j(j+1)}\,\overline{\boldsymbol{M}}. \tag{46.3}$$

[1] The classical vector model would interpret (46.3) as follows: The vector $\mathbf{s}$ precesses about the direction of $\boldsymbol{M}$. The "average of $\mathbf{s}$" then points in the same direction as $\boldsymbol{M}$, but its absolute value is smaller than $|\boldsymbol{M}|$ by the factor $(\boldsymbol{M}\cdot\mathbf{s})/M^2$.

The expectation value of $(W+\Sigma)$, to be added to the nonrelativistic energy, is then, for a state of given n, l, j, m,

$$E'_{nljm} = \Sigma_{nlj} + \mathscr{H}\mu_0 g\, m. \tag{46.4}$$

In this equation,

$$g = 1 + (g_s - 1)\frac{j(j+1) + s(s+1) - l(l+1)}{2j(j+1)} \tag{46.5}$$

is the "LANDÉ splitting factor" (with $g_s = 2$ according to DIRAC theory) and Σ_{nlj} is the eigenvalue of the operator Σ. If we multiply the orbital part of (45.9), $\mu_0 \mathscr{H}\cdot\boldsymbol{k}$, by a factor g_l, then (46.5) is modified to

$$g = g_l \frac{j(j+1) - s(s+1) + l(l+1)}{2j(j+1)} + g_s \frac{j(j+1) + s(s+1) - l(l+1)}{2j(j+1)}. \tag{46.5a}$$

In Sect. 47β we shall see that g_l differs very slightly from unity for an atom with a nucleus of finite mass. The energy shift in the magnetic field $\mathscr{H}$ is proportional to $\mathscr{H}$ (as for a spinless "electron") and to m (*not* to m_l) and also depends on the inner quantum number j through the LANDÉ factor g. If we return now to the case of a single-electron atom, $s = \frac{1}{2}$ and $j = l \pm \frac{1}{2}$. Substituting these values and the DIRAC value $g_s = 2$ into (46.5), this equation reduces to

$$g = \frac{j+\frac{1}{2}}{l+\frac{1}{2}}. \tag{46.6}$$

(46.6) could also have been obtained explicitly using the PAULI eigenfunctions (13.19).

According to (46.6) the separation of two adjacent ZEEMAN components, $m_1 = m_2 + 1$, belonging to the levels of $j = l + \frac{1}{2}$ is larger than the separation for an electron without spin ($g = 1$), and is smaller for $j = l - \frac{1}{2}$. The explanation of this lies in the fact that the spin, which interacts with the magnetic field more strongly than does the orbital angular momentum, is essentially parallel to the total angular momentum for the case $j = l + \frac{1}{2}$ and antiparallel for $j = l - \frac{1}{2}$. For some special cases one obtains:

$$\begin{array}{cccccc} g = 2 & \frac{2}{3} & \frac{4}{3} & \frac{4}{5} & \frac{6}{5} & \\ \text{for } s & p_{\frac{1}{2}} & p_{\frac{3}{2}} & d_{\frac{3}{2}} & d_{\frac{5}{2}} & \text{terms.} \end{array}$$

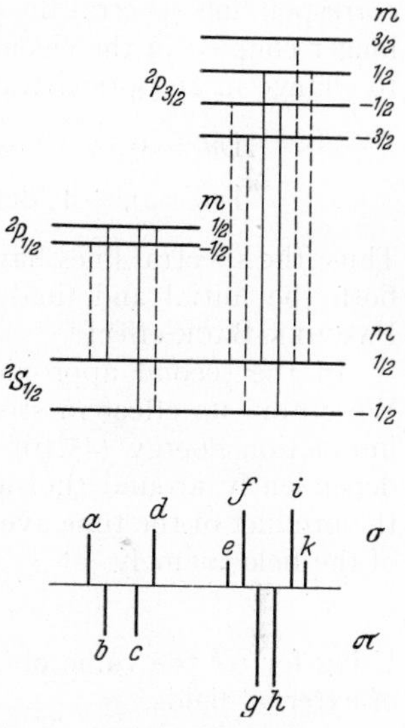

Fig. 21. Anomalous ZEEMAN effect of a line $n\,^2S - n'\,^2P$. In the upper part of the diagram, the horizontal lines denote energy levels, solid and dotted vertical lines correspond to polarization parallel and perpendicular (π- and σ-component) to the field, respectively. The lower part of the diagram shows the splitting of the spectral line.

The splitting of the spectral lines in a magnetic field naturally no longer results in the ordinary LORENTZ triplet; instead, a more complicated pattern appears which enables one to draw some conclusions about the quantum number l and j of the initial and final level corresponding to a given line. For the purpose of constructing the ZEEMAN pattern, one should note that the selection rules are the same as for an electron without spin, namely:

$\Delta m = 0$ for the line components polarized parallel to the field,

$\Delta m = \pm 1$ for the component polarized perpendicularly to the field.

In Fig. 21 the splitting of the p and s levels and the pattern of the lines $1s - 2p_{\frac{1}{2}}$ and $1s - 2p_{\frac{3}{2}}$ which results therefrom are shown. The theory of the anomalous

ZEEMAN effect which we have presented has been abundantly verified by experiment[1].

β) Strong magnetic field ("quasi-normal ZEEMAN*" or "complete* PASCHEN-BACK*" effect).* We now consider Σ as small compared with W. We first find the eigenstates and eigenvalues of W and then merely take the expectation value of Σ over the eigenfunctions of W. We put $g_s = 2$, according to the DIRAC theory.

First approximation: The eigenfunction is a product of a spatial and a spin wave function and the eigenvalue of the magnetic energy operator W is, from (46.1),

$$W = \mathcal{H}\mu_0 (m_l + 2m_s). \tag{46.7}$$

Since m_l is integral and m_s half-integral, the magnetic energy, as in the case of the electron without spin, is equal to $\mathcal{H}\mu_0$ multiplied by an integer and, thus, a normal ZEEMAN effect is simulated. This is also true for the splitting of the corresponding spectral lines: Since the spin and orbital angular momenta are no longer coupled in the eigenfunction, the spin quantum number m_s is not allowed to change in an optical transition[2] and we have the selection rule

$$\left.\begin{aligned} &\Delta m_s = 0, \\ &\Delta m_l = 0, \pm 1, \text{ depending on the polarization of the light.} \end{aligned}\right\} \tag{46.8}$$

Thus, the spectral lines have the appearance of a LORENTZ triplet, provided that both the initial and final level corresponding to the line undergo a complete PASCHEN-BACK effect[3].

In the second approximation we must consider the spin-orbit interaction. We obtain its effect in strong fields by computing the expectation value of the interaction energy (45.10) over the orbital motion. Since $\boldsymbol{k}$ and $\boldsymbol{s}$ precess independently around the magnetic field, the time average of $(\boldsymbol{k} \cdot \boldsymbol{s})$ is equal to the product of the time averages of the components of $\boldsymbol{k}$ and $\boldsymbol{s}$ along the direction of the field, namely

$$\Sigma = \tfrac{1}{2}\, \alpha^2 Z\, \overline{r^{-3}}\, m_l m_s .$$

Using for $\overline{r^{-3}}$ the value obtained from the fine structure splitting in the absence of external fields,

$$\Delta E \equiv E_{j=l+s} - E_{j=l-s} = \tfrac{1}{2}\alpha^2 Z\, \overline{r^{-3}} \left\{ \begin{aligned} &l\,(2s+1) \quad \text{if } l<s \\ &s\,(2l+1) \quad \text{if } l>s, \end{aligned} \right\} \tag{46.9}$$

we obtain

$$\Sigma = m_l m_s \Delta E \left\{ \begin{aligned} &l^{-1}(2s+1)^{-1} \quad \text{if } l<s \\ &s^{-1}(2l+1)^{-1} \quad \text{if } l>s. \end{aligned} \right\} \tag{46.10}$$

(46.10) is valid for arbitrary values of the total spin s and the orbital angular momentum l. Specializing to atoms with a single electron, $s = \frac{1}{2}$, yields

$$\Sigma = m_l m_s \frac{\Delta E}{l + \frac{1}{2}} . \tag{46.11}$$

The total energy of the atom for the state $n\, l\, s\, m_l\, m_s$ is obtained by adding (46.7) and (46.10) to the center of gravity with respect to energy of the multiplet $n\, l\, s$.

---

[1] See, for example, E. BACK, ZEEMAN-Effekt und Multiplettstruktur, Section II.

[2] The transition probability is given by

$$\sum_{s_z=-\frac{1}{2}}^{+\frac{1}{2}} \int u^*_{n'l'm'_l}(r,\vartheta,\varphi)\, \delta_{m'_s s_z}\, q\, u_{n l m_l}(r,\vartheta,\varphi)\, \delta_{m_s s_z}\, d\tau = \delta_{m'_s m_s} \int u^*_{n'l'm'_l}\, q\, u_{n l m_l}\, d\tau .$$

[3] The case in which one of the levels undergoes the PASCHEN-BACK effect, while the other level has an anomalous ZEEMAN effect is designated as a partial PASCHEN-BACK effect.

In a strong magnetic field each ZEEMAN level of the atom exhibits a splitting which is of the order of magnitude of the fine structure splitting in the absence of external fields. The same statement holds also for the spectral lines.

In Fig. 22 the splitting pattern for the transitions $1s-2p$ of an alkali atom in a strong magnetic field are shown; the term scheme is given in the upper part, the corresponding splitting of the spectral lines in the lower part.

γ) General field strength (general PASCHEN-BACK *effect).* We now derive exact expressions for the eigenfunctions and eigenvalues of the operator $(W+\Sigma)$, which are valid for arbitrary magnetic field strength, for a single-electron atom. Besides $\boldsymbol{k}^2$, M_z is still an exact constant of the motion. We consider states with fixed values of the quantum numbers n, l and m (eigenvalue of M_z). The general wave function with these quantum numbers can then be written as a superposition of two linearly independent spin wave functions. We take for these two independent states the two eigenstates of the PAULI HAMILTONian in the absence of a magnetic field, Sect. 13. These states are eigenstates of $\boldsymbol{M}^2$ with inner quantum number $j=l+\frac{1}{2}$ and $j=l-\frac{1}{2}$, respectively. We denote these states by u_+ and u_-. In this representation the unperturbed HAMILTONian H_0 and Σ are diagonal. We denote the two eigenvalues of $(H_0+\Sigma)$ by E_+ and E_- (the field-free energies of the PAULI approximation). We further define a dimensionless parameter ξ by

$$\xi=\frac{\mathscr{H}\mu_0}{\Delta E},\qquad \Delta E\equiv E_+-E_-. \tag{46.12}$$

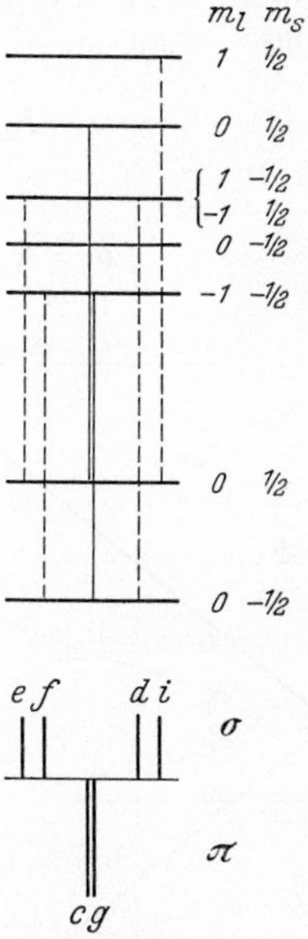

Fig. 22. Complete PASCHEN-BACK effect of a line $n\,{}^2S-n'\,{}^2P$. Energy levels in the upper, splitting of the spectral line in the lower, part of the diagrams. The letters refer back to Fig. 21. The lines a, b, h, k are supressed in strong magnetic fields. The splitting between e and f, etc. is due to the spin-orbit coupling.

We can find the explicit matrix representation of the operator W in terms of u_+ and u_- from the PAULI eigenfunctions, Eq. (13.19). The eigenvalue and eigenfunction of the total HAMILTONian $(H_0+W+\Sigma)$ can then be written in the form

$$E=\tfrac{1}{2}(E_++E_-)+E',\qquad u=a\,u_++b\,u_-. \tag{46.13}$$

E', a and b are given by the eigenvalue equation (with $g_s=2$)

$$\begin{pmatrix} \frac{1}{2}+\xi\frac{2m(l+1)}{2l+1} & \xi\frac{\sqrt{(l+\frac{1}{2})^2-m^2}}{2l+1} \\ \xi\frac{\sqrt{(l+\frac{1}{2})^2-m^2}}{2l+1} & -\frac{1}{2}+\xi\frac{2ml}{2l+1} \end{pmatrix}\begin{pmatrix} a \\ b \end{pmatrix}=\frac{E'}{\Delta E}\begin{pmatrix} a \\ b \end{pmatrix}. \tag{46.14}$$

The two possible eigenvalues E' are obtained by solving the determinantal equation of (46.14), which gives

$$E'=\Delta E\left[\xi m\pm\frac{1}{2}\sqrt{1+\xi\frac{4m}{2l+1}+\xi^2}\right]. \tag{46.15}$$

The normalized eigenfunctions (46.13) corresponding to these two eigenvalues are then given by

$$\left.\begin{aligned} a&=\sqrt{\tfrac{1}{2}(1+\gamma)}, & b&=\sqrt{\tfrac{1}{2}(1-\gamma)} & &\text{for the higher level,}\\ a&=-\sqrt{\tfrac{1}{2}(1-\gamma)}, & b&=\sqrt{\tfrac{1}{2}(1+\gamma)} & &\text{for the lower level,} \end{aligned}\right\} \tag{46.16}$$

where

$$\gamma = \frac{1 + \xi \frac{2m}{2l+1}}{\sqrt{1 + \xi \frac{4m}{2l+1} + \xi^2}} .$$

The same eigenfunctions can also be written in the form of two-component PAULI spinors, i.e. in a representation in which s_z (and hence W) is diagonal (see Sect. 12). These spinors are

$$\left.\begin{aligned} u &= R_{nl}(r) \begin{pmatrix} \sqrt{\tfrac{1}{2}(1+\delta)}\; Y_{l,m-\frac{1}{2}} \\ -\sqrt{\tfrac{1}{2}(1-\delta)}\; Y_{l,m+\frac{1}{2}} \end{pmatrix} \quad \text{for the higher level} \\ u &= R_{nl}(r) \begin{pmatrix} \sqrt{\tfrac{1}{2}(1-\delta)}\; Y_{l,m-\frac{1}{2}} \\ \sqrt{\tfrac{1}{2}(1+\delta)}\; Y_{l,m+\frac{1}{2}} \end{pmatrix} \quad \text{for the lower level,} \end{aligned}\right\} \tag{46.17}$$

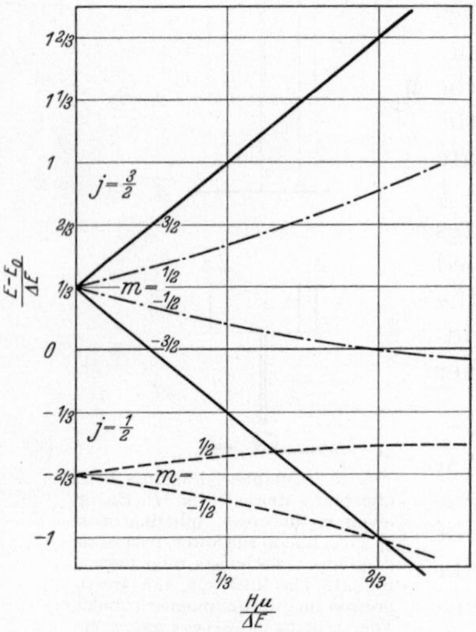

Fig. 23. Energy shift $E-E_0$ (in units of ΔE) for ^2P-states plotted against $\xi = \mathcal{H}\mu_0/\Delta E$, where $\mathcal{H}$ is the magnetic field strength and ΔE is the field-free fine structure splitting.

where

$$\delta = \frac{\xi + \frac{2m}{2l+1}}{\sqrt{1 + \xi \frac{4m}{2l+1} + \xi^2}} . \tag{46.18}$$

If $\xi \ll 1$ (weak field), (46.15) can be expanded in powers of ξ and the first two terms in this expansion give the results of Sect. 46α. Similarly, if $\xi \gg 1$ (strong field), (46.15) can be expanded in powers of $1/\xi$ and the first two terms give the results of Sect. 46β. Also, as $\xi \to 0$, the factor γ in (46.16) approaches unity. Thus either a or b in (46.13) reduces to zero and the wave function to an eigenstate of $\boldsymbol{M}^2$ (and hence of Σ). As $\xi \to \infty$, the factor δ in (46.17), (46.18) reduces to unity and the wave function (46.17) to an eigenstate of s_z and k_z (and thus of W).

The dependence of the energy on the dimensionless parameter $\xi = \mu_0 \mathcal{H}/\Delta E$ is plotted[1] in Fig. 23 from weak to fairly strong field strength for np-states in hydrogen. For $n=2$, $\Delta E = 0.365\ \text{cm}^{-1}$ and ξ equals unity for a field strength of $\mathcal{H} = 7800$ Gauss. Note that the energies of some pairs of levels cross at medium field strengths, but never for two levels with the same value of m. Note also that the energy is linear in $\mathcal{H}$ for $m = \pm(l+\frac{1}{2})$, since for these values of m only *one* eigenstate of $\boldsymbol{k}^2$ is possible and this eigenstate is independent of $\mathcal{H}$.

In general, the energy E' is not linear in $\mathcal{H}$ for medium field strength (PASCHEN-BACK region). The "moment of the atomic state" $\mu_m = \partial E'/\partial \mathcal{H}$ is then *not* independent of $\mathcal{H}$. This quantity μ_m is important in STERN-GERLACH type of experiments in which deflections of an atomic beam in an inhomogeneous magnetic field are measured. In fact, the deflection is proportional to μ_m and to the spatial gradient of $\mathcal{H}$ (see also Sect. 47γ for the "zero moment" method).

The theory presented in this section is in good semiquantitative agreement with experiment[2]. In fact, this theory, together with accurate optical measurements of ZEEMAN effect splittings, have been used in the past to get values of moderate accuracy for e/m for the electron. However, various corrections have

[1] See also K. DARWIN, Proc. Roy. Soc. Lond., Ser. A **118**, 264 (1928).
[2] For a detailed discussion see ref. [*10*], Sect. 27 d.

to be applied to the theory outlined above. Some of these are discussed in Sect. 47. The effect of the anomalous magnetic moment of the electron and some recent precision experiments are discussed in Sect. 49.

47. Some corrections to the ZEEMAN effect. We briefly discuss some small corrections which have to be applied to the theory of Sect. 46 of the ZEEMAN effect for a single-electron atom: In Sect. 46 we have approximated the DIRAC equation by the PAULI equation and, consequently, evaluated the ZEEMAN effect only to lowest order in α^2 (see Sect. 47α). We have neglected so far the effect of the motion (Sect. 47β) and the magnetic moment (Sect. 47γ) of the atomic nucleus. The effect of the term quadratic in A in (45.2) is discussed in Sect. 47δ, That of the anomalous moment of the electron in Sect. 49.

α) *Relativistic effect.* In Sect. 10 we have written down the exact DIRAC equation (10.1) for an electron in an arbitrary external electromagnetic field. This equation can be solved exactly for a uniform magnetic field of arbitrary strength in the *absence* of any electric field[1]. The DIRAC equation cannot be solved exactly for a central electrostatic field plus a uniform magnetic field $\mathscr{H}$, but the part of the energy which is *linear* in $\mathscr{H}$ can be evaluated.

We proceed from the DIRAC equation and consider the term in $\boldsymbol{\alpha}\cdot\boldsymbol{A}$ as a small perturbation ("weak" field as in Sect. 46α). One can then evaluate[2] the expectation value of this operator using the exact DIRAC wave functions (discussed in Sect. 14) for zero magnetic field. For an arbitrary central electric potential and uniform magnetic field $\mathscr{H}$ (in the z-direction) the perturbation energy can be written in the form

$$E' = \mathscr{H}\mu_0\, m\,\frac{j+\frac{1}{2}}{l+\frac{1}{2}}\left[1-\frac{2\varkappa}{\varkappa-\frac{1}{2}}\int\limits_0^\infty dr\, f^2 r^2\right]. \tag{47.1}$$

The quantum number $\varkappa$ is defined in (14.9) and f is the radial wave function for the "small component" defined in (14.10) and normalized as in (14.32). If the term in square brackets in (47.1) is replaced by unity this expression reduces to the nonrelativistic weak field expression (46.4) with (46.6). For a COULOMB potential of nuclear charge Z the radial wave functions f are known. For the ground state $1\,S_{\frac{1}{2}}$, the integral in (47.1) can be evaluated easily and the correction factor in square brackets becomes

$$1+\tfrac{2}{3}\left(\sqrt{1-Z^2\alpha^2}-1\right). \tag{47.2}$$

If the central electric field has arbitrary shape but is "weak" and the atom is essentially nonrelativistic, the integral in (47.1) can be simplified. The correction factor is obtained up to order $(Z\alpha)^2$ if f is replaced by the approximation

$$f=\frac{\hbar}{2mc}\left[\frac{dg}{dr}+(1+\varkappa)\,\frac{g}{r}\right], \tag{47.3}$$

obtained from (14.10), and if g is replaced by the radial SCHRÖDINGER wave function R_{nl}. The correction factor to this order can also be obtained by a more

[1] L. D. HUFF: Phys. Rev. **38**, 501 (1931). — M. JOHNSON and B. LIPPMANN: Phys. Rev. **76**, 828 (1949); **77**, 702 (1950). See also p. 327 of ref. [*15*] of our bibliography. We shall not discuss these solutions. The motion of a free electron in a circular orbit in a uniform magnetic field under most practical conditions (e.g. in a cyclotron) corresponds to a superposition of states with extremely large values of the magnetic quantum number m. No quantum (or spin) effects are of any importance in such "large scale" motions, e.g. the revolution frequency of the electrons' orbit is the same as that given by the relativistic theory of a classical point-charge.

[2] G. BREIT: Nature, Lond. **122**, 649 (1928). — H. MARGENAU: Phys. Rev. **57**, 383 (1940). See also ref. [*9*], p. 72.

careful treatment[1] of the PAULI type of approximation: Additional terms in (12.11) involving the magnetic field are obtained if in the approximate relation (12.7) the operator $\boldsymbol{p}$ is replaced by $(\boldsymbol{p}+e\boldsymbol{A}/c)$ [see also Eq. (12.8)]. In addition, in the term in $(E+e\varphi)^2$ in (12.11) account must be taken of the shift in energy due to the magnetic field. For a COULOMB potential, the correction factor in square brackets in (47.1) can be evaluated analytically to this order for all atomic states. For the $n\,S_{\frac{1}{2}}$-state, for instance, this factor is

$$1-\frac{1}{3}\frac{(Z\alpha)^2}{n^2}. \tag{47.4}$$

For the ground state of hydrogen, this factor is $(1-1.78\times10^{-5})$ [the first two terms in an expansion of (47.2)].

β) Nuclear motion. We have so far considered the source of the nuclear COULOMB potential as fixed. For an actual nucleus of finite mass M, a small correction to the ZEEMAN effect arises from nuclear motion. This was investigated by LAMB[1] by an extension of the method discussed in Sect. 42. Working only to order m/M, he finds that the effect of nuclear motion is to multiply the orbital term $\mu_0\,\mathcal{H}\cdot\boldsymbol{k}$ in (45.9) by a factor g_l,

$$g_l = 1-\frac{m}{M}. \tag{47.5}$$

The spin term $g_s\,\mu_0\,\mathcal{H}\cdot\boldsymbol{s}$ in (45.9) is unaffected to this order and terms of relative order $\alpha m/M$ have not been investigated yet.

These results might have been expected from the following physical arguments: A fraction $m/(M+m)$ of the orbital angular momentum $\boldsymbol{k}$ of the atom is contributed by the motion of the nucleus and the fraction $M/(M+m)$ by the electron (the momenta of the two particles are equal and opposite, their distances from the center of mass in the ratio m/M). The electron's contribution to the orbital angular momentum, and hence to the orbital term $\mu_0\,\mathcal{H}\cdot\boldsymbol{k}$, is thus reduced by the factor $M/(M+m)$ which is (approximately) (47.5). The nucleus gives a negligible orbital contribution (of order m^2/M^2), since its magnetic moment (for the *same* angular momentum) is smaller by a factor of order $\mu_N/\mu_0 = m/M$ than that of the electron. The spin term $\mu_0 g_s\,\mathcal{H}\cdot\boldsymbol{s}$, however, is connected with the electron's *intrinsic* spin and magnetic moment and is unaffected by the nuclear motion.

γ) Effect of nuclear magnetic moment. If the atomic nucleus has a non-zero magnetic moment, the atomic ZEEMAN effect will be modified. Nuclear magnetic moments are of the order of a nuclear magneton μ_N which is about 1/1836 times the electronic BOHR magneton μ_0. In the absence of a magnetic field the hyperfine structure splitting $\Delta\varepsilon$ of energy levels (magnetic electron-nucleus interaction) is generally smaller than the fine structure splitting ΔE (electronic spin-orbit interaction) by a factor of the same order. One would then also expect the effect of the nuclear magnetic moment on the ZEEMAN effect to be small. This is indeed the case for all but *very* weak magnetic fields, where the ZEEMAN pattern is altered drastically.

In Sect. 46 we have discussed the dependence on the magnetic field strength $\mathcal{H}$ of the energy eigenvalues and eigenfunctions of states in the hydrogen atom in the absence of a nuclear moment. We found that, besides n and l, also m, the eigenvalue of $M_z = k_z + s_z$, is an exact quantum number. We dealt with two

[1] W. E. LAMB: Phys. Rev. **85**, 259 (1952).

non-commuting operators: (1) The ZEEMAN effect operator W, Eq. (45.9), which is proportional to $M_z + s_z$ and whose expectation values are of order $\mu_0 \mathcal{H}$. (2) The spin-orbit coupling operator Σ, Eq. (45.10), which is proportional to $\boldsymbol{k} \cdot \boldsymbol{s}$ and whose eigenvalues lead to the field-free fine structure separation ΔE of the levels with $j = l + \frac{1}{2}$ and $l - \frac{1}{2}$. We found that j is approximately a good quantum number ($\boldsymbol{M}^2$ conserved) if $\mu_0 \mathcal{H} \ll \Delta E$ and that m_s (and hence m_l) is almost a good quantum number if $\mu_0 \mathcal{H} \gg \Delta E$. In the presence of a nuclear magnetic moment we have extra terms in the HAMILTONian and the situation is more complicated.

As discussed in Sect. 22β, many nuclei have a non-zero and fixed value I for their "spin", where $I(I+1)$ is the eigenvalue of the square of an operator $\boldsymbol{i}$ which represents the intrinsic internal angular momentum of the nucleus. The nucleus then has a magnetic moment

$$\boldsymbol{\mu} = + \mu_N g_I \boldsymbol{i},$$

where μ_N is defined in (22.7) and g_I is a constant for each nucleus. We then have two additional terms in the HAMILTONian. One represents the interaction of the nucleus with the external magnetic field $\mathcal{H}$ and is given by

$$H'' = - g_I \mu_N \mathcal{H} i_z.$$

The other operator H' is given by (22.1) and (22.6). Physically it represents the interaction of the nuclear moment with the magnetic field produced by the electron's motion and spin and does not depend explicitly on the external field $\mathcal{H}$. The operator H'' bears some analogy to the operator W and its expectation values are smaller by one order of $\mu_0/\mu_N = 1836$. The expectation values of the operator H' are smaller than those of Σ by a factor of the same order.

For external fields in the PASCHEN-BACK region, i.e., $\mu_0 \mathcal{H} \gtrsim \Delta E$, the electronic wave functions are essentially unaffected by the nuclear moment terms H' and H''. For very strong fields in particular, $\mu_0 \mathcal{H} \gg \Delta E$, one finds that the effect of H' on the energy is much smaller than that of H''. The nuclear spin is then essentially "uncoupled" from the electron's angular momenta. Each of the energy levels discussed in Sect. 46β is merely split further, according to the eigenvalue m_I of i_z (which is now a good quantum number), and the additional energy shift is given by the (small) eigenvalue $-g_I \mu_N \mathcal{H} m_I$ of the operator H''. We shall not discuss these cases further (see [*16*]), but only the case of $\mu_0 \mathcal{H} \ll \Delta E$.

If $\mu_0 \mathcal{H} \ll \Delta E$, then (see Sect. 46$\alpha$) the ZEEMAN effect operator W is small compared with the electronic spin-orbit coupling operator Σ. The hyperfine structure operator H' is small compared with Σ (by a factor of order 1836) and the nuclear ZEEMAN operator H'' is small compared with W (by a factor of the same order) and also compared with H' (by one order of $\mu_0 \mathcal{H}/\Delta E$). The stationary states are then eigenstates (to a good approximation) of Σ, and hence of $\boldsymbol{M}^2$, and j is a good quantum number. In the absence of W, H' and H'', the energy depends on j through the eigenvalue Σ_{nlj}, but is degenerate with respect to m and m_I, the eigenvalues of M_z ($\boldsymbol{M}$ is the total angular momentum of the electron) and of i_z. We consider H' and W as small perturbations which remove this degeneracy, but neglect mixing between states of different j-values. H'' is smaller than both H' and W, but H' is not necessarily smaller than W.

For transitions between states with the *same* j-value, the hyperfine structure operator H' can be written [see Eq. (22.9)] in the form

$$H' = a_{nlj} g_I \boldsymbol{i} \cdot \boldsymbol{M}, \tag{47.6}$$

where a_{nlj} is a constant for given values of n, l and j. As in Sect. 22β, we call $\boldsymbol{f}=\boldsymbol{i}+\boldsymbol{M}$ the operator for the angular momentum of the whole atom and $f(f+1)$ the eigenvalue of $\boldsymbol{f}^2$. Now $f_z=M_z+i_z$ commutes with H', W and H'' and its eigenvalue $m_f=m+m_I$ is thus an *exact* quantum number. On the other hand, H' does not commute with M_z and W does not commute with $\boldsymbol{f}^2$. Hence neither m (and therefore m_I) nor f is an exact quantum number. Calculations for arbitrary field strengths are tedious, but we discuss two simple limiting cases (neglecting H'', which is smaller than H' and W, in both cases).

Let $\Delta\varepsilon$ be the order of magnitude of the hyperfine structure splitting, i.e. of $a_{nlj}\,g_I$ in (47.6), which is of order $\Delta E/1836$. We consider first the case of extremely weak magnetic fields, $\mu_0\mathscr{H}\ll\Delta\varepsilon\ll\Delta E$ (ZEEMAN splitting less than hyperfine splitting). We then consider W as a small perturbation on H' and use the eigenfunctions of H' (for which f, *not* m, is a good quantum number) to evaluate the expectation value of W. The main splitting of a fine structure level is then the hyperfine structure splitting (eigenvalues of H') as evaluated in Sect. 22, which gives an energy depending on f, but not on m_f. Each level with given f then splits further into components with different values of m_f. This extra splitting energy is given by the expectation value of W, i.e. by $\mu_0\mathscr{H}\,g_j\overline{m}$, where g_j is the factor g defined in (46.5) and $\overline{m}$ is the expectation value of M_z for an eigenstate of $\boldsymbol{M}^2$, $\boldsymbol{f}^2$ and f_z (quantum numbers j, f and m_f). By arguments similar to those leading to (46.3), one can show that

$$\overline{m}=\frac{f(f+1)+j(j+1)-I(I+1)}{2f(f+1)}\,m_f, \tag{47.7}$$

if $f\neq 0$, and that $\overline{m}=0$ if $f=0$.

If, on the other hand, $\Delta\varepsilon\ll\mu_0\mathscr{H}\ll\Delta E$, we consider H', Eq. (47.6), as a small perturbation on the ZEEMAN operator W, Eq. (46.1). We then consider both j and m as good quantum numbers and a level with given j primarily splits into levels of different m values with the splitting energy given by (46.4) and (46.5). In addition, each m-level is split further with the splitting energy given by the expectation value $\overline{H'}$ of H', Eq. (47.6), for an eigenstate of $\boldsymbol{M}^2$, M_z and f_z (and hence of i_z). The expectation value of $\boldsymbol{i}\cdot\boldsymbol{M}$ equals that of $i_z M_z$ and

$$\overline{H'}=a_{nlj}\,g_I\,m_I\,m, \tag{47.8}$$

where $m_I=(-I,\ldots,I-1,I)$ is the eigenvalue of i_z. In either of the two limits discussed, the total number of levels (for fixed n, l, j) is $(2j+1)\,(2I+1)$.

Calculations for the energy levels in the intermediate region, $\Delta\varepsilon\sim\mu_0\mathscr{H}\ll\Delta E$ are somewhat lengthy and have to be carried out separately for each value of j. For $j=\frac{1}{2}$ one finds the following result[1], for any value of I: In the absence of a magnetic field, the level is split into a doublet with $f=I+\frac{1}{2}$ and $I-\frac{1}{2}$ and energy separation $\Delta\varepsilon=a_{nlj}\,g_I(I+\frac{1}{2})$. For arbitrary values of $\mu_0\mathscr{H}/\Delta\varepsilon$ and without neglecting the small operator H'', the energies $E_\pm$ of the two levels with fixed m_f are given by (relative to the mean energy of the field-free doublet)

$$E_\pm=-g_I\mu_N\mathscr{H}\pm\frac{\Delta\varepsilon}{2}\sqrt{1+\frac{4m_f}{2I+1}\,x+x^2};\qquad x=\frac{(g_j\mu_0-g_I\mu_N)\,\mathscr{H}}{\Delta\varepsilon}. \tag{47.9}$$

If we neglect μ_N/μ_0 in $E_\pm$ and proceed to the limits $x\to 0$ or $x\to\infty$, this expression reduces to our approximate ones above.

[1] G. BREIT and I. RABI: Phys. Rev. **38**, 2082 (1931). — S. MILLMAN, I. RABI and J. ZACHARIAS: Phys. Rev. **53**, 384 (1938). See also ref. [*16*], Chap. 2B.

The effect of the nuclear magnetic moment on the ZEEMAN effect is of practical importance for two reasons. (1) In many experiments on the atomic ZEEMAN effect it is convenient to work in the weak-field region of Sect. 46α (see, for nstance, Sect. 49β), where $\mu_0 \mathscr{H} \ll \Delta E$. Although the hyperfine splitting $\Delta\varepsilon$ is very small compared with ΔE, in these experiments $\Delta\varepsilon$ is not necessarily very small compared with $\mu_0 \mathscr{H}$ and the corrections discussed in this section may be important. (2) In the region where $\mu_0 \mathscr{H}$ and $\Delta\varepsilon$ are comparable ($x \sim 1$), the energy E of the atomic state is by no means linear in $\mathscr{H}$. In fact the "moment of the atomic state", $\mu_m = \partial E/\partial \mathscr{H}$, can vanish at a particular field strength which depends critically on g_I (i.e. on $\Delta\varepsilon$). An atomic beam passing through an *in*homogeneous magnetic field suffers a deflection proportional to μ_m and is undeflected when the atomic state has "zero moment". This fact is used in the "zero moment method[1]" to yield values for nuclear g_I-factors by measuring the values of $\mathscr{H}$ for which $\mu_m = 0$.

δ) The quadratic term[2]. We have considered so far only the perturbation term in the HAMILTONian which is linear in the magnetic field $\mathscr{H}$. Putting $g_s = 2$ in (45.9), this term is

$$W = \frac{e\hbar\mathscr{H}}{2mc}(k_z + 2s_z). \tag{47.10}$$

We have now to consider the effect of the part of the HAMILTONian which is quadratic in the vector potential $\boldsymbol{A}$ [last term in (45.2)]. This term, present both in the DIRAC and KLEIN-GORDON theories, is

$$W_Q = \frac{e^2}{2mc^2} A^2 = \frac{e^2\mathscr{H}^2}{8mc^2} r^2 \sin^2\vartheta. \tag{47.11}$$

In (47.11) we have used (45.3) for a uniform magnetic field and ϑ is the angle between $\boldsymbol{r}$ and the direction of $\mathfrak{H}$ (taken as z-axis).

We first give some order of magnitude arguments to show that the effect of W_Q is much smaller than that of W, except for states of large principal quantum number n in very strong fields. Consider a state in hydrogen with a small value of n. The order of magnitude of W_Q is given by

$$W_Q = \left(\frac{e\hbar\mathscr{H}}{2mc}\right)^2 \left(\frac{r}{\hbar}\right)^3 \frac{m}{2} \sin^2\vartheta \sim \frac{W^2}{\hbar^2/r^2 m} \sim \frac{W}{\mathrm{Ry}} W, \tag{47.12}$$

where we have replaced r by one BOHR radius and $\hbar^2/2r^2m$ by one RYDBERG. Hence W_Q is smaller than W by a factor of order W/Ry. Now the ZEEMAN energy W for all practical fields is much smaller than a RYDBERG. In particular, we have seen (Sect. 46γ) that for $\mathscr{H}$ of the order of 10^4 Gauss, W is comparable with the fine structure splitting $\Delta E \sim \alpha^2$ Ry. For such fields, then, W_Q/W is of order $\alpha^2 \sim 10^{-4}$.

The ratio of the expectation value of W_Q to that of W is negligibly small for fields of the order of 10^4 Gauss or less and for states of low principal quantum number n. At larger field strengths ("strong" field case, complete PASCHEN-BACK effect) the energy shift due to W is linear in $\mathscr{H}$, that of W_Q quadratic. Further, (3.21) shows that the expectation value of r^2 is roughly proportional to n^4. Hence W_Q/W is roughly proportional to $\mathscr{H} n^4$ and can become comparable to unity for large $\mathscr{H}$ and n. Note that the energy shift due to W changes sign when both m_l and m_s change sign, whereas the expectation value of W_Q is independent of the sign of the magnetic quantum numbers. W_Q is important even

[1] R. COHEN: Phys. Rev. **46**, 713 (1934).

[2] For a detailed discussion of these effects see L. SCHIFF and H. SNYDER, Phys. Rev. **55**, 59 (1938).

for low field strengths in cases where the expectation value of W is zero and leads to diamagnetism (for the case of helium, this is calculated in Sect. 50).

The operator W commutes with $\boldsymbol{k}^2$ and we have so far considered l as a good quantum number. On the other hand, W_Q does *not* commute with $\boldsymbol{k}^2$ and also has matrix elements for transitions between states of l-values differing by ± 2. These off-diagonal matrix elements are of the same order of magnitude as the expectation values of W_Q and result in a "mixing" of wave functions of different l-values. The amount of mixing can be calculated by first order perturbation theory and is of order $\overline{W}_Q/\Delta E$, where ΔE is the fine structure energy difference for levels of different l-values. This mixing in of excited states of H is again quite small unless $\mathscr{H}$ and n are large. The mixing is still smaller for the valence electron of an alkali atom, since the energy depends on l even nonrelativistically. The mixing is completely negligible for the ground state of H, since the biggest admixture would come from the $3d$ state with ΔE almost 1 Ry (instead of α^2 Ry for the excited states).

ε) Anomalous moment of the electron. In Sect. 18 we have discussed the various corrections to the DIRAC theory introduced by quantum electrodynamics. One simple and important effect is the anomalous magnetic moment of the electron. In the PAULI equation for the motion of an electron in an external field, the terms arising from the intrinsic moment of the electron have to be multiplied by a factor differing slightly from unity. This factor is to be used for $\frac{1}{2}g_s$ in (45.9) and can be calculated from quantum electrodynamics in the form of an expansion in powers of the fine structure constant α. The term linear in α in this expansion has been calculated by FEYNMAN and by SCHWINGER in their classic papers and the term in α^2 by KARPLUS and KROLL[1]. To this order, the correction factor is given by [see Eq. (18.5)]

$$\frac{1}{2}g_s = 1 + \frac{\alpha}{2\pi} - 2.973\frac{\alpha^2}{\pi^2} = 1.0011454. \tag{47.13}$$

Terms of order α^3 and higher have not been calculated yet, but they are expected to contribute less than $\pm 10^{-6}$ to g_s. Precision experiments by KUSCH and others, which verify (47.13), are discussed in Sect. 49.

48. Extension to many-electron atoms. *α) General theory.* In Sects. 39 to 41 we have discussed an approximately relativistic wave equation for the two-electron system. This equation, which is of the same accuracy as the PAULI approximation, can also be generalized to a many-electron atom. The HAMILTONian corresponding to this equation contains a part which depends on an external magnetic field $\mathscr{H}$. This part is in the form of sums over all electrons of terms which individually are just of the form of the field-dependent terms in the single-electron equation. We shall omit at the moment the terms quadratic in $\mathscr{H}$. We denote the sum over electrons of the orbital angular momentum, spin etc. by capital letters,

$$\boldsymbol{K} = \sum_i \boldsymbol{k}_i, \quad \boldsymbol{S} = \sum_i \boldsymbol{s}_i, \quad \boldsymbol{M} = \sum_i (\boldsymbol{k}_i + \boldsymbol{s}_i). \tag{48.1}$$

The eigenvalues of K_z, S_z, and M_z are m_L, m_S and m, those of $\boldsymbol{K}^2$, $\boldsymbol{S}^2$ and $\boldsymbol{M}^2$ are $L(L+1)$, $S(S+1)$ and $J(J+1)$. The term W in the HAMILTONian which is linear in $\mathscr{H}$ has then a form in complete analogy with (45.9),

$$W = \mu_0 \mathscr{H}(K_z + g_s S_z). \tag{48.2}$$

[1] R. KARPLUS and N. KROLL: Phys. Rev. 77, 536 (1950).

We now have to consider the parts of the HAMILTONian which are independent of $\mathcal{H}$. If one takes only the nonrelativistic approximation H_0 to this HAMILTONian one finds that $\boldsymbol{K}^2$, $\mathbf{S}^2$, K_z and S_z all commute with H_0; and L, S, m_L and m_S are all good quantum numbers. Due to the electrostatic interaction between the electrons and exchange effects, the energy eigenvalue of H_0 depends in general on the values of both L and S, but *not* on m_L and m_S (compare Sect. 28). The relativistic part of the HAMILTONian contains various types of terms, including the BREIT interaction between electrons, and some of these terms do *not* commute with $\boldsymbol{K}^2$ or $\mathbf{S}^2$. We consider only the case where the electrons are essentially nonrelativistic (low effective nuclear charge) and where the nonrelativistic energies for states of different L and S do not (accidentally) lie extremely close. One can then use the following approximation, called the RUSSELL-SAUNDERS coupling scheme.

We consider the relativistic part of the HAMILTONian as a small perturbation and consider first only the part of this perturbation which is diagonal in a representation in terms of L and S. This part can usually be written[1] in the form (to a good approximation)

$$\Sigma = a\,\boldsymbol{K}\cdot\mathbf{S}, \tag{48.3}$$

where a may depend on L and S, but not on m_L and m_S. This term Σ is then completely analogous to the operator in (45.10). In some cases (e.g. helium) the diagonal part Σ is *not* well represented by (48.3), but even in these cases Σ commutes with $\boldsymbol{M}^2$. If (for fixed L and S) we express operators in a representation in terms of J (eigenstates of $\boldsymbol{M}^2$), then Σ is diagonal,

$$\Sigma_{JJ'} = \Sigma'_J\,\delta_{JJ'}, \tag{48.4}$$

where Σ'_J is a number independent of the quantum number m. The approximate form (48.3) is a special case of operators satisfying (48.4).

The off-diagonal parts of the relativistic HAMILTONian will cause some admixture of wave functions with different values of L and S. But since the relativistic terms are small, this admixture is small and their effect on the energy is of *second* order (counting Σ as first order). The admixture will only be of order $(Z\alpha)^2\,\mathrm{Ry}/\delta E$, where δE is the energy difference between the level considered and the nearest level with different values of L and S. In He this ratio is quite small and the method used in Sect. 40 (except for ARAKI's corrections) is in fact equivalent to the RUSSELL-SAUNDERS scheme.

In alkali atoms, the neglect of off-diagonal matrix elements is again an excellent approximation for the following reason. We normally consider only states with the single valence electron outside a closed shell and L, S are simply the quantum numbers l, s for this valence electron. Now the relativistic HAMILTONian will couple this state only to those states where one of the core electrons has been lifted to a higher shell. The energy difference δE is thus large and, further, the valence electron sees a small effective nuclear charge and is essentially nonrelativistic.

If we neglect the off-diagonal relativistic matrix elements and consider L and S as exact quantum numbers, the theory of the ZEEMAN effect of a many-electron atom is very similar to the theory worked out in Sect. 46. For the weak-field case of Sect. 46α, the results of (46.4) and (46.5) were already derived by general operator methods for *arbitrary* values of l and s. These results then apply without modification for a many-electron atom (in the RUSSELL-SAUNDERS

[1] See ref. [5], p. 194.

approximation), except that l, s are replaced by L, S and j by J [the eigenvalue of $(\boldsymbol{K}+\boldsymbol{S})^2$ is $J(J+1)$]. For weak fields, J is again (almost) a good quantum number, m_L and m_S not at all. Note that these results are based only on the assumption that (48.4) holds, but not necessarily (48.3).

For strong fields (complete PASCHEN-BACK effect) the results of Sect. 46β again apply, essentially without modification. In this case m_L and m_S are (almost) good quantum numbers, J not at all. The total energy is then

$$E = E_0 + \mu_0 H (m_L + g_S m_S) + \overline{\Sigma}_{m_L m_S}, \tag{48.5}$$

where $\overline{\Sigma}$ is the expectation value of Σ, Eq. (48.4), for an eigenstate of K_z and S_z. If Σ is given by the special form (48.3), then $\overline{\Sigma}$ reduces to

$$\overline{\Sigma} = a\, m_L\, m_S, \tag{48.6}$$

in complete analogy[1] with (46.10).

For intermediate field strengths (W and Σ comparable) the situation is more complicated. For fixed L, S and m one can, for instance, use a representation in terms of eigenstates of $\boldsymbol{M}^2$ with $J = |L-S|, \ldots, L+S$. Σ, as given by (48.4), is diagonal in this representation and the matrix elements of K_z and S_z (and hence of W) can be found. One then has to find the eigenvalues and eigenstates of the matrix $(W+\Sigma)$. This must be done separately for states of different values of L and S and the calculations are lengthy for large values of S. In the case of alkali atoms with $S=\frac{1}{2}$ the theory of Sect. 46γ still holds. We only[2] discuss briefly the case of helium with $S=0$ or 1.

β) Helium. The para-states of helium have total spin zero, $S=0$. In this case the spin-orbit coupling term (48.3) and the term involving S_z in (48.2) both vanish. We then have exactly the "normal ZEEMAN effect" described in Sect. 45α as for spinless particles. The field-free wave functions are exact eigenfunctions for all field strengths and the interaction energy $\mu_0 \mathscr{H} m_L$ is strictly linear in the field (always omitting the quadratic term of Sect. 47δ). This theory is in good agreement with experiment[3].

For orthostates of helium the total spin is given by $S=1$. For states of zero orbital angular momentum, $L=0$, the field-free wave function for each value of $m=m_s=1, 0, -1$ is an exact eigenfunction and the interaction energy is simply $\mu_0 \mathscr{H} g_s m_s$. For $L \neq 0$, the correct eigenfunctions for a particular value of m are three different superpositions of three linearly independent wave functions. For weak fields these are the three eigenstates of $\boldsymbol{M}^2$ and their energies are given by (46.4). The LANDÉ factor (46.5) reduces to (with $g_s=2$ and $S=1$)

$$g = \begin{cases} (L+2)(L+1)^{-1} & \text{if} \quad J = L+1, \\ 1 + L^{-1}(L+1)^{-1} & \text{if} \quad J = L, \\ (L-1)L^{-1} & \text{if} \quad J = L-1. \end{cases} \tag{48.7}$$

By "weak" fields we mean that $\mu_0 \mathscr{H}$ is small compared with the energy difference between any two of three (field-free) fine structure components, i.e., with $\Sigma'_J - \Sigma'_{J'}$, where Σ'_J is defined in (48.4).

For strong fields ($\mu_0 \mathscr{H}$ much larger than fine structure splitting) the three eigenstates (with fixed m and L) are the eigenstates of K_z with eigenvalues

[1] The case of He, where Σ is not of form (48.3) and (48.6) does not apply, is discussed in Sect. 48β.

[2] See also ref. [5], Chap. 16.

[3] W. LOHMANN: Phys. Z. 7, 809 (1906).

$m_L = m+1$, m and $m-1$. The energies of these states are given by (48.5). The term $\bar{\Sigma}_{m_L m_S}$ is independent of $\mathscr{H}$ [and much smaller than the second term in (48.5)] and can be evaluated as follows: One first calculates the three eigenvalues Σ'_J (for $J = L+1$, L and $L-1$) of the fine structure operator Σ, as discussed in Sect. 40. One can then write the eigenstate of K_z and S_z (eigenvalues m_L and m_S) as a linear superposition of the three eigenstates of $\boldsymbol{M}^2$ (with fixed $m = m_L + m_S$), with expansion coefficients $c(m_L, m_S;\, J\, m)$ which are given in [5], Chap. 3, Sect. 14. Making use of the diagonal property (48.4) of Σ, one finds

$$\bar{\Sigma}_{m_L m_S} = \sum_{J=L-1}^{L+1} |c\,(m_L\, m_S;\, J m)|^2\, \Sigma'_J\,.$$

For intermediate field strengths one has to find the exact eigenvalues and eigenstates of the submatrix for $(W+\Sigma)$, as discussed in Sect. 48α.

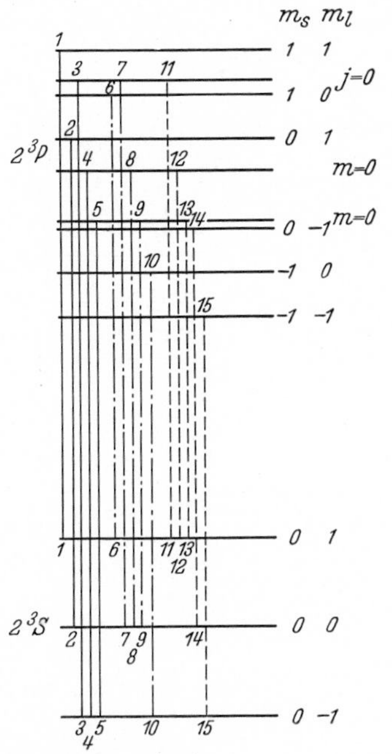

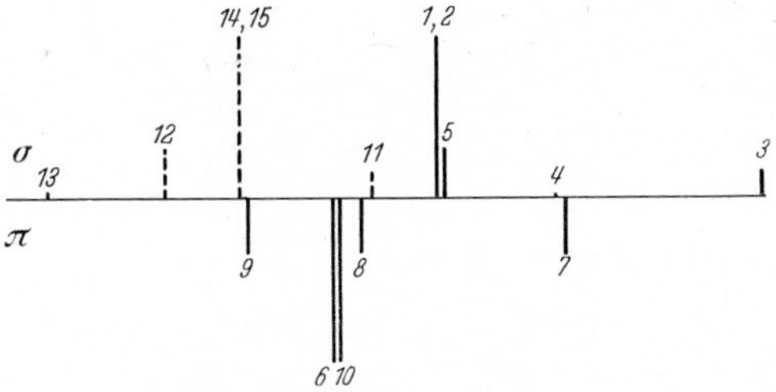

Fig. 24a and b. ZEEMAN effect for the $2\,^3P \rightarrow 2\,^3S$ line in helium for a field strength of $\mathscr{H} = 8500$ Gauss. a. The energy level scheme. The six levels with $m = \pm 1$ of the $2\,^3P$-state exhibit the complete PASCHEN-BACK effect; for $m = 0$ the uppermost level is essentially the field-free $j=0$ state, the two lower ones are combinations of $j=1$ and 2. b. The theoretical splitting diagram for the spectral line. The numbers correspond to those in Fig. 24a. Solid lines: right, broken lines: left circular polarization.

For P-states $(L=1)$ and $m=0$, for instance, the operator $(W+\Sigma)$ is represented by a three-by-three matrix, the rows and columns referring to $J = 0, 1, 2$,

$$W + \Sigma = \begin{pmatrix} \Sigma'_0 & \sqrt{\tfrac{2}{3}}\,\mu_0 \mathscr{H} & 0 \\ \sqrt{\tfrac{2}{3}}\,\mu_0 \mathscr{H} & \Sigma'_1 & \sqrt{\tfrac{1}{3}}\,\mu_0 \mathscr{H} \\ 0 & \sqrt{\tfrac{1}{3}}\,\mu_0 \mathscr{H} & \Sigma'_2 \end{pmatrix}. \tag{48.8}$$

Since $m=0$, the energies Σ'_0, Σ'_1, Σ'_2 are those without field [for $m \neq 0$, the first order ZEEMAN effect, with g given by (48.7), should be added]. The eigenvalues of this matrix are discussed in [*10*], Sect. 28. For the P-states in helium (see Sect. 40) the field-free energies Σ'_1 and Σ'_2 (for $J=1$ and 2) almost coincide accidentally and there is a region of fairly low field strengths where the $J=0$ level shows the weak-field ZEEMAN effect, but the $J=1, 2$ levels show the PASCHEN-BACK effect ([*10*], p. 401). For $m=\pm 1$, (48.8) is replaced by a two-by-two matrix, involving $J=1$ and 2, for $m=\pm 2$ there is no degeneracy and the state $J=2$ has a linear ZEEMAN effect. The level splitting for $2\,^3P$ and $2\,^3S$ for He at 8500 Gauss is shown in Fig. 24.

γ) *Relativistic corrections.* For weak magnetic fields, the LANDÉ factor g should be given by (46.5) according to the discussion of Sect. 48α. Even when

(47.12) is substituted for g_s in (46.5) this expression is still not exact. As discussed in Sect. 48α some parts of the relativistic HAMILTONian give an admixture to the wave function from states with different values of L and S, for which the expression (46.5) for g is different from the value for the state considered. These effects cannot be calculated with any great accuracy for complex atoms, but semi-quantitative estimates have been made[1] for alkali atoms in their ground state (one electron with $l=0$ outside closed shells). The effect increases with atomic number and the deviation of the LANDÉ factor g from the expression (46.5) [with g_s given by Eq. (47.12)] should be of the order of two parts in 10^5 for potassium and up to ten parts in 10^5 in cesium. According to rough estimates, the deviations of g from (46.5) for atoms with three electrons outside closed shells should not be very much greater than for alkali atoms of comparable atomic number.

Besides the effects of configuration mixing discussed above, specific relativistic corrections occur of a type similar to the BREIT-MARGENAU corrections in hydrogen (Sect. 47α). In many-electron atoms these corrections also include contributions from the BREIT interaction between electrons. For the $n\,^3S_1$-states of orthohelium these corrections have been calculated explicitly[2]. For the metastable $2\,^3S_1$-state, g differs from g_s [the value given by Eq. (46.5a)] by 4.1 parts in 10^5, compared with two in 10^5 for the hydrogen ground state. For alkali atoms and other complex atoms only semi-quantitative estimates of these relativistic effects are available[3]. These corrections to g should be of the order of magnitude of 10^{-5} to 10^{-4}.

In Sect. 49β precision experiments will be discussed which are capable of measuring the ratios of the LANDÉ factor g for states of various values of L, S and J in various atoms to an accuracy of about one part in 10^5. The value in (47.12) for g_s has been firmly established (see Sect. 49δ). The remaining discrepancies between the measured g-values and (46.5) should then be due to the corrections discussed in this section. The measured discrepancies are of the same order of magnitude as the rough theoretical estimates for them. For the ground states of the alkali atoms, for instance, the experimental g-values[4] agree with g_s to one part in 10^5 for Li, Na and K and $g/g_s=(1+5\times10^{-5})$ and $(1+13\times10^{-5})$, respectively, for Rb and Cs. For the $2\,^3S_1$-state in helium[5] $g/g_s=(1-4\times10^{-5})$, in good agreement with theory. Even for the ground state of Cr, which has five d-electrons and one s-electron outside closed shells, with $L=0$ and $J=S=3$, the LANDÉ factor is close[6] to g_s, namely $g/g_s=1-(35\pm5)\times10^{-5}$. Measurements of g-values have also been carried out[7] on $^2P_{\frac{1}{2}}$ and $^2P_{\frac{3}{2}}$ states of atoms with three electrons outside closed shells, such as Ga and In. The g-values differ from (46.5) by less than 20 parts in 10^5 in most cases.

49. Comparison with precision experiments. Numerous experimental investigations on the ZEEMAN effect in hydrogen-like and complex atoms have been carried out many years ago by means of optical spectroscopy. These experiments

---

[1] M. PHILLIPS: Phys. Rev. **88**, 202 (1952).

[2] W. PERL and V. HUGHES: Phys. Rev. **91**, 842 (1953).

[3] W. PERL: Phys. Rev. **91**, 852 (1953).

[4] P. KUSCH and H. TAUB: Phys. Rev. **75**, 1477 (1949). — P. FRANKEN and S. KOENIG: Phys. Rev. **88**, 199 (1952).

[5] HUGHES, TUCKER, RHODERICK and WEINREICH: Phys. Rev. **91**, 828 (1953).

[6] BRIX, EISINGER, LEW and WESSEL: Phys. Rev. **92**, 647 (1953).

[7] P. KUSCH and H. FOLEY: Phys. Rev. **74**, 250 (1948). — A. MANN and P. KUSCH: Phys. Rev. **77**, 435 (1950).

verified the various aspects of the theory of Sect. 46 in great detail[1], but *not* to a very high accuracy. Even with strong magnetic fields the ZEEMAN-splitting frequencies are only of the order of a few cm^{-1}, which is a small fraction of the frequency of an optical transition (order of 10^4 cm^{-1}). To within the experimental accuracy, no discrepancy with the theory of Sect. 46 (with the DIRAC value of 2 for g_s) was found. In fact, until fairly recently, the optical measurement[2] of the ZEEMAN effect together with theory provided one of the methods for measuring the ratio e/m for the electron.

Apart from confirming other details of the theory, the optical measurements confirmed the DIRAC value of 2 for g_s in (46.1) to within the experimental accuracy[3] of about one part in 500. Only recently microwave and other experimental techniques became available, which made much more accurate measurements of g_s possible. Historically, a value of g_s differing slightly from 2 (anomalous magnetic moment) was first suggested[4] by discrepancies between precision experiments and the DIRAC theory for hyperfine structure. However, the most direct measurements of g_s come from modern experiments on the ZEEMAN effect, which we shall discuss briefly.

α) Experimental techniques[5]. In optical spectra one usually deals with electric dipole transitions between two atomic states whose orbital quantum numbers L differ by unity ($\Delta L = \pm 1$). For hydrogen-like atoms the principal quantum number n also changes in an optical transition. In connection with the LAMB shift (Sect. 21) we have already considered electric dipole transitions between states in hydrogen of the *same* principal quantum number but different values of l, whose energy difference is a relativistic effect. Another type of electromagnetic transition is possible, the magnetic dipole transitions (see Sect. 66γ). For an atom in a weak (or no) external magnetic field, the selection rules for such a transition are $\Delta L = 0$, $\Delta J = 0, \pm 1$ and $\Delta m = 0, \pm 1$. We then have the possibility of a transition between two states of the *same* principal quantum number and the same L, S and J, but with $\Delta m = \pm 1$. The *whole* energy difference between two such states is then due to the interaction with the magnetic field and the frequency of the radiation emitted or absorbed in this transition gives directly the energy of the ZEEMAN splitting. In this discussion we have neglected the effects of hyperfine structure (Sect. 47γ). For atoms with a finite nuclear moment in weak magnetic fields the energy difference between two states of identical L, S and J (but different m or F) depends also on the hyperfine structure interaction energy. This complicates the measurement of the ZEEMAN effect somewhat, but also makes possible a measurement of the hyperfine structure splitting energy by observing direct transitions between states of different values of F.

The probability for such a transition with the *spontaneous* emission of radiation is negligibly small, since the frequency of the radiation is extremely small (and, further, magnetic dipole transitions generally have smaller probabilities than electric ones). On the other hand, a rotating (or oscillating) magnetic field, even

[1] For the dependence on field strength of many lines in the H-spectrum see K. FOERSTERLING and G. HANSEN, Z. Physik **18**, 26 (1923) and ref. [*10*], Sect. 27d. For a survey, of the ZEEMAN effect in complex atoms see E. BACK and LANDÉ, ZEEMAN Effect (Berlin: Springer 1925); also R. BACHER and S. GOUDSMIT, Atomic Energy States (New York: McGraw-Hill Co. 1932).

[2] L. KINSLER and W. HOUSTON: Phys. Rev. **45**, 104 (1934); **46**, 533 (1934).

[3] The more accurate measurements of KINSLER were for singlet states which show the normal ZEEMAN effect and do not involve g_s.

[4] G. BREIT: Phys. Rev. **72**, 984 (1947).

[5] For a much more detailed account see ref. [*16*], Chap. 3.

of modest field strength, represents an extremely large number of electromagnetic quanta of frequency ν, if the rotation frequency ν is much smaller than optical frequencies (order of 10^{16} cps). The rotation frequency ν in a typical experiment lies in the short wave radio or in the microwave region (order of 10^8 or 10^9 cps). Such a rotating magnetic field can thus cause transitions[1] by absorption or *induced* emission if $h\nu$ is just equal to the energy difference between the two states. If these states form part of the ground state of the atom in question, their lifetimes will be long and the resonances will be very sharp (only a small frequency range will induce transitions).

Transitions induced by a rotating field of the correct frequency form the basis of many experimental techniques. The various techniques differ mainly in their method of detecting the transitions. In the atomic beam resonance method a transition of state of a particle in an atomic beam affects its trajectory, which is detected. In the microwave resonance absorption method the absorption of energy from the imposed rotating field is detected. In the magnetic resonance induction method one essentially detects the magnetic field produced by the induced emission of radiation. In all cases one essentially measures a frequency which corresponds to the energy of ZEEMAN splitting in a constant magnetic field or of the hyperfine splitting.

One can also measure the magnetic moments of nuclei by similar methods. Consider a nucleus in ionic solution or in a certain kind of molecule, so that there is no net magnetic interaction between the nucleus and the electrons. If the nucleus changes the direction of its spin $\boldsymbol{i}$ in a uniform magnetic field $\mathcal{H}$, the only change in energy will be that due to the interaction between the nuclear magnetic moment and this magnetic field. A rotating field with $h\nu$ equal to this energy difference can then induce transitions between states of different $\boldsymbol{i}\cdot\mathcal{H}$. These transitions can again be detected by the resonance absorption or induction method. Such experiments will be discussed further in Sect. 49γ.

The order of magnitude of some rotational frequencies ν in typical experiments are as follows. For a transition between the two hyperfine structure components of the hydrogen ground state (with no magnetic field), ν is 1420 Mc/sec. For the transition between the two ZEEMAN components of any $S_{\frac{1}{2}}$-state in hydrogen in a uniform magnetic field of 1000 Gauss, ν is about 2800 Mc/sec. In the same magnetic field, for a "spin flip" of the magnetic moment of a free proton, ν is about 4.25 Mc/sec.

β) The ratio g_s/g_l. The experimental techniques discussed above make possible the measurement of frequencies, corresponding to the ZEEMAN effect energies in a constant magnetic field $\mathcal{H}$, with extremely high precision. Consider, for instance, an atomic state with no hyperfine structure in a "weak" field $\mathcal{H}$. The frequency ν corresponding to a transition in which the magnetic quantum number m changes by unity is then, according to (46.4),

$$\nu = \frac{\Delta E}{h} = \frac{e}{4\pi m c}\mathcal{H} g. \tag{49.1}$$

If the RUSSELL-SAUNDERS approximation holds, the LANDÉ factor g should be given by (46.5) or (46.5a). If, further, the unmodified DIRAC theory were correct, g_l and g_s in (46.5a) would be unity and two, respectively. We are mainly interested in investigating deviations of g_l and g_s from these values.

To obtain an accurate value for g in (49.1) we need, besides a precision measurement of the frequency ν, an accurate knowledge of the ratio e/m and of the magnetic

[1] For a detailed quantum mechanical theory see H. SALWEN, Phys. Rev. 99, 1274 (1955).

field $\mathcal{H}$. Although magnetic fields of very high uniformity can be obtained relatively easily, it is very difficult and tedious to measure the *absolute* field strength (in C.G.S. units) with high accuracy. Further, no absolute measurements of e/m of very great precision were available until recently. These difficulties can be avoided if we are satisfied with a measurement of the *ratio* of the g-values for two atomic states in the same or different atoms. One simply has to measure the ratio of the two transition frequencies in the *same* magnetic fields. This idea forms the basis of the classic experiment of KUSCH and FOLEY[1], which gave the first direct indication of the anomalous moment of the electron.

KUSCH and FOLEY used the atomic beam resonance method to measure transition frequencies for the ZEEMAN effect. To obtain sharp resonances they used atoms in their ground state and compared atoms for which the RUSSELL-SAUNDERS approximation should be very good, but which have different combinations of L, S and J. If one assumes the LANDÉ factor g to be of form (46.5a), but with g_l and g_s left arbitrary, then the ratio of the g-factors in two states with different L and/or S values immediately gives the ratio g_l/g_s. KUSCH and FOLEY used the $^2P_{\frac{3}{2}}$ and $^2P_{\frac{1}{2}}$ states in Ga and In and the $^2S_{\frac{1}{2}}$ state in Na. Assuming (46.5a), the mean of their measurements gave

$$\frac{g_s}{g_l} = 2\,(1.00119 \pm 0.00005). \tag{49.2}$$

This value clearly indicates a deviation from the DIRAC value of two. According to (47.5), the deviation of g_l from unity in the more refined theory is negligible for the reasonably heavy nuclei considered. The value of (49.2) is then in good agreement with the theoretical value given by quantum electrodynamics,

$$\frac{g_s}{g_l} \approx g_s = 2 \times 1.0011454. \tag{49.3}$$

Experimental techniques have improved still further since 1948 and the ratios of g-factors in various atomic states have by now been measured with errors of less than one part in 10^5. However, most of these measurements are for states in complex atoms. As discussed in Sect. 48γ, the actual g-factors in such atomic states can differ from the expression (46.5a) by about one part in 10^4 and these deviations cannot be calculated with any accuracy at the moment. Experiments of this type then determine the ratio g_l/g_s to not much better than one part in 10^4 at the moment, in spite of the high experimental accuracy. In fact, these experiments are used nowadays to investigate the purity of atomic states etc., after assuming the theoretical value in (49.3). It should also be pointed out that these experiments measure only the ratio g_l/g_s, not g_l and g_s separately. In Sect. 49δ we discuss an accurate absolute measurement of g_s.

γ) *Auxiliary measurements.* We have already mentioned measurements of the frequency ν_p for the "spin flip" of the magnetic moment μ_p of a free proton in a uniform magnetic field $\mathcal{H}$ by the resonance absorption or induction method. μ_p can be written in the form

$$\mu_p = \frac{1}{2}\, g'_p\, \mu_0 = \frac{1}{2}\, g_p\, \mu_{NM}, \qquad \mu_{NM} = \frac{e\hbar}{2M_p c}, \tag{49.4}$$

where μ_0 is the BOHR magneton (45.7), μ_{NM} the nuclear magneton (22.7), M_p the proton mass and the factor $\frac{1}{2}$ is the value of the spin of the proton. The frequency ν_p is then

$$\nu_p = \frac{e}{4\pi m c}\,\mathcal{H}\, g'_p = \frac{e}{4\pi M_p c}\,\mathcal{H}\, g_p. \tag{49.5}$$

[1] P. KUSCH and H. FOLEY: Phys. Rev. **74**, 250 (1948).

If the proton were a pure DIRAC particle, g_p would be exactly two. Actually it possesses an anomolous magnetic moment, like the electron, which largely stems from interaction with the virtual meson field (instead of the electromagnetic field). Unlike the fine structure constant α, the equivalent mesonic coupling constant is *not* small, g_p differs considerably from 2 and its value cannot be calculated with any accuracy from present-day meson theories.

One practical use of the proton resonance experiments is the accurate (but relative) calibration of magnetic fields. From (49.5), ν_p is directly proportional to the magnetic field $\mathcal{H}$ and measurements of ν_p in the two magnetic fields to be used in two different experiments immediately gives the ratio of the field strengths. μ_p has also been measured on an absolute scale (C.G.S. units) in a magnetic field calibrated by the U.S. Nat. Bur. Stand. in C.G.S. units[1], but only to an accuracy of about 3 parts in 10^5. This measurement is important for a determination of the absolute constants e, m and M_p, but will not be discussed further.

Experiments of great importance for our present discussion are measurements of the "cyclotron frequency" of charged particles, i.e. the frequency of revolution ν of a free particle moving in a large (on an atomic scale) circular orbit in a uniform magnetic field $\mathcal{H}$,

$$\nu = \frac{e}{2\pi M c} \mathcal{H} \tag{49.6}$$

where e and M are the charge and mass of the particle. Such measurements are not quite as accurate as those of the ZEEMAN splitting or proton resonance frequencies. The cyclotron frequency has been measured for the electron[2] and for the proton[3] together with a measurement of the proton resonance frequency ν_p. These two measurements then give values for the factors g_p' and g_p, respectively in (49.4).

$$\tfrac{1}{2} g_p' = 0.001\,521\,01\,(1 \pm 1.2 \times 10^{-5}), \qquad \tfrac{1}{2} g_p = 2.792\,76 \pm 0.000\,06. \tag{49.7}$$

The ratio of these two factors gives the ratio of the proton and electron mass. g_p alone is of importance in connection with precision measurements of the hydrogen hyperfine structure. We shall only use the value of g_p' in connection with ZEEMAN splitting frequencies.

δ) The absolute value of g_s. The limitation in the interpretation of the experiments discussed in Sect. 49β lies not in the experimental errors, but in the theoretical uncertainties in the LANDÉ factor g of (46.5) for complex atoms. For the ground state of hydrogen these difficulties do not arise. The magnetic interaction energy in weak fields can be calculated exactly and the ratio of g to g_s (after applying corrections for hyperfine structure effects), due to relativistic effects, is given by (47.4). The frequency of the ZEEMAN transition in a uniform magnetic field has been measured with extremely high precision, both by the atomic beam resonance method[4] and the resonance absorption method[5]. The proton resonance frequency ν_p is measured in the same field in each experiment. Such an experiment then gives the ratio of g_s to g_p' [see Eqs. (49.1) and (49.5)]. The two experi-

---

[1] THOMAS, DRISCOLL and HIPPLE: Phys. Rev. **78**, 787 (1950); **80**, 901 (1950).

[2] J. GARDNER and E. PURCELL: Phys. Rev. **83**, 996 (1950).

[3] F. BLOCH and C. JEFFRIES: Phys. Rev. **80**, 305 (1950). — HIPPLE, SOMMER and THOMAS: Phys. Rev. **80**, 487 (1950).

[4] KOENIG, PRODELL and KUSCH: Phys. Rev. **88**, 191 (1952).

[5] R. BERINGER and M. HEALD: Phys. Rev. **95**, 1474 (1954).

ments are in good agreement and give[1]

$$g_s/g'_p = 658.229 \pm 0.001\,. \tag{49.8}$$

The quantity of interest is not the ratio (49.8), but g_s itself. This can be obtained by combining (49.8) with g'_p, Eq. (49.7), obtained from the electron cyclotron[1] frequency, and is

$$g_s = 2\,(1.001\,147 \pm 0.000\,012)\,. \tag{49.9}$$

This value for g_s is in excellent agreement with the theoretical value, Eq. (47.12), (49.3). The term of order α^2 in (47.15) contributes about 3×10^{-5} to g_s, so the accuracy of (49.9) is sufficient to check at least the order of magnitude of even this higher order term.

It should be pointed out that, in obtaining (49.9), the proton resonance frequency was only used as a convenient intermediary. In effect, the ZEEMAN frequency of an electron in a bound state was compared with the orbital revolution frequency of an electron in the same magnetic field. The error in (49.9) comes overwhelmingly from the electron cyclotron experiment. Incidentally, a comparison of (49.9) and the values for g_s/g_l, discussed in Sect. 49β, shows that g_l for a bound state with orbital angular momentum equals unity to within the uncertainty of interpretation of about 1 part in 10^4.

50. The diamagnetism of helium[2]. The ground state of helium is a singlet state ($S=0$) and possesses no orbital angular momentum ($L=0$). The linear term W in the interaction HAMILTONian with a magnetic field is thus zero, the ground state wave function is non-degenerate and there is no ZEEMAN splitting. Nevertheless, the quadratic term (47.11) in the HAMILTONian produces a small *shift* in energy, which depends on the magnetic field. This operator is

$$W_Q = \frac{e^2}{2mc^2}\,(A_1^2 + A_2^2) = \frac{e^2\mathcal{H}^2}{8mc^2}\,(r_1^2\sin^2\vartheta_1 + r_2^2\sin^2\vartheta_2)\,. \tag{50.1}$$

Noting that the wave function is spherically symmetric and symmetric in $\boldsymbol{r}_1$ and $\boldsymbol{r}_2$ we find for the energy change ΔE (in atomic units),

$$\Delta E = \tfrac{1}{4}\,\alpha^2\mathcal{H}^2\,\overline{r^2}\,\overline{\sin^2\vartheta} = \tfrac{1}{6}\,\alpha^2\mathcal{H}^2\,\overline{r^2}\ \text{at. un.} \tag{50.2}$$

where $\overline{r^2}$ is the expectation value of r^2 for one electron. The average value may be computed by means of HARTREE's charge distribution, Table 5, resulting in

$$\overline{r^2} = 1.19\ (\text{a. u.}),\quad \Delta E = 1.05\times 10^{-5}\,\mathcal{H}^2\ (\text{a. u.})\,. \tag{50.3}$$

In the presence of a field strength $\mathcal{H} = 100\,000$ Gauss $= 0.006$ atomic units, the term shift amounts to approximately 4×10^{-10} at. units $= 0.8\times 10^{-4}\ \text{cm}^{-1}$, and thus, surely, is far below the limits of spectroscopic observability. Nonetheless, this slight term shift is responsible for the diamagnetism of helium.

The magnetic susceptibility per mole, χ, is defined by

$$\mathcal{N}\Delta E = -\tfrac{1}{2}\chi\mathcal{H}^2, \tag{50.4}$$

where ΔE is the term shift evaluated above, and $\mathcal{N}$ is AVOGADRO's number $= 6.02\times 10^{23}$. χ has the dimensions of a volume. If we insert the value of ΔE,

[1] The value quoted in (49.8) refers to g'_p for protons bound in molecules in a sample of mineral oil. Due to diamagnetic corrections this is not quite the same as for a free proton. The values quoted in (49.7) are the extrapolated ones for a free proton; the experimental value for mineral oil is $\frac{1}{2}\,g'_p = 0.001\,520\,97$.

[2] See J. C. SLATER: Phys. Rev. **31**, 333 (1928).

Laddenburg p. 357

(50.3), we obtain χ in units of a^3, where a is the radius of the hydrogen atom. In terms of cm³ we obtain the value

$$\chi = -\frac{2\Delta E}{\mathcal{H}^2}\mathcal{N}a^3 = -2\times 1.05\times 10^{-5}\times 6.02\times 10^{23}\times 0.529\times 10^{-24} = -1.87\times 10^{-6}.$$

The measured[1] value of χ is equal to -1.88×10^{-6}; the agreement is excellent.

b) STARK effect in hydrogen.

51. Linear STARK effect. *α) Symmetry considerations.* We shall consider an *arbitrary* atom in a homogeneous external electric field pointing in a direction parallel to the z-axis and of field strength F. The nonrelativistic SCHRÖDINGER equation for the atom is then, in atomic units,

$$\left(\tfrac{1}{2}\Delta + E - V - \Phi\right)u = 0, \quad \Phi = F\sum_i z_i. \tag{51.1}$$

The perturbation HAMILTONian Φ represents the sum over all electrons i of the interaction energy eFz of the electron with the electric field.

We now show that the expectation value of the perturbation potential Φ, using an eigenfunction u_0 of the field-free atom,

$$\overline{\Phi} = \int d\tau\, |u_0|^2\, \Phi,$$

vanishes in general: Consider an inversion about the nucleus of the spatial coordinates of all the electrons, i.e., change $\boldsymbol{r}_1, \boldsymbol{r}_2, \ldots, \boldsymbol{r}_n$ to $-\boldsymbol{r}_1, -\boldsymbol{r}_2, \ldots, -\boldsymbol{r}_n$ (*without* altering the spin wave functions, if any). The field-free HAMILTONian remains unchanged under such an inversion. It then follows that the field-free eigenstates have definite *parity*, i.e., u_0 either remains unchanged (even parity) or merely changes sign (odd parity) under inversion. Hence $|u_0|^2$ is unchanged but Φ *changes sign* under inversion ($z_i \to -z_i$). It then follows that the integral leading to the expectation value $\overline{\Phi}$ vanishes.

It follows from a similar argument that the matrix element of Φ for a transition between two unperturbed states a and b ($|u_0|^2$ replaced by $u_a^* u_b$ in the above integral) vanishes unless the two states have *opposite* parity. For a single electron in a central potential a state with orbital and magnetic quantum numbers l and m has odd (even) parity if l is odd (even), independent of the value of m. This follows from a property of spherical harmonics under inversion,

$$Y_{lm}(\pi - \vartheta, \pi + \varphi) = (-1)^l\, Y_{lm}(\vartheta, \varphi). \tag{51.2}$$

Thus Φ has non-zero matrix elements only for a transition from a state of odd l to one of even l (or vice versa). More explicitly, on writing $z = r\cos\vartheta$ and considering the orthogonality properties of spherical harmonics [see Eq. (A.22) of the appendix], the matrix element vanishes unless the two states have the same m and values of l differing by ± 1 (see also Sect. 60).

In complex atoms, states of different parity have different field-free energies. First order perturbation theory applied to Φ then gives no energy shift, since the expectation value $\overline{\Phi}$ vanishes. For weak fields the interaction energy is then given by *second* order perturbation theory and is *quadratic* in the field strength F. However, hydrogen-like atoms form an exception to this rule: States of different l-values (for fixed principal quantum number n) are degenerate (in nonrelativistic approximation). Since Φ has non-zero matrix elements for transitions

[1] A. P. WILLS and L. G. HECTOR: Phys. Rev. **23**, 209; **24**, 418 (1924).

between states of odd and even l, the perturbation Φ will remove this degeneracy. The eigenfunctions *with* field are then superpositions of the field-free functions with different l-values and first order perturbation theory gives an interaction which is *linear* in the field-strength (for weak fields).

β) Calculations. It is, of course, possible to evaluate the linear STARK effect of the hydrogen atom by constructing the perturbation matrix (51.1) by means of the usual eigenfunctions in polar coordinates and finding the eigenvalues of that matrix. Fortunately, the STARK effect can also be treated in a simpler fashion by calculating in parabolic instead of polar coordinates. As we have seen in Sect. 6, the SCHRÖDINGER equation of the hydrogen atom in the absence of external fields can also be separated in parabolic coordinates (a fact which is closely related to the degeneracy of the hydrogen levels with respect to l). We shall now show that the separability is maintained in the presence of the electric field. The perturbation potential of the electric field, Fz, may be expressed in parabolic coordinates according to (6.1):

$$F z = \tfrac{1}{2} F(\xi - \eta).$$

The SCHRÖDINGER equation

$$\left(\frac{1}{2}\Delta + E + \frac{Z}{r} - F z\right) u = 0,$$

on writing the Laplacian operator in parabolic coordinates according to (6.4) and multiplying the equation by $\frac{1}{2}(\xi+\eta)$, assumes the form

$$\frac{\partial}{\partial\xi}\left(\xi\frac{\partial u}{\partial\xi}\right) + \frac{\partial}{\partial\eta}\left(\eta\frac{\partial u}{\partial\eta}\right) + \left(\frac{1}{4\xi}+\frac{1}{4\eta}\right)\frac{\partial^2 u}{\partial\varphi^2} + \left[\frac{1}{2}E(\xi+\eta) + Z - \frac{1}{4}F(\xi^2-\eta^2)\right] u = 0.$$

As in Sect. 6, the above differential equation is separated by the assumption (6.5):

$$u = u_1(\xi)\, u_2(\eta)\, e^{im\varphi}, \quad Z = Z_1 + Z_2.$$

However, the functions u_1 and u_2—instead of (6.6)—now must satisfy the differential equations

$$\left.\begin{aligned} \frac{d}{d\xi}\left(\xi\frac{d u_1}{d\xi}\right) + \left(\frac{1}{2}E\xi + Z_1 - \frac{m^2}{4\xi} - \frac{1}{4}F\xi^2\right) u_1 = 0, \\ \frac{d}{d\eta}\left(\eta\frac{d u_2}{d\eta}\right) + \left(\frac{1}{2}E\eta + Z_2 - \frac{m^2}{4\eta} + \frac{1}{4}F\eta^2\right) u_2 = 0, \end{aligned}\right\} \tag{51.3}$$

which differ in the sign in front of F. The ordinary differential Eq. (51.3) may either be directly integrated—we shall do this in Sect. 53—or they may be treated by means of a perturbation procedure which has as its starting point the unperturbed eigenfunctions (6.7), (6.8) and the unperturbed eigenvalues (6.10). The perturbation procedure will be satisfactory as long as the field intensity is not too large.

The perturbation procedure differs from the usual one in that the separation parameters Z_1 and Z_2, rather than the energy E, are the eigenvalues of the problem. Solving the differential equations determines Z_1 and Z_2 as a function of E and the field intensity F. The condition that $Z=Z_1+Z_2$ gives the relation which we are after, namely, the energy E as a function of the field intensity F.

Introducing, as in Sect. 6, the quantity

$$\varepsilon = \sqrt{-2E} \tag{51.4}$$

the "eigenvalue" Z_1, in the absence of external electric field, may be expressed in terms of the electric quantum number n_1 and the magnetic quantum number m according to the formula

$$Z_1^{(0)} = \left(n_1 + \frac{m+1}{2}\right)\varepsilon. \tag{51.5}$$

The first order perturbation of this eigenvalue, produced by the field F, is given by the integral of the perturbation potential evaluated over the unperturbed eigenfunction. Except for normalization, that eigenfunction is given by (6.7) and (6.8). Normalizing according to the condition

$$\int_0^\infty u_1^2(\xi)\, d\xi = 1,$$

we obtain [cf. Eq. (3.13)]:

$$u_1(\xi) = \frac{n_1!^{\frac{1}{2}}}{(n_1+m)!^{\frac{3}{2}}}\, e^{-\frac{1}{2}\varepsilon\xi}\, \xi^{\frac{1}{2}m}\, \varepsilon^{\frac{1}{2}(m+1)}\, L_{n_1+m}^m(\varepsilon\xi), \tag{51.6}$$

and thus [cf. Eq. (3.13)]

$$\left.\begin{aligned} Z_1^{(1)} &= \frac{1}{4} F \int_0^\infty \xi^2 u_1^2\, d\xi = \frac{1}{4} F \frac{n_1!}{(n_1+m)!^3} \int \varepsilon^{m+1} \xi^{m+2} e^{-\varepsilon\xi}\, d\xi\, \left(L_{n_1+m}^m(\varepsilon\xi)\right)^2 \\ &= \frac{1}{4} F \varepsilon^{-2} (6n_1^2 + 6n_1 m + m^2 + 6n_1 + 3m + 2). \end{aligned}\right\} \tag{51.7}$$

Thus, altogether we obtain to first order [cf. Eq. (51.5)]

$$Z_1 = Z_1^{(0)} + Z_1^{(1)} = \varepsilon\left(n_1 + \frac{m+1}{2}\right) + \frac{1}{4}\frac{F}{\varepsilon^2}(6n_1^2 + 6n_1 m + m^2 + 6n_1 + 3m + 2) \tag{51.8}$$

and similarly

$$Z_2 = Z_2^{(0)} + Z_2^{(1)} = \varepsilon\left(n_2 + \frac{m+1}{2}\right) - \frac{1}{4}\frac{F}{\varepsilon^2}(6n_2^2 + 6n_2 m + m^2 + 6n_2 + 3m + 2).$$

Adding the two equations and paying due regard to the definition of the principal quantum number n, (5.8) yields

$$Z = \varepsilon n + \frac{3}{2}\frac{F}{\varepsilon^2}(n_1 - n_2)\, n \tag{51.9}$$

or, solving for ε,

$$\varepsilon = \frac{Z}{n} - \frac{3}{2} F \left(\frac{n}{Z}\right)^2 (n_1 - n_2). \tag{51.10}$$

Thus, the energy is given by

$$E = -\frac{1}{2}\varepsilon^2 = -\frac{1}{2}\frac{Z^2}{n^2} + \frac{3}{2}\frac{Fn}{Z}(n_1 - n_2). \tag{51.11}$$

Formula (51.11) for the linear STARK effect was derived by SCHWARZSCHILD and EPSTEIN on the basis of the old quantum theory and from wave-mechanics by SCHRÖDINGER in his third communication. The energy of the linear STARK effect, aside from the dependence on the principal quantum number n is a function of the difference $n_1 - n_2$ only which is also designated as the "electric quantum number"; there is no dependence on the magnetic quantum number m (m first appears in the second order approximation). The energetically highest STARK component belonging to the term with principal quantum number n is obtained by setting the parabolic quantum numbers $n_1 n_2$ equal to $n-1$ and 0, respectively, the lowest STARK component corresponds to $n_1 = 0$, $n_2 = n-1$.

The separation between these two extreme term components as given by (51.11) amounts to:

$$\Delta E = 3F\frac{n(n-1)}{Z}. \tag{51.12}$$

The separation of the terms in the STARK effect thus goes as n^2. The growth of the separation with increasing principal quantum number n is quite understandable: The larger the diameter of the electron's orbit the greater is the potential difference between diametrically opposite points in that orbit.

In order to arrive at a notion of the absolute magnitude of the STARK effect, we must remember that F is measured in atomic units. The unit of electric field intensity is the field produced by a proton at a distance equal to the radius of the first BOHR orbit of hydrogen, viz.:

$$\frac{e}{a^2} = \frac{4.80\times 10^{-10}}{(5.29\times 10^{-9})^2} = 1.71\times 10^7 \text{ e.s.u.} = 5.142\times 10^9 \text{ Volt/cm}. \tag{51.13}$$

The unit of energy is equal to twice the RYDBERG energy $2.19\times 10^5\ \text{cm}^{-1}$. Thus, if the field is measured in Volt/cm and the energy in cm^{-1}, we obtain

$$E = \left[-\frac{1.097\times 10^5}{n^2} Z^2 + \frac{F}{15620}\frac{n}{Z}(n_1 - n_2)\right] \text{cm}^{-1}. \tag{51.14}$$

The STARK splitting, especially of the highly excited terms, may attain large values. For $n=5$ the separation between the outer components, $n_1=4$, $n_2=0$ and $n_2=4$, $n_1=0$, in a field of 500000 Volt/cm is as much as

$$32\times 5\times 8 = 1280\ \text{cm}^{-1},$$

i.e., almost equal to the separation of the terms $n=5$ and $n=6$ in the absence of fields ($1400\ \text{cm}^{-1}$).

The appearance of the eigenfunctions belonging to the stationary states of the STARK effect is of interest. For the case $n_1 > n_2$, as shown in Sect. 6, the electron is predominantly on the positive side of the z-axis. Since for positive z the potential energy of the electron and the external field, eFz, is positive it is not surprising that the energy belonging to the states $n_1 > n_2$ is raised by the electric field. For a view of the asymmetry of the charge distribution, we refer the reader to Fig. 8 of Sect. 6 which gives the charge distribution of the state $n=4$, $n_1=2$, $n_2=0$ and $m=1$. Only for the case $n_1=n_2$ is there no asymmetry[1].

The experimental verification of formula (51.11) is very good[2]. Because of the dependence of the term splitting on n, the main contribution to the splitting of a spectral line comes from the upper level. The selection rule reads as usual: $\Delta m=0$ for light polarized parallel to the field, $\Delta m=\pm 1$ for perpendicular polarization. There is no selection rule with respect to the parabolic quantum numbers $n_1 n_2$, although the transitions which involve a change in the sign of $n_1 - n_2$ are mostly weak. In our approximation the STARK splitting of every term, and therefore also of every spectral line, is an integral multiple of $\frac{3}{2}F$ atomic units $= F/15620\ \text{cm}^{-1}$. The most convenient designation of a line consists of giving the shift relative to the line without field in units of $F/15620$ and specifying in addition the polarization (π parallel, σ perpendicular to the electric field).

[1] Cf., F. G. SLACK: Ann. d. Phys. **82**, 576 (1927) Fig. 2.

[2] Quantitative verification in the work of K. SJÖGREN, Z. Physik **77**, 290 (1932).

That has been done, for example, in Fig. 25. Fig. 25a shows the splitting of the second and third levels of hydrogen and the associated transitions which are allowed. The numbers which accompany the transitions designate the shift of the corresponding spectral line in units of $F/15620\ \text{cm}^{-1}$. In Fig. 25b, the resulting splitting patterns of the BALMER line H_α is shown; the length of the line has been taken to be proportional to the intensity of the line which has been calculated from formulas (65.1) and (65.2). For the purpose of comparison, Fig. 25c shows the photometric curves observed by MARK and WIERL for light polarized in directions parallel and perpendicular to the field respectively. For the higher terms of the BALMER series, see

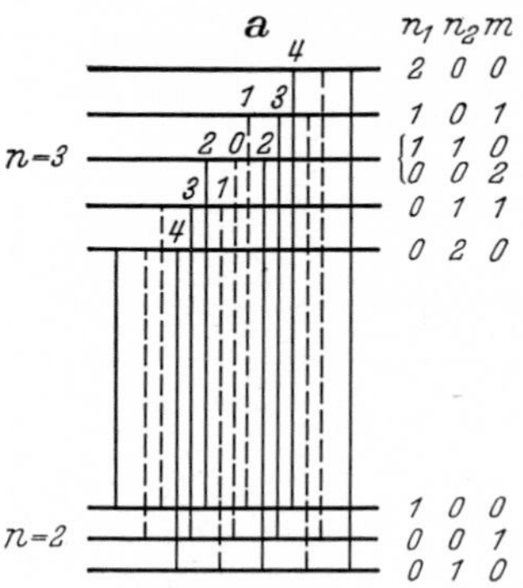

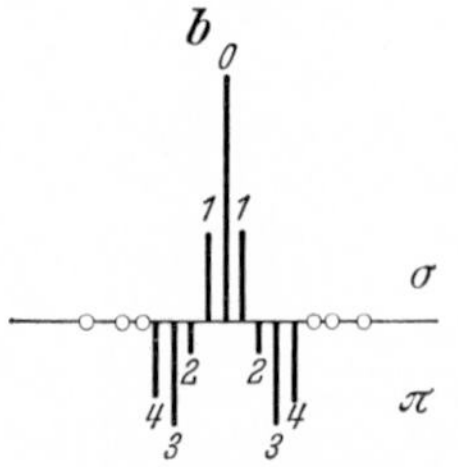

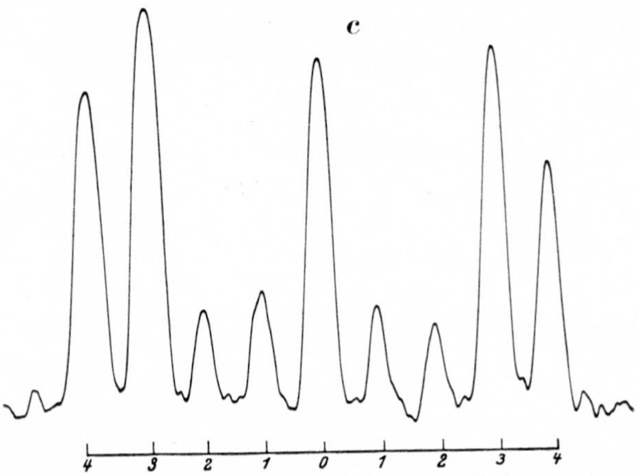

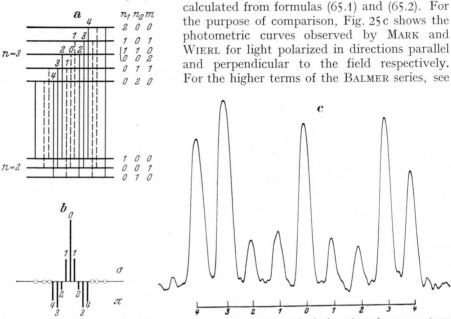

Fig. 25 a—c. STARK effect of the H_α-line in hxdrogen. a. Gives the energy level scheme (π- and σ-components are solid and dotted vertical lines, respectively). b. The theoretical splitting diagram of the spectral lines: The length of a line is proportional to its intensity (circles denote lines with very small intensity). The number against each line is the shift relative to the field-free line in units of $F/15620$. c. An experimental photometric curve (MARK and WIERL), which corresponds to the theoretical Fig. 25b (with π- and σ-components on the same picture).

E. SCHRÖDINGER, Abhandlungen zur Wellenmechanik, p. 116; H. MARK and R. WIERL, Z. Physik **53**, 526; **55**, 156; **57**, 494 (1929).

52. The quadratic STARK effect. With increasing field strength a term which is quadratic in the electric field appears in addition to the linear STARK effect, and a mixing of levels having different principal quantum numbers takes place. In order to evaluate the quadratic effect we must consider the second order perturbation of the "eigenvalue" Z_1 of the first of the differential equation (51.3). According to the general SCHRÖDINGER perturbation theory the second order perturbation is given by

$$Z_1^{(2)} = \left(\frac{1}{4} F\right)^2 \sum_{n_1' \neq n_1} \frac{|(\xi^2)_{n_1 n_1'}|^2}{Z_1^{(0)}(n_1) - Z_1^{(0)}(n_1')} . \tag{52.1}$$

The non-diagonal elements of the matrix of ξ^2 which occur in (52.1) vanish if $n_1' > n_1 + 2$ or $n_1' < n_1 - 2$. For the non-vanishing matrix elements the following values are obtained[1]:

$$\left.\begin{aligned} (\xi^2)_{n_1,\, n_1-1} &= -2\varepsilon^{-2}(2n_1 + m)\sqrt{n_1(n_1+m)}, \\ (\xi^2)_{n_1,\, n_1-2} &= \varepsilon^{-2}\sqrt{n_1(n_1-1)(n_1+m)(n_1+m-1)}. \end{aligned}\right\} \tag{52.2}$$

[1] Derivation by means of the generating function for the LAGUERRE functions (3.40).

The separation parameters Z_1 in zeroth approximation are given by (51.5), thus

$$Z_1^{(0)}(n_1) - Z_1^{(0)}(n_1') = \varepsilon\,(n_1 - n_1').$$

Evaluating the above we obtain

$$Z_1^{(2)} = -\tfrac{1}{32} F^2 \varepsilon^{-5} (m + 2n_1 + 1) \left[8m^2 + 34\,(2m\,n_1 + 2n_1^2 + m + 2n_1) + 36\right].$$

Adding to the above the corresponding expression for $Z_2^{(2)}$ gives $Z^{(2)}$ and in view of (51.9) one obtains:

$$\begin{aligned} Z &= Z^{(0)} + Z^{(1)} + Z^{(2)} \\ &= \varepsilon\, n + \tfrac{3}{2} F\, n\, \varepsilon^{-2} (n_1 - n_2) - \tfrac{1}{16} F^2 n\, \varepsilon^{-5} \left[17n^2 + 51\,(n_1 - n_2)^2 - 9m^2 + 19\right]. \end{aligned}$$

This relation between Z and ε yields the following value for the energy in second approximation:

$$\left.\begin{aligned} E_2 = -\frac{1}{2}\,\varepsilon^2 = -\frac{Z^2}{2n^2} + \frac{3}{2} F\,\frac{n}{Z}\,(n_1 - n_2) - \\ -\frac{1}{16} F^2 \left(\frac{n}{Z}\right)^4 \left[17n^2 - 3\,(n_1 - n_2)^2 - 9m^2 + 19.\right] \end{aligned}\right\} \qquad (52.3)$$

According to (52.3) the quadratic STARK effect, unlike the linear STARK effect, depends not only on n, n_1 and n_2 but also on the magnetic quantum number m. On the other hand, the second order effect remains unaltered on interchange of n_1 and n_2; thus, in so far as the second order perturbation is concerned, it does not matter whether the electron is more frequently in locations of high or low potential. Next, we note that the quadratic STARK effect always results in a lowering of the levels. Since $n_1 - n_2 < n - m$, the quantity inside the parentheses of the last term of (52.3) is always greater than $8n^2$, and consequently the depression of the term value is always greater than $F^2 n^6/2Z^4$. For $n \geq 3$ this is greater than $360F^2/Z^4$. On the other hand, it also follows from (52.3) that the components of the second quantum state which are affected to the greatest extent (namely, $n=2$, $n_1=1$, $n_2=m=0$) are shifted by only $84F^2/Z^4$, i.e., to a lesser extent than any of the higher states. Thus, all the lines of the BALMER series are shifted in the direction of smaller wave numbers, i.e., toward the red end of the spectrum. For example, measuring F in Volt/cm and wave numbers in cm^{-1}, the shift for the STARK components "+4" and "−4" for the line H_α (cf., Fig. 24a) amounts to:

$$\frac{2.19 \times 10^5}{16} \left(\frac{F}{5.14 \times 10^9}\right)^2 (81 \times 160 - 16 \times 84) \approx \left(\frac{F}{400000}\right)^2 \text{cm}^{-1}.$$

For a field strength of 400000 Volt/cm, for which the separation of the outermost components of H_α amounts to as much as 200 cm^{-1}, the red shift produced by the quadratic STARK effect amounts to only 1 cm^{-1}. On the other hand, for the same field strength, the outermost of the intense components (π 18) of H_γ, (transition $n=5$, $n_1=4$, $n_2=0$, $m=0$ to $n=2$, $n_1=1$, $n_2=0$, $m=0$) which are separated by approximately 900 cm^{-1}, undergo a red shift by as much as 22 cm^{-1}.

The perturbation expansion was carried through by ISHIDA and HIYAMA[1] up to terms of third order in the field strength F. Their result is

$$E_3 = E_2 + \frac{3}{32} F^3 \left(\frac{n}{Z}\right)^7 (n_1 - n_2)\left(23n^2 - (n_1 - n_2)^2 + 11m^2 + 39\right). \qquad (52.4)$$

[1] Y. ISHIDA and S. HIYAMA: Sci. Pap. Inst. phys. and chem. Res., Tokyo **1928**, Nr. 152.

For the two outermost components ($\pm\pi 18$) of the H_γ line, for instance[1], the frequency shift $\Delta\nu$ (in cm^{-1}), obtained from (52.4) is

$$\Delta\nu = \pm 1152.4 F - 127.1 F^2 \pm 28.3 F^3, \tag{52.5}$$

where the field strength F is expressed in units of 10^6 Volt/cm.

The experimental dependence of the STARK effect on field strength has been investigated thoroughly by RAUSCH V. TRAUBENBERG[2]. The agreement with theory is excellent. For the $\pi 18$ components of H_γ, for instance, the experimental $\Delta\nu$ has been measured up to fields of about 10^6 Volt/cm and the presence of even the *third* order term in (52.5) has been verified at the higher field strengths. A picture of the STARK effect on some lines in the BALMER series is shown in Fig. 26. The field strength increases from the bottom of the picture towards the top (the maximum field is 1.1×10^6 Volt/cm). Note that the components on the red side (to the left) of the field-free (vertical) lines are displaced more than the violet components (quadratic STARK effect). Note also that each line ceases to exist above a critical field strength F_0. This quenching of lines will be discussed in Sect. 54.

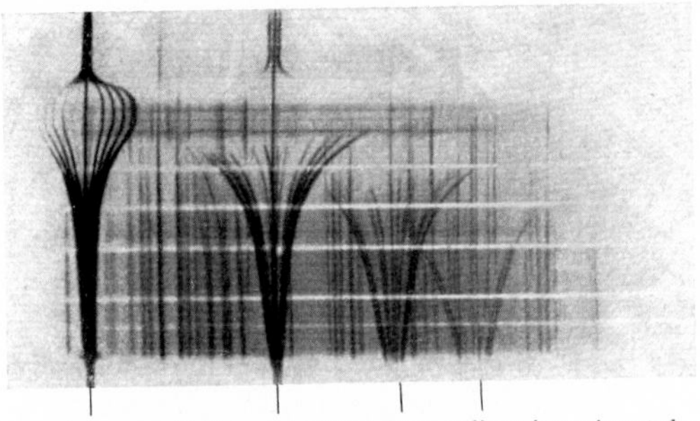

Fig. 26. STARK effect on some of the BALMER lines (experiments by RAUSCH V. TRAUBENBERG). The electric field strength increases from the bottom of the picture upwards, the maximum value (a little below the top of the picture) is 1.14 million Volt/cm, the horizontal white lines are lines of constant field strength.

53. STARK effect for strong fields[3]. The evaluation of terms of fourth order (and higher) in the field strength, according to perturbation theory, would be very tedious. For a hydrogen atom in a very strong field F, it is more convenient to solve the pair of differential equation (51.3) by an approximation method which does not involve expansions in powers of F. A suitable technique (especially for states with a reasonably large principal quantum number n) is the WENTZEL-KRAMERS-BRILLOUIN[4] (W.K.B.) method. We shall merely outline a calculation by LANCZOS[5], using this method

We eliminate first derivatives from (51.3) by substituting as new wave functions

$$\chi_1 = u_1 \sqrt{\xi}, \quad \chi_2 = u_2 \sqrt{\eta}. \tag{53.1}$$

Substituting χ_1 into the first equation of (51.3) we get

$$\frac{d^2\chi_1}{d\xi_1^2} + \Phi_1(\xi)\,\chi_1 = 0, \quad \Phi_1(\xi) = -\frac{1}{4}\varepsilon^2 + \frac{Z_1}{\xi} - \frac{m^2-1}{4\xi^2} - \frac{1}{4} F\xi, \tag{53.2}$$

where $\varepsilon = \sqrt{-2E}$. χ_2 obeys a similar equation. The function $\Phi_1(\xi)$ is essentially the "local kinetic energy" of the electron at position ξ. Φ_1 is plotted against ξ in Fig. 27, both for a finite field strength F and for zero field. In the region between the two classical turning points ξ_1 and ξ_2, the "kinetic energy" is positive

[1] For further details see ref. [*5*], p. 403.
[2] H. RAUSCH V. TRAUBENBERG: Z. Physik **54**, 307; **56**, 254 (1929); **62**, 289 (1930); **71**, 291 (1931). — Naturwiss. **18**, 417 (1930).
[3] For details see ref. [*10*], Sect. 32.
[4] G. WENTZEL: Z. Physik **38**, 518 (1926). — H. A. KRAMERS: Z. Physik **39**, 828 (1926). — L. BRILLOUIN: C. R. Acad. Sci., Paris **183**, 24 (1926).
[5] C. LANCZOS: Z. Physik **65**, 431 (1930).

and the wave function χ_1 is oscillatory and approximately of the form

$$\chi_1(\xi) = a\,\Phi_1^{-\frac{1}{4}}(\xi)\cos\left(\int\limits_{\xi_1}^{\xi}\sqrt{\Phi_1(x)}\,dx - \frac{\pi}{4}\right). \tag{53.3}$$

Since the wave function must be bounded, it must decrease exponentially on either side of the two turning points ξ_1 and ξ_2. From this requirement and considerations of continuity one can obtain the essential result of the W.K.B. method for our purpose, namely the relation

$$\int\limits_{\xi_1}^{\xi_2}\sqrt{\Phi_1(x)}\,dx = (n_1 + \tfrac{1}{2})\,\pi. \tag{53.4}$$

In (53.4), n_1 is an integer identical with the parabolic quantum number n_1 used in Sects. 6 and 51.

The relation (53.4) is only an approximation, but a fairly accurate one even for small values of n_1, and very accurate for large n_1. Using the definition (53.2) of Φ_1, the Eq. (53.4) gives a relation between the parameters ε and Z_1 for any value of F and m. From the equation for χ_2 one obtains a similar relation between ε and Z_2. These two relations, plus the condition $Z_1+Z_2=Z$, finally give a value for the energy parameter ε corresponding to any value of the field strength F.

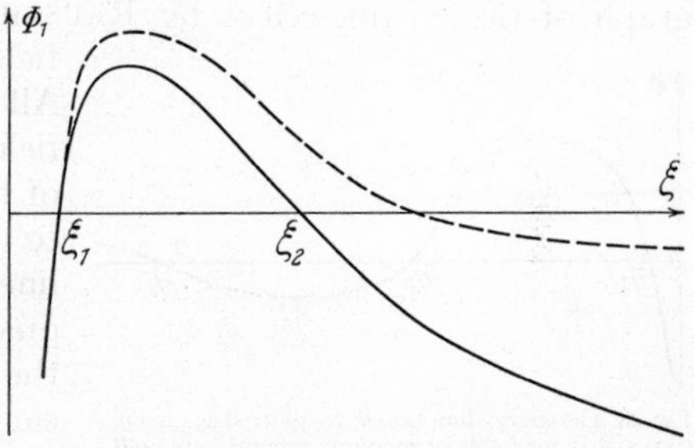

Fig. 27. The energy function $\Phi_1(\xi)$ plotted against ξ.

Such values for the energy parameter ε as a function of F were obtained numerically by LANCZOS. His results approximate those of the third order perturbation approximation (52.4) closely, except for very strong fields. For the violet component $+\pi 18$ of the H_γ line and $F = 10^6$ Volt/cm, for instance, LANCZOS' calculations give a shift of about 1052 cm^{-1}, compared with 1058 cm^{-1} from the third order approximation (52.5). For still stronger fields the difference would be much larger, but the field strengths at which observations can be made are limited by the quenching effect (see Sect. 54). For fields just below the critical (quenching) value the experimental results are in even better agreement with LANCZOS' calculations than with the third order result.

54. Ionization by the electric field. Quenching of the lines in the STARK effect[1]. Our discussion of the STARK effect must be supplemented by a very important point, namely, that the electric field is capable of altogether removing an electron from the atom. Looking at the potential energy of the electron

$$-V = -\frac{Z}{r} + F z,$$

we see that the atomic center is not the only location at which the potential is a minimum; at distances which are sufficiently far from the atom in the direction of the anode, i.e., negative z, the potential is even lower. It is well known from wave-mechanics that whenever two potential troughs exist it is always possible for the electron to pass from one trough (the atom) to the other (the anode). Evidently, once the electron has passed through the potential barrier between the two troughs it will not return to the atom but will be accelerated toward the

[1] Cf., C. LANCZOS, Z. Physik **62**, 518 (1930), and especially **68**, 204 (1931); J. R. OPPENHEIMER, Phys. Rev. **31**, 66 (1928).

anode; i.e., the atom will be left ionized. Experimentally the ionization from a given level becomes apparent in that the spectral lines initiated at that level are weakened.

Qualitatively, it is readily seen which circumstances are favorable for ionization. Above all, the radius of the electron's orbit must be large, i.e., the principal quantum number must be high. For a given principal quantum number those states are most easily ionized for which the electron's orbit is predominantly on the anode side of the atom. This is the case for the quantum states having the smallest possible n_1 and the largest possible n_2. Thus, of the terms having a given principal quantum number n, those which lie energetically the lowest are the least stable [cf. Eq. (51.11)], and, accordingly, as the field strength increases the "red" STARK components of each spectral line disappear first. This is exactly in accord with experimental observation, e.g., as in the photograph of the STARK effect by RAUSCH V. TRAUBENBERG (Fig. 26) in which the field intensity increases from bottom to top. All the lines suddenly die out at a certain field strength; the lines starting from levels of high principal quantum number n are seen to die out at lower field strengths than the lines coming from levels of lower principal quantum numbers (e.g., H_ζ before H_ε, and the latter before H_δ, etc.). Furthermore, for each line the red STARK component dies out at lower field strengths than the violet component.

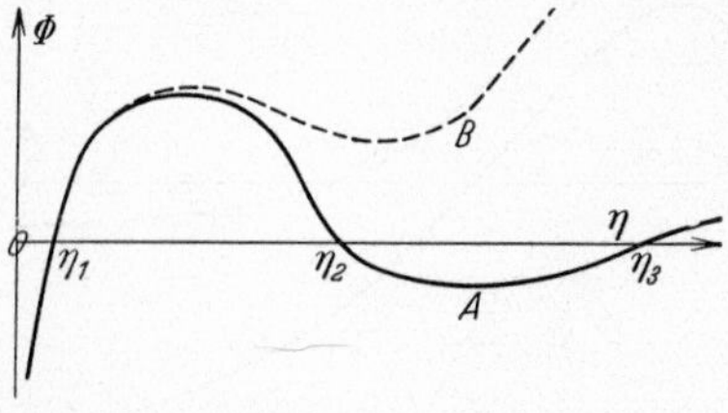

Fig. 28. The energy function $\Phi_2(\eta)$ plotted against η. Curve A is for fields of medium strength, curve B for very strong fields.

α) *Ionization limit according to classical mechanics.* For the purpose of pursuing the question of the ionization by the field quantitatively, we shall examine the differential equation for the part of the eigenfunction which depends on η. By definition the parabolic coordinate $\eta = r - z$ is large for large negative values of z, i.e., near the anode. The fact that the potential energy of the electron has a minimum near the anode is expressed in the "kinetic energy of the electron in the η direction"

$$\Phi_2(\eta) = -\frac{1}{4}\varepsilon^2 + \frac{Z_2}{\eta} - \frac{m^2-1}{4\eta^2} + \frac{1}{4}F\eta. \tag{54.1}$$

When η is large, $\Phi_2(\eta)$ is positive—contrary to the energy function $\Phi_1(\xi)$ in (53.2).

The possible types of behavior of $\Phi_2(\eta)$ are shown in Fig. 28 in which curve A corresponds to small and intermediate and B to high values of the field strength For small values of η, curve A behaves quite similarly to the curve for $\Phi_1(\xi)$ in Fig. 27; however, for large η it turns upward again and becomes positive for $\eta > \eta_3$. The "normal" motion of the electron, which we have treated so far, takes place in the "inner" region between η_1 and η_2; the ionization consists of the electron's passing into the outer region of positive kinetic energy beyond η_3. The "inner" and "outer" regions are separated by a potential barrier the height of which is of order of magnitude $|E| = \frac{1}{2}\varepsilon^2$ and the width of which is of order $|E|/F$.

As the field strength increases, the potential barrier becomes steadily lower and narrower until it finally disappears (curve B). At that stage the "inner" and "outer" regions are no longer separated by a potential barrier and ionization is possible even according to classical mechanics. The potential barrier disappears when the minimum of the function Φ_2 has the value zero, i.e., when both Φ_2 and its derivative vanish. For example, for $m=1$ one obtains

$$F_0 = \frac{E^2}{4Z_2}, \tag{54.2}$$

where F_0 is the value of F for which the expression (54.1) and its derivative is zero. According to classical mechanics, ionization would take place only if F exceeds this critical[1] value F_0. Using LANCZOS' expressions (see Sect. 53) for E and Z_2 as a function of F, one can solve (54.2) for F_0. For the "reddest component" of the level with $n=5$, which is the initial state for the H_γ-line, F_0 is about 1.1×10^6 Volt/cm. Experimentally the reddest component of H_γ is already quenched for fields of about 0.7×10^6 Volt/cm. This lowering of the critical field strength is due to the quantum mechanical effect of barrier penetration, which we shall discuss now.

β) Ionization according to wave-mechanics. We only need to deal with case A in which the "inner" and "outer" potential troughs are well defined and one can speak of the electron as being either in the atom or removed from it. Evidently up to the second zero the eigenfunction behaves almost exactly as previously, and beyond η_2 it must, as before, assume an exponential character. Thus, we are confronted with the same problem as in the theory of radioactivity (transmission of a potential step). Assuming that the electron is bound to the atom at time $t=0$, the calculation gives an outward current of electrons for all times $t>0$. Naturally, the current must be interpreted to mean that there exists a certain probability per second that the electron will escape from the atom.

A rigorous treatment of the problem has been carried through by LANCZOS. The treatment is based on the fact that in the presence of an infinitely extended potential trough there actually exist no discrete eigenvalues; rather, to any arbitrary eigenvalue there belongs an eigenfunction and the eigenfunctions differ only in that their amplitudes inside the atom vary in magnitude. This enables one to build up from these eigenfunctions a wave-function the amplitude of which vanishes exactly outside the atom. The time development of the wave-function automatically yields the migration of the charge from the atom.

We shall only use a less rigorous derivation involving the W.K.B. method, as used in the elementary theory of α-decay: Between the two classical turning points η_1 and η_2, the wave function $\chi_2(\eta)$ has the form of (53.3), with ξ and Φ_1 replaced by η and by Φ_2 [see Eq. (54.1)]. The normalization constant a in (53.3) is determined by the condition that the integral of χ_2^2 over the "classical region", from η_1 to η_2, be unity. In this integral the cos²-factor varies more rapidly than the rest of the integrand and we replace it by its average value of $\frac{1}{2}$. With this approximation, the normalization constant a is given by

$$\frac{1}{a^2} = \frac{1}{2}\int_{\eta_1}^{\eta_2} d\eta\, |\Phi_2(\eta)|^{-\frac{1}{2}}. \tag{54.3}$$

Inside the potential barrier ($\eta_2<\eta<\eta_3$), the wave function decreases exponentially[2]

$$\chi(\eta) = \tfrac{1}{2}\, a\, |\Phi(\eta)|^{-\frac{1}{4}} \exp\left[-\int_{\eta_2}^{\eta} \sqrt{|\Phi(x)|}\, dx\right]. \tag{54.4}$$

Outside the barrier ($\eta>\eta_3$), the kinetic energy is again positive and the wave function oscillatory, but its amplitude is decreased by a constant exponential

[1] In (54.2), E and Z_2 are the energy and charge parameter evaluated for field strength F_0.
[2] We drop the subscript 2 from χ and Φ.

(barrier penetration) factor

$$\chi(\eta) = \frac{1}{2} a\,|\Phi(\eta)|^{-\frac{1}{4}} \exp\left[-\int_{\eta_2}^{\eta_3} \sqrt{|\Phi(x)|}\,dx\right] \cos\left[\int_{\eta_3}^{\eta} \sqrt{|\Phi(x)|}\,dx + \frac{\pi}{4}\right]. \quad (54.5)$$

We are mainly interested in the current S outside the barrier ($\eta > \eta_3$). Since the "velocity" of the electron at the point η is $\sqrt{\Phi(\eta)}$, this current is simply $\chi^2 \sqrt{\Phi}$, where χ is given by (54.5). In the expression for χ^2 we again replace $\cos^2$ by its average value of $\frac{1}{2}$. In this approximation the current S is, as it should be, independent of the position η. Using (54.3), the current leaving the atom is then

$$S = \frac{\exp\left[-2\int_{\eta_2}^{\eta_3} \sqrt{|\Phi(\eta)|}\,d\eta\right]}{4\int_{\eta_1}^{\eta_2} \Phi^{-\frac{1}{2}}(\eta)\,d\eta}. \quad (54.6)$$

With Φ given in atomic units, as it is in (54.1), the expression (54.6) then represents the probability of ionization of the atom (in a particular state) during one atomic unit of time (2.4×10^{-17} sec).

Experimentally one does not observe the ionization directly, but the quenching by a field F of spectral lines due to radiative transitions from a particular initial atomic state to lower ones. Such spectral lines are suppressed if the probability for ionization of the initial state is greater than the probability for radiative transitions from this state. The latter probabilities (see Sect. 63, Table 15) are of the order of magnitude of 10^8 sec^{-1} or about 10^{-9} atomic units of frequency and the quenching of the spectral lines will be appreciable if the value (54.6) for S is also of order 10^{-9} or larger. When the field F is very near the "classical critical field strength" F_0, S is of order unity; thus S is of order 10^{-9} for an appreciably *smaller* field strength F_Q, the "quantum mechanical critical field strength". At these fields the smallness of S is due to the exponential term in (54.6), which depends critically on the height and width of the potential barrier and hence on F. Hence a small change in F away from F_Q produces a relatively large change in S (e.g., a 3% change in F changes S by a factor of two). Hence the intensity of a spectral line changes from essentially its field-free value to a very small value for quite a small increase in the field strength from below to above F_Q.

Numerical values for F_Q were calculated by Lanczos[1] for a number of atomic states of hydrogen. His values for the initial states of the outermost components of the H_γ and H_ε lines, for instance, are

	H_γ (red)	H_γ (violet)	H_ε (red)	H_ε (violet)
F_Q	0.69	1.01	0.20	0.32

with F_Q in units of 10^6 Volt/cm. These values are appreciably lower than the corresponding classical values F_0 and agree fairly well with the experimental values. The rapidity of the change of intensity with field strength is also verified experimentally (see Sect. 52, Fig. 26).

55. Stark effect of the fine structure of hydrogen[2]. The theory of the Stark effect which we have presented so far has been based on the Schrödinger equation without considering relativistic corrections or the spin of the electron.

[1] C. Lanczos: Z. Physik **68**, 204 (1931).

[2] Cf. V. Rojansky: Phys. Rev. **33**, 1 (1929). — R. Schlapp: Proc. Roy. Soc. Lond. **119**, 313 (1928). — G. Lüders: Ann. d. Phys. [6] **8**, 301 (1951).

This is certainly justified for electric field intensities which are ordinarily encountered in practice, namely, 100000 Volt/cm or greater which give rise to STARK splittings of 10 to several 1000 cm^{-1}. On the other hand, our treatment is not applicable to fields of less than about 1000 Volt/cm because then the STARK splitting is of the same order of magnitude as the fine structure.

α) STARK *effect small compared to fine structure.* First of all we shall deal with the case of very weak fields in which the STARK splitting is small compared to the separation of neighboring fine structure levels. In this case the quantum states have definite values of the principal quantum number n, the inner quantum number j (magnitude of the total angular momentum), and the magnetic quantum number m (component of the total angular momentum in the direction of the field, M_z). The first two quantum numbers determine the energy in the absence of field; our assumption that the STARK effect be small compared to the fine structure is equivalent to the assumption that eigenfunctions belonging to different fine structure levels are not mixed to any appreciable extent. M_z, on the other hand, is a constant of the motion for arbitrary field strengths. However, the orbital angular momentum l is a good quantum number only for vanishing field; if the field has a finite value, however small, l is not quantized[1]. Thus, in order to calculate the splitting we only need to know the matrix elements of the perturbing electric field which connect the states njm, $l=j-\frac{1}{2}$ with the states njm, $l=j+\frac{1}{2}$. The PAULI eigenfunctions of the states in question are

$$u_+=\frac{R_{n,j+\frac{1}{2}}(r)}{\sqrt{2j+2}}\begin{pmatrix}\sqrt{j-m+1}\;Y_{j+\frac{1}{2},m-\frac{1}{2}}\\ \sqrt{j+m+1}\;Y_{j+\frac{1}{2},m+\frac{1}{2}}\end{pmatrix},\quad u_-=\frac{R_{n,j-\frac{1}{2}}}{\sqrt{2j}}\begin{pmatrix}\sqrt{j+m}\;Y_{j-\frac{1}{2},m-\frac{1}{2}}\\ -\sqrt{j-m}\;Y_{j-\frac{1}{2},m+\frac{1}{2}}\end{pmatrix}. \tag{55.1}$$

and the corresponding matrix elements are given by

$$\left.\begin{aligned}\sum_\sigma\int u_-^*\,z\,u_+\,d\tau&=\int_0^{+\infty}r^2\,dr\cdot R_{n,j-\frac{1}{2}}\,R_{n,j+\frac{1}{2}}\,r\cdot\frac{1}{2\sqrt{j(j+1)}}\times\\&\times\Big[\sqrt{(j+m)(j-m+1)}\int Y^*_{j-\frac{1}{2},m-\frac{1}{2}}\,Y_{j+\frac{1}{2},m-\frac{1}{2}}\cos\vartheta\,d\omega-\\&-\sqrt{(j-m)(j+m+1)}\int Y^*_{j-\frac{1}{2},m+\frac{1}{2}}\,Y_{j+\frac{1}{2},m+\frac{1}{2}}\cos\vartheta\,d\omega\Big].\end{aligned}\right\}\tag{55.2}$$

Using (A.21), the integration over angles can readily be carried out and the quantity in the parentheses of (55.2) becomes

$$\frac{1}{2\sqrt{j(j+1)}}\left[(j+m)(j-m+1)-(j-m)(j+m+1)\right]=\frac{m}{\sqrt{j(j+1)}}.$$

The integration over r can be carried out in exactly the same way as at the beginning of Sect. 52 and yields

$$-\tfrac{3}{2}n\sqrt{n^2-(j+\tfrac{1}{2})^2}.$$

Since the diagonal elements of the perturbation matrix

$$\int u_+^*\,z\,u_+\,d\tau=\int u_-^*\,z\,u_-\,d\tau=0$$

vanish, the part of the matrix belonging to the quantum numbers njm is given simply by

$$-\frac{3n}{4}\,\frac{\sqrt{n^2-(j+\frac{1}{2})^2}}{j(j+1)}\cdot F\,m\begin{pmatrix}0&1\\1&0\end{pmatrix}. \tag{55.3}$$

[1] We neglect the LAMB shift, at the moment.

The eigenvalues of the matrix are

$$\varepsilon_m^{\pm} = \pm \frac{3}{4} \sqrt{n^2 - \left(j + \frac{1}{2}\right)^2} \frac{n\,m}{j(j+1)} F. \tag{55.4}$$

The eigenfunctions are simply the sum and the difference respectively of the eigenfunctions without field (55.1). Thus, each fine structure level is split by the electric field into $2j+1$ equidistant terms labelled by $m=-j\ldots,+j$. The separation of neighboring terms amounts to $\frac{n}{2}\frac{F}{15620}\frac{\sqrt{n^2-(j+\frac{1}{2})^2}}{j(j+1)}\,\text{cm}^{-1}$, and the splitting increases with increasing n and decreasing j. For any given n, the term belonging to the highest value of j ($j=n-\frac{1}{2}$) is not split since that term is not degenerate with respect to the orbital quantum number l (l has the fixed value $j-\frac{1}{2}=n-1$). For example, for the ground state of the BALMER series, $n=2$, only the fine structure level $j=\frac{1}{2}$ is split and, because $m=\pm\frac{1}{2}$, it is split into two equidistant levels separated by

$$\varDelta\varepsilon \equiv \varepsilon^+ - \varepsilon^- = 2\sqrt{3}\,F. \tag{55.5}$$

The splitting is of the same order of magnitude as the splitting of the second quantum state produced by the usual linear STARK effect which, according to (51.11), amounts to $6F$.

We have so far considered the two states for a given j-value to have the same energy without a field. In reality the energies of the $l=j-\frac{1}{2}$ and $j+\frac{1}{2}$ states differ slightly due to the LAMB shift (Sect. 21). The LAMB shift for $j=\frac{1}{2}$ is a reasonably small fraction of the fine structure splitting δ, (energy difference between states of different j) and is negligible for $j \geqq \frac{3}{2}$. The approximate expression (55.4) holds only if the STARK effect is small compared with the fine structure, but large compared with the LAMB shift. We derive now an expression which also holds for extremely weak fields, where the LAMB shift cannot be neglected, at least for states with $j=\frac{1}{2}$.

Consider the states with $j=\frac{1}{2}$ and fixed value of n and of m ($+\frac{1}{2}$ or $-\frac{1}{2}$). We use a representation in terms of the field-free eigenfunctions u_s and u_p, corresponding to $l=0$ and 1, respectively. We take the energy of the field-free P-state as our zero-point and call the energy displacement (LAMB shift) of the field-free S-state L. Our perturbation HAMILTONian H' is then (55.3) plus a diagonal matrix

$$H' = -n\sqrt{n^2-1}\,mF\begin{pmatrix}0 & 1\\ 1 & 0\end{pmatrix} + L\begin{pmatrix}1 & 0\\ 0 & 0\end{pmatrix}, \tag{55.6}$$

where the lower row refers to u_p. The two eigenfunctions and corresponding eigenvalues ε of (55.6) are given by[1]

$$u = a\,u_s + b\,u_p, \quad \frac{a}{b} = \frac{2n\sqrt{n^2-1}\,mF}{L \pm \sqrt{L^2 + 4(n^2-1)(n\,m\,F)^2}}, \tag{55.7}$$

$$\varepsilon = \tfrac{1}{2}L \pm \tfrac{1}{2}\sqrt{L^2 + 4(n^2-1)(n\,m\,F)^2}. \tag{55.8}$$

If the LAMB shift L is small compared with the STARK effect expression $S=n\sqrt{n^2-1}\,|mF|$ (for $n=2$, the two expressions are equal for a field strength of about 475 Volt/cm) the present results essentially reduce to our previous, less accurate, ones: $a/b=\pm 1$ for the two states, and their energies are given by (55.4) plus a shift of $+\frac{1}{2}L$ for each of the two states. If S is small compared

[1] Neglecting the ratio of STARK effect to fine structure splitting, i.e., for $F \ll \delta$.

with L, the two eigenstates are almost pure u_s and u_p, respectively, and the energies differ from the field-free values only by terms *quadratic* in the field strength, namely $\pm S^2/L$. In Fig. 29b the energy splitting between the $2S_{\frac{1}{2}}$ and $2P_{\frac{1}{2}}$-states is plotted as a function of field strength. Fig. 29b is an enlargement of the low field portion of Fig. 29a, but corrected for the LAMB shift.

β) Transition region. If the field strength is such (e.g., about 3000 Volts/cm for $n=2$) that the fine structure and STARK effect are comparable, the calculations of the level splitting are quite complicated. Only n and m are good quantum numbers, but neither j and l, nor the parabolic quantum numbers, are. The secular equations have to be solved separately for each value of n and m to find

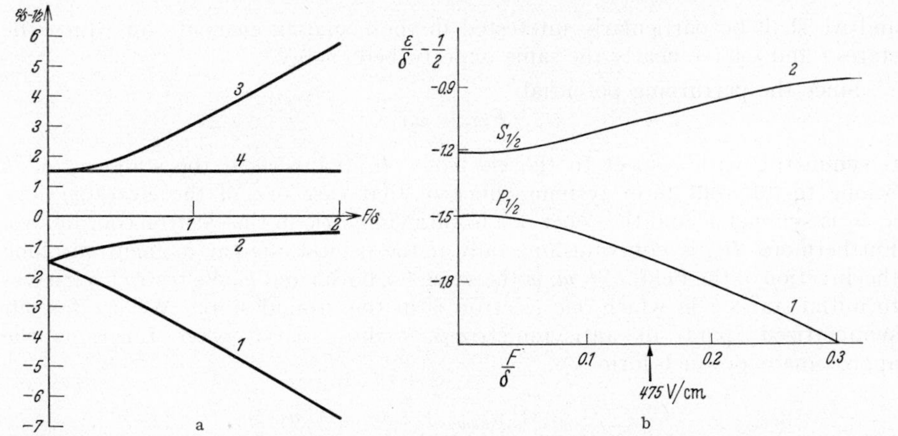

Fig. 29a and b. The STARK effect on the fine structure of the states with $n=2$ in hydrogen. Abscissa is the field strength F measured in units of $(\frac{3}{8})$ 15620 $\delta=2910$ Volt/cm, where $\delta=0.365$ cm^{-1} is the field-free fine structure splitting. Ordinate is the level energy, in units of δ, relative to the field-free mean energy. a. Level splitting (up to $F\sim 2\delta$) with the LAMB shift neglected. Note the remnant of fine structure even for strong fields in components 2 and 4. b. Level splitting for weak fields (up to $F\sim 0.3\,\delta$) of components 1 and 2, with the LAMB shift included.

the eigenvalues and eigenfunctions of each of $2(n-|m|)$ eigenstates. Such calculations were carried out by ROJANSKI[1] and, more accurately, by LÜDERS[1] for $n=2$, 3 and 4.

We reproduce in Fig. 29a the dependence on field strength F of the energies of the states with $n=2$ and positive m. We shall not discuss the results further, except for some general properties: If F (in atomic units) is small compared with the field-free fine structure splitting δ, the results essentially reduce to those of Sect. 55α. However, in addition to the energy shift (55.4) (and zero for $j=n-\frac{1}{2}$), one finds additional shifts of order F^2/δ. If F is larger than δ, one can expand the results in powers of δ/F. The leading terms are identical with the results of Sect. 51. The next term in the expansion for the energy is independent of F and is of the order of magnitude of δ.

c) STARK effect in helium.

56. The STARK effect for weak fields. In the case of helium[2], as well as for all other atoms except hydrogen, the STARK effect produced by relatively weak fields is proportional to the square of the electric field intensity. The first order perturbation in the energy vanishes since the levels are not degenerate with

[1] V. ROJANSKI: Phys. Rev. **33**, 1 (1929). — G. LÜDERS: Ann. d. Phys. [6] **8**, 301 (1951). See also ref. [*10*], Sect. 34b.

[2] Cf. J. S. FOSTER: Proc. Roy. Soc. Lond. **117**, 137 (1928.)

respect to the orbital quantum number l. Therefore, the shift of a level i produced by the electric field is given by the SCHRÖDINGER formula for the second order perturbation in the energy

$$E_i^{(2)} = \sum_k \frac{|H_{ik}|^2}{E_i - E_k}, \tag{56.1}$$

in which H_{ik} are the matrix elements of the perturbation and E_i, E_k are the energies belonging to the levels i and k of the atom in the absence of fields.

Thus, we must form the matrix elements of the perturbation energy produced by the external field,

$$H_{ik} = F \int u_i^* (z_1 + z_2)\, u_k\, d\tau, \tag{56.2}$$

and we shall be particularly interested in those matrix elements for which the states i and k have nearly the same unperturbed energy.

Since the perturbing potential

$$F(z_1 + z_2)$$

is symmetric with respect to the electrons, H_{ik} vanishes if the states i and k belong to different term systems, since in that case one of the eigenfunctions u_i, u_k is symmetric and the other one is antisymmetric in the electron coordinates. Furthermore, H_{ik} is non-vanishing only if the orbital angular momentum along the direction of the field, $k_z = m$, is the same for both i and k. We restrict ourselves to initial states i in which one electron is in the ground state. We use for our symmetrized (para) or antisymmetrized (ortho) spatial wave functions the approximate product form

$$U = \frac{1}{\sqrt{2}} \left[u_1(1)\, u_{nlm}(2) \pm u_{nlm}(1)\, u_1(2)\right],$$

where u_1 is the single-electron ground state wave function. Further, in the sum over k in (56.1), we shall retain only states k for which one electron is again in the ground state and the other in a state with the *same* principal quantum number, $u_{nl'm'}$. For the states we are neglecting, the energy denominator $(E_i - E_k)$ is much larger than for states differing only in their l-value[1]. Using the appendix Eq. (A.22), one can also show that the matrix element vanishes (for all n') unless the l-values in states i and k differ by ± 1. Substituting the eigenfunctions into (56.2), we obtain for (56.1), in our approximation,

$$E_{nl}^{(2)} = F^2 \left(\frac{|\int z\, u_{nlm} u^*_{nl+1m}\, d\tau|^2}{E_{nl} - E_{n,l+1}} + \frac{|\int z\, u_{nlm} u^*_{nl-1m}\, d\tau|^2}{E_{nl} - E_{n,l-1}}\right). \tag{56.3}$$

Thus, the perturbation of the energy level $n\,l$ consists of "interactions" with the levels $l+1$ and $l-1$, and is the larger the closer the "perturbing" levels are to the perturbed level $n\,l$. The integrations can be carried out if we substitute for the eigenfunctions u_{nlm} hydrogenic eigenfunctions with nuclear charge $Z-1$. The angular integrations can be carried out, using (A.22), and the radial integrations by the methods used in Sect. 52.

Thus, one finally obtains the following value for the perturbation in the energy:

$$E_{nlm}^{(2)} = F^2 \frac{9n^2}{4(Z-1)^2(2l+1)} \left[\frac{(n^2-(l+1)^2)\,((l+1)^2-m^2)}{(2l+3)\,(E_{nl}-E_{nl+1})} + \frac{(n^2-l^2)\,(l^2-m^2)}{(2l-1)\,(E_{nl}-E_{nl-1})}\right]. \tag{56.4}$$

According to the above, the STARK effect terms—in weak fields—depend on the square of the magnetic quantum number m, and, thus, terms which differ

[1] In this approximation we get no STARK effect at all for the ground state of helium.

only in the sign of m are degenerate. Formula (56.4) was first derived by UNSÖLD[1]. The magnitude and the direction of the term shift produced by the field are largely determined by the resonance denominators in (56.4), i.e., by the relative positions of the levels in the helium atom without field. However, as we have noted previously, for a given n and fixed term system the term values generally increase with increasing orbital quantum number l. The two ^1P terms which lie above the ^1D terms form an exception. Thus, except for the ^1P terms, the first term inside the parentheses of (56.4) is negative and the second term is positive. Furthermore, the energy differences of terms having successive values of l decrease with increasing l, i.e.,

$$E_{n,l+1} - E_{nl} < E_{nl} - E_{n,l-1},$$

and, accordingly, the absolute value of the first term in the parentheses is considerably larger than that of the second[2]. Accordingly, the STARK effect produces the following shift in the terms of helium:

In the first place, the STARK effect generally results in a reduction of the energy[2], and, secondly, in magnitude the shift is largest for $m=0$ and smallest for $m=l$.

For the purpose of getting a better quantitative understanding of the dependence of the STARK effect on the quantum numbers $n\,l$, let us examine the shift[3] of the STARK component $m=0$. We introduce the RYDBERG corrections in place of the unperturbed energy levels by setting in the usual fashion (cf. Sect. 28)

$$E_{nl} = -\frac{(Z-1)^2}{2(n-\delta_l)^2}.$$

Then we obtain

$$E^{(2)}_{nl0} = -\frac{9F^2 n^5}{16(Z-1)^4}\left\{\frac{4(l+1)^2}{4(l+1)^2-1}\,\frac{n^2-(l+1)^2}{\delta_l-\delta_{l+1}} - \frac{4l^2}{4l^2-1}\,\frac{n^2-l^2}{\delta_{l-1}-\delta_l}\right\}. \tag{56.5}$$

For $n \gg l$ the splitting grows enormously with increasing principal quantum number (as n^7) and grows rapidly also with increasing orbital quantum number since the RYDBERG corrections δ_l are reduced by a factor of 2 to 5 whenever l is increased by 1.

In order to obtain a convenient measure of the absolute magnitude of the effects which may be expected, let us define F_0 as that field strength for which the term shift of the level $m=0$ amounts to exactly one wave-number (cm^{-1}). Then for an arbitrary field the shift evidently is given by

$$E^{(2)}_{nl0} = (F/F_0)^2\ \mathrm{cm}^{-1} \tag{56.6}$$

and, for $n \gg l$,

$$F_0 = \frac{(Z-1)^2}{n^{\frac{7}{2}}} \times 1.46 \times 10^7 \times \left(\frac{4(l+1)^2}{4(l+1)^2-1}\cdot\frac{1}{\delta_l-\delta_{l+1}} - \frac{4l^2}{4l^2-1}\cdot\frac{1}{\delta_{l-1}-\delta_l}\right)^{-\frac{1}{2}}. \tag{56.7}$$

Inserting the observed values for the RYDBERG corrections from Table 4, Sect. 28, we obtain for the characteristic fields F_0

for		S terms	P terms	D terms		
orthohelium	$F_0 =$	$5.95\,n^{-\frac{7}{2}}$	$4.50\,n^{-\frac{7}{2}}$	$0.66\,n^{-\frac{7}{2}}$	million	(56.8)
parahelium		$4.86\,n^{-\frac{7}{2}}$	$1.58\,n^{-\frac{7}{2}}$	$0.60\,n^{-\frac{7}{2}}$	Volt/cm.	

[1] A. UNSÖLD: Ann. d. Phys. 82, 355 (1927).

[2] However, if $l=n-1$, the first term vanishes and the second term becomes dominant, and the energy of the terms having $l=n-1$ is increased by the electric field. Furthermore, the ^1P terms form an exception, as noted above.

[3] As noted above, this component is shifted the most.

Thus, the terms of parahelium are affected more strongly than those of orthohelium, and this is especially true of the P terms as the separation between the ^1P and the ^1D terms amounts to only about $\frac{1}{4}$ of the distance between the corresponding triplet terms. (The ^1P terms are also distinguished in that—contrary to the general rules of the STARK effect—they undergo a shift toward higher energies since they are situated above the ^1D terms to begin with; cf. above.)

In the following table we have listed the values of the characteristic fields F_0 for the individual terms of helium. The listed values (in Kilovolt/cm) of F_0 are the field strengths for which (56.4) gives a shift of 1 cm^{-1} for the component $m=0$ of states with different n and l.

n	^3S-	^1S-	^3P-	^1P-	^3D-	^1D-terms
2	735	535	735	535	—	—
3	151	115	157	42	103	45
4	52	40	42	13.8	8.3	6.5
5	23	18	17.5	6	3.3	2.6
6	12	9.5	9	3.1	1.65	1.30

A glance at the table reveals immediately the huge differences in the splittings of the individual terms. For example, a field of 10000 Volt/cm shifts the component $m=0$ of the 2^3S term by only 0.0002 cm^{-1}, whereas the corresponding component of the 6^1D term is shifted by 60 cm^{-1}. Thus, for the purpose of calculating the splittings of the lines of the helium spectrum one only needs to know the splitting of the upper level, that of the lower level is usually unobservably small. The splitting of the terms is about as large (actually somewhat smaller) as the shift of the STARK effect component $m=0$ relative to the unperturbed term, which is the quantity we have tabulated.

57. Dependence on field strength. *α) Splitting of energy levels.* For field-free states of the helium atom, we can distinguish three different orders of magnitude of energy. (i) The fine structure splitting δ, contributed by the relativistic parts of the HAMILTONian (Sect. 40). (ii) The energy differences Δ_l of states with the same principal quantum number n, but with different values of l. Δ_l is contributed by the COULOMB and exchange interaction between the electrons (Sect. 28). (iii) The energy differences Δ_n of states with principal quantum numbers n and $n+1$ (interaction with the nuclear field). These energies satisfy the inequality $\delta \ll \Delta_l < \Delta_n$ and are all approximately proportional to n^{-3}.

The calculation of the STARK effect splitting S of an energy level is very complicated if this splitting[1] is comparable with δ, Δ_l or Δ_n. We merely outline the situation for some simpler limiting cases.

Case I. $\delta \ll S \ll \Delta_l$. This is the most important case in practice and the one for which the approximations of Sect. 56 are applicable. The fine structure can be neglected, since it is even small compared with the STARK effect S, and perturbation theory can be used for S, since $S \ll \Delta_l$. The range of field strengths F for which these approximations hold depends strongly on n and l, since S increases and δ, Δ_l decrease with increasing n and l. For instance, this range of field strengths (in kilovolt/cm) is roughly 500 to 50000 for 2^3P, 2 to 200 for 4^3P and 0.1 to 20 for 4^3D. For all states of parahelium and for all S-states, there is no fine structure splitting and the equivalent ranges start from zero field strength.

[1] J. S. FOSTER: Proc. Roy. Soc. Lond. **117**, 137 (1928); ref. [*10*] Sect. 35.

To summarize the situation for Case I: n, l and m_l (and m_s) are good quantum numbers, the energy splitting is given, to a first approximation, by (56.3) and the splitting is quadratic in the fieldstrength F. If the electron spin and relativistic effects are also taken into account, one obtains an additional small splitting for triplet states with $l \neq 0$. m_s, and hence $m = m_l + m_s$, is also a good quantum number. For triplet states the splitting of the nonrelativistic energy levels into components with $m_s = -1, 0, 1$ is of the order of the field-free fine structure splitting (cf. Sect. 55).

Case II. $S \ll \delta$ (very weak field). This case exists only for triplet states with $l \neq 0$. n, l, j and m ($m = m_l + m_s$ is the component of total angular momentum in the direction of the field) are good quantum numbers, as in the field-free case. The Stark effect removes the m-degeneracy of the relativistic field-free energy levels. Unlike in hydrogen, the Stark effect splitting is quadratic (not linear) in F, since field-free levels of the same j and different l are not degenerate. In the transition region between Cases I and II only n, l and m are good quantum numbers and the effect is complicated.

Case III. $\Delta_l \ll S \ll \Delta_n$ (strong field[1]). Since the field-free energy dependence on l is small compared with the Stark effect splitting, the theory of Sect. 51 for hydrogen applies to a good approximation. The good quantum numbers then are n, m_l, m_s and the parabolic quantum numbers n_1 and n_2. To a first approximation the energy splitting is linear in F, as for hydrogen. In addition, each level is shifted by a small amount, independent of F, which is of the same order of magnitude as Δ_l.

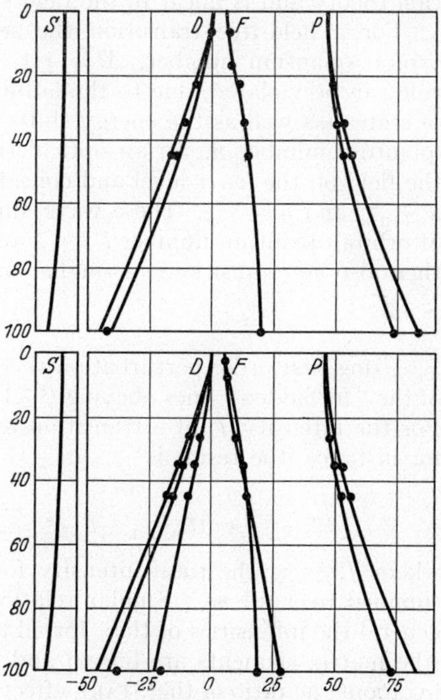

Fig. 30. The Stark effect on the lines in parahelium due to transitions from levels with $n=4$ (4 S, 4 P, 4 D, 4 F) to the 2P-state. π-components in the upper diagram, σ-components in the lower. Abscissa is field strength in kilovolt/cm. Ordinate is the line shift, relative to the field-free $4\,^1D - 2\,^1P$ line, in cm^{-1}. The curves are theoretical ones, the solid circles are experimental points.

For reasonably large values of n and a considerable range of field strengths F one has a "partial transition region" between Cases I and III. I.e., the Stark effect splitting S is large compared with the field-free energy difference between adjacent states of large l, but smaller than those with small l. For $n = 4$ and $F \sim 100$ Kilovolt/cm, for instance, the D- and F-states show a *linear* Stark effect (Case III) which is much larger than their field-free separation. The S-state, on the other hand, is still an almost pure state and shows a *quadratic* Stark effect (Case I). In Fig. 30 we show the theoretical dependence on field strength of the frequencies of transitions from the paralevels with $n = 4$ to the 2^1P-state. The splitting is almost entirely due to that of the $n = 4$ states (the Stark effect on $2P$ is negligible). The points on the theoretical curves are a few experimental ones (Foster, loc. cit.) and are seen to agree well.

[1] We shall not consider the case of extremely strong fields, where S is comparable with or larger than Δ_n. For all but very large n, $S \sim \Delta_n$ requires unreasonably large fields, e.g., a few million Volt/cm for $n = 4$.

β) *Weakening of the selection rules.* So far we have only considered the effect of the field on the *energy* of levels (splitting and shift). The field also affects the wave functions and, hence, also the selection rules for optical transitions between two states in helium. Consider weak fields, Sect. 56 and Case I of Sect. 57α. If u_{nlm} is the field-free wave function of a particular state, the equivalent eigenfunction in a weak field contains a small admixture of the two wave functions $u_{n,l\pm 1,m}$. The amount of this admixture can be calculated by first order perturbation theory and is linear in the field strength F.

For a field-free transition the selection rule (Sect. 60β) on the change in orbital quantum number, $\Delta l = \pm 1$, applies. In an electric field this selection rule can be violated, due to the admixture of states in the field. The admixture of states (as well as the energy shifts) increases rapidly with increasing principal quantum number n. In an optical transition we can then neglect the effect of the field on the *lower* level and consider only the admixture in the *upper* level of $u_{n,l+1,m}$ and $u_{n,l-1,m}$. These wave functions combine optically with lower levels of orbital quantum number $l, l+2$ and $l, l-2$, respectively. In a weak field we then also get transitions of smaller intensity which obey the selection rule

$$\Delta l = 0, \pm 2. \tag{57.1}$$

Using first order perturbation theory one can calculate the ratio of intensities of the "forbidden" lines obeying (57.1) to those of "allowed" lines with $\Delta l = \pm 1$. For the intensity J' of a transition from an upper level $n\,l$ to a lower level $n_0\,l$, for instance, the result is[1]

$$J'^{\,n_0 l}_{n l} = \frac{9}{4}\,\frac{F^2}{(E_{n,l+1} - E_{nl})^2}\,[n^2 - (l+1)^2]\,n^2\,\frac{(l+1)^2 - m^2}{4\,(l+1)^2 - 1}\,J^{n_0 l}_{n,l+1}, \tag{57.2}$$

where $J^{n_0 l}_{n,l+1}$ is the total intensity for allowed transitions $n, l+1, m$ to $n_0\,l\,m_0$, summed over all m_0. Similar relations hold for transitions with $\Delta l = \pm 2$. In general the intensities of the "forbidden" lines are quadratic in the field strength (the matrix elements are linear) and are smaller than those of the allowed lines by about the ratio of the STARK effect energy shift of the upper level to its energy separation from a level with $l+1$ (or $l-1$).

In the helium spectrum, forbidden lines from upper states ending in the $2S$ or $2P$ states fall in the visible region and are observed. In Fig. 30, for instance, lines from $4P$ and $4F$ to $2P$ occur. At a field strength of about 15 Kilovolts/cm, the theoretical intensity of the lines from $4P$ and $4F$ are about 1 and 30%, respectively, of the intensity of the allowed line from $4D$. The theoretical intensities are also verified experimentally.

In strong fields (Case III of Sect. 57α), no selection rules on l apply. Instead, the intensities are obtained in terms of the parabolic eigenfunctions, as for hydrogen (see Sect. 65).

58. The dielectric constant of helium[2]. In order to calculate the dielectric constant ε of helium we need to know the second order STARK effect for the ground level of helium. If the perturbation of the eigenvalue in the field F is given by $E_2 F^2$, then ε may be evaluated from the relation

$$\varepsilon = 1 - 8\pi N E_2, \tag{58.1}$$

[1] Neglecting a similar term involving the state $n, l-1$ (instead of $n, l+1$) which is much smaller.

[2] Cf. H. R. HASSÉ: Proc. Cambridge Phil. Soc. **26**, 542 (1930). — J. C. SLATER and J. G. KIRKWOOD: Phys. Rev. **37**, 682 (1931). The calculations of J. V. ATANASOFF, Phys. Rev. **36**, 1232 (1930) are less satisfactory.

in which N is the number of atoms per unit volume. If E_2 and F are expressed in atomic units, it is necessary to do likewise for the volume. Thus, N is the number of atoms in the volume a^3, where a is the radius of the hydrogen atom,

$$N = \mathcal{N} a^3 \frac{\varrho}{A} = 0.089 \frac{\varrho}{A} \tag{58.2}$$

in which ϱ is the density and A is the atomic weight of the substance. For a gas at standard conditions (0° C and 760 mm of pressure) $A/\varrho = 22400$, and thus

$$\varepsilon = 1 - 1.00 \times 10^{-4} E_2 . \tag{58.3}$$

The ground state of helium is the *only* state with $n=1$. The approximation used in Sect. 56 for the second order perturbation energy would thus give zero and the energy shift is in fact considerably smaller for the ground state than for any excited state. In principle one could calculate this energy shift by orthodox second order perturbation theory, but this would involve calculating matrix elements for a large number of excited P-states. We shall use instead the variation-perturbation method of Sects. 25β and 33 [see Eqs. (33.7) and (33.8)].

The unperturbed HAMILTONian (in atomic units) is

$$H_0 = -\frac{1}{2}\Delta_1 - \frac{1}{2}\Delta_2 - \frac{2}{r_1} - \frac{2}{r_2} + \frac{1}{r_{12}} . \tag{58.4}$$

The perturbation resulting from the electric field is $F(z_1+z_2)$ in which the field strength F is regarded as the perturbation parameter. In terms of the notation of Sects. 25 and 33 we simply have

$$H_1 = z_1 + z_2 . \tag{58.5}$$

The first order perturbation in the energy vanishes, and (33.8) becomes

$$E_2 = 2\int u_0^2 \left[\varphi(z_1+z_2) + \tfrac{1}{4}(\text{grad}_1\varphi)^2 + \tfrac{1}{4}(\text{grad}_2\varphi)^2\right] d\tau = \min . \tag{58.6}$$

(58.6) must be minimized by a variation of φ. Perhaps the simplest assumption for φ is the following[1]

$$\varphi = \alpha H_1 = \alpha(z_1+z_2) \tag{58.7}$$

in which α is to be varied. This gives $\text{grad}_1\varphi = \alpha$, and (58.6) becomes

$$E_2 = 2\int u_0^2 \left[\alpha(z_1+z_2)^2 + \tfrac{1}{2}\alpha^2\right] d\tau . \tag{58.8}$$

Inserting for u_0 the simple eigenfunction (32.9)

$$u_0 = e^{-\frac{1}{2}k(r_1+r_2)} \cdot k^3 , \quad k = \tfrac{27}{8} , \tag{58.9}$$

gives

$$E_2 = \frac{1024}{729}\alpha + \alpha^2 .$$

The minimum corresponds to $\alpha = -512/729$ and has the value

$$E_2 = -\left(\frac{512}{729}\right)^2 = -0.49 , \tag{58.10}$$

which is pretty far from the correct value of -0.74.

The main reason for the disagreement lies in that (58.9) represents a rather poor approximation to the true eigenfunction of the helium atom in the absence

[1] E_2 is more sensitive to small changes in u_0 than to changes in φ, since φ is always corrected to the "most favorable possible" value by the variation.

of fields. Therefore, SLATER and KIRKWOOD (loc. cit.) have substituted the HARTREE eigenfunction[1] for u_0. In addition they improved the form of the function φ by setting

$$\varphi = \alpha r_1^\nu r_2^\nu (z_1 + z_2), \tag{58.11}$$

in which the two parameters α and ν are disposable. The minimum corresponds to a ν of about $\frac{1}{2}$; this means that the eigenfunction is more strongly perturbed by the electric field when the electrons are far from the nucleus than when they are near the nucleus. This makes good sense. The calculation yields

$$E_2 = -0.715.$$

From this the dielectric constant is evaluated from (58.3) with the result

$$\varepsilon = 1.0000715,$$

whereas the observed value is

$$\varepsilon = 1.000074.$$

The agreement is satisfactory.

IV. Interaction with radiation.

a) Discrete spectrum.

59. General formulas. α) *The dipole approximation.* We start from the fundamental formula of radiation theory for the probability of a spontaneous transition of an atom from[2] a state n to a state n' (energies E_n and $E_{n'}$), with the emission of one photon. Let $\boldsymbol{k}$ be the propagation vector, $k = |\boldsymbol{k}|$ the wave number, $\nu_{nn'}$ and $\omega_{nn'}$ the "ordinary" and "angular" frequency of the photon. We then have the BOHR energy relation[3]

$$\omega_{nn'} \equiv 2\pi \nu_{nn'} \equiv c k = \frac{1}{\hbar}(E_n - E_{n'}). \tag{59.1}$$

If the photon has polarization direction x and a propagation vector $\boldsymbol{k}$ in the solid angle $d\Omega$, the fundamental transition probability per unit time is

$$W_{n'n}(\boldsymbol{k}, x)\, d\Omega = \frac{e^2 \hbar \omega_{nn'}}{2\pi m^2 c^3} |D_{nn'}^{\boldsymbol{k}x}|^2 d\Omega. \tag{59.2}$$

In (59.2), D is the following matrix element

$$D_{n'n}^{\boldsymbol{k}x} = \int u_{n'}^* \sum_i e^{i\boldsymbol{k}\cdot\boldsymbol{r}_i} \frac{\partial u_n}{\partial x_i}\, d\tau \tag{59.3}$$

where $\boldsymbol{r}_i$ is the position of the i-th atomic electron and the integral extends over the configuration space of all the electrons[4].

The fundamental expression (59.2), (59.3) is derived elsewhere[5] from quantum electrodynamics. Crudely speaking, the matrix element (59.3) is similar to that

---

[1] More correctly, they have used an analytic function derived by SLATER, which agrees very closely with the HARTREE eigenfunction.

[2] Here n denotes all the quantum numbers which specify the state, not merely the principal quantum number.

[3] $\hbar$ is the "rationalized" PLANCK's constant $h/2\pi$.

[4] We shall mainly discuss $W_{n'n}$, the probability for the spontaneous emission of a photon. Two other related quantities are the probabilities for absorption of a photon (transition of the atom from a lower to a higher state) and for the emission of a photon, which is induced by the exposure of the atom to radiation. These probabilities can be obtained from $W_{n'n}$ by the so-called EINSTEIN relations discussed in ref. [5], Chap. 4, Sect. 1 (see also our Sect. 69).

[5] See for instance, ref. [2], [5] and [6].

which one would obtain from (45.2) by putting $\boldsymbol{A}$ equal to the vector potential of a classical electromagnetic wave with polarization direction x and propagation vector $\boldsymbol{k}$. We merely list the approximations made in deriving (59.2), (59.3) from quantum electrodynamics. (1) The electrons have been treated nonrelativistically and the SCHRÖDINGER equation has been used instead of the DIRAC or PAULI equations (neglect of magnetic moment and of specific relativistic effects). (2) The interaction of the electron with the radiation field has been treated as a small perturbation (with the fine structure constant α as the perturbation parameter) and only the lowest order term kept in the expansion in powers of α. We are thus neglecting processes involving the simultaneous emission or absorption of two or more photons (and also small radiative corrections akin to the LAMB shift).

In most cases one can simplify (59.3) considerably by making a further approximation: The important distances r_i of the electrons from the nucleus are of the order of the BOHR radius of the atom, i.e. about 10^{-8} cm for low nuclear charge Z. For transitions in the discrete spectrum for low Z the wave number $k=2\pi/\lambda$ of the emitted light is much smaller than 10^8 cm^{-1}, e.g. for visible light k is of order 10^5 cm^{-1}. The exponent $\boldsymbol{k}\cdot\boldsymbol{r}_i$ in the exponential in (59.3) is thus small and we can replace the exponential by unity[1], i.e. we "neglect retardation" and use the "electric dipole approximation". In this approximation $D^{\boldsymbol{k}x}_{n'n}$ is the x-component of a vector $\boldsymbol{D}_{n'n}$ which does not depend on $\boldsymbol{k}$,

$$\boldsymbol{D}_{n'n}=\int u^*_{n'}\sum_i \operatorname{grad}_i u_n\,d\tau. \tag{59.4}$$

The vector $\boldsymbol{D}_{n'n}$ is simply $i/\hbar$ times the matrix element $\boldsymbol{p}_{n'n}$, for the transition $n\to n'$, of the total linear momentum operator $\boldsymbol{p}=\sum\boldsymbol{p}_i=-i\hbar\sum\operatorname{grad}_i$. It is often useful to write $\boldsymbol{D}_{n'n}$ in a different form (to be proved in Sect. 59β),

$$\boldsymbol{D}_{n'n}\equiv\frac{i}{\hbar}\boldsymbol{p}_{n'n}=\frac{i\,m}{\hbar}\boldsymbol{v}_{n'n}=\frac{m}{\hbar}\omega_{nn'}\boldsymbol{r}_{n'n}. \tag{59.5}$$

In (59.5), $\boldsymbol{v}$ and $\boldsymbol{r}$ are the sum of electron velocities and positions, respectively, $\omega_{n'n}$ is given[2] by (59.1) and $\boldsymbol{r}_{n'n}$ is the dipole matrix element

$$\boldsymbol{r}_{n'n}=\int u^*_{n'}\sum_i \boldsymbol{r}_i\,u_n\,d\tau. \tag{59.6}$$

Substituting (59.5) into (59.2), we obtain:

$$W(\Omega,j)\,d\Omega=\frac{e^2}{2\pi\hbar c^3}\,\omega^3_{nn'}\,(\boldsymbol{e}_j\cdot\boldsymbol{r}_{n'n})^2\,d\Omega. \tag{59.7}$$

(59.7) is the probability that an atom will undergo a transition from the state n to n' and emit light of polarization direction $\boldsymbol{e}_j$ into the solid angle $d\Omega$. The intensity of the light emitted into the solid angle $d\Omega$ in erg/sec is obtained by multiplying the probability by the energy of the light quantum $h\nu=\hbar\omega$:

$$J_j\,d\Omega=\frac{e^2}{2\pi c^3}\,\omega^4\,(\boldsymbol{e}_j\cdot\boldsymbol{r}_{n'n})^2\,d\Omega. \tag{59.8}$$

The above is precisely the classical formula for the intensity of light emitted by an oscillating dipole having dipole moment $e\,\boldsymbol{r}_{n'n}\,e^{i\nu_{nn'}t}$ and frequency $\nu_{nn'}$. For

[1] The order of magnitude of kr_i increases with Z and for very large Z this approximation is no longer very good. The approximation also fails, even for small Z, for transitions to states in the continuum of very high energy (Sects. 72 and 73). See also Sect. 66 for the effect of higher terms in the expansion of the exponential in powers of kr_i.

[2] Note that the last form of (59.5) shows that the transition probability between states of equal energy is zero ($\omega_{nn'}$, i.e. the photon frequency, is zero).

this reason the radiation obtained by neglecting the retardation [exponential factor in (59.3)] is called dipole radiation. $\boldsymbol{r}_{n'n}$ takes the place of the amplitude of the classical dipole.

If the angle between the direction of observation $\boldsymbol{k}$ and the dipole moment $\boldsymbol{r}_{n'n}$ is ϑ and the measuring device subtends a solid angle $d\Omega$ at the location of the emitting atom, the observed intensity is given by

$$J\,d\Omega = \frac{e^2}{2\pi c^3}\,\omega^4\,\mathcal{N}_n\,|\boldsymbol{r}_{n'n}|^2\sin^2\vartheta\,d\Omega \tag{59.9}$$

in which $\mathcal{N}_n$ is the number of atoms in the state n[1]. The total intensity of emitted light is obtained by integrating (59.9) over all directions of propagation of the emitted light, viz., over $d\Omega$:

$$J_{n'n} = \frac{4}{3}\,\frac{e^2\omega^4}{c^3}\,|\boldsymbol{r}_{n'n}|^2 \tag{59.10}$$

in erg/sec per emitting atom. The total transition probability for going from n to n' is obtained by dividing (59.10) by $h\nu$:

$$A_{n'n} = \frac{4}{3}\,\frac{e^2\omega^3}{\hbar c^3}\,|\boldsymbol{r}_{n'n}|^2. \tag{59.11}$$

If one finally sums (59.11) over all states n' which have energy less than that of the initial state n, one arrives at the total probability per unit of time that the state n is vacated through light emission

$$\beta_n = \sum_{E_{n'}<E_n} A_{n'n} \tag{59.12}$$

and, thus, the reciprocal of the mean life time of the state n is given by

$$T_n = \frac{1}{\beta_n} = \frac{1}{\sum\limits_{E_{n'}<E_n} A_{n'n}}\,. \tag{59.13}$$

T is of the order of magnitude 10^{-9} sec (cf. Table 15).

Finally, it is convenient to define the oscillator strength

$$f_{n'n} = \frac{2m}{\hbar}\,\omega_{n'n}\,|x_{n'n}|^2 \tag{59.14}$$

which we shall discuss further in Sects. 59β and 61. Altogether we have introduced five quantities which differ successively by a factor of ν as follows:

the square of the matrix element of the coordinate (dipole moment) $|\boldsymbol{r}_{n'n}|^2$,
the oscillator strength $f_{n'n}$, which is proportional to ν times the dipole moment,
the square of the matrix element of the momentum, $\boldsymbol{D}_{n'n}$ [cf. Eq. (59.5)], which is proportional to ν^2 times the dipole moment,
the transition probability $A_{n'n}$ proportional to ν^3 times the dipole moment,
and the intensity of emission $J_{n'n}$, proportional to ν^4 times the dipole moment.

Numerically, one obtains

$$A_{n'n} = 8.0\times 10^9\left(\frac{\nu}{\mathrm{Ry}}\right)^2 f_{n'n}\,\mathrm{sec}^{-1}, \tag{59.15}$$

$$J_{n'n} = 0.173\left(\frac{\nu}{\mathrm{Ry}}\right)^3 f_{n'n}\,\mathrm{erg/sec} \tag{59.16}$$

per emitting atom.

[1] The direction of polarization is perpendicular to $\boldsymbol{k}$. Therefore, if the direction of polarization is resolved into two components, one, $\boldsymbol{e}_1$, perpendicular to $\boldsymbol{r}_{n'n}$ the other one, $\boldsymbol{e}_2$, will lie in the plane determined by $\boldsymbol{k}$ and $\boldsymbol{r}_{n'n}$ at an angle of $\frac{\pi}{2}-\vartheta$ with $\boldsymbol{r}_{n'n}$. Light of polarization 1 is not emitted at all, and polarization 2 is emitted with intensity given by (59.9).

We finally give some crude order of magnitude arguments, for transitions in the discrete spectrum, which are based on the smallness of the fine structure constant α. For a hydrogen-like atom of nuclear charge Z, the following are characteristic orders of magnitude:

$$a_z = a/Z \sim \hbar/Z\,\alpha\, m\, c \qquad \text{for the atomic ``radius''},$$

$$p_z = \hbar/a_z \sim Z\,\alpha\, m\, c \qquad \text{for the momentum},$$

$$W_z \sim p_z^2/m \sim Z^2\,\mathrm{Ry} \sim (Z\,\alpha)^2\, m\, c^2 \qquad \text{for the level energies and}$$

$$\nu_z \sim W_z/h \sim (Z\,\alpha)^2\, m\, c^2/\hbar \qquad \text{for the ``revolution frequency''}.$$

The angular frequency ω of light emitted in radiative transitions is also of order ν_z, or about $Z^2 \times 10^{16}\,\mathrm{sec}^{-1}$, and its wave number k of order ν_z/c. The dipole matrix elements $r_{n'n}$ are of order a_z (but numerically usually smaller) and the factor $k\,r_{n'n}$ is then of order $(\nu_z/c)\,a_z$ or $Z\alpha$.

We thus see that the "dipole approximation", which consists of neglecting $k\,r_{n'n}$ compared with unity, is justified as long as $Z \ll 137$. The total decay probability β_n [see Eq. (59.12)] of an excited state is of order $\alpha\,(Z\alpha)^2\,\nu_z \sim Z^4\,10^9\,\mathrm{sec}^{-1}$. An excited state has a finite energy spread (radiation width, see Sect. 67) of order $\hbar A_n \sim \alpha\,(Z\,\alpha)^2\,W_z$ or about α times the fine structure splitting. The oscillator strength $f_{n'n}$ is dimensionless and of order (but numerically less than) unity. In fact we shall see that

$$\sum_{n'} f_{n'n} = 1\,.$$

β) Alternative forms of the matrix element. In (59.5) we have made use of a general relation between the matrix elements $\boldsymbol{p}_{n'n}$ and $\boldsymbol{r}_{n'n}$ of the momentum and position operators, respectively. This relation can be derived easily by explicit wave mechanical means[1]. We give instead a derivation using general operator manipulation[2], which we shall also find useful in later sections.

Consider a general HAMILTONian H of form

$$H = \sum_i \frac{p_i^2}{2m} + V(\boldsymbol{r}_1, \boldsymbol{r}_2, \ldots), \tag{59.17}$$

where the operators $\boldsymbol{p}_i$, $\boldsymbol{r}_i$ (for the i-th electron) satisfy the fundamental commutation relations

$$[y_i, p_{xj}] = 0, \qquad [x_i, p_{xj}] = i\,\hbar\,\delta_{ij},\ \text{etc.}, \tag{59.18}$$

and $[a, b] \equiv a\,b - b\,a$. Using (11.6), we then find

$$[\boldsymbol{r}, H] = \frac{i\,\hbar}{m}\,\boldsymbol{p}, \tag{59.19}$$

where $\boldsymbol{r} = \sum \boldsymbol{r}_i$ and $\boldsymbol{p} = \sum \boldsymbol{p}_i$. For a transition between two eigenstates of H with eigenvalues E_n and $E_{n'}$, we also have

$$[\boldsymbol{r}, H]_{n'n} = (E_n - E_{n'})\,\boldsymbol{r}_{n'n},$$

[1] One writes the two matrix elements as integrals over position space, as in (59.4) and (59.6), integrates by parts and makes use of the SCHRÖDINGER differential equation and the fact that (if at least n or n' is a *bound* state) the integrands approach zero at large distance (sec ref. [*10*], p. 249).

[2] See refs. [*1*] and [*5*].

which proves the desired relation

$$\boldsymbol{p}_{n'n} = -i\, m\, \omega_{n n'}\, \boldsymbol{r}_{n'n}. \tag{59.20}$$

A third alternative form for $D_{n'n}$ can be derived from another operator relation,

$$(E_n - E_{n'})\, \boldsymbol{p}_{n'n} = [\boldsymbol{p}, H]_{n'n} = [\boldsymbol{p}, V]_{n'n} = -i\hbar \sum_i (\mathrm{grad}_i\, V)_{n'n}, \tag{59.21}$$

where we have used the explicit wave mechanical representation for momentum in the last expression. For a general atom the potential V is of form

$$V = -Z \sum_i \frac{e^2}{r_i} + \sum_{i<j} \frac{e^2}{|\boldsymbol{r}_i - \boldsymbol{r}_j|}.$$

In this case, (59.4), (59.5) can also be rewritten as

$$\boldsymbol{D}_{n'n} = \frac{Z e^2}{\hbar\, \omega_{n n'}} \int u_{n'}^* \sum_i \frac{\boldsymbol{r}_i}{r_i^3}\, u_n\, d\tau. \tag{59.22}$$

We thus have three alternative forms for $D_{n'n}$ (with retardation neglected throughout) which involve integrals over the atomic wave functions of three different operators, the gradient operator in (59.4), $\boldsymbol{r}_i$ in (59.6) and $\boldsymbol{r}_i/r_i^3$ in (59.22). If we use exact eigenfunctions of H for u_n and $u_{n'}$ the three expressions are identical, but if we evaluate the integrals using only approximate wave functions the results can differ from each other (and from the correct expression) appreciably. Note that in the integral involving $\boldsymbol{r}_i$, the integrand is most important for rather *large* values of r_i—and in the integral involving $\boldsymbol{r}_i/r_i^3$ *small* values of r_i are important. For the integral (59.4) involving the gradient operator one finds that intermediate values of r_i are most important. Many approximate wave functions used in practice are most accurate for intermediate values of r_i. This is especially the case for wave functions of helium-like atoms obtained from the variational method (Sects. 32 and 33). These wave functions are most reliable for r_i of the order of the "atomic radius", but are poor approximations for very large or very small r_i (Sect. 36). In such cases we should expect (59.4) to be the most accurate of the three forms for $D_{n'n}$.

The three methods were compared explicitly by CHANDRASEKHAR[1] for transitions from the ground state to states in the continuum of the H^--ion. Using the most accurate (12 parameter variational) ground state wave function the three expressions for $D_{n'n}$ were indeed almost identical. Using a less accurate (six parameter) wave function, (59.4) still gave a fairly accurate value for $D_{n'n}$, but the other two expressions for $D_{n'n}$ were in error by a considerable amount. Thus (59.4) is usually the most reliable form, if approximate wave functions are used, but the form involving (59.6) is usually easier to evaluate and is most commonly used in practice (and in the following sections).

60. Selection rules for orbital and magnetic quantum numbers. *α) One-electron spectra.* First we shall consider an atom having a single electron, and in usual fashion shall express the eigenfunctions in polar coordinates:

$$u_{nlm} = R_{nl}(r)\, \mathscr{P}_{lm}(\vartheta)\, e^{im\varphi} \frac{1}{\sqrt{2\pi}}. \tag{60.1}$$

The matrix element of the coordinate z corresponding to a transition from the state having quantum numbers $n\,l\,m$ to the state $n'\,l'\,m'$, since $z = r\cos\vartheta$, is

[1] S. CHANDRASEKHAR: Astrophys. J. **102**, 223 (1945).

given by

$$\left.\begin{aligned} z_{n l m}^{n' l' m'} &= \int u_{n' l' m'}^{*}\, z\, u_{n l m}\, d\tau = \int_0^\infty r^2\, dr\, R_{n' l'}(r)\, R_{n l}(r) \cdot r \times \\ &\times \int_0^\pi \mathscr{P}_{l' m'}(\vartheta)\, \mathscr{P}_{l m}(\vartheta) \cos\vartheta \cdot \sin\vartheta\, d\vartheta \cdot \int_0^{2\pi} \frac{1}{2\pi} e^{i(m-m')\varphi}\, d\varphi. \end{aligned}\right\} \tag{60.2}$$

If $m' \neq m$ the integral over φ vanishes and we obtain the following selection rule for the magnetic quantum number for radiation emitted with polarization parallel to z

$$\Delta m \equiv m' - m = 0. \tag{60.3}$$

If the selection rule is fulfilled, the integration over φ gives exactly 1. For the purpose of evaluating the integral over ϑ we employ formula (A.22),

$$\mathscr{P}_{l m} \cos\vartheta = \sqrt{\frac{(l+1)^2 - m^2}{(2l+3)(2l+1)}}\, \mathscr{P}_{l+1\, m} + \sqrt{\frac{l^2 - m^2}{(2l+1)(2l-1)}}\, \mathscr{P}_{l-1\, m} \tag{60.4}$$

and the orthogonality relations obeyed by the associated LEGENDRE functions, viz.,

$$\int_0^\pi \mathscr{P}_{l' m} \mathscr{P}_{l m} \sin\vartheta\, d\vartheta = \delta_{l l'}. \tag{60.5}$$

From the above we obtain the result that the integral over ϑ vanishes unless the selection rule for the orbital quantum number

$$\Delta l \equiv l' - l = \pm 1 \tag{60.6}$$

is fulfilled, in which case (60.2) reduces to

$$\left.\begin{aligned} z_{n l m}^{n' l+1\, m} &= \sqrt{\frac{(l+1)^2 - m^2}{(2l+3)(2l+1)}}\, R_{n l}^{n' l+1}, \\ z_{n l m}^{n' l-1\, m} &= \sqrt{\frac{l^2 - m^2}{(2l+1)(2l-1)}}\, R_{n l}^{n' l-1}, \\ z_{n l m}^{n' l' m} &= 0 \quad \text{for all other } l', \end{aligned}\right\} \tag{60.7}$$

in which

$$R_{n l}^{n' l'} = \int R_{n' l'}(r)\, R_{n l}(r)\, r^3\, dr. \tag{60.8}$$

The integration with respect to r is more complicated and is deferred to Sect. 63.

The matrix elements of the coordinates x and y may be evaluated in a similar manner. Actually, it is more convenient to obtain the matrix elements of the linear combinations

$$x + i y = r \sin\vartheta\, e^{i\varphi} \quad\text{and}\quad x - i y = r \sin\vartheta\, e^{-i\varphi},$$

because this leads to a simplification of the integrals with respect to φ. One obtains

$$(x \pm i y)_{n l m}^{n' l' m'} = R_{n l}^{n' l'} \int_0^\pi \mathscr{P}_{l' m'} \mathscr{P}_{l m} \sin\vartheta \cdot \sin\vartheta\, d\vartheta \int_0^{2\pi} e^{i(m \pm 1 - m')\varphi} \frac{d\varphi}{2\pi}. \tag{60.9}$$

The integral with respect to φ vanishes unless

$$\Delta m = m' - m = \pm 1. \tag{60.10}$$

Thus, unless the selection rule for the magnetic quantum number is fulfilled there can be no radiation which is polarized parallel to the x and y axes. Evaluating the ϑ-integrals again with the help of formulas (A.20), (A.21) of the appendix, one again obtains the selection rule (60.6) for the orbital quantum number and also the following explicit expressions for the intensities

$$\left.\begin{aligned}
(x+iy)_{nlm}^{n'l+1\,m+1} &= \sqrt{\frac{(l+m+2)\,(l+m+1)}{(2l+3)\,(2l+1)}}\,R_{nl}^{n'l+1},\\
(x-iy)_{nlm}^{n'l+1\,m-1} &= -\sqrt{\frac{(l-m+2)\,(l-m+1)}{(2l+3)\,(2l+1)}}\,R_{nl}^{n'l+1},\\
(x+iy)_{nlm}^{n'l-1\,m+1} &= -\sqrt{\frac{(l-m)\,(l-m-1)}{(2l+1)\,(2l-1)}}\,R_{nl}^{n'l-1},\\
(x-iy)_{nlm}^{n'l-1\,m-1} &= \sqrt{\frac{(l+m)\,(l+m-1)}{(2l+1)\,(2l-1)}}\,R_{nl}^{n'l-1}.
\end{aligned}\right\}\tag{60.11}$$

All other matrix elements vanish.

From formulas (60.11) one may draw the conclusion that a change in l and in $|m|$ in the same sense is more probable than a transition in the opposite sense.

Formulas (60.7) and (60.11) have the following consequences:

1. If one adds the intensities of the transitions from a certain state nlm to all the substates m' of the level $n'l'$ without regard to the direction of polarization of the emitted radiation, one finds that the sum is independent of m:

$$\left.\begin{aligned}
\sum_{m'}|\boldsymbol{r}_{nlm}^{n'l+1\,m'}|^2 &= |z_{nlm}^{n'l+1\,m}|^2+|x_{nlm}^{n'l+1\,m+1}|^2+|x_{nlm}^{n'l+1\,m-1}|^2+\\
&\quad+|y_{nlm}^{n'l+1\,m+1}|^2+|y_{nlm}^{n'l+1\,m-1}|^2\\
&=\frac{(R_{nl}^{n'l+1})^2}{(2l+3)\,(2l+1)}\cdot\Big[(l+1)^2-m^2+\tfrac{1}{2}(l+m+2)\,(l+m+1)+\\
&\quad+\tfrac{1}{2}(l-m+2)\,(l-m+1)\Big]=\frac{l+1}{2l+1}\,(R_{nl}^{n'l+1})^2.
\end{aligned}\right\}\tag{60.12}$$

Similarly,

$$\sum_{m'}|\boldsymbol{r}_{nlm}^{n'l-1\,m'}|^2=\frac{l}{2l+1}\cdot(R_{nl}^{n'l-1})^2.\tag{60.13}$$

An immediate corollary of the above theorem is that the life time of a state is independent of its magnetic quantum number and depends only on n and l.

2. The sum of the intensities of all the Zeeman components of a spectral line which are polarized in the same direction is independent of that direction of polarization. (Thus, the summation which in case 1 was performed over all the directions of polarization (and m') with m held fixed, is now taken over m (and m') with the direction of polarization held fixed.) In view of (60.7) and (60.11) one obtains

$$\left.\begin{aligned}
\sum_{m}|z_{nlm}^{n'l-1\,m}|^2 &= (R_{nl}^{n'l-1})^2\sum_{m=-l}^{+l}\frac{l^2-m^2}{(2l+1)\,(2l-1)}=\frac{1}{3}\,l\,(R_{nl}^{n'l-1})^2,\\
\sum_{m}(|x_{nlm}^{n'l-1\,m+1}|^2+|x_{nlm}^{n'l-1\,m-1}|^2) &= \frac{1}{3}\,l\,(R_{nl}^{n'l-1})^2.
\end{aligned}\right\}\tag{60.14}$$

One conclusion which we may draw from the above is that the total intensity[1] is the same for each of the three components of the Lorentz triplet in the normal Zeeman effect.

[1] The intensity obtained by integrating over all directions of propagation.

β) General atom and helium. The results of Sect. 60α were derived for a single electron in a central (but otherwise arbitrary) field. In alkali atoms the transitions of most practical importance are those between states in which only the loosely bound valence electron is excited. For such transitions the alkali atom can be treated, to a good approximation, as a system with only one (the valence) electron which moves in a central potential $V(r)$. Although $V(r)$ is not a pure COULOMB field, but a HARTREE potential, the results of Sect. 60α still apply.

There are some selection rules which apply generally (in the dipole approximation) even to complex atoms and can be derived by general operator methods (see [5]). Consider an arbitrary many-electron atom, but treated by the RUSSELL-SAUNDERS approximation (see Sect. 43α, 48α and 64β), i.e. the spin-orbit coupling is small and L and S (the quantum numbers for total orbital and spin angular momentum, respectively) are good quantum numbers. The following selection rules then apply (for proof see ref. [5], Chap. 9):

1. The parity (defined in Sect. 51α) of the wave function must change in the transition (LAPORTE's rule)[1].

2. The total orbital angular momentum changes at most by unity, i.e. $\Delta L=0, \pm 1$.

3. The magnetic quantum number (component in the z-direction of the total orbital angular momentum) remains unchanged ($\Delta m=0$) if the emitted radiation is polarized parallel to z and changes by unity ($\Delta m=\pm 1$) if the radiation is polarized perpendicular to z.

4. The total spin quantum number S remains unchanged, $\Delta S=0$. For helium for instance, this means that transitions between an ortho- and a para-state are forbidden.

From symmetry considerations one also finds the additional selection rule that transitions between two states with $L=0$ are forbidden.

For a one-electron atom these general selection rules reduce[2] to (60.3), (60.6) and (60.10).

For a helium-like atom the situation is as follows, for transitions from an initial level in the discrete spectrum in which at least one electron is in the ground state ($l_1=m_1=0$): For emission spectra the final level must have lower energy than the initial one and must therefore also have at least one electron in the ground state. For such transitions the general selection rules again reduce exactly to Eqs. (60.3), (60.6) and (60.10). For *absorption* spectra, the general selection rules also allow transitions to doubly excited states (e.g. l_1 can change by 1, l_2 by 2, etc.). However, if one uses for both initial and final state the familiar (but approximate) product type wave functions (28.2), one finds that the matrix elements for such "double excitations" vanish. Such matrix elements are nonzero only by virtue of the polarization of the wave functions and should therefore be small. Explicit calculations[3] for He verify that transitions probabilities for double excitation are indeed small.

61. Sum rules. *α) Statement of sum rules.* In this section we state four different sum rules. The first rule is stated for any general atom, the other three

[1] If we are considering a wave function in the form of products (symmetrized, etc.) of single-electron wave functions with orbital quantum numbers $l_1, l_2, \ldots$, then LAPORTE's rule states that $\sum_i l_i$ changes by an odd integer in the transition. For a single-electron atom it states that Δl is odd.

[2] $\Delta l=0$ is forbidden, since the parity is unchanged in such a transition.

[3] J. P. VINTI: Phys. Rev. **42**, 632 (1932).

are stated for a one-electron atom (with an arbitrary central potential) and some results specific to hydrogen-like atoms derived from them. These sum rules will be proved in Sect. 62 and their generalizations to complex atoms discussed.

1. The most important sum rule is the THOMAS-REICHE-KUHN rule for the sum of the oscillator strengths for *all* transitions which start from a definite state n of the atom. This is a very general rule which holds for *any* atom or molecule, with or without external fields, for any polarization direction and no matter which (if any) of the various angular momentum operators are constants of the motion. Let Z be the total *number of electrons* in the system (for an ion this is *not* equal to the nuclear charge) and let n be a *particular* eigenstate of the total HAMILTONian and n' any one of a complete set of eigenstates[1]. The sum rule then states

$$\sum_{n'} f_{n'n} = Z. \tag{61.1}$$

2. Referring to the definition (59.14) we see that the oscillator strength corresponding to a transition $n \to n'$ depends on the orientation of the x-axis, i.e., on the direction of polarization, and therefore also on the magnetic quantum numbers m and m' of the initial and final state. Let us define an *average oscillator strength* of the transition $nl \to n'l'$, which is independent of polarization and m, as follows

$$\left.\begin{aligned} \bar{f}_{n'n} &= \frac{1}{2l+1} \sum_{m'=-l'}^{l'} \sum_{m=-l}^{l} f_{nm}^{n'm'} = \frac{2m}{3\hbar}\,\omega_{n'l'}^{nl} \sum_{m'=-l'}^{l'} |\boldsymbol{r}_{nlm}^{n'l'm'}|^2 \\ &= \frac{1}{3} \cdot \frac{\max(l, l')}{2l+1} \cdot \frac{\nu_{n'l'}^{nl}}{\mathrm{Ry}} \cdot \frac{(R_{nl}^{n'l'})^2}{a^2} \end{aligned}\right\} \tag{61.2}$$

[cf. Eqs. (59.14) and (60.12) to (60.14)], $g_n = 2l+1$ is the degree of degeneracy of the initial state.

It should be noted that $\bar{f}_{nn'}$ is not equal to $\bar{f}_{n'n}$ because, in the first place, the former is obtained by averaging over m' and summing over m, and secondly—as may be seen from the definition (59.14)—the sign of $f_{n'n}$ changes when the indices are interchanged:

$$\bar{f}_{nn'} = \frac{1}{2l'+1} \sum_{m'=-l'}^{l'} \sum_{m=-l}^{l} f_{n'm'}^{nm} = -\frac{2l+1}{2l'+1}\,\bar{f}_{n'n} = -\frac{g_n}{g_{n'}}\,\bar{f}_{n'n}. \tag{61.3}$$

The average oscillator strengths (61.2) obey a sum rule[2] which is stronger than the f sum rule. One can calculate the sum of the oscillator strengths of all the transitions from a certain level nl to the levels of a fixed orbital quantum number, with the result [cf. Eq. (61.2)]:

$$\sum_{n'} \bar{f}_{nl}^{n'l-1} = \frac{2m}{3\hbar}\,\frac{l}{2l+1} \sum_{n'} \omega_{n'l-1,nl} (R_{nl}^{n'l-1})^2 = -\frac{1}{3}\,\frac{l(2l-1)}{2l+1}, \tag{61.4}$$

$$\sum_{n'} \bar{f}_{nl}^{n'l+1} = \frac{1}{3}\,\frac{(l+1)(2l+3)}{2l+1}. \tag{61.5}$$

If the above two equations are added, one obtains the f sum rule (61.1) again.

The "partial f sum rules" (61.4), (61.5) show that among the transitions $nl \to n'l-1$ the ones which lead to energetically lower states ($\nu_{n'l-1,nl} < 0$,

[1] n and n' again denote all the quantum numbers, not only the principal one.

[2] Cf., J. G. KIRKWOOD: Phys. Z. **33**, 521 (1932). — E. WIGNER: Phys. Z. **32**, 450 (1931).

emission) predominate, whereas in the transitions $nl \rightarrow n'l+1$ absorption ($\nu_{n'l+1,nl} > 0$) makes the larger contribution; absorption predominates also in the summation of all oscillator strengths (the ordinary f sum rule). Since the energy increases with increasing principal quantum number, the sum rules (61.4) and (61.5) show that a change of principal and orbital quantum number in the same sense is more probable than a jump in the opposite sense. While we have stated the above sum rules for atoms in which a single electron makes the transitions, it should be noted that the sum rules can be generalized[1].

3. In addition to the sum rules for the oscillator strengths we can also obtain sum rules for the squares of the dipole moment; thus it can be shown [cf. Eq. (60.8)] that:

$$\sum_{n'} (R_{nl}^{n'l-1})^2 = \sum_{n'} (R_{nl}^{n'l+1})^2 = \overline{r^2_{nl}} = \int r^2 R_{nl}^2 r^2 \, dr, \tag{61.6}$$

i.e., the average value of r^2 for the initial state. Substituting from (3.26) the average value of r^2 for hydrogen we obtain

$$\sum_{n'} (R_{nl}^{n'l-1})^2 = \sum_{n'} (R_{nl}^{n'l+1})^2 = a^2 \frac{n^2}{2} \cdot (5n^2 + 1 - 3l(l+1)) \tag{61.7}$$

in which a is the radius of the hydrogen atom. Using (60.12) and (60.13) one obtains

$$\left.\begin{aligned} \sum_{n'm'} |\mathfrak{r}_{nlm}^{n'l-1m'}|^2 &= a^2 \frac{l}{2l+1} \cdot \frac{n^2}{2} (5n^2 + 1 - 3l(l+1)), \\ \sum_{n'm'} |\mathfrak{r}_{nlm}^{n'l+1m'}|^2 &= a^2 \frac{l+1}{2l+1} \cdot \frac{n^2}{2} (5n^2 + 1 - 3l(l+1)), \\ \sum_{n'l'm'} |\mathfrak{r}_{nlm}^{n'l'm'}|^2 &= a^2 \frac{n^2}{2} (5n^2 + 1 - 3l(l+1)). \end{aligned}\right\} \tag{61.8}$$

Whereas (61.6) is valid for any atom having a single transition electron, (61.7) and (61.8) hold only for hydrogen.

4. Finally, for the purpose of getting some additional orientation about the distribution of the energy levels which combine with a level of a given n, the following sum rule is useful:

$$\sum_{n'} (E_{n'l'} - E_{nl})^2 (R_{nl}^{n'l'})^2 = 4 \,\mathrm{Ry} \cdot a^2 (E_{nl} - \overline{V}_{nl}), \tag{61.9}$$

in which $\overline{V}_{nl}$ is the average value of the potential energy with respect to the eigenfunction R_{nl}. For hydrogen-like atoms this quantity is given by the virial theorem (3.29), viz.,

$$\overline{V}_{nl} = \int V R_{nl}^2 r^2 \, dr = 2E_{nl} = -\mathrm{Ry} \cdot \frac{Z^2}{n^2} \tag{61.10}$$

(Z is the nuclear charge), from which we obtain

$$\sum_{n'} (E_{n'l'} - E_{nl})^2 (R_{nl}^{n'l'})^2 = 4 \,\mathrm{Ry}^2 \cdot a^2 \cdot \frac{Z^2}{n^2} \tag{61.11}$$

and

$$\sum_{n'} \nu_{n'l'nl} f_{nl}^{n'l'} = \frac{4}{3(2l+1)} \cdot \frac{Z^2}{n^2} \,\mathrm{Ry} \cdot \begin{Bmatrix} l & \text{for } l' = l-1, \\ l+1 & \text{for } l' = l+1. \end{Bmatrix} \tag{61.12}$$

All the quantities are expressed in c.g.s. units, and a is the radius of the hydrogen atom.

---

[1] Cf., E. WIGNER, loc. cit. and our Sect. 62.

β) Examples of the application of the sum rules. 1. For the lines coming from the ground state $n=1$, $l=0$ we obtain

from (61.7) $$\sum_n (R_{1\,0}^{n\,1})^2 = 3\,a^2,$$

from (61.4) $$\sum_n (E_{n1} - E_{10})\,(R_{1\,0}^{n\,1})^2 = 3\ \mathrm{Ry}\cdot a^2,$$

from (61.11) $$\sum_n (E_{n1} - E_{10})^2\,(R_{1\,0}^{n\,1})^2 = 4\,\mathrm{Ry}^2\,a^2.$$

Thus, on the average, the energy difference between the excited and the ground state is given by

$$\frac{\sum_n (E_n - E_1)\,(R_{1\,0}^{n\,1})^2}{\sum_n (R_{1\,0}^{n\,1})^2} = \mathrm{Ry},$$

i.e., the "center of gravity" of the LYMAN series lies at the point of separation between the discrete and the continuous spectrum. The square root of the average value of the square of the excitation energy is equal to $\sqrt{\frac{4}{3}}$ Ry.

Next, we shall consider the problem of using the above sum rules for obtaining an estimate for the sum

$$\sum \frac{(R_{1\,0}^{n\,1})^2}{E_n - E_1} = S \tag{61.13}$$

which is of importance in the STARK effect of the ground level. If we replace $E_n - E_1$ by its average value 1 Ry, then we surely shall get a value of S which is too small, since transitions corresponding to a small energy difference $E_n - E_1$ make a larger contribution than the ones corresponding to a large energy difference[1]. This lower limit of S is given by

$$S_{\min} = \frac{\sum (R_{1\,0}^{n\,1})^2}{E_n - E_1} = \frac{[\sum (R_{1\,0}^{n\,1})^2]^2}{\sum (E_n - E_1)\,(R_{1\,0}^{n\,1})^2} = \frac{3}{\mathrm{Ry}} = 6 \text{ at. un.}$$

On the other hand, if we set $E_n - E_1$ equal to its smallest possible value $E_2 - E_1 = \frac{3}{4}$ Ry, we obtain a value of S which is surely too large:

$$S_{\max} = \frac{\sum_n (R_{1\,0}^{n\,1})^2}{E_2 - E_1} = \frac{4}{\mathrm{Ry}} = 8 \text{ at. un.}$$

The correct value is actually equal to 6.75 atomic units[2] corresponding to an average energy difference of $\frac{8}{9}$ Ry.

2. We shall now investigate the transition probabilities for high quantum numbers for transitions from a certain level nl to a neighboring level. In particular, we shall obtain a more quantitative result for the assertion made in subsection α2, that the transitions in which both n and l change in the same direction are more frequent than the ones in which the change is in the opposite direction.

(61.8) represents an evaluation of the sum of the squares of the dipole moments for all transitions from nl to $n'l\pm 1$ including the transition $n'=n$. If we subtract the latter we are left with the amount given by (63.6) and (63.7). For very

[1] The average value of $\frac{1}{E_n - E_1}$ is always greater than the reciprocal of the average of $E_n - E_1$.

[2] Formula (52.3) for the quadratic STARK effect for $n=1$, $n_1=n_2=m=0$ yields the perturbation energy $E_2 = -\frac{9}{4}F^2$ atomic units. On the other hand, $E_2 = -F^2 \sum_n \frac{(z_{1\,0}^{n\,1})^2}{E_n - E_1} = -\frac{1}{3}F^2 S$, since the spherical symmetry of u_{100} results in $z_{1\,0}^{n\,1} = (1/\sqrt{3})\,R_{1\,0}^{n\,1}$.

large n and l, (63.6) and (63.7) may be written as follows

$$\sum_{n'} (R_{nl}^{n'l+1})^2 = \sum_{n'} (R_{nl}^{n'l-1})^2 = \tfrac{1}{4} n^2 (n^2 + 3l^2)\, a^2. \tag{61.14}$$

Furthermore, according to (61.11) we have

$$\sum_{n'} (E_{n'} - E_n)^2 (R_{nl}^{n'l\pm 1})^2 = \frac{4}{n^2} \,\mathrm{Ry}^2 a^2. \tag{61.15}$$

Next, we note that[1] surely

$$\left.\begin{aligned}\sum_{n'} |E_{n'} - E_n| (R_{nl}^{n'l\pm1})^2 &< \sqrt{\sum_{n'} (R_{nl}^{n'l\pm1})^2 \cdot \sum_{n'} (E_{n'} - E_n)^2 (R_{nl}^{n'l\pm1})^2} \\ &= \sqrt{n^2 + 3l^2}\,\mathrm{Ry}\cdot a^2.\end{aligned}\right\} \tag{61.16}$$

On the other hand, if we assume that $l \gg 1$ in (61.5) we obtain:

$$\sum_{n'} (E_{n'} - E_n)(R_{nl}^{n'l+1})^2 = 2l\,\mathrm{Ry}\cdot a^2. \tag{61.17}$$

From (61.16) and (61.17), taking into consideration the definition of the oscillator strength (59.14), follows:

$$\frac{\sum\limits_{n'>n} f_{nl}^{n'l+1}}{\sum\limits_{n'<n} |f_{nl}^{n'l+1}|} = \frac{\sqrt{n^2 + 3l^2} + 2l}{\sqrt{n^2 + 3l^2} - 2l}. \tag{61.18}$$

Thus, for very small l (eccentric orbits) the transitions with a change of n and l in the same sense are as frequent as the ones with changes in the opposite sense. For $l = n$ (circular orbits), n and l always change in the same sense. For intermediate eccentricities, say $l = \frac{1}{2}n$, a change in the same direction is, on the average, about 7 times as frequent as a change in the opposite sense.

From (61.14) and (61.15) we can also tell by how many units, on the average, the principal quantum number changes in an optical transition. Since

$$\overline{(E_{n'} - E_n)^2} = \frac{\sum\limits_{n'} (E_{n'} - E_n)^2 (R_{nl}^{n'l\pm1})^2}{\sum\limits_{n'} (R_{nl}^{n'l\pm1})^2} = \frac{16}{n^4 (n^2 + 3l^2)}\,\mathrm{Ry}^2 \tag{61.19}$$

and since $E_n = -\frac{1}{n^2}\,\mathrm{Ry}$, i.e.,

$$E_{n'} - E_n \approx \frac{2(n' - n)}{n^3}\,\mathrm{Ry},$$

the mean square of the change in the principal quantum number is given by

$$\sqrt{\overline{(n' - n)^2}} = \frac{n^3}{2} \sqrt{\overline{(E_{n'} - E_n)^2}} = \frac{2}{\sqrt{1 + 3l^2/n^2}}. \tag{61.20}$$

Thus, for circular orbits ($l = n$) the principal quantum number always changes by unity—a result which also follows from the correspondence principle. For very eccentric orbits ($l \ll n$) the average change in n is equal to 2. and for orbits of intermediate eccentricity ($l \approx \frac{1}{2}n$) the average change amounts to about 1.5. (However, on account of the factor ν^3 [cf. Eq. (59.7)] the transition probabilities emphasize the transitions corresponding to a large jump.)

62. Proof of the sum rules. Explicit wave mechanical derivations for the four sum rules stated in Sect. 61α will be found in [*10*], Sect. 40a. We give, instead,

[1] The mean of the square is always greater than the square of the mean.

derivations based on general operator manipulation[1], some of which illustrate the use of projection operators. Rule 1 will be proved for a general system, rules 2, 3 and 4 for a one-electron atom[2].

1. Using the relation (59.20), we can rewrite the definition (59.14) for the oscillator strength in the form[3]

$$f_{n'n} = -f_{nn'} = +\frac{2i}{\hbar}(p_x)_{nn'}\,x_{n'n} = -\frac{2i}{\hbar}x_{nn'}(p_x)_{n'n}. \tag{62.1}$$

Now the states n' form a complete set of eigenstates and the following general sum rule applies for any two operators A and B

$$(A\,B)_{mn} = \sum_{n'} A_{mn'}\,B_{n'n}. \tag{62.2}$$

Taking half the sum of the last two expressions in (62.1) and using (62.2) we find

$$\sum_{n'} f_{n'n} = \frac{i}{\hbar}[p_x, x]_{nn}. \tag{62.3}$$

The operators p_x and x are sums of operators for each of the Z electrons and (59.18) gives

$$[p_x, x] = -i\hbar\sum_{i,j=1}^{Z}\delta_{ij} = -Z i\hbar \tag{62.4}$$

which is a number (not an operator). Substituting (62.4) into (62.3) gives the desired relation (61.1). Note that we have used no specific property of V in the HAMILTONian (59.17), but merely the fact that the states n' form a complete set[4].

2. We now prove the sum rules (61.4) and (61.5) for a one-electron system in a central potential, so that the square $\boldsymbol{k}^2$ of the orbital angular momentum operator is a constant of the motion. We shall use the fact that the matrix element of x (or p_x) for a transition between states[5] $n\,l\,m$ and $n'\,l'\,m'$ is non-zero only if $l'=l-1$ or $l+1$. We abreviate the eigenvalues of $\boldsymbol{k}^2$ for states with orbital quantum number l, $l+1$ and $l-1$ by

$$c_0 = l(l+1), \qquad c_+ = (l+1)(l+2), \qquad c_- = (l-1)\,l.$$

We further define the "projection operator" $(\boldsymbol{k}^2 - c_-)(c_+ - c_-)^{-1}$, which is equivalent to a multiplying factor of unity and zero, respectively, when operating on a state with orbital quantum number $l+1$ and $l-1$. Using the fact that this projection operator gives zero for $l-1$ and that the matrix element of x is zero unless $l'=l\pm 1$, we can apply the general sum rule (62.2) to derive

$$\sum_{n'm'}^{(l'=l+1)}(p_x)_{nn'}\,x_{n'n} = \sum_{n'm'l'}\left(p_x\frac{\boldsymbol{k}^2-c_-}{c_+-c_-}\right)_{nn'}x_{n'n} = \left(p_x\frac{\boldsymbol{k}^2-c_-}{c_+-c_-}\,x\right)_{nn}, \tag{62.5}$$

and a similar relation with the order of x and p_x interchanged. The sum on the left hand side is carried over all values of n' and m', but with $l'=l+1$, for a fixed initial state $n\,l\,m$. The symbol $n\,n$ on the right hand side denotes the expectation value over the state $n\,l\,m$. We are interested in the *sum* of the

---

[1] For more general proofs of these sum rules and a discussion of operator manipulation, see [*1*] and [*5*]; M. BORN, W. HEISENBERG and P. JORDAN, Z. Physik **35**, 557 (1926) and E. WIGNER, Phys. Z. **32**, 450 (1931).

[2] For other sum rules and their derivation see J. M. HARRIMAN, Phys. Rev. **101**, 594 (1956).

[3] Note that $A_{n'n}$ is the matrix element of A for a transition *from* n to n'.

[4] In the above relations n stands for *all* the quantum numbers specifying a particular state. Note that the state n in (62.3) need not be a member of the set of states n'.

[5] Here n denotes the principal quantum number only.

mean oscillator strength $\bar{f}_{nl}^{n'l'}$, defined in (61.2), over all values of n' with l' (and $n\,l$) fixed. Using (62.1) we find that this sum equals $2i/\hbar$ times the *average* over m of the left hand side of (62.5). (60.14) shows that this average is independent of the polarization direction and we can also average over this direction. We then have

$$\sum_{n'} \bar{f}_{nl}^{n',l+1} = \frac{i}{3\hbar}\left(\boldsymbol{p}\cdot\frac{\boldsymbol{k}^2 - c_-}{c_+ - c_-}\boldsymbol{r} - \boldsymbol{r}\cdot\frac{\boldsymbol{k}^2 - c_-}{c_+ - c_-}\boldsymbol{p}\right)_{nn}. \tag{62.6}$$

Making use of (11.5) and (11.7), one can show that

$$\boldsymbol{p}\cdot k^2\boldsymbol{r} - \boldsymbol{r}\cdot k^2\boldsymbol{p} = (k^2\boldsymbol{p}\cdot\boldsymbol{r} - \boldsymbol{r}\cdot\boldsymbol{p}\,k^2) + 2i(\boldsymbol{k}\times\boldsymbol{p}\cdot\boldsymbol{r} - \boldsymbol{r}\cdot\boldsymbol{p}\times\boldsymbol{k}) + 2(\boldsymbol{p}\cdot\boldsymbol{r} - \boldsymbol{r}\cdot\boldsymbol{p}). \tag{62.7}$$

Using (11.3), (11.4) and $\boldsymbol{k}\times\boldsymbol{p}\cdot\boldsymbol{r} = \boldsymbol{k}\cdot\boldsymbol{p}\times\boldsymbol{r}$, (62.7) and the term independent of $\boldsymbol{k}^2$ in (62.6) can be simplified further. Using the fact that the matrix element in (62.6) is a diagonal one for an eigenstate of $\boldsymbol{k}^2$ with eigenvalue c_0, we finally find (after some algebra)

$$\sum_{n'} \bar{f}_{nl}^{n',l\pm1} = \frac{\frac{7}{3}c_0 + 2 - c_\mp}{c_\pm - c_\mp}. \tag{62.8}$$

In (62.8) the upper signs refer to the sum (62.6) with $l' = l+1$, the lower signs to an equivalent calculation with $l' = l-1$. Substituting the explicit values for c_0, c_+ and c_-, (62.8) with the upper signs reduces to (61.5) and with the lower signs to (61.4).

3. To prove the sum rule (61.6) we note that the radial matrix element $R_{nl}^{n'l'}$ for the dipole moment can be considered as a matrix element of r between two one-dimensional wave functions χ_{nl} and $\chi_{n'l'}$, (r times the radial wave function)

$$R_{nl}^{n'l'} = \int_0^\infty dr\,\chi_{n'l'}(r)\,r\,\chi_{nl}(r) \equiv r_{nl}^{n'l'}.$$

Now $\chi_{n'l'}$ satisfies the equation

$$\left[\frac{d^2}{dr^2} - \frac{l'(l'+1)}{r^2} + \frac{2m}{\hbar^2}\left(E_{n'l'} - V(r)\right)\right]\chi_{n'l'}(r) = 0,$$

where $V(r)$ is a given central potential. Now, any bounded function of the variable r only, which also vanishes at $r=0$, can be expressed as a linear superposition of the functions $\chi_{n'l'}$ for any *fixed* values of l' but all values of n'. The $\chi_{n'l'}$ thus form a complete set (for radial functions only) and we can use the general sum rule (62.2) on the following sum over n' (with l' *fixed*)

$$\sum_{n'} (R_{nl}^{n'l'})^2 = \sum_{n'} r_{n'l'}^{nl}\, r_{nl}^{n'l'} = (r^2)_{nl}^{nl} \equiv \int_0^\infty dr\, r^2\chi_{nl}^2. \tag{62.9}$$

This sum is thus independent of the value of l' and (61.6) is a special case of (62.9).

4. To derive the relations (61.9) to (61.12) we first use (59.14) and (59.20) to write

$$\omega_{n'n} f_{n'n} = \frac{2}{\hbar m}(p_x)_{nn'}(p_x)_{n'n}. \tag{62.10}$$

As in sum rule (62.8) we are again interested in the sum of this expression over all values of the principal and magnetic quantum numbers n' and m', but for *fixed* $l'(=l+1$ or $l-1)$, averaged over all values of m. We again average over directions, use a projection operator as in (62.5) and apply (62.2) to get for this sum

$$\sum_{n'} \bar{f}_{nl}^{n',l+1}\omega_{n'n} = \frac{2}{3\hbar m}\left(\boldsymbol{p}\cdot\frac{\boldsymbol{k}^2 - c_-}{c_+ - c_-}\boldsymbol{p}\right)_{nn}.$$

Using (11.5), (11.7) and the fact that n is an eigenstate of $\boldsymbol{k}^2$ with eigenvalue c_0, we find

$$\sum_{n'} \omega_{n'n} \bar{f}_{nl}^{n',l+1} = \frac{2}{3\hbar m} (p^2)_{nn} \frac{c_0 + 2 - c_-}{c_+ - c_-}. \tag{62.11}$$

Writing $T = p^2/2m$ for the kinetic energy operator and substituting the values for c_0, $c_\pm$ into (62.11) (and in the equivalent expression with c_- and c_+ interchanged for $l' = l - 1$), we have

$$\sum_{n'} \omega_{n'l',nl} \bar{f}_{nl}^{n'l'} = \frac{4}{3(2l+1)} \frac{\bar{T}_{nl}}{\hbar} \begin{Bmatrix} l & \text{for} \quad l' = l - 1, \\ l + 1 & \text{for} \quad l' = l + 1, \end{Bmatrix}. \tag{62.12}$$

where $\bar{T}_{nl} = E_{nl} - \bar{V}_{nl}$ is the expectation value for the state $n\,l$ of the kinetic energy operator. For a COULOMB potential, $\bar{T}/\hbar$ equals $Z^2/2n^2$ atomic units of frequency (or $2\pi Z^2/n^2$ Ry) and (62.12) reduces to (61.12). For *any* potential, (61.2) shows that (61.9) and (62.12) are identical.

63. The transition probabilities for hydrogen in polar coordinates. α) *Formulas.* In order to arrive at the absolute values of the transition probabilities we must evaluate the integrals defined in (60.8), viz.:

$$R_{nl}^{n'l-1} = \int_0^\infty R_{nl} R_{n'l-1} r^3 \, dr. \tag{63.1}$$

In the above, the radial eigenfunctions are the associated LAGUERRE functions which we considered in Sects. 3 and 4. The calculation is not at all simple if it is carried out in complete generality leading to a result in closed form. Therefore, we shall at once quote the final formula obtained by GORDON[1] (for $n' \neq n$)

$$\left.\begin{aligned} R_{nl}^{n'l-1} &= \frac{(-1)^{n'-l}}{4(2l-1)!} \sqrt{\frac{(n+l)!\,(n'+l-1)!}{(n-l-1)!\,(n'-l)!}} \frac{(4nn')^{l+1} (n-n')^{n+n'-2l-2}}{(n+n')^{n+n'}} \times \\ &\times \left\{ F\left(-n_r, -n_r', 2l, -\frac{4nn'}{(n-n')^2}\right) - \left(\frac{n-n'}{n+n'}\right)^2 F\left(-n_r - 2, -n_r', 2l, -\frac{4nn'}{(n-n')^2}\right) \right\}. \end{aligned}\right\} \tag{63.2}$$

In the above,

$$F(\alpha, \beta, \gamma, x) = \sum_\nu \frac{\alpha(\alpha+1)\ldots(\alpha+\nu-1)\,\beta\ldots(\beta+\nu-1)}{\gamma\ldots(\gamma+\nu-1)\,\nu!} x^\nu \tag{63.3}$$

is the hypergeometric function and $n_r = n - l - 1$, $n_r' = n' - l$ are the radial quantum numbers of the two states. Because these numbers are integers, the series for the hypergeometric function terminate.

We shall list individually the squares of the radial integrals for the LYMAN and BALMER series, which are obtained by inserting the appropriate special values for n, n' and l in (63.2) and (63.3):

$$\left.\begin{aligned} &\text{LYMAN series:} \quad 1s - np \quad (R_{10}^{n1})^2 = \frac{2^8 n^7 (n-1)^{2n-5}}{(n+1)^{2n+5}}, \\ &\text{BALMER series:} \quad 2s - np \quad (R_{20}^{n1})^2 = \frac{2^{17} n^7 (n^2-1)(n-2)^{2n-6}}{(n+2)^{2n+6}}, \\ &\qquad 2p - nd \quad (R_{21}^{n2})^2 = \frac{2^{19} n^9 (n^2-1)(n-2)^{2n-7}}{3(n+2)^{2n+7}}, \\ &\qquad 2p - ns \quad (R_{21}^{n0})^2 = \frac{2^{15} n^9 (n-2)^{2n-6}}{3(n+2)^{2n+6}}. \end{aligned}\right\} \tag{63.4}$$

[1] W. GORDON: Ann. d. Phys. (5) **2**, 1031 (1929). The radial integrals will always be expressed in terms of the atomic unit a.

Furthermore, according to (59.14), (59.15) and (61.2), the mean oscillator strengths for the LYMAN series are given by

$$\bar{f}^{n\,1}_{1\,0} = \frac{2^8 n^5 (n-1)^{2n-4}}{3(n+1)^{2n+4}},$$

and the transition probability by

$$A^{n\,1}_{1\,0} = 8\times 10^9 \frac{2^8 n (n-1)^{2n-2}}{3(n+1)^{2n+2}} \sec^{-1},$$

provided the ground state is regarded as the initial state. The above is related to the probability for the absorption of radiation by a hydrogen atom in the ground state. (The latter quantity is obtained by multiplying the transition probability by $\frac{c^3}{4h\nu^3}\varrho_\nu$ in which ϱ_ν is the density of radiation.) On the other hand, the probability for the radiative transition of an excited np electron to the ground state is obtained by dividing the above by 3, the statistical weight of the p state

$$A^{1\,0}_{n\,1} = 8\times 10^9 \frac{2^8 n (n-1)^{2n-2}}{9(n+1)^{2n+2}} \sec^{-1}$$

and the emitted intensity per np electron [cf. Eq. (59.10)] is given by

$$J^{1\,0}_{n\,1} = 0.173 \frac{2^8 (n-1)^{2n-1}}{9n(n+1)^{2n+1}} \frac{\text{erg}}{\text{sec}}.$$

The expression (63.2) is not valid for transitions in which the principal quantum number does not change ($n\,l \to n, l\pm 1$). The radial integration for such a transition can be evaluated easily and gives

$$R^{n\,l}_{n,\,l-1} = R^{n,\,l-1}_{n\,l} = \tfrac{3}{2} n \sqrt{n^2 - l^2}. \qquad (63.5)$$

In hydrogen the frequency of the radiation emitted (or absorbed) in such transitions is in the radio or microwave region and such transitions form the basis of modern precision measurements of the fine structure and LAMB shift (Sect. 21). The square of $R^{n,\,l-1}_{n\,l}$ is, in many cases, even larger than the sum of the squares of all other matrix elements $R^{n',\,l-1}_{n\,l}$. Using the sum rule (61.7) and subtracting the square of (63.5), we find

$$\sum_{n'\neq n} (R^{n',\,l-1}_{n\,l})^2 = \tfrac{1}{4} n^2 [n^2 - 1 + 3(l-1)^2], \qquad (63.6)$$

and similarly

$$\sum_{n'\neq n} (R^{n',\,l+1}_{n\,l})^2 = \tfrac{1}{4} n^2 [n^2 - 1 + 3(l+2)^2]. \qquad (63.7)$$

For $n=2$, for instance, we get

$$(R^{2\,1}_{2\,0})^2 = (R^{2\,0}_{2\,1})^2 = 27, \quad \sum_{n'\neq 2} (R^{n'\,0}_{2\,1})^2 = 3, \quad \sum_{n'\neq 2} (R^{n'\,1}_{2\,0})^2 = 15, \quad \sum_{n'\neq 2} (R^{n'\,2}_{2\,1})^2 = 30.$$

For a fixed initial state $n\,l$, the transition probability to a final state with principal quantum number n' decreases roughly as n'^{-3} with increasing n'. Note that the energy separation of levels with n' and $(n'+1)$ is also proportional to n'^{-3} for large n' (and so are the fine structure and hyperfine structure splittings).

β) Tables. We give below some tables for various quantities connected with transition probabilities in the hydrogen spectrum. Numerical values for the radial integrals, oscillator strengths, line intensities, and lifetimes have been tabulated

Table 13. *Squares of the dipole moments* $(R_{nl}^{n'l'})^2 = (\int R_{nl} R_{n'l'} r^3\, dr)^2$ *for hydrogen.*

Initial	1s	2s	2p		3s	3p		3d	
Final	np	np	ns	nd	np	ns	nd	np	nf
$n=1$	—	—	1.67	—	—	0.3	—	—	—
2	1.666	27.00	27.00	—	0.9	9.2	—	22.5	—
3	0.267	9.18	0.88	22.52	162.0	162.0	101.2	101.2	—
4	0.093	1.64	0.15	2.92	29.9	6.0	57.2	1.7	104.6
5	0.044	0.60	0.052	0.95	5.1	0.9	8.8	0.23	11.0
6	0.024	0.29	0.025	0.41	1.9	0.33	3.0	0.08	3.2
7	0.015	0.17	0.014	0.24	0.9	0.16	1.4	0.03	1.4
8	0.010	0.10	0.009	0.15	0.5	0.09	0.8	0.02	0.8
$n=9$ to ∞ together	0.032	0.31	0.025	0.42	1.4	0.22	2.0	0.05	1.8
asymptotic	$4.7n^{-3}$	$44.0n^{-3}$	$3.7n^{-3}$	$58.6n^{-3}$	$169n^{-3}$	$28n^{-3}$	$248n^{-3}$	$5n^{-3}$	$198n^{-3}$
Discrete spectrum	2.151	39.30	29.820	27.62	202.56	179.18	174.54	125.88	122.85
Continuous spectrum	0.849	2.70	0.180	2.38	4.44	0.82	5.46	0.12	3.15
Total	3.000	42.00	30.00	30.00	207.00	180.00	180.00	126.00	126.00

Initial	4s	4p		4d		4f	
Final	np	ns	nd	np	nf	nd	ng
$n=1$	—	0.09	—	—	—	—	—
2	0.15	1.66	—	2.9	—	—	—
3	6.0	29.8	1.7	57.0	—	104.7	—
4	540.0	540.0	432.0	432.0	252.0	252.0	—
5	72.6	21.2	121.9	9.3	197.8	2.75	314.0
6	11.9	2.9	19.3	1.3	26.9	0.32	27.6
7	5.7	1.4	7.7	0.5	8.6	0.08	7.3
8	2.1	0.6	3.2	0.2	3.9	0.04	3.0
$n=9$ to ∞ together	4.3	1.0	5.9	0.3	6.9	0.07	4.5
asymptotic	$445n^{-3}$	$102n^{-3}$	$655n^{-3}$	$33n^{-3}$	$687n^{-3}$	$6n^{-3}$	$393n^{-3}$
Discrete spectrum	642.7	598.7	591.7	503.50	496.0	359.95	356.4
Continuous spectrum	5.3	1.3	8.3	0.50	8.0	0.05	3.6
Total	648.0	600.0	600.0	504.00	504.0	360.00	360.0

by KUPPER[1], SUGIURA[2], SLACK[3] and MAXWELL[4]. Our tables are taken from these papers with a few corrections. Much more accurate values for the oscillator strengths (our Table 14) have been tabulated recently by HARRIMAN[5] for initial states up to $4f$ and final states up to $n=50$.

In Table 13 we have tabulated the squares of the radial integral

$$(R_{nl}^{n'l'})^2 = \left(\int_0^\infty R_{nl} R_{n'l'} r^3\, dr\right)^2$$

in terms of the atomic unit a^2 for $n=1$ to 4, $n'=1$ to 8. In addition, we list the sum of the squares for the transitions from a fixed state to the higher discrete states ($n' \geq 9$), and a corresponding sum for the transitions from nl to all the discrete states, and finally the sum of $(R_{nl}^{n'l'})^2$ for all the transitions into the continuous spectrum. The last sum is evaluated by taking the difference between

1 A. KUPPER: Ann. d. Phys. **86**, 511 (1928).
2 V. SUGIURA: J. Phys. Radium **8**, 113 (1927).
3 F. G. SLACK: Phys. Rev. **31**, 527 (1928).
4 L. R. MAXWELL: Phys. Rev. **38**, 1664 (1931).
5 J. M. HARRIMAN: Phys. Rev. **101**, 594 (1956).

Table 14. *Oscillator strengths for hydrogen.*

Initial	1s	2s	2p		3s	3p		3d	
Final	np	np	ns	nd	np	ns	nd	np	nf
$n=1$	—	—	−0.139	—	—	−0.026	—	—	—
2	0.4162	—	—	—	−0.041	−0.145	—	−0.417	—
3	0.0791	0.4349	0.014	0.696	—	—	—	—	—
4	0.0290	0.1028	0.0031	0.122	0.484	0.032	0.619	0.011	1.016
5	0.0139	0.0419	0.0012	0.044	0.121	0.007	0.139	0.0022	0.156
6	0.0078	0.0216	0.0006	0.022	0.052	0.003	0.056	0.0009	0.053
7	0.0048	0.0127	0.0003	0.012	0.027	0.002	0.028	0.0004	0.025
8	0.0032	0.0081	0.0002	0.008	0.016	0.001	0.017	0.0002	0.015
$n=9$ to ∞ together	0.0109	0.0268	0.0007	0.023	0.048	0.002	0.045	0.0007	0.037
asymptotic	$1.6\,n^{-3}$	$3.7\,n^{-3}$	$0.1\,n^{-3}$	$3.3\,n^{-3}$	$6.2\,n^{-3}$	$0.3\,n^{-3}$	$6.1\,n^{-3}$	$0.07\,n^{-3}$	$4.4\,n^{-3}$
Discrete spectrum	0.5650	0.6489	−0.119	0.928	0.707	−0.121	0.904	−0.402	1.302
Continuous spectrum	0.4350	0.3511	0.008	0.183	0.293	0.010	0.207	0.002	0.098
Total	1.000	1.000	−0.111	1.111	1.000	−0.111	1.111	−0.400	1.400
$\overline{E}$	0.54	0.61	0.6	0.42	0.78	0.47		0.39	

Initial	4s	4p		4d		4f	
Final	np	ns	nd	np	nf	nd	n'g
$n=1$	—	−0.010	—	—	—	—	—
2	−0.009	−0.034	—	−0.073	—	—	—
3	−0.097	−0.161	−0.018	−0.371	—	−0.727	—
4	—	—	—	—	—	—	—
5	0.545	0.053	0.610	0.028	0.890	0.009	1.345
6	0.138	0.012	0.149	0.006	0.187	0.0016	0.183
7	0.060	0.006	0.063	0.002	0.072	0.0005	0.058
8	0.033	0.003	0.033	0.001	0.037	0.0003	0.027
$n=9$ to ∞ together	0.082	0.006	0.075	0.002	0.081	0.0006	0.045
asymptotic	$9.3\,n^{-3}$	$0.7\,n^{-3}$	$9.1\,n^{-3}$	$0.3\,n^{-3}$	$8.6\,n^{-3}$	$0.05\,n^{-3}$	$3.5\,n^{-3}$
Discrete spectrum	0.752	−0.126	0.912	−0.406	1.267	−0.715	1.658
Continuous spectrum	0.248	0.015	0.199	0.006	0.133	0.001	0.056
Total	1.000	−0.111	1.111	−0.400	1.400	−0.714	1.714
$\overline{E}$	1.25	0.72		0.45		0.32	

the total sum of all R^2 [which may be obtained from the sum rules (61.7)] and the sum for the transitions to the discrete spectrum. Finally, the asymptotic formula for $(R_{nl}^{n'l'})^2$ is given for high values of n', for fixed $n\,l\,l'$, under the heading "asymptotic".

Table 14 contains the average oscillator strengths, as defined in (61.2), for the (partial) LYMAN, BALMER, PASCHEN, and BRACKETT series. The arrangement of the table is the same as that of Table 13; however, we have added a row on the bottom which contains the average energy of the states in the continuum which combine with the state $n\,l$ (the particular values of $n\,l$ are specified at the top of each column). The average energy expressed in terms of the absolute value of the energy of the state $n\,l$ is given by

$$\overline{E} = \frac{\int\limits_{\text{cont. spectr.}} E'(R_{nl}^{E'l'})^2\,dE'}{\int (R_{nl}^{E'l'})^2\,dE'} \cdot \frac{n^2}{\text{Ry}}.$$

Table 15. *Transition probabilities for hydrogen in 10^8 sec^{-1}.*

Initial	Final	$n=1$	2	3	4	5	Total	Lifetime in 10^{-8} sec
$2s$	np	—	—	—	—	—	0	∞
$2p$	ns	6.25	—	—	—	—	6.25	0.16
2	mean	4.69	—	—	—	—	4.69	0.21
$3s$	np	—	0.063	—	—	—	0.063	16
$3p$	ns	1.64	0.22	—	—	—	1.86	0.54
$3d$	np	—	0.64	—	—	—	0.64	1.56
3	mean	0.55	0.43	—	—	—	0.98	1.02
$4s$	np	—	0.025	0.018	—	—	0.043	23
$4p$ {	ns	0.68	0.095	0.030	—	—	} 0.81	1.24
	nd	—	—	0.003	—	—		
$4d$	np	—	0.204	0.070	—	—	0.274	3.65
$4f$	nd	—	—	0.137	—	—	0.137	7.3
4	mean	0.12_8	0.083	0.089	—	—	0.299	3.35
$5s$	np	—	0.012_7	0.008_5	0.006_5	—	0.027_7	36
$5p$ {	ns	0.34	0.049	0.016	0.007_5	—	} 0.415	2.40
	nd	—	—	0.001_5	0.002	—		
$5d$ {	np	—	0.094	0.034	0.014	—	} 0.142	7.0
	nf	—	—	—	0.000_5	—		
$5f$	nd	—	—	0.045	0.026	—	0.071	14.0
$5g$	nf	—	—	—	0.042_5	—	0.042_5	23.5
5	mean	0.040	0.025	0.022	0.027	—	0.114	8.8
$6s$	np	—	0.007_3	0.0051	0.0035	0.0017	0.0176	57
$6p$ {	ns	0.195	0.029	0.0096	0.0045	0.0021	} 0.243	4.1
	nd	—	—	0.0007	0.0009	0.0010		
$6d$ {	np	—	0.048	0.0187	0.0086	0.0040	} 0.080	12.6
	nf	—	—	—	0.0002	0.0004		
$6f$ {	nd	—	—	0.0210	0.0129	0.0072	} 0.0412	24.3
	ng	—	—	—	—	0.0001		
$6g$	nf	—	—	—	0.0137	0.0110	0.0247	40.5
$6h$	ng	—	—	—	—	0.0164	0.0164	61
6	mean	0.0162	0.0092	0.0077	0.0077	0.0101	0.0510	19.6

For example, the states of the continuum which combine with the level $3s$ have an average energy of $\bar{E}=0.78\times\frac{1}{9}$ Ry$=0.087$ Ry. However, it is not claimed that these numbers have a high degree of accuracy.

In Table 15 are listed the transition probabilities [with regard to their evaluation from the f values compare (59.15)] from the sublevels $s, p, d \ldots$ of the states $n=2, 3, 4, 5, 6$ to all the lower states in terms of 10^8 sec^{-1}. By summing the individual transition probabilities one obtains the decay constants given in the next to the last column under the heading "Total". The reciprocal of the decay constant is equal to the lifetime and is given in the last column. In addition, we have calculated the average value of the transition probabilities from the states of a certain principal quantum number n to that of another principal quantum number n', namely

$$A_{n'n} = \sum_{l l'} \frac{2l+1}{n^2} A_{nl}^{n'l'} . \tag{63.8}$$

The average transition probability, as given above, assumes importance if the excited atoms suffer a great many collisions during their lifetime or if some other perturbation, such as an electric field, assures that the atoms occupy the substates of various orbital quantum numbers l in proportion to their statistical weights (see below).

Table 16. *Intensities for hydrogen in 10^{-4} erg/sec.*

	LYMAN series	BALMER series				PASCHEN series					
	$1s-np$	$2s-np$	$2p-ns$	$2p-nd$	total	$3s-np$	$3p-ns$	$3p-nd$	$3d-np$	$3d-nf$	total
a) *Absorption or emission*, if one electron is *present* in the initial state (on the average).											
$n=2$	304	—	—	—	—	—	—	—	—	—	—
3	94	1.97	0.19	9.6	11.8	—	—	—	—	—	—
4	41	1.15	0.10	4.13	5.38	0.096	0.019	0.37	0.011	1.01	1.51
5	21	0.67	0.06	2.14	2.87	0.074	0.013	0.261	0.007	0.483	0.84
6	12	0.42	0.035	1.15	1.50	0.052	0.009	0.168	0.004_5	0.265	0.500
7	8	0.27	0.02	0.75	1.04	0.035	0.007	0.109	0.002_5	0.162	0.315
8	5	0.18	0.01_5	0.53	0.73	0.024	0.005	0.077	0.001_5	0.113	0.220
9 to ∞	19	0.64	0.05	1.70	2.4	0.09	0.01	0.25	0.006	0.34	0.70
b) Emission, if one electron per second is *put into* the initial state.											
$n=2$	48.6	—	—	—	—	—	—	—	—	—	—
3	50.5	1.06	3.0	15.0	19.0	—	—	—	—	—	—
4	51.0	1.42	2.3	15.0	18.7	0.12	0.44	1.35	0.014	7.4	9.3
5	50.5	1.61	2.2	15.0	18.8	0.17	0.45	1.85	0.017	6.8	9.3
6	49.5	1.73	2.0	14.4	18.1	0.21	0.51	2.10	0.018	6.4	9.2

Finally, Table 16 gives the line intensities under various conditions of excitation: If the electrons are distributed according to the statistical weights, i.e., if on the average there is exactly one electron in each excited state $n\,l\,m$, the intensity of the line $n\,l \to n'\,l'$ is given by

$$J_{nl}^{n'l'} = (2l+1)\,h\,\nu_{nl,n'l'}\,A_{nl}^{n'l'}. \tag{63.9}$$

These so-called statistical intensities are listed in Table 16a. If, on the other hand, precisely one electron arrives in each state $n\,l\,m$ per unit of time (for example, through collisions, absorption of radiation, cascading from higher states, etc.), then the number of electrons which, on the average, occupy the state $n\,l\,m$ is equal to the lifetime T_{nl} of that state, and the emitted intensity is given by

$$[J_{nl}^{n'l'}] = J_{nl}^{n'l'}\,T_{nl} = (2l+1)\,\frac{A_{nl}^{n'l'}}{\sum\limits_{n'l'} A_{nl}^{n'l'}}\,h\,\nu_{nl,n'l'}\,. \tag{63.10}$$

These so-called dynamical intensities are listed in Table 16b.

γ) Discussion of the tables. 1. By inspecting Tables 13 and 14, the frequently mentioned rule (Sects. 61α2, 61β2) may be verified, which states that the transitions in which n and l change in the same sense are more frequent than those in which there is a change in the opposite sense. For example, the transition probabilities for $2p \to 3s$ and $2p \to 3d$ are as 1:25. The rule also applies to transitions to the continuous spectrum. In such transitions l is practically always increased by unity.

2. For high orbital quantum numbers (the circular orbits of the BOHR theory), jumps of unity in the principal quantum number are by far the most frequent [cf. Eq. (61.20)]; transitions into the continuum are very rare. For small orbital quantum numbers (eccentric orbits), transitions to the continuum are more frequent.

One may compare, for example, the oscillator strengths of the lines having initial levels $4s$ and $4f$. For $4f \to 5g$ the oscillator strength is about $2\frac{1}{2}$ times as large as that of $4s \to 5p$. On the other hand, the transitions from $4s$ to the continuum have oscillator strengths about 5 times as large as the ones initiated at $4f$. Thus, circular orbits are difficult to ionize.

3. For a fixed value of l, the total oscillator strengths for all the transitions into the continuous spectrum generally decrease with increasing principal quantum number. Thus for the initial level $1s$ it amounts to 0.436, for $4s$ to 0.248. The average energy of the levels in the continuum which combine with a certain discrete level, is roughly half the magnitude of the ionization potential of the discrete level in question. More precisely, the ratio (last row of Table 14) increases somewhat with increasing principal quantum number and declines fairly rapidly with increasing orbital quantum number.

The transition probabilities may be obtained by multiplying the oscillator strengths by ν^2. As a consequence, the transitions corresponding to a high frequency ν are the most probable, in spite of the fact that the oscillator strengths are largest when the principal quantum number changes by the least amount, i.e., when ν is as small as possible. For example, in the transitions from $4p \to 1s$, $2s$ and $3s$, the ratio of the oscillator strengths is 1:3.5:16, whereas the ratio of the transition probabilities is 23:3:1 (see Tables 14 and 15). The above has several important consequences as follows:

4. Of all the possible transitions (in emission) from an initial state $n\,l$, the transition to the state of lowest energy (compatible with the selection rules) is by far the most probable one, i.e. to the state $n'=l$, $l'=l-1$. *Cascade transitions*, which involve a series of transitions before the atom ends up in its ground state, are likely only insofar as they are required by the l-selection rule. I.e. the most likely form of cascade from a state $n\,l$ is the shortest possible one with l steps (via $n'=l$, $l'=l-1$, then $n''=l-1$, $l''=l-2$) down to the ground state. Hence, states with $n>l+1$ are more easily obtained by direct excitation from the ground state, rather than indirectly by excitation to a higher state followed by a radiative transition[1] (or ionization plus recombination). However, states with $n=l+1$ are likely to be produced by such cascade from higher states, if the excitation conditions allow appreciable excitation to higher states[2].

As an example we give in Table 17 the theoretical relative probabilities of various cascade processes, which all start from the $5d$ level in hydrogen. All

Table 17. *Relative probabilities of various transitions from the 5d-state.*

$4f \to 3d \to 2p \to 1s$	0.3%	$4p \to 2s$	1.1%
$4p \to 3d \to 2p \to 1s$	0.1%	$3p \to 2s$	2.9%
$4p \to 3s \to 2p \to 1s$	0.3%		4.0%
$4p \to 1s$	8.0%		
$3p \to 1s$	21.2%		
$2p \to 1s$	66.1%		
	96.0%		

[1] An important exception is the metastable $2s$-state, which cannot be excited by a direct radiative transition from the ground state. States with $l>1$ also cannot be obtained by direct radiative excitation from the ground state. Such states, as well as the $2s$-state, can be obtained by electronic excitation.

[2] For experimental confirmation see L. ORNSTEIN and H. LINDEMANN, Z. Physik **63**, 8 (1930). A study of cascade transitions is also important in connection with "mesic atoms" where negatively charged mesons are captured by the nuclear COULOMB field to form atomic states with large values of n.

cascades end either in the ground state or the $2s$-state and the $5d \to 2p \to 1s$ cascade has indeed the largest probability.

5. Of all the sublevels $n\,l$ of the n-th quantum state, the p level has by far the shortest life-time because it combines with the $1s$ ground state, and the probability corresponding to that transition is by far greater than any other. The lifetimes of all the other levels arrange themselves according to their orbital quantum numbers, except for the lifetime of the ns levels which do not fit into the regular scheme. Their lifetimes are always very long since the transitions $ns \to n'p$ are very rare, as n and l change in the opposite sense (cf. Table 15).

6. The lifetimes of the quantum states go up with increasing principal quantum number. This is true both for a fixed orbital quantum number and for the average over l. For a fixed value of l, we have with pretty good accuracy

$$T_{nl} \sim n^3,$$

whereas the following holds for the average lifetime of the n-th quantum state[1]:

$$T_n = \left(\sum_l \frac{2l+1}{n^2}\,\frac{1}{T_{nl}}\right)^{-1} \sim n^{4.5}.$$

7. Within a given series the line intensities decline strongly, if the number of electrons which on the average occupy an excited state, is the same for all the levels (Table 16a). This assumption is fulfilled when thermodynamic equilibrium exists and the temperature is very (infinitely) high. That condition is nearly fulfilled in the hot stars. When one talks about the "intensities" of spectral lines (e.g., SCHRÖDINGER), what is usually meant is the intensities at infinitely high temperature excitation.

On the other hand, if thermodynamic equilibrium does not exist, and the excitation process is of such a nature that the same number of electrons arrive in each excited state per second, then the line intensities in a given series are constant within the accuracy of the calculation (Table 16b). Thus, the decline of the intensities within a given series has its origin solely in the different excitation probabilities of the different levels.

8. We consider finally the sum of the oscillator strengths $f_{nlm}^{n'l'm'}$, summed over *all* l, l', m' and m, with fixed n and $n'(n \neq n')$. The following approximate formula[2] represents this sum accurately for large n and n' (and to within a factor of about two for *all* values of $n \neq n'$)

$$F_{n'n} \equiv \sum_{l l' m m'} f_{nlm}^{n'l'm'} \approx \frac{2^6}{3\sqrt{3}\pi}\left(\frac{1}{n^2} - \frac{1}{n'^2}\right)^{-3}\frac{1}{n^3}\,\frac{1}{n'^3} = 3.92\left(\frac{E_{n'} - E_n}{\mathrm{Ry}}\right)^{-3}\frac{1}{n^3}\,\frac{1}{n'^3}. \qquad (63.11)$$

64. Intensity of fine structure lines. *α) The* PAULI *and dipole approximations.* We consider next the effect of the electron's spin on the transition probabilities. In (59.3) we have essentially taken the matrix element between the nonrelativistic wave functions[3] for two atomic states of $e^{i\boldsymbol{k}\cdot\boldsymbol{r}}\boldsymbol{p}$, where $\boldsymbol{p}$ is the electron's momentum operator and $\boldsymbol{k}$ is the propagation vector (k the wave number) of the photon. According to the relativistic DIRAC theory for electrons, in this matrix element the operator $\boldsymbol{p}$ is replaced by mc times the DIRAC operator $\boldsymbol{\alpha}$

[1] The more rapid rise of the average lifetime with n is explained by the fact that when n is increased by 1, a circular orbit having a long lifetime is included with the other values of the orbital quantum number.

[2] A. UNSÖLD: Physik der Sternatmosphären, 2nd ed. Berlin: Springer 1955.

[3] We again use units such that $\hbar = 1$.

(and the wave functions by DIRAC spinors). We consider, for simplicity, a one-electron system. Written in momentum space representation, the matrix element is then (apart from numerical factors)

$$\xi = m c \int d^3p \langle u_{n'}^* (\boldsymbol{p} + \boldsymbol{k}) \boldsymbol{\alpha} u_n(\boldsymbol{p}) \rangle, \tag{64.1}$$

where $\langle\ \rangle$ denotes the scalar product of the four-component DIRAC spinors $u_{n'}^*$ and $\boldsymbol{\alpha} u_n$.

We restrict ourselves now to an "essentially nonrelativistic" system, so that the important values of momentum p in the atomic DIRAC wave functions are small compared with mc and we shall only work to the accuracy of the PAULI approximation (Sects. 12 and 13). Following the work of Sect. 16, we then approximate the wave functions $u_n(\boldsymbol{p})$ by eigenfunctions of the operator $\beta mc + \boldsymbol{\alpha}\cdot\boldsymbol{p}$ with positive eigenvalue (and similarly for $u_{n'}(\boldsymbol{p}+\boldsymbol{k})$). We can then reduce (64.1) to a matrix element involving only two-component PAULI spinors and operators. Using further the approximation (16.14), the matrix element (64.1) reduces to

$$\xi = \int d^3p \left\langle u_{n'}^* (\boldsymbol{p} + \boldsymbol{k}) \left[\boldsymbol{p} + \tfrac{1}{2}\boldsymbol{k} + \tfrac{i}{2}\boldsymbol{k}\times\boldsymbol{\sigma}\right] u_n(\boldsymbol{p})\right\rangle, \tag{64.2}$$

where u_n and $u_{n'}$ are now PAULI spinors and $\boldsymbol{\sigma}$ is the two-by-two PAULI spin matrix. It can be shown that the errors made in replacing (64.1) by (64.2) are of relative order of magnitude $(p/mc)^2$ and $(|\boldsymbol{p}+\hbar\boldsymbol{k}|/mc)^2$. For an electron in a COULOMB potential (charge Z) this error is of order $(Z\alpha)^2$, as is the case generally for the PAULI approximation.

The matrix element (64.2) can be simplified further if, in addition to the PAULI approximation, we also use the "electric dipole" approximation discussed in Sect. 59. In position space this involves neglecting kr_0 compared with unity, where r_0 is of the order of the "atomic radius". In momentum space the important values of p are of order $\hbar/r_0$ and the dipole approximation consists of neglecting $\hbar k$ compared with p. Thus, if we replace $\boldsymbol{k}$ by zero in (64.2), this expression reduces to

$$\xi = \int d^3p \langle u_n^* (\boldsymbol{p}) \boldsymbol{p} u_n(\boldsymbol{p})\rangle = \int d^3r \langle u_{n'}^* (\boldsymbol{r}) \boldsymbol{p} u_n(\boldsymbol{r})\rangle = \boldsymbol{p}_{n'n}. \tag{64.3}$$

We have thus shown that, in the electric dipole (and PAULI) approximation, the matrix element obtained in the DIRAC theory is identical with that of the nonrelativistic theory [see Eq. (59.5)], except that the wave functions are now PAULI spinors. For a COULOMB potential the relative error made in replacing (64.2) by (64.3) is of order $Z\alpha$ (which is larger than the error due to using the PAULI approximation).

The expression (64.2) can also be simplified somewhat even if we want to keep terms of relative order $Z\alpha$. We only need the component ξ_e of the vector matrix element (64.2) in the polarization direction $\boldsymbol{e}$ of the photon. The photon's propagation direction $\boldsymbol{k}$ is always perpendicular to $\boldsymbol{e}$, and $k_e = 0$; also $(\boldsymbol{k}\times\boldsymbol{\sigma})_e = k\sigma_\perp$, where $\perp$ denotes the direction perpendicular to both $\boldsymbol{k}$ and $\boldsymbol{e}$. We can rewrite the matrix element ξ_e in terms of a position space integral and get

$$\xi_e = (p_e e^{i\boldsymbol{k}\cdot\boldsymbol{r}})_{n'n} + \frac{i}{2} k (\sigma_\perp e^{i\boldsymbol{k}\cdot\boldsymbol{r}})_{n'n}. \tag{64.2a}$$

The first term in (64.2a) is the *full* nonrelativistic matrix element (without neglect of retardation). The second term in (64.2a) is a correction term (of relative order $Z\alpha$), characteristic of the DIRAC theory, and will be discussed in Sect. 66α in connection with magnetic dipole radiation. The neglect of retardation (replacing the exponential by unity) in this *second* term only introduces errors of order $(Z\alpha)^2$.

For electrons moving in a central potential the electron's spin affects the selection rules, etc. for radiative transitions even if the approximation (64.3) is used, i.e. even if specific relativistic effects are neglected. This is due to the degeneracy of the nonrelativistic energy of states differing only by their quantum number m_l (see Sect. 13).

β) Selection rules. For a system of any number of electrons in a central potential, the z-components of the total orbital angular momentum (quantum number m_L) and of the total spin (m_S) are *not* constants of the motion individually. On the other hand $m = m_L + m_S$ and J [eigenvalue of $\boldsymbol{M}^2 = (\boldsymbol{K}+\boldsymbol{S})^2$ is $J(J+1)$] *are* good quantum numbers for any atom (in the absence of external fields). This change in the quantization rules immediately leads to new selection rules. If we restrict ourselves to the dipole approximation, i.e. use the matrix element (59.5) or (64.3), one can prove some general selection rules using only the commutation properties of $\boldsymbol{p}$, $\boldsymbol{r}$ and $\boldsymbol{M}$ (for proofs see [3] and [5]). For any atom the following rigorous selection rules hold

$$\Delta m = 0, \quad \pm 1 \quad \text{(for polarization parallel and perpendicular, resp., to } z) \tag{64.4}$$

and

$$\Delta J = 0 \quad \text{or} \quad \pm 1, \tag{64.5}$$

$$J = 0 \rightarrow J = 0 \quad \text{forbidden.} \tag{64.6}$$

As discussed in Sect. 48α, for many atoms (especially for low Z) the Russell-Saunders approximation is a fairly good one. I.e. the spin-orbit coupling is treated as a small perturbation and the quantum numbers L and S are (almost) "good" quantum numbers. In this approximation the four selection rules at the beginning of Sect. 60β also apply. For a single-electron atom[1] the first two of these rules again reduce to (60.6).

We merely outline how some of the above selection rules can be verified explicitly for a single-electron atom in the Pauli approximation. The wave function for a stationary state can be written in the form

$$u_{nljm} = \sum_{m_l + m_s = m} \alpha_{m_s}^{ljm} v_{nlm_l}(\boldsymbol{r}) \xi_{m_s}, \tag{64.7}$$

where the α_{m_s} are numerical coefficients, $v(\boldsymbol{r})$ spatial wave functions (for quantum numbers n, l, and m_l) which do not depend on the spin coordinates. ξ_{m_s} for $m_s = \pm\frac{1}{2}$ are two ortho-normal Pauli spinors which are eigenstates of s_z with eigenvalues $\pm\frac{1}{2}$. One can then write out the matrix element (64.3) of the operator $\boldsymbol{p}$ (or similarly for $\boldsymbol{r}$) for the transition from a state $nljm$ to $n'l'j'm'$ as a double sum over m_s and m_s', using (64.7) for the initial and final wave functions. Using the fact that the operator $\boldsymbol{p}$ (or $\boldsymbol{r}$) does *not* contain any Pauli matrices and that the ξ_{m_s} form an orthonormal set, one finds

$$\boldsymbol{r}_{nljm}^{n'l'j'm'} = \sum_{m_s} \alpha_{m_s}^{ljm} (\alpha_{m_s}^{l'j'm'})^* \boldsymbol{r}_{nl,m-m_s}^{n'l',m'-m_s} \tag{64.8}$$

where the term in $\boldsymbol{r}$ on the right hand side denotes the spatial matrix element (59.6) of $\boldsymbol{r}$ between the wave functions

$$v_{nl,m-m_s} \quad \text{and} \quad v^*_{n'l',m'-m_s}.$$

From the form of (64.8) and the work of Sect. 60α, the selection rules (64.4) and $\Delta l = \pm 1$ follow immediately. Since $j = l \pm \frac{1}{2}$, the selection rule $\Delta l = \pm 1$

[1] In this case the Russell-Saunders and Pauli approximations are identical.

does not, by itself, forbid transitions with $\Delta j = \pm 2$. That the matrix element (64.8) for such transitions is in fact zero, as stated in (64.5), can be verified explicitly by substituting the explicit expressions for the coefficients α_{m_s} into (64.8).

γ) Sum rules. For any many-electron atom, to which the RUSSELL-SAUNDERS approximation is applicable, we have the following sum rule:

(I) The total probability of all transitions from a fixed state $nLJm$ to all states with fixed $n'L'$ (but all possible values of $J'm'$) is independent of the total angular momentum J and magnetic quantum number m of the initial state. Further, this total probability is the same as the total probability of transitions in the theory *without* spin from the state nLm_L to all states with fixed $n'L'$ (but all values of m_L').

We merely outline the proof of this rule for a one-electron system. We have to evaluate the sum over all j' and m' of the square of (64.8). From the definition (64.7) of the coefficients α_{m_s} and the fact that both the functions u_{nljm} and $v_{nlm_l}\,\xi_m$ form complete orthonormal sets, follow the relations

$$\sum_{j'} (\alpha_{m_s}^{l'j'm'})^* \alpha_{m_s'}^{l'j'm'} = \delta_{m_s m_s'}, \qquad \sum_{m_s} |\alpha_{m_s}^{ljm}|^2 = 1.$$

From (60.12) and (60.13) we also find that

$$\sum_{m'} |\boldsymbol{r}_{nl,\,m-m_s}^{n'l',\,m'-m_s}|^2 \equiv |\boldsymbol{r}_{nl}^{n'l'}|^2$$

is independent of $m - m_s$. Using these relations and (64.7) one finally obtains

$$\sum_{j'm'} |\boldsymbol{r}_{nljm}^{n'l'j'm'}|^2 = |\boldsymbol{r}_{nl}^{n'l'}|^2, \tag{64.9}$$

which is the required relation.

It should be remembered that the sum rule I above holds also for a many-electron system, but only in the RUSSELL-SAUNDERS approximation, i.e. if L is (to a good approximation) a good quantum number and the (spin-orbit) splitting of multiplets small. For X-ray levels (inner electrons) in heavy atoms (large Z), relativistic effects are quite appreciable and the spacing of multiplets large. The wave functions deviate appreciably from the PAULI approximations and the sum rule I is not a very good approximation. We shall only consider cases where the above approximations are applicable (see, however, Sects. 66 and 68).

It follows from the sum rule I that the lifetime of any fine structure component of a level with fixed quantum numbers n and L is *independent* of the "total" and magnetic quantum numbers J and m (at least for unperturbed atoms) and has the same value as in the theory without spin. At least under the usual excitation conditions (no preferred spatial direction), the probability of excitation of a component $nLJm$ is also independent of J and m. In this case, for fixed values of n and L, the *number* of electrons *present in* a state $nLJm$ is also independent of J and m. The following sum rule also holds in this case:

(II) The total intensity of all spectral lines for transitions from a level nLJ (summed over all ZEEMAN components, i.e. all m) to all levels with fixed $n'L'$ (all J', m') is proportional to $(2J+1)$, the statistical weight of the initial level.

The sum rule II has been verified experimentally for closely spaced multiplets in different types of atoms, especially for alkali atoms. For hydrogen-like atoms, however, the assumptions leading to the rule II do *not* apply under the usual *practical* conditions although the fine structure splitting is small and the PAULI approximation good (for unperturbed atoms): This is due to the degeneracy of the nonrelativistic energy of levels with the same n but different l. This degeneracy is only removed to a slight extent by the fine structure and LAMB shift and the wave functions are perturbed severely by the presence of even quite weak external electric fields or other pertubations (see Sect. 55). We shall show in Sect. 67 that such perturbations also affect the lifetimes of the various fine structure levels and hence also the number of electrons present in various excited states.

δ) *Intensity formulas.* For doublet spectra, such as the spectrum of hydrogen, the sum rules in conjunction with the selection rules suffice to determine completely the transition probabilities for all the lines.

We shall consider the transitions from the states $n\,l$, $j=l+\frac{1}{2}$ and $j=l-\frac{1}{2}$ to the states n', $l-1$, $j'=l-\frac{3}{2}$ and $j=l-\frac{1}{2}$ (cf. Fig. 31). One of these, $j=l+\frac{1}{2}\rightarrow j'=l-\frac{3}{2}$ is forbidden by the j selection rule. Thus, only one line is initiated at the level $j=l+\frac{1}{2}$ (a in Fig. 31). On the other hand, there are two lines from the initial level $j=l-\frac{1}{2}$ (b, c). According to our sum rule, the ratio of the sum of the transition probabilities of the two lines b and c to that of a, must be the same as the ratio of the statistical weights, viz.,

$$(b+c):a=2l:(2l+2). \qquad (64.10)$$

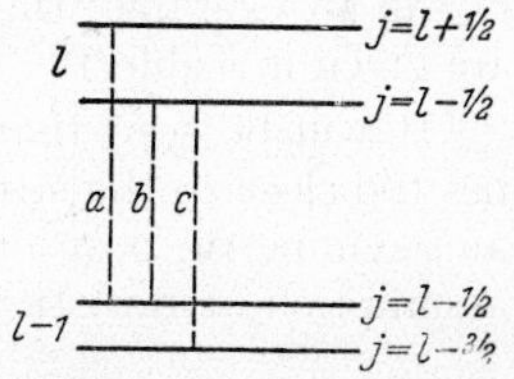

Fig. 31. Diagram of the transitions from a state with orbital quantum number l to one with $l-1$ for a one-electron atom (doublet spectrum), including fine structure.

On the other hand, if we regard the primed levels as initial states, we obtain in an analogous fashion

$$(a+b):c=l:(l-1). \qquad (64.11)$$

From (64.10) and (64.11) follows the ratio of the three transition probabilities, namely

$$a:b:c=[(l+1)(2l-1)]:1:[(l-1)(2l+1)]. \qquad (64.12)^{1}$$

The ratios of line intensities and transition probabilities are the same, provided the initial states are excited in proportion to their statistical weights. The most important special cases are the following:

$$\left.\begin{aligned}
&s\,p \text{ transitions: } s\,p_{\frac{3}{2}}:s\,p_{\frac{1}{2}}=2:1\\
&\qquad (=a:b;\ c \text{ does not exist, since } s \text{ levels do not split}),\\
&p\,d \text{ transitions: } p_{\frac{3}{2}}d_{\frac{5}{2}}:p_{\frac{3}{2}}d_{\frac{3}{2}}:p_{\frac{1}{2}}d_{\frac{3}{2}}=9:1:5,\\
&d\,f \text{ transitions: } d_{\frac{5}{2}}f_{\frac{7}{2}}:d_{\frac{5}{2}}f_{\frac{5}{2}}:d_{\frac{3}{2}}f_{\frac{5}{2}}=20:1:14.
\end{aligned}\right\} \qquad (64.13)$$

For large values of l, the intensity of the line b, i.e., the transition in which j does not change, is very small compared to the intensity of the transition in which j and l change by the same amount. This statement is a companion of the rule (60.11) which states that l and m change predominantly in the same sense, and also of the theorem in Sect. 63γ1 which makes the same claim for n and l.

The intensity ratios (64.13) have been verified in many instances, for example for the alkali spectra. For a comparison with experiment see Sect. 67ε and Sect. 68.

The absolute intensities may be obtained by evaluating first the intensities without considering spin and then multiplying the results by the relative intensities given in (64.12) and dividing by $\frac{1}{2}(2l+1)(2l-1)$.

[1] This was obtained at an early date. See, for example, H. HÖNL, Ann. d. Phys. **79**, 273 (1925).

Table 18. *Fine structure intensities of H_α.*
($\Delta\nu$ is the line frequency in cm^{-1} relative to that of line *c*. $2j+1$ is the statistical weight of the initial level.)

Initial state	Final state	$\Delta\nu$	Transition	Oscillator strength	$2j+1$	Total oscillator strength	
a) $j=\frac{1}{2}$	$j'=\frac{3}{2}$	-0.144	$3s \to 2p_{\frac{3}{2}}$	$\frac{2}{3}\times 0.041$	2	0.05	2.83
b) $\frac{3}{2}$	$\frac{3}{2}$	-0.036	$3d_{\frac{3}{2}} \to 2p_{\frac{3}{2}}$	$\frac{1}{6}\times 0.417$	4	0.28	
c) $\frac{5}{2}$	$\frac{3}{2}$	0	$3d_{\frac{5}{2}} \to 2p_{\frac{3}{2}}$	1×0.417	6	2.50	
d) $\frac{1}{2}$	$\frac{1}{2}$	0.220	$3s \to 2p_{\frac{1}{2}}$	$\frac{1}{3}\times 0.041$	2	0.03	0.31
			$3p_{\frac{1}{2}} \to 2s$	1×0.142	2	0.28	
e) $\frac{3}{2}$	$\frac{1}{2}$	0.328	$3p_{\frac{3}{2}} \to 2s$	1×0.142	4	0.57	1.96
			$3d_{\frac{3}{2}} \to 2p_{\frac{1}{2}}$	$\frac{5}{6}\times 0.417$	4	1.39	

As an example, the intensities[1] of the components of the hydrogen line H_α are given in Table 18.

It will be seen that the intensity of the line *a* is too small and that line *b* lies too close to the strong line *c* to permit separate observation. Line *d* occupies an asymmetric position among the short wave components of H_α. Under the assumption of statistical distribution, the intensity ratios are

$$(a+b+c):d:e = 1:0.11:0.69.$$

The center of gravity of the complex $a+b+c$ is shifted by $-0.006\ cm^{-1}$ relative to the line *c*, the center of gravity of $d+e$ is shifted by $-0.015\ cm^{-1}$ relative to *e*, and the separation between the two centers of gravity amounts to $0.319\ cm^{-1}$.

The intensities may be derived without the help of the sum rules directly from the PAULI eigenfunctions (13.19) in a way which we used in Sect. 64β for the verification of the selection rule for *j*. This yields, at the same time, the intensities of the ZEEMAN components: For transitions in which *j* changes by unity that intensity is given, as before, by (60.7) and (60.11) provided we replace *l* by *j* and *m* by the *z* component of the total angular momentum. For transitions in which there is no change in *j*, one obtains

$$z_{nljm}^{n'l'jm} = m\, C_{lj}^{l'j} R_{nl}^{n'l'}, \tag{64.14}$$

$$(x+iy)_{nljm}^{n'l'jm+1} = (x-iy)_{n'l'jm+1}^{nljm} = \sqrt{(j+m+1)(j-m)}\, C_{lj}^{l'j} R_{nl}^{n'l'}. \tag{64.15}$$

Formulas (64.14) and (64.15) have general validity for any multiplet spectrum. In the case where there is only one valence electron, $R_{nl}^{n'l'}$ is the radial integral (60.8). For a doublet spectrum the *C* factors are given by

$$C_{lj}^{l-1j} = \frac{1}{2j(j+1)}, \qquad C_{lj}^{l-1j-1} = \frac{1}{2j}. \tag{64.16}$$

Even for hydrogen, transitions between fine structure components with the *same* principal quantum number *n* and with $\Delta l = \pm 1$, $\Delta j = 0, \pm 1$ are not forbidden by the selection rules. But the frequency of "photons" emitted or absorbed in such transitions is extremely low (radio waves rather than light) and depends strongly on the *j*-values of the two states (for $\Delta j = \pm 1$ the energy difference is of the order of the fine structure, for $\Delta j = 0$ of the order of the LAMB shift). *Induced* transitions of this sort are of great importance in modern experiments on the LAMB shift and fine structure (Sect. 21), but the probability *A* of a *spontaneous* transition is extremely small, since the frequency ν is so low, ($A_{n'n}$

[1] A. SOMMERFELD and A. UNSÖLD: Z. Physik **38**, 237 (1926).

is proportional to $\nu^3 x^2_{n'n}$). The radial integral for a transition with $\Delta n = 0$ is given by (63.5), and (64.16) still holds. For $n = 2$ in hydrogen, for instance, a spontaneous transition from $2P_{\frac{3}{2}}$ to $2S_{\frac{1}{2}}$ is possible with the emission of a "photon" of frequency 9912 Mc/sec. The transition probability is about 10^{-6} sec^{-1}, which is negligible compared with the probability of 6×10^8 sec^{-1} for the transition $2P_{\frac{3}{2}}$ to the ground state. Similarly a spontaneous transition from $2S_{\frac{1}{2}}$ to $2P_{\frac{1}{2}}$ is possible with a "photon" frequency of 1058 Mc/sec and a transition probability of about 10^{-9} sec^{-1} (lifetime of about 30 years). Although transitions from the $2S$-state to the ground state are forbidden in the dipole approximation, two-quantum transitions to the ground state, etc., have a much larger probability than 10^{-9} sec^{-1} (see Sect. 67β).

ε) The intensities of the helium fine structure lines. The intensities in triplet spectra cannot be immediately derived from the sum rules, except for the combinations between S and P levels. Since S terms are not split by the interaction with the spin, the ratio of the intensities of the transitions from the one ^3S term to the three ^3P terms $j = 0, 1, 2$ is equal to the ratio of the statistical weights

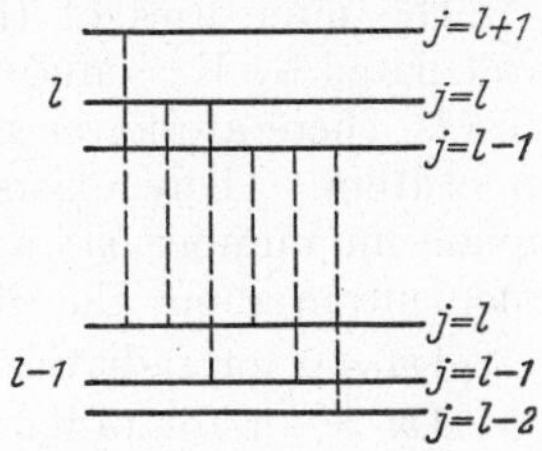

Fig. 32. Diagram of the transitions from a state with orbital quantum number l to one with $l-1$ for a triplet spectrum.

$$^3S_1\,^3P_2 : {^3S_1}\,^3P_1 : {^3S_1}\,^3P_0 = 5:3:1.$$

More generally, the intensity ratio of the lines which arise in the transition from the triplet nl to the triplet $n'l-1$ (cf. Fig. 32) is given in Table 19a.

Table 19a. *Relative intensities of the multiplet components in triplet spectra.*

Final state	j of initial state			Sum
	$j = l+1$	l	$l-1$	
$j' = l$	$(2l+3)(2l-1)l^2$	$(2l+1)(2l-1)$	1	$(2l+1)^2 l^2$
$l-1$	—	$(2l+1)(2l-1)(l+1)(l-1)$	$(2l+1)(2l-1)$	$(2l+1)(2l-1)l^2$
$l-2$	—	—	$(2l+1)(2l-3)l^2$	$(2l+1)(2l-3)l^2$
Sum	$(2l+3)(2l-1)l^2$	$(2l+1)(2l-1)l^2$	$(2l-1)^2 l^2$	$3(2l+1)(2l-1)l^2$

Naturally, the intensity ratios are again valid only if the initial states are occupied in proportion to their statistical weights. As a specific example we shall put down the intensity relationships for a PD transition.

Table 19b. *Relative intensities of the components of the multiplet* $^3D \rightarrow {^3P}$.

Final state	Initial state			Sum
	$^3D_3$	$^3D_2$	$^3D_1$	
$^3P_2$	84	15	1	100
$^3P_1$	—	45	15	60
$^3P_0$	—	—	20	20
Sum	84	60	36	180

Both in the special example given in Table 19b and in the more general case of Table 19a, we have included the sum of the intensities of all the lines which arise from the same initial state in order to show that these sums are indeed proportional to the statistical weight $2j+1$ of the initial level. Furthermore, it will readily be seen from the tables that the transitions in which j and l change in the same sense are the most frequent; that the transitions in which there is no change in j are rarer; and that the transitions in which j and l change in the opposite sense are extremely weak. For large values of l only the transitions of the first type occur.

65. Intensities in parabolic coordinates (STARK effect). We consider next the effect of a moderately strong uniform external electric field on the intensities of spectral lines. We discuss only hydrogen-like atoms[1], for which the effect is very marked because of the l-degeneracy of the nonrelativistic energies. The effect in very weak electric fields (STARK effect $\ll$ fine structure splitting, see Sect. 55) is discussed in Sect. 67. We consider here only field strengths such that the STARK effect splitting is large compared with the fine structure and the linear STARK effect (Sect. 51) approximation holds. The atomic eigenstates are then those described by the wave functions expressed in parabolic coordinates (Sect. 6) with quantum numbers n_1, n_2 and m.

The intensities of the STARK components of the BALMER lines were first calculated by E. SCHRÖDINGER[2] and have been put to an extensive experimental test[3]. There are fewer selection rules for an atom in an external field than for a free atom. There exists only one selection rule with respect to the magnetic quantum number m, which determines the component of the orbital angular momentum about the direction of the electric field, namely,

$\Delta m = 0$ for radiation polarized in a direction parallel to the field,

$\Delta m = \pm 1$ for radiation polarized in a perpendicular direction.

There is no strict selection rule with respect to the parabolic quantum numbers n_1 and n_2; however, there is a quasi-selection rule which predicts that the outermost components, which according to the term scheme may be expected to appear in the line pattern, will generally have unobservably small intensities. This is the case, for example, with the components $\pi 8$ of H_α which are shifted by $8F/15\,620\ \text{cm}^{-1}$ relative to the unperturbed line and correspond to the transition from the state $n=3$, $n_1=2$, $n_2=m=0$ to the state $n=2$, $n_1=0$, $n_2=1$, $m=0$.

The general formula for the coordinate matrix element has been obtained by GORDON[4], and for radiation polarized parallel to the field is given by

$$\left.\begin{aligned} z_{n_1 n_2 m}^{n_1' n_2' m} &= (-)^{n_1'+n_2'} \frac{a}{4\,(m!)^2} \sqrt{\frac{(n_1+m)!\,(n_2+m)!\,(n_1'+m)!\,(n_2'+m)!}{n_1!\quad n_2!\quad n_1'!\quad n_2'!}} \left(\frac{4\,n\,n'}{(n-n')^2}\right)^{m+2} \left(\frac{n-n'}{n+n'}\right)^{n+n'} \times \\ &\times \left\{\left[2\,(n_1'-n_2')\frac{n^2+n'^2}{(n+n')^2} - (n_1-n_2)\frac{4\,n\,n'}{(n+n')^2}\right] \Psi_m(n_1 n_1')\,\Psi_m(n_2 n_2') - \right. \\ &\left. - 2\left[n_1'\,\Psi_m(n_1, n_1'-1)\,\Psi_m(n_2, n_2') - n_2'\,\Psi_m(n_1 n_1')\,\Psi_m(n_2, n_2'-1)\right]\right\} \end{aligned}\right\} \quad (65.1)$$

and for radiation polarized perpendicularly to the field by

$$\left.\begin{aligned} x_{n_1 n_2 m}^{n_1' n_2' m-1} &= (-)^{n_1'+n_2'} \frac{a}{4\,(m-1!)^2} \sqrt{\frac{(n_1+m)!\,(n_2+m)!\,(n_1'+m-1)!\,(n_2'+m-1)!}{n_1!\quad n_2!\quad n_1'!\quad n_2'!}} \left(\frac{4\,n\,n'}{(n-n')^2}\right)^{m+1} \left(\frac{n-n'}{n+n'}\right)^{n+n'} \times \\ &\times \left\{\Psi_{m-1}(n_1 n_1')\,\Psi_{m-1}(n_2 n_2') - \left(\frac{n-n'}{n+n'}\right)^2 \Psi_{m-1}(n_1+1, n_1')\,\Psi_{m-1}(n_2+1, n_2')\right\}. \end{aligned}\right\} \quad (65.2)$$

In the above, Ψ is the hypergeometric function

$$\Psi_m(n_i n_i') = F\left(-n_i, -n_i', m+1, -\frac{4\,n\,n'}{(n-n')^2}\right) = 1 - \frac{n_i\,n_i'}{m+1} \cdot \frac{4\,n\,n'}{(n-n')^2} + \cdots. \quad (65.3)$$

---

[1] For He see S. FOSTER, Proc. Roy. Soc. Lond., Ser. A **117**, 137 (1927).

[2] E. SCHRÖDINGER: Ann. d. Phys. **80**, 468 (1926).

[3] H. MARK and R. WIERL: Z. Physik **53**, 526; **55**, 126; **57**, 494 (1929) referred to as I, II and III respectively. See also J. STARK, Ann. d. Phys. **48**, 193 (1915); Handbuch der Experimentalphysik, Bd. XXI, 427; J. ST. FOSTER and L. CHALK, Proc. Roy. Soc. Lond. **123**, 108 (1929); Nature, Lond. **118**, 693 (1926).

[4] W. GORDON: Ann. d. Phys. **2**, 1031 (1929). A numerical error in this paper was corrected by A. B. UNDERHILL, Publ. Dominion Astrophys. Obs. **8**, 386 (1951).

For the LYMAN series ($n'=1, n_1'=n_2'=m'=0$) the formulas for the squares of the coordinate matrix elements are especially simple and are given by

$$\left.\begin{aligned} (z_{000}^{n_1 n_2 0})^2 &= a^2 \cdot \frac{2^8 n^6 (n-1)^{2n-6}}{(n+1)^{2n+6}} (n_1 - n_2)^2, \\ (x_{000}^{n_1 n_2 1})^2 = (x_{000}^{n_1, n_2, -1})^2 &= a^2 \cdot \frac{2^8 n^6 (n-1)^{2n-6}}{(n+1)^{2n+6}} (n_1+1)(n_2+1). \end{aligned}\right\} \quad (65.4)$$

By summing over the values of n_1 and n_2 which belong to the same principal quantum number ($n_1 = 0 \ldots n-1$, $n_2 = n-1-m-n_1$), one arrives again at the intensity formula (63.4) for the LYMAN series which we have previously derived in polar coordinates.

Below we give a table of the intensities of the STARK effect components of the second LYMAN line L_β, and of the first BALMER line H_α which has the same initial level ($n=3$). The former was obtained from (65.4), the latter from the tables of SCHRÖDINGER.

The first part of the Table, 20a, enables one to calculate the lifetime of the STARK effect terms having principal quantum number $n=3$. In it are entered the probabilities for a transition from each term to the first and second quantum states. The second part of the Table, 20b, is to be used in the calculation of the actual intensities of the components of H_α under two different assumptions (cf. Table 16) as follows:

Table 20a. *Probabilities for transitions starting from the* STARK *effect levels with* $n=3$.

($n_1 n_2 m$ denote the quantum numbers of the initial state; π and σ the two polarization possibilities; A_{rel} is the transition probability in arbitrary units, A_{abs} in units of 10^8 sec^{-1} and T is the mean lifetime in 10^{-8} sec.

$n_1 n_2 m$	LYMAN series			BALMER series						A_{abs}	T
				pol. π		pol. σ		$\pi + 2\sigma$			
	pol.	A_{rel}	A_{abs}	Final state	A_{rel}	Final state	A_{rel}	A_{rel}	A_{abs}		
002	—	0	0	—	0	001	2304	4608	0.64	0.64	1.56
110	—	0	0	100 010	729 729	001	882	3222	0.45	0.45	2.22
101	σ	4	0.82	001	1152	100 010	968 8	3104	0.43	1.25	0.80
200	π	4	0.82	100 010	1681 1	001	18	1718	0.24	1.06	0.94

Table 20b. *The intensities of the* STARK *effect components of the* H_α*-line.*

($\Delta\nu$ is the displacement of the line, relative to the field-free line, in units of $F/15620$ cm^{-1}; J_S and J_D are the statistical and dynamical intensities, respectively, in units such that the strongest component has intensity 100; $\bar{J}_S$ is the calculated J_S in the units given by SCHRÖDINGER.)

Initial state	Statis. weight	Final state	$\Delta\nu$	Calculated $\bar{J}_S$	Calculated J_S	Calculated J_D	Observed J_S	Observed J_D
Polarization parallel to the field								
110	1	010	2	729	32	89	31	79
101	2	001	3	2304	100	100	100	100
200	1	100	4	1681	73	86	76	92
200	1	010	8	1	0	0	0	0
Polarization perpendicular to the field								
002	2	001	0	4608 }	100	100	100	100
110	1	001	0	882 }				
101	2	100	1	1936	35	17	38	38
101	2	010	5	16	0	0	0	0
200	1	001	6	18	0	0	0	0

1. The occupation of each of the STARK effect levels is proportional to its statistical weight (i.e., on the average each level is occupied by the same number of atoms).

2. The excitation of each level is proportional to its statistical weight (i.e., the same number of atoms arrive in each level per unit time).

Under assumption 1, the intensities, the so-called statistical intensities, are calculated by multiplying the transition probabilities of Table 20a by the statistical weight of the initial state, and the results agree with those of SCHRÖDINGER. One arrives at the intensities under assumption 2, the dynamical intensities, by multiplying the statistical intensities by the lifetime of the initial state. The statistical and dynamical intensities differ considerably. The measured intensities of MARK and WIERL (loc. cit. II) are also included in the Table. They are the results of two different experiments: In the first, a hydrogen-nitrogen mixture is maintained at a considerable pressure (0.02 to 0.03 mm Hg) and the hydrogen atoms are continually excited by collisions. In the second experiment, the emission takes place essentially in a vacuum (10^{-4} mm Hg), and, accordingly, only those atoms emit which are already in an excited state when they enter the region of space under observation. It will be noted that the pressure experiments agree well with SCHRÖDINGER'S statistical intensities, the experiments in vacuum with the dynamical intensities. That is to be expected. In the experiments which are carried out under pressure, the continual collisions assure a uniform distribution of the atoms over the STARK levels. On the other hand, in the vacuum experiments one may probably assume that there is a fairly uniform distribution ln the beginning which in the course of time shifts in favor of the long-lived ievels 110 and 002.

66. Higher multipole radiation[1]. *α) The multipole expansion.* As discussed in Sects. 59 and 64α, we have used throughout the "dipole approximation" (neglect of retardation). Let $\boldsymbol{k}_\omega$ be the[2] propagation vector of the photon. We have replaced the operator $e^{i\boldsymbol{k}_\omega\cdot\boldsymbol{r}} m c \boldsymbol{\alpha}$, occurring in the DIRAC theory, by the nonrelativistic operator $e^{i\boldsymbol{k}_\omega\cdot\boldsymbol{r}}\boldsymbol{p}$ and have further replaced the exponential by unity. This replacement is based on the assumption that $k_\omega a$ is small, where a (the "atomic radius") is a distance characteristic of the linear dimensions of the atomic wave functions.

The neglect of retardation is a poor approximation for X-ray radiation emitted by the inner electrons of an atom with large Z. For such atoms $Z\alpha$ is not very small and relativistic effects are important[3]. The effects of retardation are also important for the continuous spectrum (e.g., photoeffect), where photons of high frequency (wave length not necessarily larger than a) are emitted or absorbed. This will be discussed in Sects. 72 and 73. In this section we restrict ourselves to the discrete spectrum for atoms with $Z \ll 137$. In this case $k_\omega a$ is indeed small and the effect of retardation is small in general. However, in the dipole approximation used so far some types of transitions are forbidden completely by selection rules. For some of these "forbidden" transitions the more exact theory will give non-zero probabilities (although small compared with dipole probabilities for "allowed" transitions).

We consider first the operator $e^{i\boldsymbol{k}_\omega\cdot\boldsymbol{r}}\boldsymbol{p}$ of the SCHRÖDINGER theory. The product $\boldsymbol{k}_\omega\cdot\boldsymbol{r}$ is small and, instead of neglecting it completely, we expand the

[1] For details see [5], Chap. 4, 9 and 11; [7], p. 728 to 743; H. C. BRINKMAN, Ph. D. Diss. Utrecht, 1932 and M. E. ROSE, Multipole Fields. New York: John Wiley & Sons 1955.

[2] We denote the constant propagation vector by $\boldsymbol{k}_\omega$, the orbital angular momentum operator by $\boldsymbol{k}$.

[3] E. SEGRÈ: Rend. Lincei (6) **14**, 501 (1931).

exponential in a TAYLOR series,

$$e^{i\boldsymbol{k}_\omega\cdot\boldsymbol{r}} = 1 + i\,\boldsymbol{k}_\omega\cdot\boldsymbol{r} - \tfrac{1}{2}(\boldsymbol{k}_\omega\cdot\boldsymbol{r})^2 + \cdots. \tag{66.1}$$

The first term (unity) in this expansion leads exactly to the electric dipole approximation of the previous sections. The higher terms in the expansion lead to transitions which are somewhat analogous to the types of radiation obtained by a multipole expansion in classical radiation theory. We shall consider only the effect of the second term of the expansion (66.1) on the matrix element (59.3). We call the propagation direction $\boldsymbol{k}_\omega$ of the photon the x-axis and its polarization direction $\boldsymbol{e}$ the y-axis ($\boldsymbol{k}_\omega$ and $\boldsymbol{e}$ are always perpendicular) and consider a transition of the atom from a state n to n'. From the BOHR energy relation (59.1) the wave number k_ω of the emitted photon equals $\omega_{n'n}/c$. We then have to add to the electric dipole matrix element (59.5) the correction term

$$D'_{n'n} = \frac{i}{\hbar}\Big(\sum_j i\,k_\omega\, x_j\, p_{y,j}\Big)_{n'n} = -\frac{\omega_{n'n}}{c\hbar}\sum_j (x_j\, p_{y,j})_{n'n}, \tag{66.2}$$

where j denotes the j-th electron and $n'n$ denotes the matrix element of an operator.

The matrix element (66.2) can be rewritten as follows. We first write (for one electron)

$$x\,p_y = \tfrac{1}{2}(x\,p_y + p_x\,y) + \tfrac{1}{2}(x\,p_y - p_x\,y).$$

Using (59.19), the explicit definition (11.4) for the operator $\boldsymbol{k}$ for the orbital angular momentum, and the fact that x commutes with p_y, we find

$$x\,p_y = \frac{i\,m}{2\hbar}(H\,x\,y - x\,y\,H) + \frac{\hbar}{2}\,k_z, \tag{66.3}$$

where k_z is the z-component of the operator $\boldsymbol{k}$ for the particular electron[1]. Since the states n and n' are eigenstates of the HAMILTONian H with eigenvalues E_n and $E_{n'}$, we have [using (59.1)]

$$D'_{n'n} = -\frac{\omega_{n'n}}{2c\hbar}\sum_j\big[-i\,m\,\omega_{n'n}(x_j\,y_j)_{n'n} + \hbar\,(k_{zj})_{n'n}\big]. \tag{66.4}$$

The matrix element (66.4) was obtained using the nonrelativistic operator $\boldsymbol{p}$ instead of $mc\boldsymbol{\alpha}$, which occurs in the DIRAC theory. This replacement was discussed in Sect. 64α and is equivalent to replacing the vector in square brackets in (64.2) by $\boldsymbol{p}$. If the DIRAC theory is used, as it should be, one has to evaluate the component of the vector matrix element (64.2) in the polarization direction[2] $\boldsymbol{e}$, which results in the expression (64.2a). The first term in this expression is the full nonrelativistic matrix element, whose expansion leads to the electric dipole expression plus (66.4) plus higher terms. The second term in (64.2a) is of the same (small) order of magnitude as (66.4) and we approximate it by replacing the exponential by unity. If this term is added to the matrix element (66.4), the operator k_z in (66.4) is replaced by $k_z + \sigma_z = k_z + 2s_z$, where s is the PAULI spin-operator for the particular electron. $D'_{n'n}$ plus this additional term is then

[1] An error in a similar derivation in [10], p. 473, was kindly pointed out by Dr. M. A. PRESTON.

[2] $\boldsymbol{e}$ is perpendicular to $\boldsymbol{k}_\omega$, which is called $\boldsymbol{k}$ in Sect. 64.

the sum of two matrix elements

$$\left.\begin{aligned} D_{n'n}^{(e2)} &= \frac{i\,m\,\omega_{n'n}^2}{2c\hbar}\sum_i (x_j\,y_j)_{n'n}; \\ D_{n'n}^{(m1)} &= -\frac{\omega_{n'n}}{2c}(K_z+2S_z)_{n'n} \end{aligned}\right\} \tag{66.5}$$

where $\boldsymbol{K}=\sum_j \boldsymbol{k}_j$ and $\boldsymbol{S}=\sum_j \boldsymbol{s}_j$ are the operators for the total orbital and spin angular momentum, respectively.

The matrix elements (66.5) are to be compared with the electric dipole matrix element [see (59.5)]

$$D_{n'n}^{(e1)} = \frac{m}{\hbar}\,\omega_{nn'}\sum_j (y_j)_{n'n}.$$

These matrix elements bear some analogy to expressions found in classical radiation theory: The matrix element $e\,y_{n'n}$ corresponds to the classical electric dipole moment in the direction of polarization of the emitted radiation. Similarly $e(xy)_{n'n}$ corresponds to the electric quadrupole moment and $D^{(e2)}$ is called an electric quadrupole matrix element. Note that $D^{(e2)}$ depends both on the propagation (x) and polarization (y) directions of the photon. Finally, $(e/2mc)\times(K_z+2S_z)_{n'n}$ is the quantum mechanical equivalent of the magnetic dipole moment of a charge and current distribution possessing angular momentum[1]. Note that the magnetic dipole matrix element $D^{(m1)}$ depends on the direction (z) perpendicular to the plane containing the propagation and polarization directions. Apart from selection rules, the order of magnitude of both $D^{(e2)}$ and $D^{(m1)}$ should be smaller than that of $D^{(e1)}$ by $k_\omega a \sim \omega a/c \sim \hbar/mca \sim Z\alpha$. The selection rules are discussed below.

β) Electric quadrupole radiation. We consider now the selection rules for $D^{(e2)}$, the electric quadrupole matrix element. We restrict ourselves to single-electron atoms, but consider different orientations of the polarization and propagation directions relative to the quantization direction of the atom (to which the magnetic quantum number m refers). We also restrict ourselves to the PAULI approximation, so that l is a good quantum number.

The selection rules for the magnetic quantum number m are an immediate consequence of (66.5). If, for example, the direction of quantization is along z, then the following rules hold:

Observation direction	Polarization direction	Matrix element of	Selection rule for m
parallel to the field (z)	x or y	$xz = r^2\cos\vartheta\sin\vartheta\cos\varphi$	$\Delta m = \pm 1$
perpendicular to the field (x)	parallel (z)	same	$\Delta m = \pm 1$
	perpendicular (y)	$xy = \frac{1}{2}r^2\sin^2\vartheta\sin 2\varphi$	$\Delta m = \pm 2$
at 45° to the field $\left(\frac{1}{\sqrt{2}}(x+z)\right)$	45° to the field $\left(\frac{1}{\sqrt{2}}(z-x)\right)$	$\frac{1}{2}(z^2-x^2) = \frac{1}{2}r^2\left(\frac{3}{2}\cos^2\vartheta-\frac{1}{2}\right) - \frac{1}{4}r^2\sin^2\vartheta\cos 2\varphi$	$\Delta m = 0$ and $\Delta m = \pm 2$
	perpendicular (y)	$\frac{1}{\sqrt{2}}(xy+zy)$	$\Delta m = \pm 1$ and ± 2

[1] Note that this magnetic moment combination also occurs in the ZEEMAN effect.

As in the case of the dipole radiation of Sect. 60, the above selection rules follow simply from a consideration of the φ integral which occurs in the matrix element.

The integrals with respect to ϑ give rise to the selection rules for l. Examining, for example, the integral which corresponds to the transition $\Delta m = 0$

$$\int R^*_{n'l'}(r)\,\mathscr{P}_{l'm}(\vartheta)\,r^2\left(\tfrac{3}{2}\cos^2\vartheta - \tfrac{1}{2}\right) R_{nl}(r)\,\mathscr{P}_{lm}(\vartheta)\,r^2\,dr\,\sin\vartheta\,d\vartheta,$$

it is readily seen that l' and l may only differ by an even integer since $P_2(\vartheta) = \frac{3}{2}\cos^2\vartheta - \frac{1}{2}$ is an even function of $\cos\vartheta$, and, furthermore, they may differ by at most by 2 since $P_2(\vartheta)$ contains only the second power of $\cos\vartheta$. Therefore,

$$\Delta l = 0 \quad \text{or} \quad \pm 2 \quad \text{and} \quad l = 0 \to 0 \quad \text{is forbidden.} \tag{66.6}$$

The above selection rule may also be arrived at in another way. According to the usual rules of matrix multiplication we have

$$(x\,y)_{n'n} = \sum_{n''} x_{n'n''}\,y_{n''n}.$$

Applying the selection rule for dipole radiation $\Delta l = \pm 1$ we obtain

$$l'' - l = \pm 1 \quad \text{and} \quad l'' - l' = \pm 1$$

from which (66.6) follows immediately. Similarly, one obtains the J selection rule for quadrupole radiation from the rule for dipole radiation (64.5):

$$\Delta J = 0, \quad \pm 1 \quad \text{or} \quad \pm 2. \tag{66.7}$$

Evidently, in similar fashion one can also derive specialized intensity formulas for the ZEEMAN components, fine structure components, etc. There are also sum rules which correspond exactly to those derived for dipole radiation. For example, for reasons of symmetry the quadrupole radiation is independent of the direction of propagation and polarization if all the ZEEMAN components are summed. The quadrupole radiation within a given multiplet is independent of the magnetic and total angular momentum quantum numbers of the initial state, if a summation over all the directions of propagation and polarization is performed. For the details we refer the reader to the papers by RUBINOWICZ[1] and for experimental verifications to the work of SEGRÈ[2] and others.

In order to obtain a notion of the magnitude of the line intensities in question, we shall calculate the intensity of the transition from the ground state to the $3d$ state of hydrogen. Carrying out the integrations over angles and over the directions of propagation and polarization of the emitted light, one obtains

$$\int d\Omega \sum |D^{kj}_{n'n}|^2 = \left(\frac{m}{2\hbar c}\,\omega^2\right)^2 \frac{8\pi}{15} \left(\int_0^\infty R_{10}(r)\,r^2\,R_{32}(r)\,r^2\,dr\right)^2.$$

Inserting the eigenfunctions (3.18) into the radial integral yields $\frac{81}{256} \times \sqrt{30}\,a^2$, in which a is the radius of the hydrogen atom. Defining the oscillator strength as

$$\overline{f}_{n'n} = \frac{2}{3}\,\frac{\hbar}{m\,\omega_{nn'}}\,\frac{1}{8\pi}\int d\Omega \sum_j |D^{kj}_{n'n}|^2 \tag{66.8}$$

---

[1] A. RUBINOWICZ: Z. Physik **61**, 338 (1930); **65**, 662 (1930); with J. BLATON, Ergebn. exakt. Naturwiss. **11**, 176 (1932) which also contains additional references.

[2] E. SEGRÈ: Z. Physik **66**, 827 (1930); with C. J. BAKKER, Z. Physik **72**, 724 (1931); S. SAMBURSKY, Z. Physik **68**, 774 (1931); **76**, 132, 266 (1932).

[for dipole radiation the definition goes over to (59.14)], one obtains after some numerical computation, for the transition $1s \rightarrow 3d$

$$f_{1s}^{3d} = 0.033\,\alpha^2 = 1.8 \times 10^{-6}. \tag{66.9}$$

Transitions which have an oscillator strength of such a small magnitude can, of course, be observed only in two ways: either in absorption—this has been done, for example, by SEGRÈ for the transition $3s \rightarrow 3d$ of Na—or if the upper level is metastable. If, for example, the $3d$ state of hydrogen were metastable (assuming for a moment that the transition $3d \rightarrow 2p$ does not exist), the lifetime of the $3d$ state would be given by[1] [cf. Eq. (59.15)]:

$$T = \left(\frac{\nu}{\mathrm{Ry}}\right)^{-2} 1.25 \times 10^{-10} \times \frac{5}{1.8 \times 10^{-6}} = 4.4 \times 10^{-4}\,\text{sec}. \tag{66.10}$$

The above agrees in order of magnitude with the lifetimes of metastable states as generally found experimentally.

γ) Magnetic dipole radiation. We consider first the most general selection rules for the magnetic dipole matrix element $D^{(m1)}$. For any complex atom (without external fields), $\boldsymbol{M}^2$ and M_z are constants of the motion ($\boldsymbol{M} = \boldsymbol{K} + \boldsymbol{S}$) with eigenvalues $J(J+1)$ and m, respectively. In addition, the atomic states can be classified into states with even or odd parity (for a nonrelativistic product wave function the parity is even (odd) if $\sum_j l_j$ is even (odd), where l_j is the orbital quantum number for the j-th electron). We need the matrix element, between two atomic states, of the component of $\boldsymbol{K} + 2\boldsymbol{S} = \boldsymbol{M} + \boldsymbol{S}$ in the direction ξ which is perpendicular to the plane containing the propagation and polarization directions of the photon. One can derive (see [5]) the following three general selection rules:

$$(1) \qquad \Delta m = 0 \quad (\text{if } \xi \parallel z), \quad \pm 1 \quad (\text{if } \xi \perp z), \tag{66.11}$$

$$(2) \qquad \Delta J = 0 \quad \text{or} \quad \pm 1 \quad (J = 0 \rightarrow 0 \text{ forbidden}). \tag{66.12}$$

and (3) the parity must remain unchanged in the transition[2].

If the RUSSELL-SAUNDERS approximation (see Sects. 43α, 48α and 64β) holds, much more restrictive selection rules apply. Consider first the HARTREE product type wave functions belonging to a particular "configuration" i.e., with *given* values of the quantum numbers $n_1 l_1$, $n_2 l_2$, etc. for the various electrons, but arbitrary values of m_{1l}, m_{1s}; m_{2l}, m_{2s}; etc. The spatial part of each single-electron wave function (in this approximation) is independent of m_s and the radial part is also independent of m_l. In the RUSSELL-SAUNDERS approximation one then forms a linear superposition of these wave functions (from a particular configuration), for which L, S and J are good quantum numbers (as well as $n_1 l_1$, $n_2 l_2$, etc.). Now the operator $\boldsymbol{K} + 2\boldsymbol{S}$ commutes with $\boldsymbol{K}^2$, $\boldsymbol{S}^2$ and also with $\boldsymbol{k}_2^2$, $\boldsymbol{k}_1^2$, etc. One then finds the following selection rule for a matrix element of $\boldsymbol{K} + 2\boldsymbol{S}$,

$$\Delta L = \Delta S = \Delta l_1 = \Delta l_2 = \cdots = 0, \tag{66.13}$$

in addition to (66.11) and (66.12). But in our present approximation the radial part of a wave function is simply a product of single-particle radial functions

[1] The factor 5 has its origin in the fact that the oscillator strength 1.8×10^{-6} must be shared by the five magnetic substates of the $3d$ level.

[2] For electric dipole transitions (see Sect. 64β), we also have rules (1) and (2) (with the polarization direction taking the place of ξ) but (3) is replaced by the rule that the parity must change. For electric quadrupole transitions the rule (3) also applies, but (1) is replaced by $\Delta m = 0, \pm 1, \pm 2$ and in (2), $\Delta J = \pm 2$ is now also possible.

which depend only on $n_1 l_1, n_2 l_2$, etc. Now the operator $\boldsymbol{K}+2\boldsymbol{S}$ leaves the radial part of any wave function unchanged and two radial wave functions with the same l, but different n, are orthogonal. We then find the additional selection rule

$$\Delta n_1 = \Delta n_2 = \cdots = 0. \tag{66.14}$$

We have thus found that, in the RUSSELL-SAUNDERS approximation, magnetic dipole transitions are only possible between two states belonging to the *same* configuration and having the *same* values of L and S. Two such states belong to the same fine structure multiplet and their energy difference is extremely small (compared with 1 Ry, say). The emitted radiation is then in the microwave or radio region, *not* in the optical region, and $\omega_{nn'}$ in (66.5) is extremely small. Spontaneous transitions of this type thus have a negligibly small probability, but induced transitions of this type can be important: For an atom in a weak external magnetic field, for instance, the energy of a level depends on the magnetic quantum number m. Magnetic dipole transitions are then possible between two ZEEMAN components of the same[1] fine structure level ($\Delta L = \Delta S = \Delta J = 0$, $\Delta m = \pm 1$) and can be used to measure the ZEEMAN effect energy splitting (see Sect. 49). For an atom whose nucleus has a magnetic moment, one can also get magnetic dipole transitions between two hyperfine structure components of the same fine structure level ($\Delta L = \Delta S = \Delta J = 0$, $\Delta f = \pm 1$) (see [*16*] and our Sect. 22).

δ) Applications. The transition probabilities for electric quadrupole transitions with $\Delta l = \pm 2$ (or 0) are an order of $(Z\alpha)^2$ smaller than for "allowed" electric dipole transitions with $\Delta l = \pm 1$. For hydrogen-like atoms the frequencies of quadrupole lines coincide with those of much stronger dipole lines (because of the l-degeneracy) and cannot be investigated experimentally. For alkali and more complex atoms the frequencies of quadrupole lines are distinct and have been measured in absorption (see [*5*], Chap. 9, Sect. 5). Electric octupole transitions with $\Delta l = \pm 3$ have probabilities an order of $(Z\alpha)^4$ smaller than dipole transitions and are of little interest for atomic spectra.

We have already discussed magnetic dipole transitions between components of the same fine structure multiplet. Magnetic dipole transitions in the optical region (between different fine structure multiplets) have probabilities an order of $(Z\alpha)^2 \xi^2$ smaller than electric dipole transitions, where ξ is the order of magnitude of the matrix element $(K_z + 2S_z)_{n'n}$. In the RUSSELL-SAUNDERS approximation, ξ is zero—and is generally very small for atoms with small nuclear charge Z. Magnetic dipole transitions thus have very small probabilities, but occur nevertheless in interstellar gas[2] (emission nebulae): Interstellar gas contains some doubly ionized O^{++}-ions at extremely low pressure, so that atomic collisions are very rare. The ground state configuration of O^{++} has two valence electrons in p-states which can form a $^1D_2$ state, as well as ^3P-states with $J = 0, 1$ or 2 at lower energies. This $^1D_2$-state is metastable since electric dipole transitions to the ^3P-states are strictly forbidden (parity unchanged) and higher order transitions are also forbidden in a pure RUSSELL-SAUNDERS approximation ($\Delta S = 1$). The exact wave functions deviate slightly from pure RUSSELL-SAUNDERS coupling and the exact singlet $^1D_2$-state has a slight admixture of the triplet $^3P_2$ wave functions (and vice versa). The order ξ of the matrix elements for magnetic

---

[1] For a single-electron atom in an S-state, for instance, $l = 0$ and $s = j = \frac{1}{2}$ for both states and $m = -\frac{1}{2}$ and $+\frac{1}{2}$ respectively. For such a transition the matrix element $(K_z + 2S_z)_{n'n}$ is simply unity if z is perpendicular to the axis of quantization.

[2] See ref. [*5*], Chap. 11, Sect. 5 and J. A. HYNEK, Astrophysics, Chap. 13. New York: McGraw-Hill 1951.

dipole transitions is then not exactly zero, but small (less than 0.01). Spontaneous magnetic dipole transitions from the $^1D_2$-state to $^3P_2$ and $^3P_1$ are responsible for the "nebular emission lines" in interstellar gas and the lifetime of the $^1D_2$-state is about 40 sec. The lifetime of the metastable $2\,^2S_{\frac{1}{2}}$-state in hydrogen is discussed in Sect. 67α.

Radiative transitions of higher multipole type are much more common between energy levels of *nuclei* than in atoms[1]: "Metastable states" occur very frequently and in some cases the J-value of a first excited state differs by ± 3 from that of the ground state. Such states (called nuclear isomers) may decay by electric octupole transitions. Electric quadrupole transitions are more common still in nuclear spectroscopy. In complex nuclei spin-orbit coupling is very much stronger than in atoms and the nuclear wave functions are not of RUSSELL-SAUNDERS type. The selection rules (66.13) and (66.14) do not apply and the probabilities for magnetic dipole transitions may be quite appreciable.

67. Lifetimes of excited states in hydrogen. In Sect. 63 we have calculated the probabilities for transitions between states in hydrogen which are eigenstates of $\boldsymbol{k}^2$ (l is a good quantum number, wave function separable in spherical polar coordinates). The corresponding mean lifetimes for such states are given in Table 15 and depend strongly on the orbital quantum number l. In Sect. 64 we have taken the electron's spin into account and shown that the lifetime of a state with a definite l-value (in the PAULI approximation) is the same as in nonrelativistic theory and the same for the states with $j=l-\frac{1}{2}$ and $l+\frac{1}{2}$. The lifetimes of excited states of hydrogen atoms in a reasonably strong electric field (STARK effect $\gg$ fine structure) were discussed in Sect. 65. In this case l is not at all a good quantum number (we have instead the parabolic quantum numbers) and the lifetimes are quite different from those of Table 15. In the absence of any perturbations or in *very* weak electric fields, levels with different j-values are well separated in energy. On the other hand, the two states of given j value (with $l=j-\frac{1}{2}$ and $j+\frac{1}{2}$) have the same energy, if the LAMB shift is neglected. We shall discuss in this section under what circumstances these two degenerate states (with l differing by unity) decay separately with the different lifetimes given in Table 15. We restrict ourselves throughout to weak enough electric fields so that the STARK effect is smaller than the fine structure splitting.

We shall use in our discussion the concept of the "radiation width" Γ of an energy level: If an atomic state of energy E decays exponentially with a mean lifetime of $\hbar/\Gamma$ seconds, the time dependence of its wave function will be proportional to

$$\exp\left[-i\left(E-\tfrac{1}{2}i\Gamma\right)t/\hbar\right]. \tag{67.1}$$

The quantity $\frac{1}{2}\Gamma$ has the dimensions of energy and is called the "half-width" of the level. In the language of the uncertainty principle, Γ corresponds to a spread or uncertainty in the energy of the level. Radiation theory leads to the following related result: Consider a radiative transition from the excited state of energy E and mean lifetime $\hbar/\Gamma$ to the ground state of energy E_0 (and infinite lifetime). The energy $h\nu$ of the emitted photon is then not exactly $(E-E_0)$, but photons of different energies can be emitted with a probability approximately proportional to

$$\left[(h\nu-E+E_0)^2+\left(\tfrac{1}{2}\Gamma\right)^2\right]^{-1}. \tag{67.2}$$

For hydrogen-like atoms of nuclear charge Z, the width Γ (see Sect. 59α) is of order $\alpha(Z\alpha)^2 W_Z$, where $W_Z=Z^2$ Ry is the ionization potential. Thus Γ is extremely small compared with the energy differences (E_2-E_1) between levels

[1] See J. BLATT and V. WEISSKOPF, Theoretical Nuclear Physics, Chap. 12. New York: Wiley 1952; R. G. SACHS, Nuclear Theory, Chap. 9 (Cambridge- Addison-Wesley 1953), and Vols. XXXIX to XLII of this Encyclopedia.

with different principal quantum numbers n, and Γ is even one order of α smaller than the fine structure splitting. We are also interested in the ratio of Γ for excited states to the LAMB shift splitting S_L between the two states $l=j+\frac{1}{2}$ and $j-\frac{1}{2}$ for fixed j. This ratio is roughly independent of n (both Γ and S_L are roughly proportional to n^{-3}) but depends strongly on j: For $j \geqq \frac{3}{2}$ and for any n, the LAMB shift splitting S_L is appreciably smaller than the width Γ of either of the two states (for $j=\frac{3}{2}$, for instance, Γ for the $P_{\frac{3}{2}}$-state is about 10 times the splitting energy S_L). For $j=\frac{1}{2}$ and any n, on the other hand, S_L is appreciably larger than the width Γ of the $P_{\frac{1}{2}}$-state (the width Γ is smaller still for the $S_{\frac{1}{2}}$-state). For $n=2$, for instance, the mean-life $\hbar/\Gamma$ of the $2P_{\frac{1}{2}}$-state is

$$\frac{\hbar}{\Gamma} = \frac{3c^2}{4\alpha\,\omega_{21}^3\,|\boldsymbol{r}_{12}|^2} = 1.595 \times 10^{-9}\ \text{sec}. \tag{67.3}$$

The width in frequency units is then $\Gamma/h = 99.8$ Mc/sec (corresponding to $0.0033\ \text{cm}^{-1}$), compared with the LAMB shift splitting[1] between $2S_{\frac{1}{2}}$ and $2P_{\frac{1}{2}}$ of $S_L/h = 1058$ Mc/sec.

We shall discuss separately the case of levels with $j=\frac{1}{2}$ and those with $j>\frac{1}{2}$. For all $j=\frac{1}{2}$ states (see Table 15) the lifetime (without perturbations) of the S-state is appreciably longer than that of the P-state. The situation is particularly interesting for $n=2$ where the 2 S-state is metastable.

α) The unperturbed 2 S-state. We consider first the lifetime of a hydrogen atom in the metastable $2S_{\frac{1}{2}}$-state in the absence of any perturbations such as an electric field or atomic collisions. The only states with lower energy are the $1S$ ground state and the $2P_{\frac{1}{2}}$-state. Spontaneous transitions to the 2 P-state have a negligibly small probability (lifetime about 20 years), since the energy difference is so small. Electric dipole transitions to the ground state are strictly forbidden, since the $1S$ and $2S$-states have the same parity. In the PAULI approximation, $2S_{\frac{1}{2}}-1S_{\frac{1}{2}}$ electric quadrupole transitions (Sect. 66β) are forbidden[2] (since both states have $l=0$) and magnetic dipole transitions (Sect. 66γ) are also forbidden since the radial wave functions of the two states are orthogonal in this approximation. If the exact DIRAC wave functions are used, the matrix element ξ of the spin operator is not exactly zero, but the relative deviations of the exact from the PAULI wave functions, and hence ξ, are only of order $(Z\alpha)^2$. Magnetic dipole transitions from $2S_{\frac{1}{2}}$ to $1S_{\frac{1}{2}}$ are therefore not strictly forbidden, but their probability is smaller than those for allowed electric dipole transitions by an order of $(Z\alpha)^6$ or about 10^{-13} for hydrogen. An explicit calculation[3] of this effect leads to a lifetime of the $2S_{\frac{1}{2}}$-state in hydrogen of about 2 days!

The largest probability for a $2S-1S$ transition comes from a type of process which we have neglected so far, namely the simultaneous emission of two photons whose combined energies equal the energy difference between the two atomic states. For such two-quantum processes $l=0 \rightarrow l=0$ transitions are not forbidden, but their probabilities turn out to be smaller than those of *allowed* single quantum transitions by an order of $\alpha(ka)^2 \sim \alpha(Z\alpha)^2$. The total probability for two-quantum transitions from $2S$ to $1S$ in hydrogen has been calculated[4] and

[1] We shall neglect any hyperfine structure splitting in hydrogen, which is less than the LAMB shift for all $j=\frac{1}{2}$ states and less than the radiation width Γ for all states with $j \geqq \frac{3}{2}$.

[2] In fact, electric quadrupole transitions are strictly forbidden unless $j_1+j_2 \geqq 2$ (here $j_1=j_2=\frac{1}{2}$).

[3] G. BREIT and E. TELLER: Astrophys. J. **91**, 215 (1940).

[4] G. BREIT and E. TELLER: Astrophys. J. **91**, 215 (1940). For a discussion of other two-quantum processes see M. GÖPPERT-MAYER, Ann. Phys. **9**, 273 (1931).

is about 7 sec^{-1}. The mean lifetime of $\frac{1}{7}$ sec of the $2S$-state is thus extremely long compared with that of the $2P$-state (1.6×10^{-9} sec).

The effect of electric fields on the lifetime of the metastable state in hydrogen is discussed below. The effect of collisions transferring hydrogen atoms from the $2S$ to other states has been investigated by various authors[1]. In a partially ionized hydrogen gas under conditions of thermal equilibrium the main effect is due to collisions of the atom in the $2S$-state with hydrogen ions (protons) resulting in a transition to either of the $2P$-states. At temperatures around 10000 °K the probability for the removal of a hydrogen atom from the $2S$-state by collisions[2] is about $7\times 10^{-4} N_i$ sec^{-1}, where N_i is the number of positive ions per cm^3. The lifetime of an atom in the $2S$-state is then appreciably longer than for the $2P$-state if N_i is much less than 10^{12} ions/cm^3. Collisions with neutral hydrogen atoms contribute only a removal probability of the order of $10^{-8} N$ sec^{-1} $\sim 10^7 p$ sec^{-1}, where N is the number of atoms/cm^3 and p the pressure in mm Hg. In terrestrial low pressure discharge tubes with *low* ion densities (and also in the outermost atmospheres of stars) the removal rate of $2S$-state atoms by collisions is appreciably less than the inverse lifetime of about 10^9 sec^{-1} of the $2P$-state. In interstellar gas clouds N and N_i are only of the order of about 100 and removal by collisions is even slower than the two-quantum decay to the ground state. In the LAMB shift experiments (Sect. 21) unidirectional atomic beams in a very good vacuum are used and the effect of collisions can be neglected.

β) The $j=\frac{1}{2}$ states in an electric field. We consider next the effect of a uniform, constant and weak electric field of field strength F on the lifetime of the metastable $2S_{\frac{1}{2}}$-state in hydrogen. In the absence of the electric field (and all other perturbations) the two $n=2$, $j=\frac{1}{2}$ states decay separately with vastly different lifetimes: $t_P = 1.6\times 10^{-9}$ sec for the $2P_{\frac{1}{2}}$-state and $t_S=\frac{1}{7}$ sec for the $2S_{\frac{1}{2}}$-state. If, for instance, at time $t=0$ we have a wave function which is a linear superposition of the $2S$ and $2P$ eigenfunctions,

$$u(0) = a\,u_{2S} + b\,u_{2P}, \tag{67.4}$$

the two parts of the wave function decay quite independently. At a later time t where $t_P \ll t \ll t_S$, for instance, the $2P$ part has practically all decayed to the ground state ($1S$) and the $2S$ part practically not at all. The wave function is then approximately

$$u(t) = a\,u_{2S}\,e^{-iE_{2S}t/\hbar} + b\,u_{1S}\,e^{-iE_{1S}t/\hbar}. \tag{67.5}$$

We consider now the two stationary states with $n=2$, $j=\frac{1}{2}$ in the presence of an electric field F, weak enough so that the STARK effect is small compared with the fine structure splitting (but not necessarily smaller than the LAMB shift). We neglect the effect[3] of hyperfine structure and of the radiation width of the $2P$-state, which are smaller than the (field free) LAMB shift splitting S_L between $2S$ and $2P$ of 1058 Mc/sec (in frequency units). In the presence of the electric field F (but neglecting radiation) there are two stationary states with $n=2$, $j=\frac{1}{2}$ and given m ($+\frac{1}{2}$ or $-\frac{1}{2}$), which are discussed in Sect. 55α. The wave function for each of these two states is a linear superposition of form (67.4). The ratio a/b for each of these states as a function of F is given by (55.7) and their energy

[1] See E. M. PURCELL: Astrophys. J. **116**, 457 (1952).

[2] Collisions with electrons (instead of protons) contribute only about 10% of this probability.

[3] For states with $j \gtrless \frac{3}{2}$ we shall use a different approximation in Sect. 67γ. More general expressions (which neglect neither the LAMB shift nor the radiation width) have been obtained by W. LAMB and R. RETHERFORD, Phys. Rev. **79**, 549 (1950) (see their Appendix II) and by G. LÜDERS, Z. Naturforsch. **5**a, 608 (1950); see also (67.14).

difference by (55.8). For $n=2$, the ratio 2ξ of the STARK effect splitting $2\sqrt{3}F$ to the (field-free) LAMB shift splitting S_L is about $F/475$ Volt/cm. (55.7) then gives for the ratio a/b

$$\frac{a_\pm}{b_\pm} = + \frac{2\xi}{1 \pm \sqrt{1+4\xi^2}}, \tag{67.6}$$

where the plus sign refers to the stationary state which reduces to $2P$ for $\xi=0$ and the minus sign to that which reduces to $2S$.

(55.8) shows that the energy separation between the two stationary states with $n=2$, $j=\frac{1}{2}$ increases with increasing field strength F and is larger than the radiation width of the $2P$-state for all F. Each of the two states, with wave functions given by (67.4) and (67.6), will then decay to the ground state separately with its own lifetime $t_\pm(F)$. The transition matrix element from the part of the wave function involving u_{2S} is negligible and the transition probability essentially all comes from the admixture of u_{2P} in the wave function. The lifetimes of the two states are then given by

$$t_\pm(F) = t_P \frac{a_\pm^2 + b_\pm^2}{b_\pm^2}, \tag{67.7}$$

where t_P is the lifetimes of the field-free $2P$-state and $a_\pm$, $b_\pm$ are given by (67.6). For $\xi \gg 1$, both t_+ and t_- are nearly equal to $2t_P$ and no trace of metastability remains in either state. For $\xi \ll 1$, one of the two states is almost pure $2P$ and t_+ nearly equals the field-free t_P. The other state is almost pure $2S$ with a small admixture of $2P$ which gives a lifetime of (neglecting again the direct $2S-1S$ transition probability)

$$t_-(F) = \xi^{-2} t_P = \left(\frac{F}{475 \text{ Volt/cm}}\right)^{-2} t_P. \tag{67.8}$$

Under the conditions of the LAMB shift experiment all external electric fields can be kept down to about 5 Volt/cm or less and the $2S$-state is almost pure and has a much longer lifetime than the $2P$-state[1]. The situation is more complicated if a uniform and constant weak magnetic field $\mathscr{H}$ is also present: In the presence of the magnetic (and the absence of an electric) field the components with $m=\frac{1}{2}$ and $-\frac{1}{2}$ of both the $2S_{\frac{1}{2}}$ and $2P_{\frac{1}{2}}$ energy levels split as shown in Fig. 33 (see also Sect. 46α). At about 575 Gauss the $m=-\frac{1}{2}(S)$ and the $m=\frac{1}{2}(P)$ levels coincide and the $m=\frac{1}{2}(S)$ and $m=-\frac{1}{2}(P)$ levels are separated by about 2150 Mc/sec (compared with 1058 Mc/sec for zero field). If an additional electric field, with direction *perpendicular* to that of the magnetic field, is applied it will couple the m-component of the S-level with the $P_{\frac{1}{2}}$-level with $m'=-m$. In a very weak electric field the mixing of the wave functions is much larger[2] for the $m=-\frac{1}{2}(S)$ level (whose energy coincides with that of the relevant P-level)

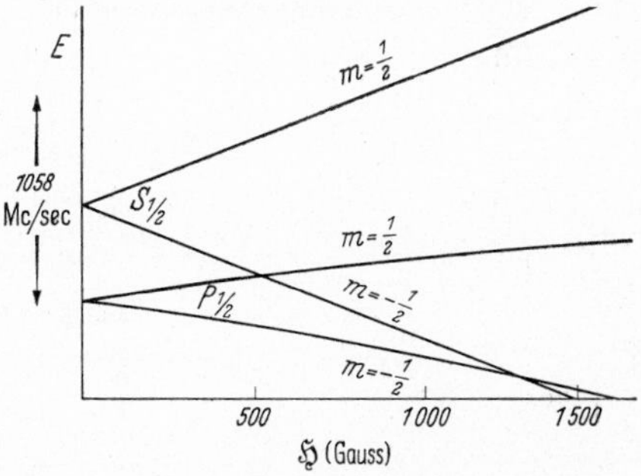

Fig. 33. ZEEMAN effect on the levels with $n=2$, $j=\frac{1}{2}$ in hydrogen for weak magnetic fields $\mathscr{H}$ (including the LAMB shift).

[1] Although we have assumed a uniform and constant electric field, the results can be extended to apply to the varying electric fields produced in a discharge tube or atomic beam apparatus by passing electrons and ions. Note, however, that these fields would have to be less than about 0.05 Volt/cm for the lifetime of the $2S$-state to have its field-free value of $\frac{1}{7}$ sec.

[2] In our approximation by an infinite factor, in reality by a factor of $\sqrt{1850}$ [see Sect. 67γ and also W. E. LAMB, Rep. Progr. Phys. **14**, 19 (1951)].

than for the $m=\frac{1}{2}(S)$ level. The lifetime of the $m=-\frac{1}{2}(S)$ level is then much shorter than for $m=\frac{1}{2}(S)$. The experimental conditions in the LAMB shift experiment can be so arranged that the $m=-\frac{1}{2}(2S)$ and all $(2P)$ levels decay in flight to the ground state and a polarized beam of $2S$-atoms with $m=\frac{1}{2}$ reaches the detector.

We have considered so far only the $j=\frac{1}{2}$ levels with $n=2$. For $j=\frac{1}{2}$ but larger values of n (in an electric, but no magnetic, field) the situation is *qualitatively* similar. The field-free lifetime of the nS-state is no longer (practically) infinite, but nevertheless appreciably larger than that of the nP-state and the LAMB shift is much larger than the radiation widths. The lifetimes of the two states again become comparable with each other for field strengths F for which the STARK effect is comparable with the LAMB shift. However, the STARK effect increases and the LAMB shift decreases with increasing principal quantum number n. The critical field strength thus decreases very rapidly (inversely as $n^4\sqrt{n^2-1}$) with increasing n and is approximately 475, 58, 12 and 1.7 Volt/cm for $n=2, 3, 4$ and 6, respectively.

γ) Lifetimes of other excited states. We now consider the effect of a weak electric field on the "mixing" of the wave functions and the lifetimes of the two states with $l=j+\frac{1}{2}$ and $j-\frac{1}{2}$ in hydrogen for $j\geqq\frac{3}{2}$. The field-free LAMB shift is small compared with the radiation widths for such states and, for simplicity, we neglect the LAMB shift completely. Since the two energy levels are assumed to coincide in the absence of an external field, one might at first sight expect that an external electric field of *arbitrarily* small strength F would "mix up" the wave functions and lifetimes of the two field-free states. We shall now show that this is *not* the case until the field strengths are large enough so that the STARK effect splitting is larger than the difference between the radiation widths of the two states.

Let $u_1(\boldsymbol{r}, t)$ and $u_2(\boldsymbol{r}, t)$ be the wave functions of the states with $l=j+\frac{1}{2}$ and $j-\frac{1}{2}$ (and fixed m) in the absence of both the electric field and the interaction with radiation. We consider a state of the atom in the electric field whose wave function is a linear superposition of u_1, u_2 and wave functions for levels of lower energy. The part of this wave function which contains u_1 and u_2 is then

$$u(t) = a_1(t)\,u_1 + a_2(t)\,u_2, \tag{67.9}$$

where the coefficients a_1 and a_2 satisfy[1] the coupled differential equations (derived from the wave equations)

$$\left.\begin{aligned}\frac{da_1}{dt} &= -if a_2 - 2\beta_1 a_1,\\ \frac{da_2}{dt} &= -if a_1 - 2\beta_2 a_2.\end{aligned}\right\} \tag{67.10}$$

The coefficients f and β in (67.10) have the following meaning: $\hbar f$ is the magnitude of the matrix element between the states 1 and 2 of the perturbation HAMILTONian due to the presence of a weak electric field of strength F parallel to the quantization direction. From (55.3) we have

$$\hbar f = \left|\pm\frac{3}{4}\sqrt{n^2-\left(j+\frac{1}{2}\right)^2}\,\frac{n\,m}{j(j+1)}\,F\right|. \tag{67.11}$$

$4\beta_1$ and $4\beta_2$ are the reciprocal mean lifetimes of the pure states 1 and 2 as given in Table 15 (and $\beta_1>\beta_2$). In the absence of the electric field, $a_1(t)$ would be a multiple of $e^{-2\beta_1 t}$ and similarly for a_2.

[1] E. WIGNER and V. WEISSKOPF: Z. Physik **63**, 54 (1930).

We can look for a solution of (67.10) for which a_1 and a_2 have the *same* purely exponential (but possibly complex) time dependence. One finds two different solutions satisfying this requirement and the corresponding two wave functions (67.9) are

$$\left.\begin{aligned} u_a &= [f u_1 + i(\beta_- - \gamma)\, u_2]\, e^{-(\beta_1+\beta_2+\gamma)t}, \\ u_b &= [f u_1 + i(\beta_- + \gamma)\, u_2]\, e^{-(\beta_1+\beta_2-\gamma)t}; \\ \beta_- &\equiv \beta_1 - \beta_2, \quad \gamma = \sqrt{\beta_-^2 - f^2}. \end{aligned}\right\} \tag{67.12}$$

The general solution of (67.9) with (67.10) is a linear superposition of the wave functions u_a and u_b. Note, however, that u_a and u_b are in general *not* orthogonal except in the limits of $\beta_-^2 \ll f^2$ and of $\beta_-^2 \gg f^2$.

It is convenient to consider separately the two cases of β_-^2 larger than and smaller than f^2:

(i) $\beta_-^2 > f^2$: In this case, γ and the exponents in the exponentials in (67.12) are real. The time dependence of u_a (and of u_b) represents a purely exponential decay. The real energies of the two states a and b are then equal (as in the absence of the electric field) but the lifetimes of the two exponential decays are different (except in the limit of $\beta_-^2 = f^2$). (67.12) simplifies if we assume $\beta_-^2 \gg f^2$, i.e. if the STARK effect splitting is small compared with the difference between the radiation widths. The states a and b are then almost identical with the two field-free states: The ratio $|a_2/a_1|$ is then approximately $f/2\beta_-$ for u_a and $2\beta_-/f$ for u_b and the lifetimes t_a and t_b differ little from the field-free values,

$$t_a^{-1} \approx 4\beta_1 - \frac{f^2}{\beta_-}, \qquad t_b^{-1} \approx 4\beta_2 + \frac{f^2}{\beta_-}. \tag{67.13}$$

(ii) $\beta_-^2 < f^2$: In this case, γ is purely imaginary and the exponents in the exponentials in (67.12) are complex. The terms $e^{\pm i|\gamma|t}$ represent energy shifts of the two states in opposite directions and their energy difference is $2|\gamma|\hbar$. If $\beta^2 \ll f^2$ then $2|\gamma|$ reduces to $2f - \beta_-^2/f$, compared with $2f$ in the absence of radiation. The inverse lifetimes of the two states a and b are then the same and equal to $2(\beta_1+\beta_2)$. Note also that $|a_2/a_1|$ is unity for both states in this limit.

The above equations would also hold for states with $j=\frac{1}{2}$ if the LAMB shift (in the absence of an electric field) were zero. More general relations can also be derived which take into account both the LAMB shift and the radiation widths. We only give a special case of these relations for $n=2$ and $j=\frac{1}{2}$: Let $\Gamma_P = 4\hbar\beta_P = \hbar/t_P$ be the radiation width of the $2P$-state and $\hbar L$ the energy separation between $2S$ and $2P$ in the absence of the electric field. If the STARK effect is small compared with the LAMB shift and/or Γ_P and if we neglect Γ_S completely, one then finds for the lifetime t_b of the state which is "almost pure $2S$",

$$\frac{t_P}{t_b} = \frac{f^2}{4\beta_P^2 + L^2}. \tag{67.14}$$

This expression for t_b reduces to (67.13) if $L \ll \beta_P$ and to (67.8) if $L \gg \beta_P$. In the absence of any magnetic field the ratio $L/2\beta_P$ is about 21; in a magnetic field of about 575 Gauss (see end of Sect. 67β) this ratio is zero and about 43, respectively, for the $m=-\frac{1}{2}$ and $+\frac{1}{2}$ states.

We can summarize the dependence on electric field strength F of the lifetimes of the various states with $n=3$, for instance, as follows. For the levels with $j=m=\frac{3}{2}$, $\beta_- = 0.31\times 10^8\ \text{sec}^{-1}$ and f, as given by (67.11), equals β_- for the critical field strength of $F_c = 1.9$ Volt/cm. For $F \ll F_c$ the inverse lifetimes (in $10^8\ \text{sec}^{-1}$) are as given in Table 15, i.e. 0.06 for $S_{\frac{1}{2}}$, 1.86 for $P_{\frac{1}{2}}$ and $P_{\frac{3}{2}}$ and 0.64

for $D_{\frac{3}{2}}$ and $D_{\frac{5}{2}}$. As F approaches F_c the $P_{\frac{3}{2}}$ and $D_{\frac{3}{2}}$ states are "mixed" into two different states and the inverse of the lifetime of each of these states (in $10^8\,\text{sec}^{-1}$) approaches 1.25 (and remains 1.25 for $F > 1.9$ Volt/cm). As F approaches 60 Volts/cm (see Sect. 67β) the $S_{\frac{1}{2}}$ and $P_{\frac{1}{2}}$ states also begin to be "mixed" and the inverse lifetime of each of the two resulting states approaches 0.96 for F much larger than this value (the $D_{\frac{5}{2}}$ lifetime is unchanged). Finally, for F of the order of 500 Volt/cm or larger, mixing of the states with different values of j sets in and the lifetimes approach those given in Table 20. For larger values of n the situation is qualitatively similar, but the critical values of field strength are roughly proportional to n^{-5}.

δ) Occupation numbers and excitation conditions. We have only discussed so far the effect of perturbations such as a weak electric field on the lifetimes of two states in hydrogen which have identical values of n and j. We have found the linear combinations u_a and u_b of the field-free wave functions u_1 and u_2 which have a purely exponential time-dependence. Another quantity of interest is the occupation number n_1 (and similarly n_2), i.e. the time average of the number of atoms per cm³ which are in the state u_1 (and u_2, respectively). These occupation numbers are of importance since the intensities of different spectral lines (both in absorption and in emission) depend on them for the following reason: The states u_1 and u_2 correspond to different values of the orbital quantum number, $l = j + \frac{1}{2}$ and $j - \frac{1}{2}$ respectively, and combine optically with different states. Consider, for instance, transitions from the two levels with $n = 3$ and $j = \frac{3}{2}$ to various levels with $n = 2$. The part of the $n = 3$ wave function involving $u_2(3\,P_{\frac{3}{2}})$ gives transitions only to the levels with $j = \frac{1}{2}$ (to the $2\,S_{\frac{1}{2}}$-component). The part involving $u_1(3\,D_{\frac{3}{2}})$, however, can also give transitions to the level with $j = \frac{3}{2}\,(2\,P_{\frac{3}{2}})$.

The occupation numbers n_1 and n_2 depend not only on the perturbing electric field, but also on the excitation conditions, and can be calculated as follows. Consider a particular excitation process which excites at time $t = 0$ one electron into a state which is a definite superposition of the field-free states 1 and 2,

$$u(0) = a_1(0)\,u_1 + a_2(0)\,u_2; \qquad |a_1(0)|^2 + |a_2(0)|^2 = 1. \tag{67.15}$$

We consider, for simplicity, states with $j \geqq \frac{3}{2}$, so that we can neglect the LAMB shift. Using the solutions (67.12) of (67.9) and (67.10), one can then find the wave function $u(t)$, Eq. (67.9), at later times t which satisfies the Eq. (67.10) and the boundary condition (67.15) at $t = 0$. One can then evaluate the time integral I_1 of the partial probability that the electron be in the state u_1. The result is

$$I_1 = \int_0^\infty |a_1(t)|^2\,dt = \frac{f^2 + 4(\beta_1 + \beta_2)\,\beta_2\,|a_1(0)|^2 - 4f\beta_2\,\text{Im}\,[a_1(0)\,a_2^*(0)]}{4(\beta_1 + \beta_2)\,(4\beta_1\beta_2 + f^2)}, \tag{67.16}$$

where Im denotes the imaginary part of an expression and f, β_1, and β_2 are defined in Sect. 67γ. A similar expression holds for I_2, the time integral of $|a_2(t)|^2$.

If N excitations of the type (67.15) take place per sec per cm³, then the occupation number n_1 (average number of atoms in state 1 per cm³) is simply NI_1 and similarly $n_2 = NI_2$. In practice, excitation conditions are usually such that different excitations can occur with different ratios of $a_1(0)/a_2(0)$ for an *individual* process but with definite *average* values for $|a_1(0)|^2$, $|a_2(0)|^2$ and for the phase relation between $a_1(0)$ and $a_2(0)$. Note that I_1 (in an electric field) for an individual process depends not only on $|a_1(0)|^2$ but also on the phase relation through the term $\text{Im}(a_1 a_2^*)$. Under most practical excitation conditions, the *average* of $\text{Im}(a_1 a_2^*)$ is zero: (i) Excitation by collisions with electrons. A linear combination of u_1 and u_2 is excited in an individual collision, but the phase relation varies in a random manner from one collision to the next. (ii) Excitation from a lower atomic state by light absorption. Because of the selection rule on l, either u_1 alone or u_2 alone is excited in an individual transition so that Im $(a_1 a_2^*)$ is zero for each transition[1].

We assume now that the average of $\mathrm{Im}(a_1 a_2^*)$ in (67.16) is zero and denote the average number $N|a_1(0)|^2$ of excitations to state u_1 per sec cm³ by N_1 (similarly for N_2). We then get for the average occupation number n_1 from (67.16),

$$n_1 = \frac{N_1[4(\beta_1+\beta_2)\beta_2 + f^2] + N_2 f^2}{4(\beta_1+\beta_2)(4\beta_1\beta_2 + f^2)}, \tag{67.17}$$

and a similar expression for n_2. Note that n_1 depends in general on N_2 as well as N_1, i.e. even if only states 2 are excited directly ($N_1 = 0$) some probability for the electron being in state 1 is built up by the mixing effect of the electric field. For weak enough fields, so that $f^2 \ll 4\beta_1\beta_2$, we have approximately

$$n_1 = \frac{N_1}{4\beta_1}\left[1 + \frac{N_2}{N_1}\frac{f^2}{4(\beta_1+\beta_2)\beta_2}\right]. \tag{67.18}$$

Unless N_2/N_1 is very large, (67.18) approximates the field-free values of $n_1 = N_1/4\beta_1$ ($4\beta_1$ is the inverse lifetime) and also $n_2 = N_2/4\beta_2$. If, on the other hand, the electric field is strong enough so that $f^2 \gg 2(\beta_1^2 + \beta_2^2)$, then (67.17) and the equivalent relation for n_2 reduce (approximately) to

$$n_1 = n_2 = \frac{N_1 + N_2}{4(\beta_1+\beta_2)}. \tag{67.19}$$

The relations (67.16) to (67.19) hold only in the absence of a Lamb shift (field-free energy separation between the states 1 and 2), but the situation is *qualitatively* similar if such a shift is present (e.g. for states with $j=\frac{1}{2}$): (i) If either the Lamb shift or the radiation widths are large compared with the Stark effect splitting, the occupation numbers are given approximately by their field-free values. (ii) If the Stark effect is large compared with both the Lamb shift and the two radiation widths, the occupation numbers n_1 and n_2 are approximately equal and given by (67.19). In case (i) the two states with the same l and $j = l \pm \frac{1}{2}$ have the same lifetime and the total intensity of all lines from all Zeeman components of the level with either j-value is proportional to the statistical weight $(2j+1)$ under the usual excitation conditions (rule II, Sect. 64β). Note that this is *not* true in case (ii), where levels with different j-values have different lifetimes.

The situation is again different if the Stark effect is even large compared with the total fine structure splitting of the levels with fixed n (e.g. for $F \gg 500$ Volt/cm if $n=3$ and $F \gg 10$ Volt/cm if $n=6$). If the electric field F is constant in magnitude and direction we deal with the Stark effect components, whose energies are discussed in Sect. 51 and their lifetimes in Sect. 65. Under many practical conditions the perturbing electric field varies in direction and magnitude in a random manner, (e.g. the field due to electrons and ions passing by). In this case the spectral lines coming from states with fixed n are broadened (rather than shifted) and the *average* lifetimes of *all* levels with the same n should be

[1] If we neglect the mixing by the electric field of states with different l values in the lower states from which absorption takes place. Even with mixing the average of Im $(a_1 a_2^*)$ is usually still zero (this is certainly the case if the orientation of the electric field varies in a random manner).

approximately the same. Under most excitation conditions, the occupation number of a component with particular values of n, l, j and m will then only depend on n.

ε) Summary. In the last few sections we have mainly discussed oscillator strengths, transition probabilities and line intensities for transitions between states of a single-electron atom which can be characterized by the orbital quantum number l. In Sect. 63 we have evaluated the required radial matrix elements explicitly for the special case of hydrogen-like atoms (pure COULOMB potential). As we discussed in Sect. 67, experimental verification of the theoretical results for hydrogen are very difficult in practice, because of the l-degeneracy. Under most practical conditions some weak perturbations, such as fluctuating electric fields or atomic collisions are present. These perturbations "mix up" the two fine structure levels with the same j-value (except, possibly, for $j=\frac{1}{2}$ and small values of n where the LAMB shift is appreciable) to an extent which depends on the details of the experimental conditions. Further, the thermal motions of the atoms give a DOPPLER shift to the frequency of a spectral line, with sign and magnitude varying from one atom to the next, so that each experimental spectral line is broadened considerably (DOPPLER broadening). The line broadening due to the DOPPLER effect may even be larger than the fine structure separations for large principal quantum number n.

We shall not discuss the many experiments on the line intensities in hydrogen, which have been carried out by means of optical spectroscopy in spite of these difficulties (they are described in Sect. 44 of [*10*]). It should be mentioned, however, that the LAMB shift experiments (Sect. 21) verify at least one entry for hydrogen in Table 15 quite accurately: The natural line width and shape for the $2P_{\frac{1}{2}}$- (and also the $2P_{\frac{3}{2}}$) level in H, D, and He^+ are measured accurately under (atomic beam) conditions where the DOPPLER and STARK broadening is kept to a minimum. The natural width is related to the lifetime of the level by (67.1) and (67.2) and the LAMB experiments agree well with the theoretical lifetime of 1.595×10^{-9} sec.

68. Alkali and X-ray spectra. There are two other kinds of spectra, to which the theory of single-electron spectra is often applied, which are not complicated by any l-degeneracy. These are the spectra of valence electrons in alkali atoms and the X-ray spectra due to transitions of inner electrons in heavy atoms. We shall not discuss these spectra in detail, but merely outline to what extent the theory of single-electron atoms applies and how these spectra differ from the hydrogen spectrum.

α) Alkali spectra. An alkali atom in its ground state consists of one or more closed shells of electrons plus one single (valence) electron in a new shell in a ns-state ($n=2$ for Li, $n=3$ for Na, etc.). We shall only consider those excited states of alkali atoms which contain the same closed shells with only the valence electron excited. The closed shells have zero total orbital angular momentum and zero total spin and are essentially unchanged in a transition between two states of the valence electron. In Sect. 17β we outlined briefly how one can calculate (most accurately by the HARTREE method) the effective central potential $V(r)$, due to the closed shells plus the nuclear COULOMB potential, which acts on the valence electron. Alkali spectra are usually treated theoretically by simply assuming that the valence electron makes transitions between stationary states in a *fixed* central potential $V(r)$. This treatment is, of course, only an approximation: The field of the valence electron acts on the electrons in the closed shells and the radial HARTREE wave functions of the closed shell electrons depend very slightly on the state in which the valence electron is. Hence the closed shells are not completely unaffected by a transition of the valence electron and the effective potential $V(r)$ acting on this electron depends slightly on its state. Further, the total wave function cannot be exactly of the assumed product form, but can be written as a superposition of all possible product wave functions. In this superposition, terms (with small coefficients) will occur in which more than one electron is excited ("configuration mixing", see Sect. 49β). For all alkali atoms these effects are very small and the single-electron approximation is excellent.

The effective potential $V(r)$ for alkali atoms is radically different from a COULOMB potential, especially for *large* nuclear charge Z: At very small distances r the effective charge $Z_p = r\,V(r)$ is close to Z, whereas at large distances the screening is almost complete and the effective charge is close to unity. The dependence of the level energies on the orbital quantum number is very strong (much larger than the fine structure splittings). The radial dipole matrix elements, and especially the oscillator strengths $f_{n'n}$, are numerically quite different from the hydrogenic ones. Some approximate oscillator strengths, as calculated from HARTREE wave functions[1], for the principal series in Li ($2S-nP$) and Na ($3S-nP$) are compared with the hydrogenic ones (Table 14) below:

n	2	3	4	5	6
Li$-2S$	0.75	0.006	0.005	0.003	0.00_2
H$-2S$	0	0.43	0.10	0.042	0.022
Na$-3S$		0.98	0.014	0.002	0.001
H$-3S$		0	0.48	0.12	0.05

One striking feature of the alkali spectra is the fact that the oscillator strength for a transition between an S- and a P-state with the *same* principal quantum number n is not only non-zero, but actually close to unity. The oscillator strengths for $nS-n'P$ with $n \neq n'$ are very much smaller than for $n=n'$ and also much smaller than the equivalent strengths in hydrogen. The most prominent line in the absorption spectrum of an alkali, with a nS valence electron for its ground state, is the doublet corresponding to the transitions to the $nP_{\frac{3}{2}}$ and $nP_{\frac{1}{2}}$ states. According to the discussion of Sect. 64, the matrix elements for the transitions to $P_{\frac{3}{2}}$ and $P_{\frac{1}{2}}$ should be identical. This leads to the simple rule that the intensities of the two components of the doublet should have the same ratios as the statistical weights $(2j+1)$ of the final states, i.e., a ratio of $1:2$ for $P_{\frac{1}{2}}:P_{\frac{3}{2}}$. This rule is satisfied very well by the experimental intensity ratios for the first member of the principal series for alkalis ($nS-nP$).

This rule is violated for the doublets $nS-n'P$ with $n'>n$ (at least for alkalis with large Z) for the following reason[2]. Because of the relativistic spin-orbit interaction, a nonrelativistic $n'P$ wave function is not an exact eigenfunction of the total HAMILTONian, but the correct eigenfunction is a linear superposition of various wave functions. Although the $n'P$ function is by far the leading term in this superposition, a small admixture of nP is also contained. The expansion coefficient for nP is of order $(Z\alpha)^2$ and its value is *different* for the $P_{\frac{1}{2}}$ and $P_{\frac{3}{2}}$ states. Although this coefficient is small, the transition matrix element for $nS-nP$ is much larger than for $nS-n'P$. For alkalis with large Z, most of the transition probability then comes from this small admixture and the probability,

[1] B. TRUMPY: Z. Physik **61**, 54 (1930), **66**, 720 (1930).
[2] E. FERMI: Z. Physik **59**, 680 (1929).

like the admixture coefficient, is *different* for $P_{\frac{1}{2}}$ and $P_{\frac{3}{2}}$. For Cs, for instance, ($Z=55$, $n=6$ for the ground state) the intensity ratio for $6S-7P_{\frac{3}{2}}$ to $6S-7P_{\frac{1}{2}}$ is about 3.5:1 (but 2:1 for the $6S-6P$ doublet).

β) X-ray spectra. In a heavy atom (large Z) in its ground state a number of the innermost shells are completely filled and only some outer shells are partially unfilled. Thus, for $Z>30$ all possible electronic states with $n=1$, 2 and 3 (and $4s$) are occupied and for $Z>70$ all states with n up to 4 (also $5s$, $5p$ and $6s$) are occupied, etc. Consider now a highly excited state of such an atom in which one of the electrons in an inner shell has been removed (either completely by ionization or by excitation to one of the outermost partially empty shells), say a $1s$-electron (K-shell). Spontaneous radiative transitions can then take place in which one electron from one of the filled shells outside the K-shells makes a transition to the vacant $1s$-state. In the initial state we have a single "hole" in the K-shell, in the final state a single hole in the L- or M-shell ($n=2$ or 3), etc. For such a transition the effect of the very outermost shells, which are only partially filled, can be neglected and the closed shells can be replaced (to a good approximation) by a central screening potential. As regards angular momentum quantum numbers, selection rules, etc., a single hole in a closed shell behaves similarly to a single electron in the shell (because of the exclusion principle). To quite a good approximation such transitions can be treated theoretically as transitions of a single electron in some effective central potential $V(r)$.

The effective potentials $V(r)$ to be used for the initial and final states are not quite the same but, since the nuclear charge Z is much larger than unity, this difference is not important. Also, for large Z, the deviation of $V(r)$ from the nuclear Coulomb potential Z/r is not very marked at the small distances r at which the wave function of an inner electron is concentrated. We have discussed the energies of X-ray levels in Sect. 17γ and seen that the energy splitting of levels with different l and same j (due to the non-Coulomb screening potential) becomes less marked as Z increases and the wave functions approach hydrogenic ones. On the other hand relativistic effects (e.g. the energy splitting of levels with the same l and different j) become more important as Z increases.

Exact matrix elements have been calculated recently[1] for a single electron in a completely *unscreened* Coulomb potential. These calculations use relativistic Dirac wave functions and do *not* neglect retardation in evaluating matrix elements (operator $mc\boldsymbol{\alpha} e^{i\boldsymbol{k}\cdot\boldsymbol{r}}$ not replaced by $\boldsymbol{p}$, see Sects. 64 and 66). For $Z=82$ (Pb, screening neglected) and for transitions between $1s$ and $2p_{\frac{3}{2}}$ or $2p_{\frac{1}{2}}$ (called the $K\alpha_1$ or $K\alpha_2$ lines, respectively) the results are as follows. The completely nonrelativistic and non-retarded oscillator strengths f (valid only for low Z) of Table 14 for these two transitions are $\frac{2}{3}$ and $\frac{1}{3}$ of 0.416, respectively, i.e. 0.277 and 0.139. The corresponding relativistic values for $Z=82$ are 0.195 and 0.112 (ratio of 1.73 instead of 2). The frequency ω of the $K\alpha_1$ X-ray line is larger than that of the $K\alpha_2$ by a factor of 1.035 for this value of Z and the calculated *intensity* ratio for the two lines (intensity proportional to $\omega^3 f$) is 1.93.

For electrons in the K- and L-shells for heavy atoms, the effects of screening are not very important and the above mentioned calculation for the intensities of the $K\alpha$-doublet should be quite a good approximation. For transitions to electron states in higher shells (M, N, etc.) screening should not be neglected[2]

[1] W. B. Payne: Ph. D. Thesis. Louisiana State Univ. 1955. — W. Payne and J. Levinger: Phys. Rev. **101**, 1020 (1956).

[2] Screening reduces the overlap between the K-shell and the higher shells. The oscillator strengths in the discrete spectrum are thus reduced and those in the continuum enhanced by screening.

even for the heaviest atoms. Intensity ratios are then rather complicated functions of Z (since both the effect of screening and relativistic and retardation effects depend on Z) and are only in qualitative agreement with the nonrelativistic hydrogenic results of Sect. 63. Rather few accurate calculations[1] and experiments are available for the various intensity ratios.

In practice another process, called the AUGER effect, which has no analogue in single-electron spectra, competes with the emission of X-rays: Consider again a spontaneous transition of an electron from, say, the L, M or N shell to a state in a lower shell. In heavy atoms the energy release of such an electronic transition is larger than the ionization potential of electrons in the *outermost* shells. This energy release can then be taken up by the ejection from the atom of one of the outer electrons unaccompanied by any radiation (instead of a photon taking up the energy release). The relative probabilities[2] of radiative and AUGER effect transitions depend strongly on Z and on the particular states involved. For very large Z and for electronic transitions between the innermost shells, the AUGER effect is less likely than the emission of X-rays.

b) The photoeffect.

69. General survey[3]. In Sect. 59 we gave general formulae for radiative transitions of an atom from any state of higher to one of lower energy, accompanied by the spontaneous emission of a photon. In the last few sections we have largely restricted ourselves to transitions between atomic states in the *discrete* spectrum (or "bound-bound" transitions). We shall consider in the next few sections the case where one of the two atomic states is in the discrete, but the other in the *continuous*, spectrum ("bound-free" transitions). Transitions from a free to a bound state with the emission of a photon (called recombination or radiative capture) are discussed in Sect. 75. We shall mainly be concerned with the inverse process, the photoeffect, i.e., the absorption of radiation by an atom in a bound state accompanied by the ejection of one of the atom's electrons into a "free" state (i.e., a state of positive energy in the continuum).

Consider electromagnetic radiation of definite frequency ν, propagation vector $\boldsymbol{k}_\nu$ and polarization direction $\boldsymbol{j}$, incident on an atom in some bound state b. Let I_b be one of the ionization potentials of this atomic state, i.e., the energy required to remove one electron to the free state with zero kinetic energy with the remaining electrons forming *some* bound state of the remaining positive ion[4]. If $h\nu > I_b$, an absorption process can take place to this state of the positive ion plus a free electron of kinetic energy W. W is related to the energy $h\nu$ of the absorbed photon by

$$W = h\nu - I_b, \tag{69.1}$$

and, since the energy W is in the continuous spectrum, absorption is possible for a continuous range of frequencies ν.

The continuous spectrum for the ejected electron is highly degenerate (even for a *non*-COULOMB potential), i.e., there are infinitely many electronic states each with energy W. We can take as a set of linearly independent states of energy

[1] H. MASSEY and E. BURHOP: Proc. Roy. Soc. Lond., Ser. A **153**, 661 (1936).

[2] For calculations see E. RAMBERG and F. RICHTMYER, Phys. Rev. **51**, 913 (1937).

[3] For more detailed accounts of the photoeffect and for further references, see ref. [7], Chap. 6 and ref. [6], Chap. IV and V; also H. HALL, Rev. Mod. Phys. **8**, 358 (1936); G. R. WHITE, U. S. Nat. Bur. Stand. Circular 1003 (May 1952, Washington 25, D.C.) and K. H. SPRING, Photons and Electrons (London: Methuen 1954).

[4] We shall often consider the special case of a single-electron atom, where the remaining positive ion is simply a bare nucleus and there is only one ionization potential I_b.

W those with wave functions separable in spherical polar coordinates, characterized by quantum[1] numbers l and m. Let u_W denote the wave function for a particular one of these states (definite l and m, as well as energy W), normalized per unit energy interval [see Eqs. (4.11) and (4.19)]. Let $D_{Wb}^{\boldsymbol{k}_\nu j}$ be the matrix element (59.3) with $u_{n'}$ replaced by u_W (and u_n by the wave function u_b for the bound state). We form the following quantity, which has the dimensions of cm² and is called a cross-section,

$$\sigma_W = \frac{2\pi e^2 \hbar^2}{m^2 c \nu} |D_{Wb}^{\boldsymbol{k}_\nu j}|^2. \tag{69.2}$$

From the transition probability (59.2) and the EINSTEIN relations between the probabilities of inverse processes (see [5] to [7]), one can derive the following physical significance for the absorption cross-section σ_W: Let N_0 be the number of photons in the incident beam of radiation (considered monochromatic) which cross 1 cm² per sec (energy flux of $N_0 h\nu$ per cm² per sec) and $\mathcal{N}$ the number of atoms per cm³ in state b. Let w_W be the probability per sec for one such atom being excited to state W and τ_W the probability for one photon being absorbed in a path length of 1 cm (in a $b \to W$ transition). One then finds that

$$w_W = N_0 \sigma_W, \qquad \tau_W = \mathcal{N} \sigma_W. \tag{69.3}$$

The expressions (69.2) and (69.3) refer to absorption processes which lead to a continuum state of the ejected electron with *specific* values of l and m. To get the total absorption coefficient τ (for fixed ν and initial atomic state b) we have to sum τ_W (and similarly for w_W and σ_W) over all possible values of l and m. In the dipole approximation, which we discuss below, the selection rules of Sect. 60 apply and (since the initial state b has fixed values of l and m) only a few terms in this sum are non-zero.

There is an alternative scheme for classifying the final states and evaluating the absorption probabilities, which involves the continuum wave functions discussed in Sects. 6γ, 7β and 9β. One can show[2] that the wave functions representing plane waves plus *incoming* spherical waves should be used for the electron's continuum wave function, which appears as the *final* state in the transition[3]. The angular distribution of the ejected electron can be obtained as follows in this method: Let $\hbar\boldsymbol{k}$ be a possible momentum of the electron with $\hbar^2 k^2/2m = W$ and with the direction of $\boldsymbol{k}$ inside a cone of infinitesimal solid angle $d\Omega$ (axis of the cone denoted by Ω). Let $D_{\Omega b}^{\boldsymbol{k}_\nu j}$ denote the matrix element (59.3) with $u_{n'}$ (in atomic units) replaced by

$$u_\Omega(\boldsymbol{r}) = \sqrt{\frac{k}{(2\pi)^3}}\, [e^{i\boldsymbol{k}\cdot\boldsymbol{r}} + v(\boldsymbol{r})], \tag{69.4}$$

where $v(\boldsymbol{r})$ is the "scattered part" of this eigenstate[4] of the atomic HAMILTONian. Instead of (69.2), we then have a partial cross-section, for absorption processes

[1] We are considering the nonrelativistic theory at present and are neglecting spin.

[2] See ref. [7], p. 457 and also G. BREIT and H. BETHE, Phys. Rev. **93**, 888 (1954) and H. A. BETHE, Ann. d. Phys. **4**, 443 (1930).

[3] A wave packet can be formed by a superposition of electronic wave functions of this type, which approximates a plane wave without *any* spherical waves for large *positive* times. This wave packet would contain incoming spherical waves at large *negative* times, but, since it occurs as a *final* state in a transition, the wave packet is only built up after a certain time (at which the photon wave packet is absorbed).

[4] The normalization factor under square roots in (69.4) is the "density of states per unit energy" ϱ_E; see, for instance, ref. [6], p. 205.

in which $\boldsymbol{k}$ lies within the solid angle $d\Omega$, given by

$$\sigma_\Omega\, d\Omega = \frac{2\pi e^2 \hbar^2}{m^2 c \nu} \,|D^{k_\nu j}_{\Omega b}|^2 d\Omega. \tag{69.5}$$

The total cross-section σ is the integral of the differential cross-section σ_Ω over $d\Omega$ and the total absorption coefficient is $\tau = \mathcal{N}\sigma$.

Exact expressions for the photoeffect cross-sections are not available and a number of different approximations are usually used under different circumstances. A list of some common approximations, and their range of applicability, follows.

α) *Single-electron approximation and screening.* The calculations are simplified enormously if hydrogenic wave functions can be used both for the initial and final states of the photo-electron. Besides being exact for one-electron ions, such wave functions yield quite good approximations also for the photo-electric absorption of high-frequency radiation (X-rays) by atoms with fairly large Z. It will be shown in Sects. 70 and 71 that the *inner* electrons (mainly the K- and L-shells) contribute most to the absorption of X-rays. As for transitions in the discrete spectrum (Sect. 68β), the photo-ejection of an inner electron from an atom with large Z can be described fairly well by using single-electron HARTREE wave functions both for the initial (bound) and final states of this electron. Further, if Z is fairly large, the HARTREE potential acting on one electron depends very little on the state of the electron and the same potential $V(\boldsymbol{r})$ can be used for the electron's initial and final states.

The wave function u_b for a bound state with small principal quantum number n is concentrated in a small range of radial distances r around some value r_{0n}. The integrand in the matrix element (59.3) is then most important also for r near r_{0n}. As discussed in Sect. 17β, the HARTREE potential can be approximated, in this region, by (17.5),

$$V_n(r) = -\frac{(Z - s_n)}{r} + V_{0n}. \tag{69.6}$$

For atoms with large Z, the effect of the "inner screening" constant s_n is rather small and we shall choose $s_1 = 0.3$ for $n=1$ (K-shell) and $s_2 = 4.1_5$ for $n=2$ (L-shell). The "outer screening" constant V_{0n} is chosen most conveniently such that the ionization potential (17.6),

$$I_n = \left[\left(\frac{Z - s_n}{n}\right)^2 - 2V_{0n}\right] \mathrm{Ry}, \tag{69.7}$$

agrees with the experimental ionization potential. For Cu ($Z=29$) and $n=1$, for instance, the experimental I_1 is 662 Ry and $2V_0 = 161$ Ry.

For the initial bound state wave function u_b for an electron in the potential (69.6), we shall then use a hydrogenic one with principal quantum number n and nuclear charge $Z - s_n$. For the wave function u_W or u_Ω of the final state in the continuum we shall use the following approximation. The *total* energy W of the electron in the final state is given by (69.1), where I_n is the experimental ionization potential which is also given by (69.7). At very large radial distances r the kinetic energy of the electron equals W, at intermediate distances r the potential energy is given by the rather complicated HARTREE potential and only in the neighbourhood of the small distance r_{0n} is the potential approximated by (69.6). Since the integrand of the matrix element D, (59.3), is needed mainly for r of order r_{0n} we shall approximate the final state by a wave function for total energy W in the potential (69.6). This approximate wave function is then identical with a hydrogenic one for nuclear charge $Z-s_n$ and for an *apparent* total energy $\hbar^2 k'^2/2m$ of

$$\frac{\hbar^2 k'^2}{2m} = W - 2V_{0n} = h\nu - I_n - 2V_{0n} = h\nu - \left(\frac{Z-s_n}{n}\right)^2 \text{Ry}. \tag{69.8}$$

This approximation for the final continuum state is a more drastic one than for the bound state, since the correct potential in the asymptotic region (large r) does *not* approach V_{0n}, as given by (69.6), but approaches zero. In the frequency region $I_n < h\nu < (Z-s_n)^2 n^{-2}$ Ry, in particular, W is positive and the photoeffect is possible but the *apparent* total energy (69.8) is *negative*. We shall see in Sect. 71 that the final results are not very sensitive to the value and sign of k'^2 in this region and we shall simply substitute (69.8) for k'^2 (even when negative) into the final expressions for the matrix elements.

The hydrogenic approximation is rather poor for electrons of principal quantum number n much larger than 2 or 3, especially if the nuclear charge Z is not very large. Fortunately these cases are not of very great importance[1], except for calculations on the opacity in stellar atmospheres. In particular, photoeffect from the outer electrons of *negative* atomic ions takes place in stellar atmospheres, for which the single-electron approximation breaks down completely. More accurate calculations for such cases will be discussed in Sect. 74α.

β) Nonrelativistic treatment. As discussed before, the bound state of the electron can be treated nonrelativistically and its spin neglected, if $p_0/mc \sim Z\alpha \ll 1$, where p_0 is the BOHR momentum for nuclear charge Z and electronic mass m. If, in addition, the kinetic energy W of the ejected electron is small compared with the electron's restmass energy mc^2, the ejected electron can also be treated nonrelativistically (Sects. 70 to 72 and 74). Calculations for $Z\alpha$ of the order of unity are very difficult (see Sect. 73) but, if $Z\alpha \ll 1$, the case of arbitrarily large W can be treated (Sect. 73α).

γ) Neglect of retardation. We restrict ourselves, for the moment, to cases with $Z\alpha \ll 1$. We then have the following inequalities between three different orders of magnitude of energy, the ground state ionization potential I_1, c times the BOHR momentum p_0 and the electron's restmass energy mc^2.

$$I_1 \sim (Z\alpha)^2 mc^2 \ll p_0 c \sim (Z\alpha)\, mc^2 \ll mc^2. \tag{69.9}$$

If the energy of the incident photon $h\nu$ is small compared to mc^2, then also $W \ll mc^2$ [see Eq. (69.1)] and the nonrelativistic approximation applies. If the more stringent condition $h\nu \ll p_0 c \sim Z\alpha mc^2$ is also satisfied, then the wave length of the photon is also large compared with the "radius" of the bound state of the electron and the photon's momentum small compared with the BOHR momentum p_0. In this case we can again neglect retardation, i.e., replace the factor $e^{i\boldsymbol{k}_\nu\cdot\boldsymbol{r}}$ in the matrix element (59.3) by unity, just as for the electric dipole approximation to the discrete spectrum.

In this approximation we can again write the matrix element (59.3) in the form (59.5), which involves $\boldsymbol{r}$ instead of the momentum operator. Calculations with retardation neglected are discussed in Sects. 70 and 71. Note that in this dipole approximation the matrix element does not depend explicitly on the propagation direction of the photon and the angular distribution of the ejected

[1] For the photoeffect from the valence electron in an alkali atom, the single-electron approximation is again applicable, but the appropriate single-electron wave functions differ radically from hydrogenic ones (Sect. 68α).

electrons is rather simple. The effect of retardation on the angular distribution is discussed in Sect. 72.

*δ) The "*BORN *approximation".* If $h\nu \gg I_1$, then the kinetic energy W of the ejected electron is also large compared with the ionization potential I_1. In this case the wave function of the ejected electron can be treated by BORN approximation (see Sects. 7 and 9). In fact, for the photoeffect from a bound state with zero orbital angular momentum the effect of the nuclear potential on the ejected electron can be neglected completely if $h\nu \gg I_1$. If $Z\alpha \ll 1$, it follows from (69.9) that there is a range of $h\nu$ for which *both* the BORN approximation can be used *and* retardation neglected. The BORN approximation is discussed in Sects. 70 and 72β.

We shall neglect throughout higher order radiative corrections, i.e., treat the interaction with the radiation field in lowest order perturbation theory (with α as the coupling constant). Besides neglecting radiative corrections, we also do not treat processes involving two (or more) real photons, although one such process, the COMPTON scattering of photons, is of great importance (see Sect. 73β).

70. The BORN approximation. We consider first the photoeffect from a single-electron atom with $Z\alpha \ll 1$ and for a photon frequency ν such that $mc^2 \gg h\nu \gg I_1 = Z^2$ Ry. We shall use the matrix element $D_{\Omega b}^{\boldsymbol{k}_\nu \boldsymbol{j}}$ which involves the wave function u_Ω (69.4), which represents a plane wave plus scattered waves. We discuss first the simplest approximation to u_Ω, a plane wave.

α) Plane wave approximation. Consider the wave function u_Ω for an electron with asymptotic momentum $\hbar k$, where

$$W = \frac{\hbar^2 k^2}{2m} = h\nu - I_b \tag{70.1}$$

and I_b is the ionization potential of the initial bound state b. If $h\nu \gg Z^2$Ry, then $\hbar k$ is large compared with the BOHR momentum p_0. In this case the second part $v(\boldsymbol{r})$ of the wave function (69.4) is small compared with the first part $e^{i\boldsymbol{k}\cdot\boldsymbol{r}}$, which simply represents a plane wave state of the electron in the absence of any COULOMB potential. We first evaluate the part of the matrix element D which involves only the plane wave part of (69.4). We shall see later that this gives a good approximation to D *only* if the bound state b is an S-state.

Let u_b be any normalized bound state wave function. The matrix element $D_{\Omega b}^{\boldsymbol{k}_\nu \boldsymbol{j}}$, with $v(r)$ in (69.4) neglected completely, is then given by

$$D_{\Omega b}^{\boldsymbol{k}_\nu \boldsymbol{j}} = i\sqrt{\frac{k}{(2\pi)^3}} \int d^3r\, e^{-i\boldsymbol{k}\cdot\boldsymbol{r}} e^{i\boldsymbol{k}_\nu\cdot\boldsymbol{r}} p_j u_b(\boldsymbol{r}), \tag{70.2}$$

where $\hbar p_j$ is the component of the electron's momentum operator in the polarization direction $\boldsymbol{j}$ of the photon. $\boldsymbol{j}$ is perpendicular to the photon's propagation vector $\boldsymbol{k}_\nu$, so that p_j commutes with $e^{i\boldsymbol{k}_\nu\cdot\boldsymbol{r}}$. The function $e^{i\boldsymbol{k}\cdot\boldsymbol{r}}$ is an eigenstate of p_j with eigenvalue $k\cos\vartheta$, where ϑ is the angle between the vectors $\boldsymbol{k}$ and $\boldsymbol{j}$. We can then rewrite (70.2) in the form

$$D_{\Omega b}^{\boldsymbol{k}_\nu \boldsymbol{j}} = i\, k^{\frac{3}{2}} \cos\vartheta\, \psi_b(\boldsymbol{k} - \boldsymbol{k}_\nu), \tag{70.3}$$

where $\psi_b(\boldsymbol{p})$ is the FOURIER-transform of $u_b(\boldsymbol{r})$, i.e., the normalized momentum-space wave function for the state b (discussed in Sect. 8). For a state b, characterized by the quantum numbers n, m, l, in a central potential, $\psi_b(\boldsymbol{p})$ is of form $F_{nl}(p)\, Y_{lm}(\vartheta, \varphi)$ where Y_{lm} is a *normalized* spherical harmonic.

We consider now the special case of a COULOMB potential with nuclear charge Z and an initial bound state b with principal quantum number n and with $l=0$

(S-state). We are only considering the case of k large compared with the BOHR momentum and can use the asymptotic approximation (8.11) for F_{n0}. The wave function ψ_b is then, in *atomic* units,

$$\psi_b(\boldsymbol{k}-\boldsymbol{k}_\nu) = \frac{2\sqrt{2}}{\pi n^{\frac{3}{2}}} \frac{Z^{\frac{5}{2}}}{|\boldsymbol{k}-\boldsymbol{k}_\nu|^4}. \tag{70.4}$$

On substituting (70.3) with (70.4) into (69.5), we obtain the differential cross-section σ_Ω. The momentum $|\boldsymbol{k}|$ in (70.3) and (70.4) is given by (70.1), but $I_b = I_1/n^2 \ll h\nu$ and we can replace $(\hbar k)^2$ by $2mh\nu$ in the final expression for σ_Ω.

If we had neglected retardation, the k_ν would have been replaced by zero in (70.2) and hence also in (70.3) and (70.4). As discussed in Sect. 69γ this neglect of retardation is always justified if $h\nu \ll Z\alpha mc^2$, in which case $\hbar k_\nu$ is much smaller than the BOHR momentum. But k_ν enters our expressions only through (70.4) and the neglect of k_ν in (70.4) causes a small error as long as $k_\nu = 2\pi\nu/c \ll k$. From (70.1) this is the case as long as $h\nu \ll mc^2$, *even* if $\hbar k_\nu$ is *not* smaller than the BOHR momentum. If we replace k_ν by zero[1] in (70.4), our approximation for the differential cross-section σ_Ω (from a bound S-state) becomes (in C.G.S. units):

$$\sigma_\Omega = \frac{2^4}{\pi n^3} \frac{e^2}{mc} \frac{\nu_1^{\frac{5}{2}}}{\nu^{\frac{7}{2}}} \cos^2\vartheta, \tag{70.5}$$

where $\nu_1 = Z^2$ Rydberg is $Z^2(4\pi)^{-1}$ times one atomic unit of frequency. The total cross-section σ, obtained by integrating σ_Ω over all solid angles, is then

$$\sigma = \frac{2^6}{3n^3} \frac{e^2}{mc} \frac{\nu_1^{\frac{5}{2}}}{\nu^{\frac{7}{2}}}. \tag{70.6}$$

In our present approximation the cross-section for the photoeffect decreases with the minus third power of the principal quantum number n (for an S-state) and with the minus $\frac{7}{2}$ power of the frequency ν of the photon. If we use the hydrogenic approximation for complex atoms and if $\nu \gg \nu_1$, then the contribution to the photoeffect from the two 1s-electrons is appreciably larger than from all other ns-electrons combined. In deriving (70.5) and (70.6) we have used the asymptotic expression for the momentum space wave function ψ_b, which is valid only if $W \sim h\nu \gg I_b$ ($k \gg p_0$). It is interesting to note the energy dependence of the cross-section near the long-wave-length limit ($h\nu$ near I_b), obtained by substituting the exact expression for ψ_b into (70.3), even though the BORN approximation expression (70.3) is not valid in this energy range: For k less than the BOHR momentum, the correct ψ_b does not increase indefinitely with decreasing k but [unlike (70.4)] approaches a constant limit as $k \to 0$. Thus, for $W = h\nu - I_b \ll I_b$, the main energy dependence of the BORN approximation matrix element (70.3) is the factor $k^{\frac{3}{2}}$ and the cross-section is approximately proportional to $W^{\frac{3}{2}}$, where W is the energy of the ejected electron. Thus the BORN approximation cross-section is zero at threshold ($h\nu = I_b$, $W = 0$), rises to a maximum at W of the order of I_b and then decreases as $W^{-\frac{7}{2}}$ for large W, (70.6). For a 1s-electron in hydrogen, for instance, we find, using the explicit wave function (8.10),

$$\sigma \propto \frac{W^{\frac{3}{2}}}{(W+I_1)^5} \propto \frac{(\nu-\nu_1)^{\frac{3}{2}}}{\nu^5}. \tag{70.6a}$$

In (70.6a), $I_1 = h\nu_1$ is the ionization potential for the 1s-state. We shall see that the correct cross-section for hydrogen-like atoms (Sect. 71α) has a *finite* value

[1] The effect of the term dropped here is discussed in Sect. 72β.

(and a maximum) at threshold ($W=0$), but for negative atomic ions (Sect. 74α) the energy dependence is similar to that given by the BORN approximation (70.6a).

For an initial bound state b with non-zero orbital quantum number l, one again obtains (70.3) for the matrix element D, *if* one again neglects $v(\boldsymbol{r})$ in (69.4) completely. In the region $h\nu \sim W \gg Z^2$ Ry, we can use the asymptotic expression (8.12) with (8.4) for ψ_b. For a bound p-state ($n, l=1, m$), for instance, with retardation (i.e., k_ν) neglected, we have

$$D_{\Omega b}^{\boldsymbol{k}_\nu \boldsymbol{j}} = i\,\frac{8}{3}\sqrt{\frac{2}{\pi}}\sqrt{\frac{n^2-1}{n^5}}\left(\frac{Z}{k}\right)^{\frac{7}{2}}\cos\vartheta\, Y_{1m}(\vartheta,\varphi), \tag{70.7}$$

where (k, ϑ, φ) are spherical polar coordinates (with $\boldsymbol{j}$ as polar axis) for $\boldsymbol{k}$ and Y_{1m} is the normalized spherical harmonic. On substituting (70.7) into (69.5) one again obtains the lowest order BORN approximation for the differential cross-section σ_Ω. If one *averages* σ_Ω over the three possible values of the magnetic quantum number m for the initial bound state and uses the appendix Eq. (A.42), one finds (for $l=1$) instead of (70.5),

$$\sigma_\Omega = \frac{2^6(n^2-1)}{9\pi n^5}\,\frac{e^2}{m c}\,\frac{\nu_1^{\frac{7}{2}}}{\nu^{\frac{9}{2}}}\cos^2\vartheta. \tag{70.8}$$

In the present approximation one obtains qualitatively similar results for bound states with higher values of l: σ_Ω, averaged over all possible values of m from $-l$ to l, is proportional to $\cos^2\vartheta$ and to $\nu^{-l-\frac{7}{2}}$ and approximately proportional to n^{-3} (for $n \gg l$). We shall see below that the neglect of $v(\boldsymbol{r})$ in (69.5) is *not* justified for $l \gtrless 1$ even if $h\nu \sim W \gg Z^2$ Ry so that (70.8) and similar expressions for $l > 1$ are *wrong*, (although the dependence on n and ν and the order of magnitude is correct).

β) First order BORN *approximation.* We now investigate the effect of the second term $v(\boldsymbol{r})$ in (69.4), which we have omitted in Sect. 70α. We shall neglect retardation, i.e., omit the factor $e^{i\boldsymbol{k}_\nu\cdot\boldsymbol{r}}$ in the matrix element D, which can then be written as an integral over momentum space

$$D_{\Omega b}^{\boldsymbol{k}_\nu \boldsymbol{j}} = i\int d^3r\, u_\Omega^*(\boldsymbol{r})\, p_j\, u_b(\boldsymbol{r}) = i\sqrt{k}\int d^3p\, \psi_\Omega^*(\boldsymbol{p})\, p_j\, \psi_b(\boldsymbol{p}). \tag{70.9}$$

In (70.9), $\sqrt{k}\,\psi_\Omega(\boldsymbol{p})$ is the FOURIER transform of the exact continuum wave function $u_\Omega(\boldsymbol{r})$, Eq. (69.4), and ψ_b that of u_b. In Sect. 9β we have discussed the first order BORN approximation expression for ψ_Ω. If $V'(p)$ is $(2\pi)^{-\frac{3}{2}}$ times the FOURIER transform of the central potential (not necessarily COULOMB) in which the electron moves, then the BORN approximation [see Eqs. (9.7) and (9.11)] is

$$\psi_\Omega(\boldsymbol{p}) = \delta^{(3)}(\boldsymbol{p}-\boldsymbol{k}) + \frac{2}{k^2-p^2}\,V'(|\boldsymbol{p}-\boldsymbol{k}|). \tag{70.10}$$

On substituting the delta-function part (zero order BORN approximation) of (70.10) into (70.9), we again obtain (70.3), after neglecting k_ν. We now investigate the additional contribution D' to (70.9), obtained by substituting the second part of (70.10), in the region where $W=k^2/2m$ is much larger than the ionization potential.

In this energy region, k is large compared with the "average momentum" p_0. One can then show that the main contribution to the integral

$$D' = 2i\sqrt{k}\int d^3p\,\frac{V'(|\boldsymbol{p}-\boldsymbol{k}|)}{k^2-p^2}\,p_j\,\psi_b(\boldsymbol{p}) \tag{70.11}$$

comes from values of p of the order of $p_0 \ll k$, where the bound wave function ψ_b is large. For a bound S-state one can show that (70.11) is small compared with (70.3), if $p_0 \ll k$. For a bound p-state ($l=1$), the following approximation to (70.11) is sufficient: For $p \sim p_0 \ll k$, the functions $V'(|\boldsymbol{p}-\boldsymbol{k}|)$ and k^2-p^2 vary very slowly with p and we replace p by zero in these expressions. In this approximation we have

$$D' = 2i\,k^{-\frac{3}{2}}\,V'(k)\int d^3p\,p_j\,\psi_b(\boldsymbol{p}). \tag{70.12}$$

After a partial integration we have

$$p_x\,\psi_b(\boldsymbol{p}) = -\frac{i}{(2\pi)^{\frac{3}{2}}}\int d^3r\,e^{-i\boldsymbol{r}\cdot\boldsymbol{p}}\,\frac{\partial u_b(\boldsymbol{r})}{\partial x},$$

where u_b is the FOURIER transform of ψ_b and the x-axis is parallel to $\boldsymbol{j}$. Using the relation

$$\int d^3p\,e^{-i\boldsymbol{r}\cdot\boldsymbol{p}} = (2\pi)^3\,\delta^{(3)}(\boldsymbol{r})$$

we find

$$D' = 2(2\pi)^{\frac{3}{2}}\,k^{-\frac{3}{2}}\,V'(k)\left[\frac{\partial u_b(\boldsymbol{r})}{\partial x}\right]_{r=0}. \tag{70.13}$$

The approximate expression (70.13) is non-zero only if the bound state b has quantum numbers $l=1$ and $m=0$ ($u \propto x$) where the quantization (x) direction is along $\boldsymbol{j}$. For the special case of a COULOMB potential, $V'(k)$ is given by (8.6a) and the derivative at the origin of $u_b(\boldsymbol{r})$ can be obtained from (1.3), (1.8) and the expansion (3.17). For a bound state ($n, l=1, m$) of a hydrogen-like atom with charge Z we find[1]

$$D' = -i\,\frac{2}{\pi}\sqrt{\frac{2}{3}}\sqrt{\frac{n^2-1}{n^5}}\left(\frac{Z}{k}\right)^{\frac{7}{2}}\delta_{m0}, \tag{70.14}$$

where δ_{m0} is the KRONECKER delta function. The first order BORN expression (70.14) has to be added to the zero order expression (70.7). Note that the two expressions are of the *same* order of magnitude (for $l=1$). We substitute the sum of the two expressions into (69.5) and again *average* σ_Ω over the three values -1, 0 and 1 of m. Using the explicit expressions (1.8) for Y_{lm}, we find

$$\sigma_\Omega = \frac{2^4}{9\pi}\,\frac{n^2-1}{n^5}\,\frac{e^2}{mc}\,\frac{\nu_1^{\frac{7}{2}}}{\nu^{\frac{9}{2}}}. \tag{70.15}$$

The angular distribution is thus *isotropic* [unlike the incorrect result (70.8)], and the total cross section is $\sigma = 4\pi\sigma_\Omega$. The range of validity of (70.15) is given by $\nu_1 \ll \nu \lesssim \nu_1/Z\alpha$.

For bound states with $l>1$, the approximation (70.12) to (70.11) vanishes. For these higher l-values one can expand $V'(\boldsymbol{p}-\boldsymbol{k})/(k^2-p^2)$ in terms of spherical harmonics and powers of p/k and keep only the lowest order term which gives a non-zero contribution to the integral (70.11). This term will again be of the same order of magnitude as (70.3) for all values of l except zero: This can be seen

---

[1] Since we will have to add this matrix element to (70.7) we must take for $u_b(\boldsymbol{r})$ *exactly* the FOURIER transform of ψ_b, given by (8.12) with (8.4), which was used in deriving (70.7). This form for u_b is i times the wave function defined by (3.17) with (1.8).

most easily by considering the continuum wave functions which are separable in spherical polar coordinates (used in the next sections) with quantum numbers l' and m': For $l>0$, transitions are possible with $l'=l+1$ and $l-1$. For $l'=l-1$, the first order BORN wave function $F_{l'}(p)\,Y_{l'm'}(\vartheta\,\varphi)$ is still sufficiently large "far off the energy shell" (i.e., for $p\sim p_0\ll k$) so that the first order contribution is of the same order as the zero order one. For $l'=l+1$, on the other hand, $F_{l'}(p)$ is so small for $p\ll k$ that the first order contribution is negligible. The transitions to $l'=l-1$ are absent only if $l=0$.

Note how rapidly the total cross-section σ *per electron* decreases with increasing n and l. For s- and p-states, for instance,

$$\sigma_{1s}=n^3\sigma_{ns}=3\,\frac{n^5}{n^2-1}\,\frac{\nu}{\nu_1}\,\sigma_{np}\,. \tag{70.16}$$

This dependence on n and l reflects the behavior of the bound state wave functions in momentum space at large momenta (or in position space at small radial distances r).

71. The absorption coefficient without retardation. We shall neglect retardation and relativistic effects throughout this section. However, we shall *not* replace the continuum wave functions by their BORN approximation, but use the exact hydrogenic nonrelativistic wave functions which give valid results also very near threshold (i.e., near the long wave length limit, $h\nu=I_b$). We consider a bound state b and a wave function u_W, separable in spherical polar coordinates, for the continuum state. With retardation neglected, (69.2) and (69.3) with (59.5) then gives for the absorption coefficient τ_W,

$$\tau_W=\frac{8\pi^3 e^2\mathcal{N}\nu}{c}\left|\int u_W^*\sum_i x_i\,u_b\,d\tau\right|^2, \tag{71.1}$$

where x is the polarization direction of the photon.

α) The K-shell. We shall evaluate the above integral for the hydrogen atom. Let u_b be the eigenfunction of the ground state. The continuum eigenfunction depends not only on the energy but also on two additional quantum numbers such as l and m. In order to obtain the total absorption coefficient, (71.1) must be evaluated for all values of l and m and the results must be summed. However, in our particular case, since the eigenfunction of the ground state is spherically symmetric, only those continuum eigenfunctions contribute which have an angular dependence of the form $\sin\vartheta\cos\varphi$; otherwise the integrals over angles in (71.1) vanish. Accordingly, the orbital quantum number of the contributing continuum state is $l=1$. The integral in (71.2) becomes

$$\left.\begin{aligned}
x_{W1}&=\int_0^\infty r^3\,dr\,R_{W,l=1}(r)\cdot 2e^{-Zr}\cdot Z^{\frac{3}{2}}\int_0^\pi \sin\vartheta\,d\vartheta\int_0^{2\pi}d\varphi\,\times\\
&\times\sqrt{\frac{3}{4\pi}}\sin\vartheta\cos\varphi\cdot\sqrt{\frac{1}{4\pi}}\cdot\sin\vartheta\cos\varphi=\frac{4Z^2\sqrt{1+n'^2}}{\sqrt{3}\sqrt{1-e^{-2\pi n'}}}\,\times\\
&\times\frac{1}{2\pi}\int_0^\infty(2kr)^{-2}r^3\,dr\,e^{-Zr}\oint\left(\xi+\frac{1}{2}\right)^{-in'-2}\left(\xi-\frac{1}{2}\right)^{in'-2}e^{-2ikr\xi}\,d\xi.
\end{aligned}\right\} \tag{71.2}$$

In the above, we have inserted the expressions for the spherical harmonics Y_{00} Y_{11} as given by (1.8) and the continuum eigenfunction from (4.22). The contour integral is defined in Sect. 4, $n'=Z/\sqrt{2W}$ and $k=\sqrt{2W}$. Interchanging the order of integration with respect to r and ξ, and disregarding for the moment the coefficient in front of the first integral sign, we obtain

$$J = \frac{1}{4k^2} \oint d\xi \frac{(\xi + \frac{1}{2})^{-in'-2} (\xi - \frac{1}{2})^{in'-2}}{(Z + 2ik\xi)^2}$$

$$= \frac{-1}{16k^4} \int d\xi \left(\xi + \frac{1}{2}\right)^{-in'-2} \left(\xi - \frac{1}{2}\right)^{in'-2} \left(\xi - \frac{1}{2} i n'\right)^{-2}.$$

The integrals must be taken around the two branch points $\xi = \frac{1}{2}$ and $\xi = -\frac{1}{2}$[1]; however, since the integrand goes to zero as ξ^{-6}, the contour may be extended to infinity. The contour goes around the pole $\xi = \frac{1}{2} i n'$ in the negative sense and the integration therefore yields simply the residue at that pole, namely

$$\left.\begin{aligned} J &= \frac{2\pi i}{16k^4} \cdot \frac{d}{d\xi} \left[\left(\xi + \frac{1}{2}\right)^{-in'-2} \left(\xi - \frac{1}{2}\right)^{in'-2} \right]_{\xi = \frac{1}{2} i n'} \\ &= \frac{64 n' \cdot 2\pi}{16k^4 (1 + n'^2)^3} \left(\frac{i n' - 1}{i n' + 1}\right)^{in'} = \frac{8\pi k Z}{(Z^2 + k^2)^3} \cdot e^{-2n' \operatorname{arc\,cot} n'}. \end{aligned}\right\} \tag{71.3}$$

Substitution into (71.2) yields

$$|x_{W1}|^2 = \frac{2^8}{3} \cdot \frac{Z^6}{(Z^2 + k^2)^5} \frac{e^{-4\frac{Z}{k} \arctan \frac{k}{Z}}}{1 - e^{-2\pi Z/k}} = \frac{2^8}{3Z^4} \left(\frac{n'^2}{1 + n'^2}\right)^5 \cdot \frac{e^{-4n' \operatorname{arc\,cot} n'}}{1 - e^{-2\pi n'}} \text{ at. un.} \tag{71.4}$$

The dimensions are those of an area divided by an energy; in atomic units the dimensions are a^3/e^2.

Next, we substitute (71.4) into (71.1). In doing so we note that the long wave length limit of the photoeffect is given by

$$\nu_1 = \frac{E_1}{h} = Z^2 \text{ Ry} = \frac{Z^2}{4\pi} \text{ at. un. of frequency} \tag{71.5}$$

according to the photoelectric equation (69.1). Furthermore, according to the definition of n', $W = k^2 = Z^2/n'^2$ Rydberg, and thus

$$\nu = (Z^2 + k^2) \text{ Ry} = \nu_1 \cdot \left(1 + \frac{1}{n'^2}\right), \quad n' = \sqrt{\frac{\nu_1}{\nu - \nu_1}}. \tag{71.6}$$

Taking into consideration that an atom has two K electrons, the absorption coefficient becomes

$$\tau = 2 \cdot (2\pi a)^3 \mathcal{N} \frac{\nu}{c} |x_{W1}|^2 = \frac{2^8 \pi e^2}{3mc} \mathcal{N} \cdot \frac{\nu_1^3}{\nu^4} \cdot \frac{e^{-4n' \operatorname{arc\,cot} n'}}{1 - e^{-2\pi n'}}, \tag{71.7}$$

in which a is the radius of the hydrogen atom. If ϱ denotes the density and A the atomic weight of the absorbing substance, the total absorption by the K shell has the value

$$\tau = 4.1 \times 10^8 \cdot \frac{\varrho}{AZ^2} \left(\frac{\nu_1}{\nu}\right)^4 \cdot f(n'), \tag{71.8}$$

in which $f(n')$ is the last fraction in (71.7). For small and intermediate values of k (say, $k < 3Z$), $f(n')$ is closely approximated by

$$f(n') = f(k) = e^{-4} \left(1 + \frac{4}{3n'^2}\right) = e^{-4} \left(1 + \frac{4}{3} \frac{k^2}{Z^2}\right), \tag{71.9}$$

[1] See Fig. 6. For more details compare A. SOMMERFELD and G. SCHUR, Ann. d. Phys. **4**, 409 (1930).

and for very large values of k by

$$f(n') = \frac{1}{2\pi n'} = \frac{k}{2\pi Z}. \tag{71.10}$$

For $k \ll Z$, i.e. so close to the long wave length limit that the energy of the photoelectrons is small compared to the ionization potential of the atom, we obtain, in view of (71.9), (71.5) and (71.6),

$$f(n') = e^{-4}\left(\frac{\nu}{\nu_1}\right)^{\frac{4}{3}},$$

and thus

$$\frac{\tau}{\varrho} = \frac{7.6\times 10^6}{A Z^2}\left(\frac{\nu_1}{\nu}\right)^{\frac{8}{3}}. \tag{71.11}$$

The absorption coefficient at the K absorption limit is seen to decline about as Z^{-3} with increasing atomic number. For a fixed value of Z, τ varies as $\nu^{-\frac{8}{3}}$ in the immediate neighborhood of the absorption edge[1]. At a more considerable distance from the edge, for example, if the energy of the photoelectrons is approximately equal to the ionization potential, then (71.9) is nearly $\frac{4}{3} e^{-4} \frac{\nu}{\nu_1}$ and the absorption coefficient goes as the inverse third power of ν. Finally, if the incident frequency becomes very high, say 100 times as great as the frequency corresponding to the K absorption edge, then in view of (71.10),

$$\frac{\tau}{\varrho} = \frac{6.5\times 10^7}{AZ^2}\left(\frac{\nu_1}{\nu}\right)^{\frac{7}{2}}.$$

This expression is identical with the BORN approximation result, obtained from (70.6). Thus, the decline with growing frequency becomes increasingly steeper, and this agrees with experiment. However, if the frequency ν of the incident light becomes so high that retardation plays a role, the decline becomes less steep again.

The results above are strictly valid only for hydrogen-like atoms, but we shall adapt them to give approximate results for the photoeffect for K-shell electrons in complex atoms. Following the discussion of Sect. 69α, we use hydrogenic wave functions for the bound and continuum state of the photoelectron, both for the same nuclear charge $Z - s$ where we take $s_1 = 0.3$, SLATER's inner screening constant for the K-shell. Following (69.8) we simply use (71.7) with ν still standing for the actual frequency of the photon but with ν_1 and n' modified to

$$\nu_1 = (Z - s_1)^2 \text{ Rydberg}, \qquad n'^2 = \frac{\nu_1}{\nu - \nu_1}. \tag{71.12}$$

We then have for τ_K, the absorption coefficient for both K-shell electrons, instead of (71.8)

$$\tau_K = 4.1\times 10^8 \frac{\varrho}{A} (Z - 0.3)^6 \left(\frac{\text{Ry}}{\nu}\right)^4 f\left(\sqrt{\frac{\nu_1}{\nu - \nu_1}}\right). \tag{71.13}$$

Note, however, that the experimental K-absorption edge or threshold frequency $\nu_K = I_1/h$ (at which the *actual* energy W of the ejected electron is zero) does *not* equal ν_1, as defined by (71.12). In fact, ν_K is *smaller* than ν_1 and the difference

[1] Not as ν^{-4} as has been frequently claimed in the literature, e.g., B. M. STOBBE and F. SAUTER, loc. cit.

is due to the outer screening constant V_{01}, Eq. (69.7). Near the absorption edge ν_K, the function $f(n')$ is well represented by (71.9) and no difficulty is encountered by substituting a negative (or zero) value for n'^{-2} from (71.12) into (71.9).

In Fig. 34a the theoretical absorption coefficient τ_K, Eq. (71.13), is plotted against wavelength of the incident photon for Sn ($Z=50$).

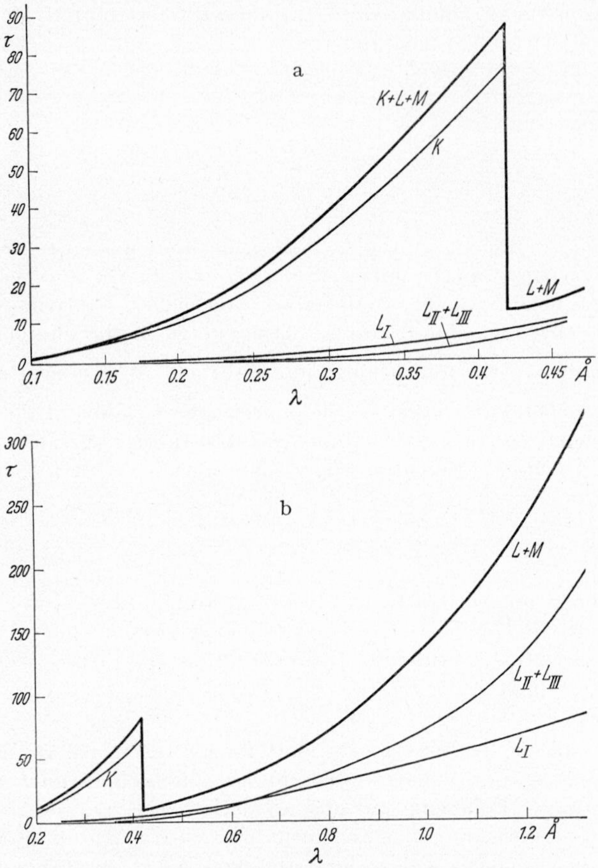

Fig. 34a and b. The theoretical photoelectric absorption coefficient τ (actually absorption cross-section in units of 10^{-22} cm²/atom) for Sn, plotted against photon wave-length λ (in Ångström units). The letters K, L, etc. denote the contribution to τ from the corresponding electron shells

β) Contribution of higher shells. The contribution to the absorption coefficient due to the $2s$- and $2p$-electrons has been calculated by STOBBE[1]. His calculations are similar to those for the K-shell electrons—retardation effects are neglected and hydrogenic wave functions are used. The contribution of the L_I-shell (the two $2s$-electrons) to the absorption coefficient τ is

$$\tau_{L_I}=\frac{2^{11}\pi e^2\mathcal{N}}{3mc}\frac{\nu_2^3}{\nu^4}\left(1+3\frac{\nu_2}{\nu}\right)\frac{e^{-4n_2'\operatorname{arc\,cot}(\frac{1}{2}n_2')}}{1-e^{-2\pi n_2'}}, \tag{71.14}$$

and that of the L_{II}- and L_{III}-shell combined (the six $2p$-electrons) is[2]

$$\tau_{L_{II}}+\tau_{L_{III}}=\frac{2^{11}\pi e^2\mathcal{N}}{3mc}\frac{\nu_2^4}{\nu^5}\left(3+8\frac{\nu_2}{\nu}\right)\frac{e^{-4n_2'\operatorname{arc\,cot}(\frac{1}{2}n_2')}}{1-e^{-2\pi n_2'}}. \tag{71.15}$$

[1] M. STOBBE: Ann. d. Phys. 7, 661 (1930).
[2] The formula in STOBBE's paper is too large by a factor of two.

In these expressions, ν_2 and n_2' are defined by

$$\nu_2 = \frac{1}{4}(Z - s_2)^2\,\mathrm{Ry}, \qquad n_2' = 2\sqrt{\frac{\nu_2}{\nu - \nu_2}}, \tag{71.16}$$

where we use $s_2 = 4.15$ for SLATER's inner screening constant[1]. A similar calculation for the eighteen electrons in the M-shell ($3s$, $3p$ and $3d$) has been carried out by HALL[2].

In Fig. 34 we have plotted the contribution to the absorption coefficient τ for Sn ($Z = 50$) of the K, L_{I} and $L_{\mathrm{II}} + L_{\mathrm{III}}$ shells, as well as the total from the K, L and M shells, using the above formulae[3]. The units for τ are 10^{-22} cm^2/atom [actually the absorption cross section σ, Eq. (69.3)]. The agreement with experiment[4] is quite good, in spite of the simple screening approximations used in the calculations.

At high frequencies ($\nu \gg \nu_1$), the expressions (71.14) and (71.15) reduce to those obtained from the BORN approximation, (70.6) and (70.15). As discussed in Sect. 70, the contribution to the absorption coefficient of the higher shells is small compared with that of the K-shell at high frequencies (in spite of the larger number of electrons in the higher shells). Including the effects of screening we find for the L-shell (for $\nu \gg \nu_1$)

$$8\tau_{L_{\mathrm{I}}} = \frac{8}{3}\frac{\nu}{\nu_2}(\tau_{L_{\mathrm{II}}} + \tau_{L_{\mathrm{III}}}) = \left(\frac{Z - s_2}{Z - s_1}\right)^5 \tau_K. \tag{71.17}$$

Another quantity of interest is the "K-absorption jump" δ_K, i.e., the ratio of the absorption coefficient just above and just below the experimental threshold frequency ν_K for the photoeffect from the K-shell,

$$\delta_K = \left(\frac{\tau_K + \tau_L + \tau_M + \cdots}{\tau_L + \tau_M + \cdots}\right)_{\nu = \nu_K}. \tag{71.18}$$

If we neglect both outer and inner screening (i.e., put ν_K equal to ν_1 and $s_1 = s_2 = 0$) and neglect the contributions from the M- and higher shells, we have

$$\delta_K = 1 + \frac{8}{3}\exp\left(\frac{8}{\sqrt{3}}\arctan\sqrt{3} - 4\right) = 7.15.$$

The effect of screening on δ_K is quite appreciable, except for very large Z. We use $s_1 = 0.3$, $s_2 = 4.1_5$ and evaluate δ_K at a value of the frequency ν equal to the experimentally *observed* ν_K. Still omitting the contribution from the M-shell, one finds $\delta_K = 11.2$, 9.3 and 8.5, respectively, for Fe ($Z = 26$), Ag ($Z = 47$) and W ($Z = 74$). Including a rough estimate for absorption from the M-shell, one finally gets

$$\delta_K = 9._2 \text{ for Fe}, \quad 7._4 \text{ for Ag}, \quad 6._5 \text{ for W},$$

in fair agreement with experiment[5].

The absorption coefficient $\tau_{L_{\mathrm{I}}}$ for the L_{I}-subshell, Eq. (71.14), is proportional to $\nu^{-3.5}$ for high frequencies ($\nu \gg \nu_1$) and approximately proportional to $\nu^{-2.1}$ for

---

[1] Actually, a slightly larger value of s_2 should be used for $2p$- than for $2s$-electrons. In any case the present screening approximation is accurate only for fairly large Z, say, $Z > 20$.

[2] H. HALL: Rev. Mod. Phys. **8**, 358 (1936). More detailed expressions for the states with $n = 3$ and $n = 4$ are given by J. HARRIMAN, Phys. Rev. **101**, 594 (1956).

[3] More accurate graphs and tables for the K- and L-shells are given in HALL's review article and total absorption coefficients are given by G. WHITE, U.S. Nat. Bur. Stand. Circ. 1003 (May 1952, Washington, D.C.).

[4] S. J. ALLEN: Phys. Rev. **27**, 266; **28**, 907 (1926) and HALL's article.

[5] E. JÖNSSEN: Diss. Upsala 1928.

ν near the frequency ν_2, defined in (71.16). The ratio $\delta=(\tau_{L_{II}}+\tau_{L_{III}})/\tau_{L_I}$ equals $3\nu_2/\nu$ for $\nu\gg\nu_1$ and is thus very small for high frequencies. The ratio δ is still approximately proportional to ν^{-1} even at lower frequencies and equals 2.75 for $\nu=\nu_2$. The experimental L-shell absorption edge lies at a frequency ν_L which is still *lower* than ν_2 (due to outer screening) and at this frequency δ is even larger than 2.75. The calculated values for δ for radiation of wavelength 1.54 Å (the Cu $K\alpha$-line) for two elements follow: For Cu ($Z=29$), $\nu/\nu_2=3.80$ and $\delta=0.75$; for Ba ($Z=56$), $\nu/\nu_2=0.87$ and $\delta=3.1$. The calculated values for δ for various elements and frequencies are in moderate, but *not* good, agreement with experiment (see HALL's article).

Exact calculations for the photoelectric cross section from shells higher than the M-shell are tedious, but an approximate formula, for frequencies not much larger than the threshold frequency, can be derived as follows[1]. Consider the photoelectric cross-section $\sigma_{nl}(\nu)$ from a single nl-level in a hydrogen-like atom. Using (69.2) and the definition of the mean oscillator strengths (Sect. 61), we can write[2]

$$\sigma_{nl}(\nu)=\frac{2\pi^2 e^2\hbar}{m c}\frac{d\bar{f}_{nl}}{dE}, \tag{71.19a}$$

where df/dE is the oscillator strength per unit energy interval for a transition from the state nl to a continuum state of energy $E=h\nu-E_n$. Similarly the cross-section σ_{nl}, summed over all $2n^2$ electrons with principal quantum number n, is

$$\sigma_n(\nu)=\frac{2\pi^2 e^2\hbar}{m c}\frac{dF_n}{dE}, \tag{71.19}$$

where F is the summed oscillator strength discussed at the end of Sect. 63.

Consider now the approximate expression (63.11) for large values of n'. The number of integral values of n' per unit energy interval is proportional to n'^3 and $dF_n/dE_{n'}$, as given by (63.11), is a slowly varying function of $E_{n'}$. We can therefore expect this expression to be still reasonably accurate for small *positive* values $h\nu-E_n$ of $E_{n'}$. With the frequency ν expressed in units of ν_1 (i.e., $\nu'\equiv h\nu/Z^2\,\mathrm{Ry}=\nu/\nu_1$) we then have

$$\frac{dF_n}{d\nu'}\approx 1.96\,\nu'^{-3}n^{-3}. \tag{71.20}$$

This very simple approximate expression is reasonably accurate[3] even for low n and for ν a few times the threshold frequency. For $n=1$, for instance, the correct expression for low ν, (71.7) with (71.9) and (71.19), gives

$$\frac{dF_1}{d\nu'}=\frac{2^8 e^{-4}}{3}\nu'^{-2.7}=1.56\,\nu'^{-2.7},$$

compared with $1.96\,\nu'^{-3}$ from (71.20). Similarly (71.14) and (71.15) give, for $n=2$ and for ν not much larger than ν_2, $dF_2/d\nu'=0.282\,\nu'^{-2.9}$, compared with $0.245\,\nu'^{-3}$ from (71.20).

72. Angular distribution and retardation. *α) Angular distribution without retardation*[4]. The angular distribution of the ejected photoelectron is given by the differential cross-section σ_Ω, Eq. (69.5): For a fixed propagation direction $\boldsymbol{k}_\nu$

[1] See also the end of Sect. 78.

[2] H. BETHE, L. BROWN and J. STEHN: Phys. Rev. **77**, 370 (1950).

[3] For corrections to this expression see D. MENZEL and C. PEKERIS, M.N.R. Astron. Soc. **96**, 77 (1935). See also J. A. GAUNT, Phil. Trans. Roy. Soc. Lond., Ser. A **229**, 163 (1930).

[4] For further details, and for references to the experimental literature, see ref. [*10*], Sect. 47d and HALL's review article, p. 369.

and polarization direction $\boldsymbol{j}$ of the incident photon, the cross-section for the ejection of an electron with momentum $\boldsymbol{k}$ (per unit solid angle around this direction) is σ_Ω with u_Ω given by (69.4). We discuss first general results which can be obtained from symmetry considerations if retardation and relativistic effects are neglected.

We consider first a single-electron atom with an arbitrary central potential $V(r)$ and an initial bound state b with wave function $u_{nlm}(\boldsymbol{r})$ separable in spherical polar coordinates. If we take the polarization direction $\boldsymbol{j}$ of the photon as our x-axis, the matrix element to be substituted into (69.5) becomes, with retardation *neglected*,

$$D^{\boldsymbol{j}}_{\Omega b} \propto \int d^3r\, u^*_\Omega(\boldsymbol{r})\, x\, u_{nlm}(\boldsymbol{r}). \tag{72.1}$$

This matrix element, and hence σ_Ω, does not depend explicitly on the propagation direction of the incident photon, but does depend on the angle ϑ between the polarization (x-) direction of the photon and the propagation direction $\boldsymbol{k}$ of the emitted electron. For a single initial state u_{nlm}, (72.1) also depends on the quantization direction and magnetic quantum number m for this state. We now restrict ourselves to the *average* σ_Ω, averaged over all possible m values from $-l$ to l for the initial state u_{nlm} (but with n and l fixed). For a closed subshell in a complex atom, the state with each m-value is occupied (twice) and the cross-section from the whole subshell is $2(2l+1)$ times this average. For a partially filled subshell the average occupation number is also independent of the m-value, as long as no external (or crystal lattice) fields are present. Such an average over all m-values is independent of the quantization direction used for the initial state. The angular distribution for the averaged $\bar{\sigma}_\Omega$ thus depends only on the single angle ϑ between $\boldsymbol{k}$ and $\boldsymbol{j}$ ($\cos\vartheta = k_x/k$ in our notation).

We show first that σ_Ω remains *unchanged* when the electron's propagation direction is changed from $\boldsymbol{k}$ to $-\boldsymbol{k}$ (with the direction of $\boldsymbol{j}$, the x-axis, fixed): We change the variable of integration in (72.1) from $\boldsymbol{r}$ to $-\boldsymbol{r}$ and reverse the quantization direction of u_{nlm}. The integrand is then unchanged except for a change of sign, *each* integral of form (72.1) changes sign and $\bar{\sigma}_\Omega$ is unchanged. Changing the sign of $\boldsymbol{k}$ changes the sign of $\cos\vartheta$ and $\bar{\sigma}_\Omega$ is thus an *even* function of $\cos\vartheta$. We show next that this function must be of form $(\alpha+\beta\cos^2\vartheta)$: We use a spherical polar coordinate system $(r, \vartheta', \varphi')$ for the variable $\boldsymbol{r}$ in (72.1) with the direction of $\boldsymbol{k}$ as polar axis (and quantization direction for u_{nlm}). Using the spherical harmonics addition theorem we can write x in (72.1) in the form

$$x = \boldsymbol{r}\cdot\boldsymbol{j} = r(\cos\vartheta\cos\vartheta' + \sin\vartheta\sin\vartheta'\cos\varphi'), \tag{72.2}$$

where we have taken $\varphi' = 0$ for the azimuthal plane which contains the unit polarization vector $\boldsymbol{j}$. The matrix elements (72.1) thus depend on ϑ only through the two terms in (72.2) which are linear in $\cos\vartheta$ and $\sin\vartheta$, respectively. The averaged cross-section $\bar{\sigma}_\Omega$ is obtained by summing the absolute squares of these matrix elements over all m-values. From the above symmetry argument the coefficient of the cross-term $\cos\vartheta\sin\vartheta$ must vanish and we have

$$\bar{\sigma}_\Omega \propto \alpha\sin^2\vartheta + \beta'\cos^2\vartheta = \alpha + \beta\cos^2\vartheta. \tag{72.3}$$

More explicitly, the coefficients α and β are given by the following expressions. The exact continuum wave function u_Ω for a central potential can be written as a sum of wave functions $u_{\Omega l'}$, where $u_{\Omega l'}$ is expressible in spherical polar coordinates (with $\boldsymbol{k}$ as polar axis) with orbital quantum number l' and zero magnetic quantum number m' [see (7.2)]. Using the orthogonality properties of spherical harmonics, we then find

$$\left.\begin{aligned} \alpha &= \tfrac{1}{4} \sum_{m=-1,1} \left| \sum_{l'=l-1,\, l+1} \int d^3r\, u^*_{\Omega l'}\, r \sin\vartheta'\, e^{-im\varphi'}\, u_{nlm} \right|^2 \\ \beta' &= \beta + \alpha = \left| \sum_{l'=l-1,\, l+1} \int d^3r\, u^*_{\Omega l'}\, r \cos\vartheta'\, u_{nl0} \right|^2. \end{aligned}\right\} \tag{72.4}$$

If the initial bound state is an s-state ($l=0$), then there are no states u_{n0m} with $m=\pm 1$ and the coefficient α in (72.3) and (72.4) vanishes. Thus the angular distribution is proportional to $\cos^2\vartheta$ for an s-state in any central potential. For a p-state we have already shown in Sect. 70β that the angular distribution is isotropic ($\beta=0$) in BORN approximation. An explicit calculation[1], valid also at low frequencies ν near the threshold ν_2, Eq. (71.16), for $2p$-electrons ($L_{\mathrm{II}}+L_{\mathrm{III}}$-shell) gives[2]

$$\bar{\sigma}_\Omega \propto 1 + \frac{2(Z-s_2)^2\,\mathrm{Ry}}{\nu} \cos^2\vartheta. \tag{72.5}$$

β) Retardation effects. Let (Θ, Φ) be the spherical polar coordinates of the propagation direction $\boldsymbol{k}$ of the ejected electron in a coordinate system with the photon's propagation direction $\boldsymbol{k}_\nu$ as polar (z-) axis and its polarization direction $\boldsymbol{j}$ as x-axis ($\Phi=0$ plane). We have seen that the angular distribution $\bar{\sigma}_\Omega$ only depends on $\cos^2\vartheta$, if retardation is neglected, where

$$\cos^2\vartheta = \sin^2\Theta \cos^2\Phi. \tag{72.6}$$

With retardation included, $\bar{\sigma}_\Omega$ also depends on Θ itself, although we shall see that the retardation effects are small at nonrelativistic velocities. We still restrict ourselves to the nonrelativistic SCHRÖDINGER theory for both the initial and final states of the electron. *Exact* (within the frame work of the nonrelativistic theory) calculations are available[3] for the differential cross-section σ_Ω for the K- and L-shells of hydrogen-like atoms. These results take retardation into account fully and are also valid for low photon frequencies. We shall merely evaluate the retardation correction in the BORN approximation for s-electrons and also restrict ourselves to nonrelativistic velocities for the ejected electron[4], i.e., $(Z\alpha)^2 mc^2 \ll h\nu \ll mc^2$.

In zero order (plane wave) BORN approximation, the differential cross section σ_Ω from a bound s-state is given by (69.5) with (70.3), if retardation is taken into account fully. The only effect of retardation is that $\psi_b(\boldsymbol{k}-\boldsymbol{k}_\nu)$ occurs in (70.3) instead of $\psi_b(\boldsymbol{k})$. This effect can be pictured physically by saying that the absorbed photon imparts its own momentum $\hbar\boldsymbol{k}_\nu$ to the ejected electron (in addition to the momentum it receives in the dipole approximation)[5]. The angular distribution is no longer symmetric about the polarization direction, but the direction of maximum intensity is shifted towards the direction of propagation of the photon: Using the explicit hydrogenic wave function (70.4), the

---

[1] G. SCHUR: Ann. d. Phys. **4**, 433 (1930).

[2] (72.5) is exact only for a COULOMB potential $(Z-s_2)/r$. In a complex atom the actual effective (HARTREE) potential deviates appreciably from $(Z-s_2)/r$ for large r. The coefficient β in (72.4) is quite sensitive to the exact shape of the potential at large r, especially at low frequencies. Thus (72.5) is not very accurate for complex atoms and the correct coefficient β of $\cos^2\vartheta$ is smaller than that given by (72.5).

[3] J. FISCHER, Ann. d. Phys. **8**, 821; **11**, 489 (1931); F. SAUTER, Ann. d. Phys. **9**, 217; **11**, 454 (1931) and especially A. SOMMERFELD and G. SCHUR, Ann. d. Phys. **4**, 409 (1930) and ref. [7], Chap. 6, Sects. 4 and 6.

[4] J. FRENKEL: Phys. Rev. **37**, 1276 (1931).

[5] This picture must not be taken too seriously: The factor $k^{\frac{3}{2}}$ in (70.3) is *not* replaced by $|\boldsymbol{k}-\boldsymbol{k}_\nu|^{\frac{3}{2}}$, as the picture might imply.

differential cross-section σ_Ω with retardation equals the dipole approximation (70.5) times the correction factor F,

$$F = \frac{k^8}{|\boldsymbol{k} - \boldsymbol{k}_\nu|^8}. \tag{72.7}$$

$\hbar k$ is given by (70.1) and the photon momentum $\hbar k_\nu$ equals $h\nu/c$. Neglecting I_b compared with $h\nu$ [we are assuming $h\nu \gg (Z\alpha)^2 mc^2$], we have

$$\frac{k_\nu}{k} = \frac{\hbar k}{2mc} = \frac{1}{2}\frac{v}{c}, \tag{72.8}$$

where v is the velocity of the ejected electron. Since $v \ll c$ (we assume $h\nu \ll mc^2$) we find, after expanding (72.7) in powers of v/c and keeping only the first two terms,

$$F = \left(1 - \frac{v}{c}\cos\Theta\right)^{-4} \approx 1 + 4\frac{v}{c}\cos\Theta. \tag{72.9}$$

We have thus shown that the angular distribution from s-state electrons is not given by (72.6), but by

$$\sigma_\Omega \propto \sin^2\Theta\cos^2\Phi\left(1 + 4\frac{v}{c}\cos\Theta\right). \tag{72.10}$$

Note that the correction factor in (72.9) is quite small still even when the photon's wavelength is comparable with the atomic radius. We have so far neglected all other specifically relativistic effects, but the correction factor (72.9) is nevertheless meaningful since it is linear in v/c, whereas the other relativistic effects (see Sect. 73) are of order $(v/c)^2$ or smaller. For the *total* cross-section σ, (72.10) integrated over all angles, however, the correction linear in v/c integrates to zero and the retardation correction is also only of order $(v/c)^2$.

In the same energy region, $Z^2\,\mathrm{Ry} \ll h\nu \ll mc^2$, the angular distribution for the $L_{II} + L_{III}$ shell (the six $2p$-electrons) is given by ([7], p. 477)

$$\bar\sigma_\Omega \propto \left(1 + 2\frac{v}{c}\cos\Theta\right) + \sin^2\Theta\cos^2\Phi\left[2\,\frac{(Z - s_2)^2\,\mathrm{Ry}}{\nu} + 4\frac{v}{c}\cos\Theta\right]. \tag{72.11}$$

SOMMERFELD and SCHUR, and SCHUR[1], respectively, have calculated more accurate results for K- and for L-electrons, which do not neglect $Z^2\,\mathrm{Ry}/\nu$ at all, but omit higher powers of v/c. These results reduce to (72.10) and (72.11) for small $Z^2\,\mathrm{Ry}/\nu$ (and small v/c).

For s-state electrons, the maximum of the differential cross-section (72.10) still lies at zero azimuthal angle Φ. For constant Φ, however, the maximum intensity is obtained not at $\Theta = \frac{1}{2}\pi$ ($\cos\Theta = 0$), but at an angle $\Theta_{\max}$, given by (for $v \ll c$)

$$\cos\Theta_{\max} \approx \frac{\pi}{2} - \Theta_{\max} \approx 2\frac{v}{c} = 2\beta. \tag{72.12}$$

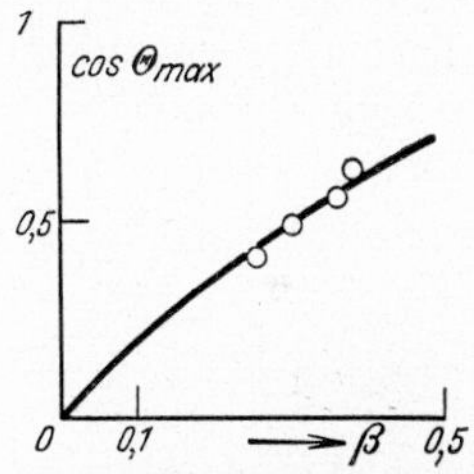

Fig. 35. Forward shift of the maximum of the photoelectric cross-section. The function $\cos\vartheta_{\max}$ is plotted against $\beta = v/c$ (v is the velocity of the photoelectron).

$\cos\Theta_{\max}$ is plotted against β in Fig. 35. For larger values of β, the more accurate relativistic expression (73.3) was used to evaluate the plotted expression of $\cos\Theta_{\max}$.

73. Relativistic effects. We discuss now the effects introduced by using the relativistic DIRAC theory for the electron instead of the nonrelativistic SCHRÖDINGER theory. The matrix element D to be substituted into (69.5) is modified in two ways. Relativistic DIRAC spinor wave functions must be used for u_Ω and for u_b and the momentum operator $\boldsymbol{p}$ is to be replaced by $mc\boldsymbol{\alpha}$, i.e.

$$D_{\Omega b}^{\boldsymbol{k}_\nu j} = \frac{imc}{\hbar}\int u_\Omega^* \sum_i e^{i\boldsymbol{k}_\nu\cdot\boldsymbol{r}_i}\,\alpha_j^{(i)}\,u_b\,d\tau. \tag{73.1}$$

[1] G. SCHUR: Ann. d. Phys. 4, 433 (1930).

No exact analytic calculations have been carried out so far using the DIRAC theory, but various useful formulae are available. We discuss first approximate analytic formulae, which hold if $Z\alpha \ll 1$.

α) Relativistic BORN *approximation.* We restrict ourselves to hydrogenic wave functions with $Z\alpha \ll 1$. Relativistic effects for the bound state wave function u_b are only of relative order $(Z\alpha)^2$ and we shall ignore them (e.g. by using the PAULI approximation for u_b). On the other hand we require expressions which are also valid for $h\nu \gtrsim mc^2$ and have to use DIRAC wave functions u_Ω for the continuum state. Since $h\nu_1 \sim (Z\alpha)^2 mc^2$ and since the relativistic effects are small if $h\nu \ll mc^2$, we can also restrict ourselves to the energy region $\nu \gg \nu_1$, where the BORN approximation can be used. Such a calculation, analogous to those of Sect. 70, [except that a DIRAC wave function u_Ω and (73.1) was used] has been carried out by SAUTER[1] for K-electrons. We discuss first the angular distribution of SAUTER's results.

We define the following dimensionless variables,

$$\beta = \frac{v}{c}, \quad \gamma = \frac{1}{\sqrt{1-\beta^2}} \approx 1 + \frac{h\nu}{mc^2}, \tag{73.2}$$

where v is the velocity of the ejected electron [neglecting $I_b/h\nu$ in (69.1)]. SAUTER's angular distribution is then given by

$$\sigma_\Omega \propto \frac{\sin^2\Theta}{(1-\beta\cos\Theta)^4}\left\{\frac{\cos^2\Phi}{\gamma}\left[1-\frac{1}{2}(\gamma-1)(1-\beta\cos\Theta)\right]+\frac{1}{4}(\gamma-1)^2(1-\beta\cos\Theta)\right\}, \tag{73.3}$$

where Θ and Φ are the angles defined at the beginning of Sect. 72β. At relatively low energies, $\beta \ll 1$, the parameter γ is approximately unity and $\gamma - 1 \approx \frac{1}{2}\beta^2 \ll \beta$. In this case the first term in (73.3) is the leading one and this expression reduces to (72.10). At extremely relativistic energies, on the other hand, we have

$$\frac{h\nu}{mc^2} \approx \gamma \gg 1, \quad 1-\beta \approx \frac{1}{2\gamma^2} \ll 1. \tag{73.4}$$

The last term in (73.3) is then the leading one and the angular distribution is strongly peaked in the forward direction (Θ small). For $\Theta \ll 1$ and $\gamma \gg 1$, (73.3) then gives, instead of (72.10) and (72.12),

$$\sigma_\Omega \propto \frac{\Theta^2}{(1+\gamma^2\Theta^2)^3}, \quad \Theta_{\max} = \frac{1}{\sqrt{2}\,\gamma}. \tag{73.5}$$

Note that, in this limit, σ_Ω is independent of the photon's polarization direction (i.e. of Φ).

The total cross-section σ_K per electron (σ_Ω integrated over angles) for the K-shell (τ_K equals $2\mathcal{N}\sigma_K$) according to SAUTER's formula, can be written in the following form

$$\frac{\sigma_K}{\varphi_0} = Z^5\alpha^4\left(\frac{mc^2}{h\nu}\right)^5(\beta\gamma)^3\left[1+\frac{3}{4}\frac{\gamma(\gamma-2)}{\gamma+1}\left(1-\frac{1}{2\beta\gamma^2}\log\frac{1+\beta}{1-\beta}\right)\right]. \tag{73.6}$$

In this expression, φ_0 is a constant of dimensions cm^2, called the THOMSON scattering cross-section,

$$\varphi_0 = \frac{8\pi}{3} r_0^2 = 6.65\times10^{-25}\,\mathrm{cm}^2, \quad r_0 = \frac{e^2}{mc^2} = \alpha\,\lambda_c = 2.818\times10^{-13}\,\mathrm{cm}, \tag{73.7}$$

[1] F. SAUTER: Ann. d. Phys. **11**, 454; **9**, 217 (1931). See also ref. [7], Chap. 6, Sect. 8.

where r_0 is the "classical radius" and $\lambda_c = \hbar/mc = 3.86\times 10^{-11}$ cm is the "rationalized COMPTON wave length" of the electron. In the nonrelativistic region, $\beta \ll 1$, $\gamma \approx 1$ and the expression in square brackets in (73.6) reduces to unity. Using the fact that $h\nu = \frac{1}{2} mc^2\beta^2$, (73.6) for $\beta \ll 1$ reduces to

$$\sigma_K = 2^{\frac{5}{2}} Z^5 \alpha^4 \left(\frac{m c^2}{h\nu}\right)^{\frac{7}{2}} \varphi_0 . \tag{73.8}$$

Using the fact that $h\nu_1 = \frac{1}{2}(Z\alpha)^2 mc^2$ and the definition (73.7), one finds that (73.8) is identical with the nonrelativistic BORN approximation (70.6). For extremely relativistic energies, on the other hand, (73.4) applies and (73.6) reduces to

$$\sigma_K = \frac{3}{4} Z^5 \alpha^4 \left(\frac{m c^2}{h\nu}\right) \varphi_0 = Z^5 \alpha^6 \lambda \lambda_c , \tag{73.9}$$

where λ_c is defined in (73.7) and λ is the wave length of the incident photon. At relativistic energies $h\nu$ of the photon, the absorption cross-section thus decreases only with the minus *first* power of this energy.

β) Attenuation of photons. We have been mainly concerned with the photoelectric absorption of high frequency radiation (X-rays and γ-rays of a few keV and more) in elements with medium and large Z. In this energy region the photoeffect comes mainly from the inner electrons of the atoms (especially the two K-electrons). There are two other effects which also contribute to the attenuation of X-rays and γ-rays while passing through matter[1]. We shall not discuss these in detail, but merely mention some results. One of these is the *scattering* of a photon by an electron[2]. For a single *free* electron in the nonrelativistic energy region $h\nu \ll mc^2$ the photon is scattered with only a small decrease of frequency ν and the total scattering cross-section is simply φ_0, Eq. (73.7), and is independent of ν. Note that the THOMSON scattering cross-section φ_0 is proportional to e^4, since the electron interacts with the radiation field *twice* (absorption of the incident and emission of the scattered photon).

For an electron bound in an atom, the scattering of the photon is still given approximately by φ_0, if the wave length λ of the photon is small compared with the "radius" of the bound state electronic wave function. In this case the electron is ejected from the atom, but with energy small compared with that of the photon (still for $h\nu \ll mc^2$). At smaller frequencies (larger λ), the effect of the binding of the electron is more important (and complicated), both coherent and incoherent scattering of the photon takes place and the total scattering cross section is somewhat larger than φ_0. In elements with large Z, most of the Z electrons are in the outer shells with large radii and the total scattering cross-section from the whole atom is roughly $Z\varphi_0$ for frequencies larger than the K-shell absorption edge[3]. In the energy region $(Z\alpha)^2 mc^2 \ll h\nu \ll mc^2$, the ratio of the total photoelectric absorption cross-section σ_{ph} [approximately twice σ_K, Eq. (73.8)] to the scattering cross-section σ_{sc} is then

$$\frac{\sigma_{\text{ph}}}{\sigma_{\text{sc}}} = 2^{\frac{5}{2}} (Z\alpha)^4 \left(\frac{m c^2}{h\nu}\right)^{\frac{7}{2}} . \tag{73.10}$$

[1] See E. SEGRÈ, Experimental Nuclear Physics, Vol. 1, Part II by J. ASHKIN and H. BETHE. New York: J. Wiley 1953.

[2] See ref. [*6*], Sects. 19 and 22; see also G. R. WHITE, U.S. Nat. Bur. Stand. Circular 1003 (May 1952, Washington, D.C.).

[3] For the *coherent* scattering of photons from K-shell electrons in atoms with very large Z, see S. BRENNER, G. BROWN, R. PEIERLS and J. WOODWARD, Proc. Roy. Soc. Lond., Ser. A **227**, 51, 57 (1954).

This ratio is of order $(Z\alpha)^{-3}$ for ν near the K-absorption edge and is also large for even lower frequencies (photoeffect mainly from the L-shell). At large frequencies, however, this ratio is small [of order $(Z\alpha)^4$ for $h\nu \sim mc^2$] and most of the attenuation is due to photon-scattering. The ratio (73.10) is unity at an energy of approximately

$$h\nu = 1.6 (Z\alpha)^{1.14} m c^2 = 0.84 (Z\alpha)^{1.14} \text{MeV}. \tag{73.11}$$

At relativistic photon energies $h\nu > mc^2$, the scattered photon has an appreciably lower frequency than the incident one (the electron takes up the momentum difference). The total cross-section σ_{sc} for scattering from the Z electrons (which can certainly be considered as though they are unbound) is given by the KLEIN-NISHINA formula for the COMPTON effect ([*6*], Sect. 22) in this energy range. σ_{sc} decreases with increasing ν slightly less rapidly than σ_{ph}, Eq. (73.9), and the

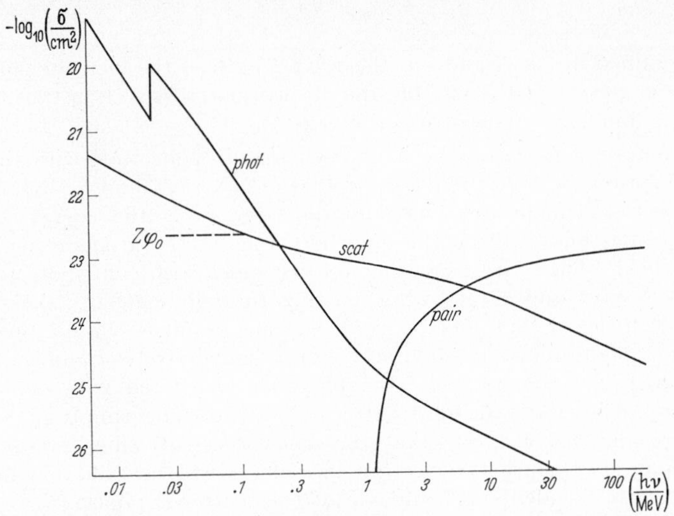

Fig. 36. The cross-sections σ for various processes undergone by a photon of energy $h\nu$ in passing through molybdenum (Z=42), plotted on a log-log scale. The curves labelled "phot", "scat" and "pair" are for photoelectric absorption, photon scattering and pair creation, respectively. The dotted line labelled $Z\varphi_0$ is the THOMSON cross-section from Z free electrons.

photoeffect is much less important than COMPTON scattering for all $h\nu \gtrsim mc^2$. In the extreme relativistic region $h\nu \gg mc^2$,

$$\sigma_{sc} = \frac{3}{8\gamma}\left(\log 2\gamma + \frac{1}{2}\right) Z\varphi_0, \tag{73.12}$$

where γ is given by (73.4).

At relativistic energies, photon attentuation by pair creation ([*6*], Sect. 26) competes with scattering and the photoeffect (see also Sect. 79γ). This is an effect specific to DIRAC pair theory and the creation of the electron-positron pair can be thought of as follows: An (unobservable) electron in the sea of negative-energy states (under the influence of the nuclear COULOMB potential) absorbs the photon and makes a transition to a positive-energy state (the "hole in the sea" is observed as the positron). The effect of pair creation by a photon depends only on the presence of the nuclear COULOMB potential, *not* on the presence of any real atomic electrons. The total pair creation cross-section σ_{pair} rises rapidly at first with increasing ν from zero at the threshold $h\nu = 2mc^2 = 1.02$ MeV. For $h\nu/mc^2 \approx \gamma \gg 1$, σ_{pair} *increases* logarithmically with increasing γ and is of order $Z\alpha\gamma\sigma_{sc}$. At extremely relativistic energies, pair creation is thus more important than the COMPTON effect (and the photoeffect is negligible). In Fig. 36

the three cross-sections σ_{ph}, σ_{scat} and σ_{pair} are plotted against $h\nu$ on a logarithmic scale for Mo ($Z=42$, $Z\alpha=0.31$).

γ) Deviations from BORN *approximation.* For elements with small enough Z, so that $Z\alpha \ll 1$, we have discussed quite accurate approximation formulae for the photoeffect which cover the whole range of photon frequencies ν. Thus, for $h\nu \ll mc^2$ the STOBBE formulae of Sect. 71 (relativity neglected), and for $h\nu \gg (Z\alpha)^2 mc^2$ the SAUTER formula (73.6) may be used. Since $Z\alpha \ll 1$, the range of validity of the two approximations overlap and one can even combine them in a semi-empirical way: For the K-shell multiply (73.6) by $2\pi\sqrt{\nu_1/\nu}\, f(n')$ with $f(n')$ defined by (71.7). This formula then reduces to (71.7) for small frequencies ν and to (73.6) for[1] large ν. However, both the SAUTER and STOBBE formulae neglect some relativistic effects of relative order $(Z\alpha)^2$ and, for very heavy elements, $Z\alpha$ is by no means very small (although never larger than unity, e.g. $Z\alpha=0.67$ for U, $Z=92$).

HULME *et al.*[2] have evaluated the exact DIRAC expressions (no neglect of $Z\alpha$) for the total photoelectric absorption cross-section σ_K for the K-shell for a few values of Z and of $h\nu$. Since no analytic DIRAC continuum wave functions separable in parabolic coordinates are available, these calculations involved summing a number of terms in the multipole expansion and some numerical work had to be carried out separately for each value of Z and $h\nu$. HALL[3] has obtained an analytic expression for σ_K, valid for all $Z\alpha$, for the limit of high frequency $h\nu \gg mc^2$. His expression for σ_K equals the limit (73.9) of the SAUTER formula multiplied by the factor

$$F = \exp\left[-\pi Z\alpha + 2Z^2\alpha^2(1-\log Z\alpha)\right]. \tag{73.13}$$

Table 21. *Correction factors* F_n *and* F *to the* SAUTER *formula for Pb.*

$\frac{h\nu}{mc^2}$	0.69	2.2	∞
F_n	0.28	0.47	1
F	0.27	0.53	0.46

In Table 21, we give the ratio F (for two frequencies) of HULME's numerical values of σ_K to those obtained from SAUTER's expression (73.6) [and HALL's factor (73.13) for $h\nu \gg mc^2$] for Pb, $Z=82$, $Z\alpha=0.60$. In the same table, F_n is the factor $2\pi\sqrt{\nu_1/\nu}\, f(n')$, Eqs. (71.7) and (71.8), with n' given by the nonrelativistic formula (71.6). The empirical factor F_n is quite close to the correct expression F at moderately low energies, even for such large values of Z. The departure of F_n from F for large values of the energy and of Z is not surprising: As $h\nu/mc^2 \to \infty$, the relativistic expression $Ze^2/\hbar v$ for n' tends to $Z\alpha$, whereas the nonrelativistic value for n', used in F_n, tends to zero.

It should be noted that the frequency dependence $\nu^{-3.5}$ of the nonrelativistic BORN approximation (70.6) for σ_K does not hold for *any* frequencies ν for elements with large Z: The BORN approximation factor (71.10) would be accurate only for rather large values of ν/ν_1, (say, $\nu \gg 10\nu_1$) and for such large frequencies the nonrelativistic approximation is no longer accurate. If we write $\sigma_K \propto \nu^{-n}$, then n varies almost monotonically from $n \approx 2.7$ at $\nu \sim \nu_1$, to $n=1$ for $h\nu \gg mc^2$ (see also Fig. 36) without ever attaining the value $n=3.5$, if Z is larger than about 30 or 40.

74. The optical region. *α) Negative ions and helium.* We have considered so far mainly the photoelectric absorption of X-rays and γ-rays in atoms with large Z. In such cases most of the contribution comes from the innermost atomic

[1] For large ν, $n' \approx \sqrt{\nu_1/\nu}$ and $2\pi n' f(n') \approx 1$ from (71.10).

[2] H. HULME, J. MCDOUGAL, R. BUCKINGHAM and R. FOWLER: Proc. Roy. Soc. Lond., Ser. A **149**, 131 (1935).

[3] H. HALL: Phys. Rev. **45**, 620 (1934) and Rev. Mod. Phys. **8**, 358 (1936).

electrons for which screening effects are not too important and one obtains good results by using single-electron hydrogenic wave functions for both the initial and the final state of the photoelectron. For radiation of frequency much lower than the threshold for the ejection of inner electrons, the photoeffect can take place only from the more loosely bound outer electrons, for which the hydrogenic approximation is rather poor. Few calculations have been done for such states in complex atoms, but the photoeffect from the negative hydrogen ion H^- (see Sect. 34), a loose structure for which the hydrogenic approximation breaks down, has been studied extensively.

As discussed in Sect. 34, the negative hydrogen ion has only one bound state with ionization potential $I_1 = h\nu_1 = 0.75$ eV and its wave function is represented rather poorly by a simple product of two single-electron wave functions (polarization effects are important). CHANDRASEKHAR[1] has calculated the photoelectric cross-section $\sigma(\nu)$ for H^-, using different approximations for the bound state wave function. He finds that rather accurate bound state wave functions are required (the best one being an eleven-parameter variational one) to obtain reliable results for $\sigma(\nu)$. The continuum wave function for the final state of the electron is also very different from a hydrogenic one for ν near the threshold value ν_1 and the frequency dependence near threshold is drastically different from that of Sect. 71α. This can be seen as follows.

The final state wave function represents an electron of positive energy $k^2/2m$ moving in the potential $V(r)$ due to a *neutral* hydrogen atom in its ground state. This potential $V(r)$ approximates e/r for small r but approaches zero very rapidly for r larger than the BOHR radius a_0 (complete screening). Since the ground state of H^- is an s-state, the final state is a p-state. For $r > a_0$, where $V \to 0$, r times the radial wave function for the p-state is approximately of the form

$$\sqrt{\frac{\pi}{2}}\,\chi(r) = \frac{\sin(kr+\delta)}{kr} - \cos(kr+\delta), \tag{74.1}$$

if we use the same normalization for $kr \to \infty$ as in (4.18). For such a "short-range" potential $V(r)$, one finds that the phase shift δ in (74.1) is very small if $ka_0 \ll 1$, i.e. δ is of the order of $(ka_0)^3$. For $r \sim a_0$, the range of radial distances of importance for the photoelectric matrix element, one then finds $\chi(a_0) \sim (ka_0)^2$. For such small values of k, i.e. near the low-frequency limit $\nu \approx \nu_1$, the cross-section $\sigma(\nu)$ is then proportional to $k^3 \propto (\nu - \nu_1)^{\frac{3}{2}}$ and goes to *zero* at threshold, just as the BORN approximation result of Sect. 70α. In fact, if we replace δ by zero in (74.1), we obtain exactly the wave function used in the BORN approximation calculation (solution for zero potential). If δ were small compared with $(ka_0)^3$, $\sigma(\nu)$ would not only be of the same order of magnitude as, but very close to, the BORN approximation result. If, on the other hand, the final state electron moves in a potential which is COULOMBic at large distances, then $\chi(a_0)$ is[2] of order $(ka_0)^{\frac{1}{2}}$ [instead of $(ka_0)^2$] and $\sigma(\nu)$ tends to a *finite* limit at threshold ($k \to 0$), as for the hydrogenic calculations of 71α.

Explicit calculations[3], using more accurate final state wave functions, show that the BORN approximation result for $\sigma(\nu)$ is in fact within 5% of the correct value for a large range of frequencies ν. CHANDRASEKHAR'S cross-section is plotted against ν/ν_1 (in arbitrary units) in Fig. 37, where $h\nu_1$ is the ionization potential of H^-. It rises from zero at threshold (wavelength about 16500 Å) to a maximum at a wavelength of about 8500 Å.

---

[1] S. CHANDRASEKHAR: Astrophys. J. **100**, 176 (1944); **102**, 223 (1945).
[2] This can be seen by comparing (4.19) and (4.23) for $n' \gg 1$.
[3] S. CHANDRASEKHAR: Astrophys. J. **102**, 395 (1945).

The situation is different again for the photoeffect from the ground state of neutral helium: Even at large radial distances r the potential acting on the photoelectron is not zero but $-e/r$, the COULOMB potential of the nucleus ($Z=2$) minus that of *one* electron. The cross-section $\sigma(\nu)$ has a finite value (in fact, a maximum) at the threshold frequency ν_1 as for hydrogen. This cross-section[1] is plotted against ν/ν_1 in Fig. 37, together with the hydrogenic expression (71.7) (normalized to agree at $\nu=1.5\nu_1$). Note that the He-curve is closer to the hydrogenic one than to that for H^-.

β) Stellar opacity[2]. The photoeffect is one of the most important causes of opacity (i.e. the attenuation of electromagnetic radiation) in the interior and atmosphere of the sun and of stars. Typical stellar matter consists largely of hydrogen plus about 10% (by mass) of helium and of the order of a few percent (or less) by mass for the elements with $Z\sim 6$ to $Z\sim 30$ combined. The stellar matter is partly ionized and photons can also be absorbed by a process we have not discussed so far, the "free-free" transitions:

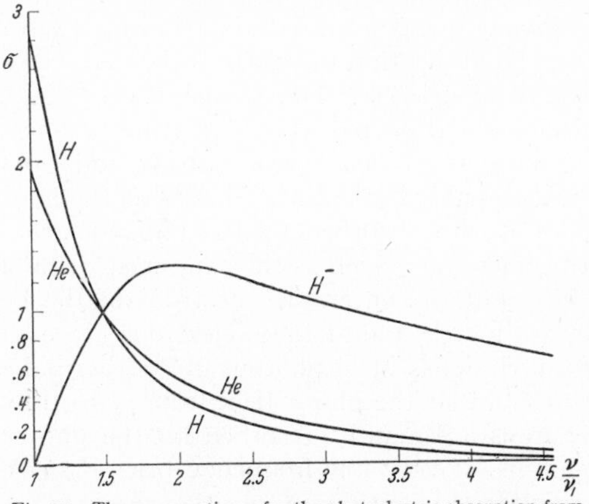

Fig 37. The cross-section σ for the photoelectric absorption from the ground states of H^-, He and H. The abscissa is the frequency ν divided by the threshold frequency ν_1 for the particular atom or ion, the ordinate is σ in units such that $\sigma=1$ for $\nu=1.5\nu_1$.

An electron of *positive* energy moving in a *continuum* state in some atomic potential can make a transition to another continuum state with higher energy and simultaneously absorb a photon. This process is thus the analogue of the photoeffect for an initial state of the electron in the continuum (instead of in the discrete spectrum) and there is no minimum threshold value for the frequency ν of the photon to be absorbed. This process is the inverse of Bremsstrahlung (discussed in Sects. 76 to 79) and the photon absorption cross-section can be derived from related expressions for Bremsstrahlung. We shall not discuss calculations[3] for the photon absorption cross-section $\sigma_{FF}(\nu)$ due to free-free transitions under stellar conditions, but merely note that for an electron with initial velocity v in a COULOMB potential of charge Z the approximate relation

$$\sigma_{FF}(\nu) \propto Z^2 v^{-1} \nu^{-3} \tag{74.2}$$

holds[4].

In the interior of a typical star, where most of its mass is concentrated, the temperature is of the order of 10^6 to 10^7 °K ($kT\sim 10^2$ to 10^3 eV) and the density of the order of 10^{-2} to 10^2 gm/cm³. Energy is transported outwards from the interior by electromagnetic radiation, which is continually absorbed and reemitted and has a thermal frequency distribution. Under these circumstances

[1] Calculated by using a six-parameter variational wave function for the ground state and COULOMB wave function with charge $Z-1=1$ for the continuum state; S. HUANG, Astrophys. J. **108**, 354 (1948).

[2] L. H. ALLER: Astrophysics, Vol. I and II. New York: Ronald Press Co. 1953 and 1954. G. KELLER and R. MEYEROTT: Argonne Nat. Lab. Rep 4771 and 4856 (1952). — A. UNSÖLD: Physik der Sternatmosphäre, 2nd ed. Berlin: Springer 1955.

[3] H. ZIRIN: Astrophys. J. **119**, 371 (1954). — R. KULSRUD: Astrophys. J. **119**, 386 (1954).

[4] See also the end of Sect. 78 and (78.10).

essentially all the hydrogen and helium is completely ionized. The heavier atoms with $Z \sim 6$ to 30 are ionized to a high degree and only the innermost electrons remain bound. The photoeffect then is due only to the bound electrons of these heavier atoms and the photoelectric cross-sections can be obtained approximately from (71.19) and (71.20) and small corrections to this formula have also been calculated. If the abundance of these heavier atoms is very low, the free-free transitions of an electron in the potentials of ionized hydrogen and helium are an important source of photon absorption [especially at low photon frequencies where only bound states with large principal quantum number n could contribute to the photoeffect, cf. Eq. (71.20)]. For large photon frequencies, the *scattering* of photons by the free electrons is more important than either the photoeffect or free-free transitions, and the scattering cross-section per electron is given to a good approximation by φ_0, Eq. (73.7).

The absorption of radiation in the atmospheres of the sun and of other stars is also of interest. The temperature T_s in the "photosphere" (i.e. depths from which radiation has about an equal chance of escaping and of being absorbed) of most stars lies between 3000 and 20000 °K and the density is very low. In reasonably hot stars ($T_s \sim 10^4$ °K) the hydrogen is only partly ionized and most photons are absorbed by the photoelectric effect from bound hydrogen atoms. In cooler stars, such as the sun, most of the hydrogen is neutral and in its *ground* state, but the outermost electrons of the heavier atoms have been removed by ionization. Some of these electrons are captured by neutral hydrogen atoms to form H^--ions. Most photons in the thermal radiation have frequencies well below threshold for the photoeffect from neutral hydrogen in the ground state and such photons are mainly absorbed by the photoeffect from the bound H^--ions. For photons of very low frequency ($h\nu < 0.75$ eV) absorption by free-free transitions from the H^--continuum (positive energy electrons moving in the field of a *neutral* hydrogen atom) is also important[1].

γ) The average excitation energy for the LAMB *shift.* We consider first a bound S-state with principal quantum n_0 and energy E_0 of a hydrogen-like atom. In (19.10) we have defined a dimensionless quantity K_0/Z^2 Ry which represents, in some sense, the "average excitation energy" in units of the ground state energy. Using the definition (59.14) of the oscillator strength f_{0n} and (59.20), we can rewrite (19.10) as

$$\log \frac{K_0}{Z^2\,\mathrm{Ry}} = \frac{\sum\limits_n f_{0n}\,\nu_{0n}^2 \log|\nu_{0n}|}{\sum\limits_n f_{0n}\,\nu_{0n}^2}\,, \tag{74.3}$$

where $\nu_{0n} = (E_n - E_0)/Z^2$ Ry. The sums over n are to be carried over *all* stationary states of the hydrogen atom, including those in the continuum, and can be written as

$$\sum_n f_{0n}\,\nu_{0n}^2 = \sum_n{}' f_{0n}\,\nu_{0n}^2 + \int\limits_{-2\log n}^{\infty} \frac{df}{d\nu}\,\nu^3\,d\log\nu\,, \tag{74.4}$$

with a similar relation for the sum involving $\log\nu$. In (74.4), $\sum'$ denotes summation over bound states n only and $df/d\nu$ is the oscillator strength per unit frequency interval and is related to the photoelectric absorption cross-section from the state n_0 by (71.19a). It should be remembered that the calculations of Sect. 19β were nonrelativistic ones with retardation neglected and hence f_{0n} in (74.3) is also the nonrelativistic, non-retarded oscillator strength.

[1] S. CHANDRASEKHAR and F. BREEN: Astrophys. J. **104**, 430 (1946).

Analytic expressions for f_{0n} for the discrete spectrum were given in Sect. 63 and $df/d\nu$ for the continuum can be derived from STOBBE's analytic formulae for the photoelectric cross-section, discussed in Sect. 71. The sums and integrals in (74.3) with (74.4) can then be evaluated by numerical work, separately for each value of n_0. Such calculations have been carried out[1] for $n_0=1$ to 4. The results are

n_0	1	2	3	4	∞
K_0/Z^2 Ry	19.770	16.640	15.921	15.640	15.2

including an extrapolated value for $n_0 \to \infty$. Note that the values of K_0/Z^2 Ry are numerically rather large and do not depend on the value of n_0 very strongly. This result is at first sight somewhat surprising: Using (19.13) and (21.1) we can write

$$\sum_n f_{n0}\,\nu_{0n}^2 = \frac{16\,\pi}{3\,Z^3}\,\delta^{(3)}(r)_{n_0 n_0} = \frac{16}{3\,n_0^3}\,. \tag{74.5}$$

Since $\sum_n f_{n0}=1$, the square root of the expression (74.5) also represents an average of ν, in some sense. This "average" is only about 2.3 for $n_0=1$ and decreases with increasing n_0 as $n_0^{-1.5}$ quite unlike the other "average", K_0/Z^2 Ry.

The dependence on n_0 of K_0 and of (74.5) can be understood as follows: Table 14, and also (63.11), shows that f_{0n} is of order unity if n is close to n_0 but falls off rapidly with increasing $n-n_0$, if n_0 is large. For small $n-n_0$, the energy difference ν_{0n} in (74.4) is very small and the sum over the discrete spectrum $\sum' f_{0n}\,\nu_{0n}^2$ is of order n_0^{-6}. On the other hand $df/d\nu$ is roughly proportional to n_0^{-3} and $\nu^3\,df/d\nu$ increases with ν, for ν of the order unity, and has a maximum at a rather large numerical value ν_m of ν. Only for very large values of ν does $\nu^3\,df/d\nu$ approach its BORN approximation expression (see Sect. 70α), which is proportional to $\nu^{-0.5}$. The deviation from the BORN approximation is largely due to the effect of the COULOMB potential on the *continuum* wave function. Consequently ν_m does not depend very strongly on n_0 and is rather large ($\nu_m \sim 7$ for $n_0=2$). The ratio ϱ of the first (discrete sum) to the second (continuum integral) term on the right side of (74.4) thus decreases rapidly with increasing n_0 (and ϱ is already only 0.068 for $n_0=1$). Thus the major contribution to both the numerator and denominator of (74.3) comes from the continuum and K_0/Z^2 Ry is of order (actually larger than) ν_m, which is almost independent of n_0.

The situation is different for states $n_0 l_0$ with non-zero orbital quantum number l_0. In this case the dimensionless quantity K_0/Z^2 Ry, to be substituted into (21.3), is defined by

$$\log\frac{K_0(n_0,\,l_0)}{Z^2\,\text{Ry}} = \frac{3\,n_0^3}{16}\sum_n \bar{f}_{0n}\,\nu_{0n}^2\log|\nu_{0n}|\,, \tag{74.6}$$

where $\bar{f}_{0n}$ is the mean oscillator strength for $n_0 l_0 m_0 \to n,\, l_0 \pm 1,\, m$ (averaged over m_0 or over the polarization direction). If $\log|\nu_{0n}|$ were replaced by a constant on the right hand side of (74.6), it follows from (74.5) that the sum $\sum f\nu^2$ would vanish exactly[2] since the wave function at the origin is zero for $l_0 \neq 0$. For non-zero l_0, the integral over the continuous spectrum [cf. (74.4)] contributes very *little*, since $\nu^3\,df/d\nu$ *decreases* with increasing ν already at threshold ($\nu = n_0^{-2}$) and decreases even more strongly in the BORN approximation region (as $\nu_0^{-l_0-0.5}$, see

[1] H. BETHE, L. BROWN and J. STEHN: Phys. Rev. **77**, 370 (1950). — J. M. HARRIMAN: Phys. Rev. **101**, 594 (1956).

[2] Note that f_{0n} is negative for negative ν_{0n}.

Sect. 70 and 71 β). The negative and positive contributions in the sum (74.6) cancel to an appreciable extent and the total sum is rather small for all n_0. Some of the numerical results are

$n_0 l_0$	$2P$	$4P$	$3D$
$\log (K_0/Z^2 \text{Ry})$	-0.0300	-0.0419	-0.0052

Similar calculations are required for evaluating the LAMB shift (41.7) for the ground state of helium-like atoms. K_0 is again defined by (74.3) and the dipole matrix elements (or oscillator strengths) are required for transitions from the ground state to excited states of the two-electron atom. These matrix elements are not known exactly, but reasonably good approximations are available. The calculation of K_0 has to be carried out separately for each value of the nuclear charge Z. One finds that the most important transitions are those to singly excited states and especially to those in the continuum. The oscillator strengths for the continuum for He ($Z=2$) can be obtained from HUANG's expression for the photoelectric cross-section, discussed in Sect. 74α, and plotted in Fig. 37. One check for the accuracy of the oscillator strengths is the sum rule corresponding to (74.5),

$$\sum_n f_{0n} \nu_{0n}^2 = \frac{16\pi}{3 Z^3} \left(\delta^{(3)}(\boldsymbol{r}_1) + \delta^{(3)}(\boldsymbol{r}_2)\right)_{n_0 n_0}. \tag{74.7}$$

The expectation value over the ground state wave function on the right hand side of (74.7) is known quite accurately (see Table 10, Sect. 36). The numerical results[1] for He ($Z=2$) are

$$K_0 = (84.3 \pm 5) \text{ Ry}. \tag{74.8}$$

For large Z, K_0/Z^2 Ry must approach the hydrogenic value for $n_0=1$, $l=0$. Combined with (74.8) this gives the semi-empirical result

$$K_{0(Z)} \approx 19.77 (Z + 0.06)^2 \text{ Ry}. \tag{74.9}$$

75. Recombination. α) *General formulas for the probability of the processes.* In the preceding sections we discussed the absorption processes in the continuous spectrum. Now we shall deal with the emission processes. If an electron is incident on a bare nucleus the following events may occur:

The electron may be captured by the nucleus with the emission of light, i.e., the electron may reach a discrete energy level;

or the electron may merely have its velocity reduced—with the emission of light—and continue on its flight in a different direction;

or, finally, the electron may simply be deflected without change in velocity.

The third process has already been dealt with in Sect. 6γ, and is of no interest to us here since it is not accompanied by the emission of light. The probability of the first two processes is directly given by (59.2):

$$w(\Omega, j)\, d\Omega = \frac{e^2 \hbar \omega}{2\pi m^2 c^3} \,|D_{n'n}^{\boldsymbol{k}\boldsymbol{j}}|^2\, d\Omega \tag{75.1}$$

is the probability that the electron undergoes the transition from the state n to the state n' and emits light, of frequency $\nu_{nn'}$ and polarization $\boldsymbol{j}$, into the solid angle $d\Omega$.

[1] P. KABIR and E. SALPETER: Bull. Amer. Phys. Soc. 1, 46 (1956).

In the evaluation of D, the eigenfunctions u_n and $u_{n'}$ must be taken to be those of an electron in the field of the nucleus which causes the emission. Furthermore, u_n must have the form of an incident plane wave at large distances from the nucleus. This condition is fulfilled by the eigenfunction in parabolic coordinates (cf. Sect. 6γ):

$$u_k = \sqrt{\frac{2\pi n'}{1 - e^{-2\pi n'}}}\, e^{\frac{1}{2} i k \xi} \cdot \frac{1}{2\pi i \sqrt{v}} \int d\zeta\, e^{-ik\eta\zeta} \left(\zeta + \frac{1}{2}\right)^{-in'} \left(\zeta - \frac{1}{2}\right)^{in'-1}, \tag{75.2}$$

in which z is the direction of incidence of the electron, $\xi = r + z$, $\eta = r - z$, $k = \sqrt{\frac{W}{\text{Ry}}}$ is the wave number, $n = -in' = -iZ/k$ is the "principal quantum number". The normalization of the wave function differs from the usual one and is chosen so that one electron is incident on a unit of area per unit of time [see the remark following Eq. (6.24)]. With this normalization (75.1) simply becomes the cross-section of the nucleus for the processes under consideration.

It is also possible, of course, to express the wave of the incident electron (75.2) in terms of the eigenfunctions in polar coordinates[1]:

$$u_k = \frac{\sqrt{h}}{2k} \sum_l (2l+1)\, i^l P_l(\cos\vartheta)\, \frac{\Gamma(l+1-in')}{|\Gamma(l+1-in')|} \cdot R_{Wl}(r). \tag{75.3}$$

In general, the above representation is not as convenient as (75.2).

β) Recombination processes[2]. The probability of capturing the incident electron in a $1s$ orbit may be written down at once, since we have already calculated the pertinent matrix elements in the treatment of the photoelectric effect (Sect. 71). Assuming that the velocity of the incident electron is not too large, the retardation factor may again be neglected in the evaluation of the matrix element D, and we obtain [cf. Eq. (75.3)]

$$|D^{kj}_{1W}| = \frac{m\omega}{\hbar} \int u_1 z\, u_{W10}\, d\tau \cdot \sqrt{3} \cdot \sqrt{4\pi} \cdot \frac{\sqrt{h}}{2k}. \tag{75.4}$$

Evidently, in a transition to the ground state only radiation which is polarized in the z direction—the direction of incidence—is emitted, as in all other cases the matrix element D vanishes, provided the retardation is neglected. For the same reason only the part of the eigenfunction (75.3) of the incident electron which corresponds to $l = 1$ makes a contribution (l selection rule). Thus, we finally arrive at

$$u_{W10} = R_{W1}(r)\, Y_{10}(\vartheta, \varphi) = \sqrt{\frac{3}{4\pi}}\, R_{W1}(r)\, P_1(\cos\vartheta), \tag{75.5}$$

---

[1] Cf., for example, B. M. Stobbe, Ann. d. Phys. **7**, 682 (1930). For large z, u_k must behave as an incident plane wave; thus, using the well known expansion of a plane wave in terms of spherical waves

$$u_k = \frac{1}{\sqrt{v}} \cdot e^{ikz} = \sqrt{\frac{\pi}{2v}} \cdot \frac{1}{\sqrt{kr}} \cdot \sum_l (2l+1)\, i^l P_l(\cos\vartheta)\, J_{l+\frac{1}{2}}(kr)$$

$$= \frac{1}{\sqrt{v}} \cdot \frac{1}{kr} \cdot \sum_l (2l+1) \cdot i^l P_l(\cos\vartheta) \cdot \cos\left(kr - (l+1)\frac{\pi}{2}\right).$$

(75.3) is obtained by comparing the above expression with the asymptotic representation of the eigenfunction normalized per unit energy.

[2] M. Stobbe, loc. cit., E. C. G. Stückelberg and P. M. Morse: Phys. Rev. **35**, 116 (1930). — W. Wessel: Ann. d. Phys. **5**, 611 (1930).

in which Y_{10} is the normalized spherical harmonic and P_1 is the unnormalized LEGENDRE polynomial. Next, we insert the value of the matrix element (71.4) into (75.4) and the resulting expression into (75.1), and integrate over all possible directions of propagation of the emitted light quantum.

Then we obtain the following expression for the cross-section for recombination

$$\left.\begin{aligned} \sigma_1(\nu) &= \frac{2^7\pi}{3}\,\frac{e^2}{m c^2}\,\frac{h}{m c}\,\frac{\nu_1^3}{\nu^2(\nu-\nu_1)}\cdot\frac{e^{-4\sqrt{\frac{\nu_1}{\nu-\nu_1}}\,\mathrm{arc\,tg}\sqrt{\frac{\nu-\nu_1}{\nu_1}}}}{1-e^{-2\pi\sqrt{\frac{\nu_1}{\nu-\nu_1}}}} \\ &= 9.1\times 10^{-21}\,\frac{\nu_1^3}{\nu^2(\nu-\nu_1)}\cdot f\left(\sqrt{\frac{\nu_1}{\nu-\nu_1}}\right). \end{aligned}\right\} \tag{75.6}$$

We note that e^2/mc^2 is the classical electron radius, and h/mc the COMPTON wave length of the electron. For hydrogen, the cross-section is equal to 2.1×10^{-21} cm² if the velocity of the incident electron corresponds to 1 electron volt. Thus, the cross-section is seen to be very small, and is inversely proportional to the square of the velocity for low speeds and to the fifth power for high velocities. The recombination processes in which the electron is caught in a higher shell are even rarer[1].

As for the photoeffect, we can get a *rough* approximation from (71.19) and (71.20) for the total cross-section σ_n for recombination with the electron being captured into any of the bound states with principal quantum number n. This approximation, roughly valid up to frequencies ν about $10\nu_1$, is ($\nu_n = \nu_1/n^2$)

$$\sigma_n = 1.96\pi^2\,\frac{e^2\hbar}{m^2c^3}\,\frac{\nu_1^2}{\nu(\nu-\nu_n)}\,n^{-3}. \tag{75.7}$$

For large frequencies, $\nu \gg 10\nu_1$, the BORN approximation applies and (75.7) breaks down. In this region the correct cross-section decreases with increasing ν more rapidly than (75.7) by approximately one power of $\nu^{-\frac{1}{2}}$.

The RUTHERFORD scattering formula (6.24) shows that the cross-section for radiationless scattering of the electron by the COULOMB potential, through large angles (say, $\vartheta > 90°$), is of the order of magnitude of $\sigma_R = (Ze^2/E)^2$, where E is the energy of the incident electron. (75.7) then gives the following order of magnitude relation

$$\sigma_n \sim Z^2\alpha^3\,\frac{\nu-\nu_n}{\nu}\,n^{-3}\sigma_R\,. \tag{75.8}$$

Although recombination is much less likely than RUTHERFORD scattering, it is nevertheless important in a partially ionized gas in thermal equilibrium. Atoms are continuously ionized by the photoeffect (photons from the thermal radiation) and electrons must be recaptured at an equal rate (at equilibrium).

We have only discussed so far the radiative capture of an electron by a bare nucleus. For the capture of an electron by a positive ion, screening corrections must be applied as for the photoeffect. Since the recombination cross-section decreases rapidly with increasing principal quantum number n, the electron is most likely to be captured into the innermost empty (or partially unfilled) shell.

---

[1] If the velocity of the incident electron is low, the small magnitude of the cross-section has its origin in the factor ν^3 which multiplies the square of the matrix element of the coordinate [cf. Eqs. (75.1), (75.4)]. If the initial velocity is high, the matrix elements D become small through destructive interference.

c) Bremsstrahlung.

76. General survey[1]. We consider now the case of radiative transitions of an electron between two states in the continuum. We shall discuss mainly transitions in which a photon is emitted, i.e. the following process called Bremsstrahlung: An electron of positive kinetic energy E_0 and momentum $\boldsymbol{p}_0$ impinges on an atomic ion (or bare nucleus), emits a photon of momentum $\boldsymbol{k}$ (energy $h\nu = kc$) and polarization direction $\boldsymbol{j}$ (perpendicular to $\boldsymbol{k}$) and the electron emerges with momentum $\boldsymbol{p}$ and energy E. The energies of the photon and the electron are related by the expression

$$h\nu = E_0 - E, \tag{76.1}$$

but there is no conservation of momentum for the electron-photon system. If the electron impinges on an atom or ion (instead of a bare nucleus) we have, strictly speaking, a many-electron problem. In most cases the polarization of the atomic electrons by the incident electron is unimportant and we shall always replace the atom or ion by a fixed central potential $V(r)$.

Let $u_0(\boldsymbol{r})$ be the wave function for a stationary state of the electron in the potential $V(r)$, which behaves asymptotically like a plane wave of momentum $\boldsymbol{p}_0$ plus scattered outgoing spherical waves. We normalize u_0 per unit current crossing unit area, so that (75.2) is the special case of u_0 for a Coulomb potential. Similarly $u(\boldsymbol{r})$ is a wave function which behaves asymptotically like a plane wave of momentum $\boldsymbol{p}$ plus *incoming* spherical scattered waves. As discussed in the beginning of Sect. 69, the "incoming" type of solution must be used, since it is to represent a *final* state[2]. Further, we shall normalize $u(\boldsymbol{r})$ per unit *energy* interval, as for the wave function (69.4). Following (75.1), we write

$$\left.\begin{aligned} \sigma(E, \Omega_p, \Omega_k, \boldsymbol{j}) &= \frac{e^2 h\nu}{2\pi m^2 c^3} |D|^2, \\ D &= \frac{i}{\hbar} \int u^*(\boldsymbol{r})\, p_j\, e^{-i\boldsymbol{k}\cdot\boldsymbol{r}/\hbar}\, u_0(\boldsymbol{r})\, d^3r. \end{aligned}\right\} \tag{76.2}$$

For fixed initial momentum $\boldsymbol{p}_0$, consider a Bremsstrahlung process in which the outgoing electron has its energy in an energy interval dE (centered around E) and the direction of its momentum in an infinitesimal cone of solid angle $d\Omega_p$ (centered around $\boldsymbol{p}$, denoted by Ω_p) and the photon has polarization direction $\boldsymbol{j}$ and momentum direction $\boldsymbol{k}$ in a cone of solid angle $d\Omega_k$ (axis direction denoted by Ω_k). The probability per unit time for such a process is then given by

$$\sigma(E, \Omega_p, \Omega_k, \boldsymbol{j})\, dE\, d\Omega_p\, d\Omega_k. \tag{76.3}$$

Since u_0 is normalized per unit current density, (76.3) is of the dimensions of cm^2 and we shall call $\sigma(E, \Omega_p, \Omega_k, \boldsymbol{j})$ the differential cross-section for short. We shall also be interested in the expression obtained by summing (76.3) over two polarization directions perpendicular to $\boldsymbol{k}$ and integrating this expression over both $d\Omega_p$ and $d\Omega_k$. We shall write this integrated cross-section in either of two forms,

$$\sigma(E)\,|dE| = \sigma(\nu)\,|d\nu| \tag{76.4}$$

where ν is related to E by (76.1).

[1] For more detailed discussions of Bremsstrahlung, see ref. [7], Chap. 7 and ref. [6], Sect. 25; also the article by H. A. Bethe and J. Ashkin in E. Segrè, Experimental Nuclear Physics, Vol. 1, Part II (New York: J. Wiley 1953), and L. P. Smith, Rev. Mod. Phys. **6**, 69 (1934).

[2] See, however, H. Olsen, Phys. Rev. **99**, 1335 (1955).

We have already made one approximation, namely to replace the atom on which the electron impinges by a fixed central potential $V(r)$. Calculations of Bremsstrahlung cross-sections are more difficult still than for the photoeffect (a larger number of momentum variables are involved) and various additional approximations have to be used under different circumstances. Two regions for the incident energy E_0 are of greatest practical interest. (1) For the production of the continuous X-ray spectrum in X-ray tubes, nonrelativistic energies $E_0 \ll mc^2$ are most important. In this case E_0 may not be large compared with the K-shell ionization potential of the struck atom. (2) For the passage of electrons from cosmic rays or from high energy accelerators through matter, the relativistic effects for $E_0 \gg mc^2$ are of greatest interest. In both cases 1 and 2, the struck atom is usually neutral and has a reasonably large nuclear charge Z. We outline now some of the approximations made under different circumstances.

α) Nonrelativistic treatment. If $Z\alpha \ll 1$ and if $E_0 \ll mc^2$, then both the initial and final states of the electron can be treated nonrelativistically. (E is always less than E_0.) In this case SCHRÖDINGER wave functions can be used and the various energies and momenta are related by [see Eq. (76.1)],

$$E_0 = \frac{p_0^2}{2m}, \qquad E = \frac{p^2}{2m}, \qquad k = \frac{p_0^2 - p^2}{2mc}. \tag{76.5}$$

Since $p_0 \ll mc$, (76.5) shows that the photon momentum k is always small compared with the momentum change $|\boldsymbol{p}_0 - \boldsymbol{p}|$ of the electron. As for the photoeffect, the neglect of retardation (neglecting $k/|\boldsymbol{p}_0 - \boldsymbol{p}|$) then introduces rather small errors at nonrelativistic energies. Nevertheless, the effect of retardation on the *angular* distribution is of relative order p_0/mc, whereas specifically relativistic effects are of order $(p_0/mc)^2$ and $(Z\alpha)^2$. These retardation effects are discussed briefly in Sect. 77γ. For a COULOMB potential and with retardation and relativistic effects omitted, both the differential and integrated cross sections have been evaluated analytically. These results are discussed in Sect. 78.

If the incident electron energy is relativistic, $E_0 \gtrsim mc^2$, the DIRAC theory has to be used for the electrons. Thus DIRAC spinor wave functions must be used for u_0 and u in the matrix element D, (76.2), and the momentum operator $\boldsymbol{p}$ is replaced by the DIRAC matrix $mc\boldsymbol{\alpha}$. We also have to use the relativistic relation $E = \sqrt{m^2c^4 + p^2c^2}$ between energy and momentum and (76.1) takes the form

$$k = \sqrt{(mc)^2 + p_0^2} - \sqrt{(mc)^2 + p^2}. \tag{76.6}$$

At extremely relativistic energies, $p \gg mc$, the photon momentum k is approximately equal to $p_0 - p$, which can be very close to the electron's momentum transfer $|\boldsymbol{p}_0 - \boldsymbol{p}|$ and retardation effects are extremely important. No exact relativistic calculations for arbitrary values of $Z\alpha$ are available. Approximate calculations, which neglect $(Z\alpha)^2$ compared with unity, have been carried out for arbitrary energy and arbitrary potential $V(r)$. The results of these calculations, the so-called BETHE-HEITLER formula, are discussed in Sect. 79α. Some calculations for extremely relativistic energies, which neglect only $Z\alpha\, mc/p_0$ (not $Z\alpha$), are discussed in Sect. 79β.

β) The BORN *approximation.* If $Z\alpha \ll 1$ and if both E_0 and E are large compared with the K-shell ionization potential $I_1 \sim \frac{1}{2}(Z\alpha)^2 mc^2 = Z^2$ Ry, the BORN approximation (Sect. 7 and 9) can be used for the wave functions u_0 and u. We shall see (Sect. 77α) that u_0 and u can not *both* be replaced by plane waves, but methods somewhat similar to those of Sect. 70β have to be used. The BORN approximation results are reasonably simple even for an arbitrary potential $V(r)$ (see Sects. 77β and 79α).

At relativistic momenta $p_0 \gg mc$, the expansion parameter for the BORN approximation to the DIRAC wave functions is no longer $Z\alpha\, mc/p$, but $Ze^2/\hbar v$, where v is the velocity corresponding to the momentum p. Since v approaches the velocity of light c (not ∞) as $p/mc \to \infty$ the expansion parameter is of order $Z\alpha$ at extreme relativistic energies. The BETHE-HEITLER formula (Sect. 79α) is based on such a BORN approximation expansion and is in error by a factor of relative order $(Z\alpha)^2$ even at the highest energies.

γ) Screening. We consider next the various approximations used for the effective central potential $V(r)$ due to the struck atom (see also the discussion of Sect. 17β). This potential can also be written in the form

$$V(r) = -\frac{Ze^2}{r} + e^2 \int d^3r' \frac{\varrho(\boldsymbol{r}')}{|\boldsymbol{r} - \boldsymbol{r}'|}, \tag{76.7}$$

where Z is the nuclear charge and $e\varrho(r')$ is the (spherically symmetric) average charge distribution of the atomic electrons in the struck atom or ion. In Bremsstrahlung calculations which employ the BORN approximation, the quantity required is $V'(\boldsymbol{q})$, the three-dimensional FOURIER transform of $V(\boldsymbol{r})$ times $(2\pi)^{-\frac{3}{2}}$. Working in atomic units, we find from (76.7)

$$V'(q) = -\frac{Z - F(q)}{2\pi^2 q^2}, \qquad F(q) = \int d^3r\, \varrho(r)\, e^{i\boldsymbol{q}\cdot\boldsymbol{r}}. \tag{76.8}$$

As discussed in Sect. 7γ, the differential cross-section for *radiationless* scattering of an electron by the potential $V(r)$ is proportional to the quantity $|V'(q)|^2$, if $\boldsymbol{q}$ is the momentum change of the electron and if BORN approximation is used [see (7.11)]. The most accurate expressions for $V(r)$ and $\varrho(r)$ are obtained by means of the HARTREE method. The quantity $V'(q)$, or the atomic form-factor $F(q)$, can be obtained by numerical integration from the HARTREE potentials, but the integrations have to be carried out separately for each atom or ion and for each value of q. This HARTREE form-factor has been evaluated for a number of light and medium-heavy atoms (see [9], p. 188). For atoms with large nuclear charge Z, the THOMAS-FERMI approximation to the effective potential $V(r)$ is sufficiently accurate. For a neutral atom, $V(r)$ is given by a single function of $Z^{\frac{1}{3}}r$ for all Z and $F(q)$ as a function of $Z^{-\frac{1}{3}}q$. These functions have been tabulated ([9], p. 190); $V(r)$ falls off rapidly for $r \gg Z^{-\frac{1}{3}}$ (in atomic units) and $F(q)$ approaches Z rapidly for $q \ll Z^{\frac{1}{3}}$, so that $V'(q)$ in (76.8) is much smaller than the expression for the unscreened COULOMB potential ($F=0$). Note that the BOHR momentum for charge Z is $Z \gg Z^{\frac{1}{3}}$ (in atomic units). A very simple form for the effective potential, which only gives a *qualitative* account of screening, is

$$V(r) = -\frac{Z}{r} e^{-Qr}, \qquad V'(q) = -\frac{Z}{2\pi^2 (q^2 + Q^2)}, \tag{76.9}$$

where Q is a constant of the order of magnitude of $Z^{\frac{1}{3}}$.

In Sect. 78 we shall discuss exact nonrelativistic results, valid for the special case of a COULOMB potential. These calculations can be adapted to take screening into account, at least in a very crude way, by choosing $V(r)$ of form (69.6)

$$V(r) = \left(-\frac{Z-s}{r} + V_0\right) \text{a.u.} \tag{76.10}$$

The wave functions in the matrix element (76.2) are needed most accurately for radial distances r of the order of $\hbar|\boldsymbol{p}_0 - \boldsymbol{p}|^{-1}$ ($\boldsymbol{p}_0$ and $\boldsymbol{p}$ are the initial and final electron momenta). One can then choose s and V_0 so that (76.10) approximates the THOMAS-FERMI potential most closely for these radial distances. For atoms with large Z, the values of $|\boldsymbol{p}_0-\boldsymbol{p}|$ of most practical interest are usually large compared with $Z^{\frac{1}{3}}$. In this case[1] one puts $s=0$ in (76.10).

The replacement of a complex atom by a fixed effective potential $V(r)$ only takes account of the influence of the atomic electrons for processes in which these atomic electrons remain in their bound orbits after the emission of the photon (coherent effects). We are thus omitting "electron-electron Bremsstrahlung", where the momentum change of the incident electron is not taken up by the fixed potential, but by one of the atomic electrons, which is ejected from the atom in the process. In such a process the ejected atomic electron also carries away energy. The ratio of the cross-section for such processes to that of ordinary "potential Bremsstrahlung" is proportional to $1/Z$ and at nonrelativistic energies[2] is very small even if Z is small (see also Sect. 79γ).

77. Nonrelativistic BORN approximation. α) *The matrix element.* We first rewrite the matrix element (76.2) as an integral over momentum space. We use atomic units and denote the FOURIER transforms of the two wave functions $u_0(\boldsymbol{r})$ and $u(\boldsymbol{r})$ by $(2\pi)^{\frac{3}{2}}p_0^{-\frac{1}{2}}\psi_0(\boldsymbol{p}')$ and by $p^{\frac{1}{2}}\psi(\boldsymbol{p}')$, respectively. With u_0 and u normalized per unit current density and per unit energy interval, respectively, the asymptotic "plane wave parts" of both $\psi_0(\boldsymbol{p}')$ and $\psi(\boldsymbol{p}')$ are then simply three-dimensional DIRAC delta functions. Using the fact that the photon's momentum $\boldsymbol{k}$ is perpendicular to its polarization direction $\boldsymbol{j}$, one can rewrite the matrix element D in (76.2) in the form

$$D=i\sqrt{\frac{p\,(2\pi)^3}{p_0}}\int d^3p'\,\psi^*(\boldsymbol{p}')\,p'_j\,\psi_0(\boldsymbol{p}'+\boldsymbol{k}), \tag{77.1}$$

where p'_j is the component of $\boldsymbol{p}'$ in the direction of $\boldsymbol{j}$.

ψ_0 and ψ are momentum space wave functions for eigenstates of the electron in the potential (76.7) which have "asymptotic momentum" $\boldsymbol{p}_0$ and $\boldsymbol{p}$, respectively. If both p_0 and p are *large* compared with the BOHR momentum Z (E_0 and E large compared with the ground state binding energy Z^2 Ry), then we can replace ψ_0 and ψ by their BORN approximation expressions [see (9.7) and (9.11)],

$$\left.\begin{aligned}\psi_0(\boldsymbol{p}')&=\delta^{(3)}(\boldsymbol{p}'-\boldsymbol{p}_0)+\frac{2}{p_0^2-p'^2}V'(\boldsymbol{p}'-\boldsymbol{p}_0),\\ \psi(\boldsymbol{p}')&=\delta^{(3)}(\boldsymbol{p}'-\boldsymbol{p})+\frac{2}{p^2-p'^2}V'(\boldsymbol{p}'-\boldsymbol{p}),\end{aligned}\right\} \tag{77.2}$$

where $V'(q)$ is given[3] by (76.8). The terms involving V' in (77.2) represent the second term in an expansion in powers of Z/p_0 (or Z/p). On substituting (77.2) into (77.1) we obtain the sum of four integrals. Since $Z\ll p_0$, p we might expect the leading term (cf. Sect. 70α) to be the one involving both $\delta^{(3)}(\boldsymbol{p}_0-\boldsymbol{p}'-\boldsymbol{k})$ and $\delta^{(3)}(\boldsymbol{p}-\boldsymbol{p}')$. However, $\boldsymbol{p}_0-\boldsymbol{p}-\boldsymbol{k}$ can never vanish if the equation of energy conservation (76.6) [or (76.5) if $p_0, p\ll mc$] is satisfied. The "leading" term in (77.1) is then identically zero: Physically speaking, this is due to the fact that an absolutely free electron cannot emit a photon without violating the conservation of either energy or momentum. For Bremsstrahlung to take place

[1] V_0 can then be chosen so that (69.7) with $s=0$, $n=1$ agrees with the experimental K-shell ionization potential.

[2] J. KATZENSTEIN: Phys. Rev. **78**, 161 (1950).

[3] In the denominators in (77.2) we have omitted the infinitesimal imaginary parts $\pm i\,\varepsilon$, since we shall not need these functions for p' equal to p_0 or p in our approximate calculations.

the atomic potential V must then "absorb some momentum", i.e. we have to consider the effect of the potential V' on at least one of the wave functions ψ_0 and ψ.

We shall see that the two terms involving one delta function and one power of V', obtained by substituting (77.2) into (77.1), are non-zero. The fourth term involving two powers of V is smaller by a factor of order Z/p and we shall omit it. Carrying out the integrals for these two terms, we find

$$D = 2i\, V'(q) \sqrt{\frac{p\,(2\pi)^3}{p_0}} \left(\frac{p_{0j}}{p^2 - |\boldsymbol{p}_0 - \boldsymbol{k}|^2} + \frac{p_j}{p_0^2 - |\boldsymbol{p} + \boldsymbol{k}|^2} \right), \tag{77.3}$$

where

$$\boldsymbol{q} = \boldsymbol{p}_0 - \boldsymbol{p} - \boldsymbol{k} \tag{77.4}$$

is the "momentum transfer absorbed by the atomic potential". (77.3) is the required BORN approximation result for the matrix element (expressed in atomic units) and can be substituted into (76.2) to give the differential cross-section.

Identically the same BORN approximation result (77.3) can also be obtained by a slightly different method (see [6], p. 242). One considers *both* the atomic potential $V(r)$ and the electron's interaction with the radiation field as perturbations on the HAMILTONian $H_0 = p^2/2m$. One then uses second order perturbation theory to calculate the probability amplitude for the transition of the electron from a free state of momentum $\boldsymbol{p}_0$ to one of momentum $\boldsymbol{p}$ with the emission of the photon. The two terms in (77.3) correspond to the photon being emitted by the electron before or after the electron is scattered by the potential V.

β) Cross-section without retardation. The following inequalities can be derived from the nonrelativistic relation (76.5),

$$\frac{k}{|\boldsymbol{p}_0 - \boldsymbol{p}|} \leq \frac{p_0}{m c}, \quad (2\boldsymbol{p}_0 \cdot \boldsymbol{k}) \frac{m c}{p_0} \leq p_0^2 - p^2 \geq (2\boldsymbol{p} \cdot \boldsymbol{k}) \frac{m c}{p}.$$

Since $p < p_0 \ll mc$, we can then neglect retardation with only a small loss of accuracy. I.e. we can replace k by zero both in (77.4) and in the two denominators in (77.3).

With retardation neglected, (77.3) reduces to

$$D = -2i\, V'(|p_0 - p|) \sqrt{\frac{p}{p_0}\,(2\pi)^3}\; \frac{p_0 x_0 - p x}{p_0^2 - p^2}, \tag{77.5}$$

where x_0 and x are the cosines of the angles which $\boldsymbol{p}_0$ and $\boldsymbol{p}$, respectively, make with the polarization direction $\boldsymbol{j}$. Note that (77.5) does not depend explicitly on the propagation direction $\boldsymbol{k}$ of the photon (except that $\boldsymbol{j}$ must be perpendicular to $\boldsymbol{k}$). Substituting (77.5) into (76.2), using (76.1) and reverting to C.G.S. units, we find for the differential cross-section

$$\sigma(E, \Omega_p, \Omega_k, j) = [Z - F(q)]^2 \alpha^3 \frac{\hbar^2}{\pi^2} \frac{p}{p_0} \frac{1}{E_0 - E} \frac{(p_0 x_0 - p x)^2}{q^4}, \tag{77.6}$$

where $\boldsymbol{q} = \boldsymbol{p}_0 - \boldsymbol{p}$ and F is defined in (76.8).

The differential cross-section (77.6), for fixed p_0, depends on a number of variables: On one energy variable E [or p or k, since E, p, k are connected by (76.5)], on the direction of $\boldsymbol{p}$ through the factor $q = |\boldsymbol{p}_0 - \boldsymbol{p}|$, on the polarization direction $\boldsymbol{j}$ through the cosine factors x_0 and x, and indirectly on the electron's propagation direction $\boldsymbol{k}$ (since $\boldsymbol{j}$ and $\boldsymbol{k}$ must be perpendicular). We shall outline a few properties of the Bremsstrahlung spectrum, derivable from (77.6), all for a fixed value of $\boldsymbol{p}_0$ (directed along the x-axis, say).

We consider first the polarization of photons which are emitted with a given momentum $\boldsymbol{k}$. The absolute value, but not the direction Ω_p, of $\boldsymbol{p}$ is then fixed. If one neglects screening [i.e. replaces F in (77.6) by zero], the integral over $d\Omega_p$ can be carried out[1]. If, for instance, $\boldsymbol{k}$ is perpendicular to the direction of incidence $\boldsymbol{p}_0$ of the electron ($\boldsymbol{p}_0$ in the x-direction, $\boldsymbol{k}$ in the y-direction), then the polarization direction $\boldsymbol{j}$ must lie in the xz-plane. Let $J_\parallel$ and $J_\perp$ be the relative probabilities for polarization $\boldsymbol{j}$ in the x-direction and z-direction, respectively. After integrating over $d\Omega_p$, one finds the following expression for P, a measure of the degree of polarization,

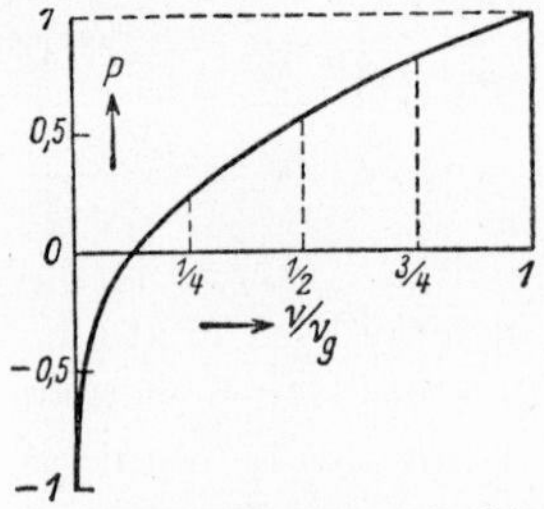

Fig. 38. The measure P, defined in (77.7), of polarization of Bremsstrahlung photons emitted at right angles to the momentum of the incident electron. The abscissa is the photon frequency ν divided by the high-frequency limit ν_g (called ν_0 in the text).

$$P \equiv \frac{J_\parallel - J_\perp}{J_\parallel + J_\perp} = \frac{(p_0^2 - 3p^2)\log\dfrac{p_0+p}{p_0-p} + 6p_0 p}{(3p_0^2 - p^2)\log\dfrac{p_0+p}{p_0-p} + 2p_0 p}. \tag{77.7}$$

As $p/p_0 \to 0$, i.e. near the high-frequency limit ν_0 of the photon spectrum,

$$h\nu_0 = k_0 c = E_0 = p_0^2/2m, \tag{77.8}$$

P approaches $+1$, i.e. the photons are all polarized in the x-direction. As $p \to p_0$ (i.e. as ν and k approach zero) P approaches -1, i.e. the photons are all polarized in the z-direction. In Fig. 38 the quantity P, Eq. (77.7), is plotted against $\nu/\nu_0 = 1 - p^2/p_0^2$.

For a fixed direction and absolute value of $\boldsymbol{p}$, the indirect dependence of the cross-section on the photon's propagation direction $\boldsymbol{k}$ is obtained as follows. Let ϑ and ϑ_0 be the angles which $\boldsymbol{k}$ makes with $\boldsymbol{p}$ and $\boldsymbol{p}_0$, respectively, and φ the angle between the $(\boldsymbol{p}, \boldsymbol{k})$ and $(\boldsymbol{p}_0, \boldsymbol{k})$ planes. Further, let χ be the angle between $\boldsymbol{k}$ and the fixed vector (momentum transfer) $\boldsymbol{q} = \boldsymbol{p}_0 - \boldsymbol{p}$. We now have to sum the expression $(p_0 x_0 - p x)^2 = (p_{0j} - p_j)^2$ in (77.6) over two polarization directions $\boldsymbol{j}$, perpendicular to each other and to $\boldsymbol{k}$. The result can be written in various forms,

$$\left.\begin{aligned}\sum_{j \perp k} (p_{0j} - p_j)^2 &= q^2 - (\boldsymbol{q}\cdot\boldsymbol{k})^2/k^2 = q^2 \sin^2\chi \\ &= p_0^2 \sin^2\vartheta_0 + p^2 \sin^2\vartheta - 2p_0 p \sin\vartheta_0 \sin\vartheta \cos\varphi.\end{aligned}\right\} \tag{77.9}$$

The intensity ($\propto \sin^2\chi$) thus has a maximum for $\boldsymbol{k}$ in (and is symmetric about) the plane perpendicular to the direction of the momentum transfer $\boldsymbol{q}$. If $p \ll p_0$ (ν near the high frequency limit ν_0), the direction of $\boldsymbol{q}$ is almost parallel to $\boldsymbol{p}_0$ (direction of incidence) and $\chi \approx \vartheta_0$. The expression (77.9) holds with or without screening.

With screening neglected and for a fixed absolute value of p and fixed vector $\boldsymbol{k}$, one can integrate the differential cross-section over $d\Omega_p$ and sum over polarization directions. The dependence of the resulting cross-section on the direction of $\boldsymbol{k}$ is then proportional to

$$J_\parallel \sin^2\vartheta_0 + J_\perp (1 + \cos^2\vartheta_0), \tag{77.10}$$

where the ratio of $J_\perp$ to $J_\parallel$ is given by (77.7). This distribution for $\boldsymbol{k}$ is again symmetric about the yz-plane ($\vartheta_0 = \pi/2$).

For a fixed direction and momentum $\boldsymbol{p}$ of the outgoing electron, one can also integrate (77.6) over the photon's propagation direction $d\Omega_k$ (after summing over

[1] For details, see ref. [7], Chap. 7, Sect. 3.

polarization directions), using (77.9). The angular distribution of the outgoing electrons[1] is then given by the cross-section

$$\sigma(E,\Omega_p)\,dE\,d\Omega_p = \alpha^3 \frac{8\hbar^2}{3\pi}\frac{dE}{E_0-E}\,d\Omega_p\,\frac{[Z-F(q)]^2}{q^2}, \tag{77.11}$$

in which expression only the last fraction depends on the direction of $\boldsymbol{p}$. If we neglect screening (put $F=0$), this factor reduces to

$$Z^2 q^{-2} = Z^2(p_0^2+p^2-2p_0 p\cos\alpha)^{-1}, \tag{77.12}$$

where α is the angle between $\boldsymbol{p}_0$ and $\boldsymbol{p}$. According to (77.12), the intensity of the scattered electrons has a maximum for forward scattering ($\alpha=0$) and a minimum for backward scattering ($\alpha=\pi$) and the dependence of the intensity on α is strongest if p_0-p is small (small photon energy).

We consider next the effect of screening, i.e. of the atomic form factor $F(q)$, on (77.11). Our BORN approximation is in any case only valid for p_0 and p large compared with the BOHR momentum, Z atomic units. As discussed in Sect. 76γ, $F(q)\ll Z$ if $q\gg Q$, where Q is a momentum of the order of $Z^{\frac{1}{3}}$ atomic units. Q is thus small compared with p_0 and p, especially for atoms with large Z. Since $q\gtrsim p_0-p$, we can neglect screening over most of the range of values of p (0 to p_0) and need consider it only for $p_0-p\lesssim Q\ll p_0$. If we use the very approximate form (76.9) for the screening potential, we get for the last fraction in (77.11)

$$Z^2 q^2 (q^2+Q^2)^{-2}, \tag{77.13}$$

instead of (77.12). The situation is qualitatively similar if more accurate screening potentials are used: The approximation (77.12) is accurate for $q\gg Q$, but for $p\to p_0$ the last fraction in (77.11) has a *finite* maximum value of the order of $Z^2 Q^{-2}$.

We finally come to the integrated cross-section (76.4). If we neglect screening, (77.11) with (77.12) can easily be integrated over $d\Omega_p$ to give

$$\sigma_B(\nu)\,d\nu = \sigma_0\frac{d\nu}{\nu}\log\frac{p_0+p}{p_0-p}, \tag{77.14}$$

where $\nu=kc/h$ is related to p_0, p by (76.5) and

$$\sigma_0 = \frac{16}{3}Z^2\alpha^3\left(\frac{\hbar}{p_0}\right)^2. \tag{77.15}$$

The BORN approximation $\nu\sigma_B(\nu)/\sigma_0$ is plotted against ν in Fig. 39, Sect. 78. As ν approaches the high frequency limit ν_0, Eq. (77.8), this function approaches zero as $2p/p_0$. However, the BORN approximation breaks down for $p\ll Z$ atomic units and we shall see in the next section that the correct cross-section approaches a *finite* limit as $\nu\to\nu_0$.

As ν approaches the low frequency limit zero ($p\to p_0$), $\nu\sigma_B(\nu)/\sigma_0$ for an unscreened COULOMB potential approaches infinity as $\log\left(2p_0/(p_0-p)\right)$. For an actual neutral atom, however, (77.13) shows that $\nu\sigma(\nu)/\sigma_0$ with screening included deviates from the unscreened expression for very low values of ν ($p_0-p\lesssim Q$) and approaches a *finite* value of the order[2] of $\log(p_0/Q)$ as $\nu\to 0$.

---

[1] O. SCHERZER: Ann. d. Phys. **13**, 137 (1932).

[2] For a more detailed account of screening see F. SAUTER, Ann. d. Phys. **18**, 486 (1933); **20**, 404 (1934).

We finally compare the order of magnitude of the cross-section σ_0, Eq. (77.15), with that of large-angle COULOMB scattering and of recombination. We find

$$\sigma_0 \sim \alpha \left(\frac{p_0}{m c}\right)^2 \sigma_R \sim \left(\frac{p_0}{Z \text{ at. un.}}\right)^2 \sigma_{\text{rec}}, \tag{77.16}$$

where $\sigma_R \sim (Z e^2/E_0)^2$ is the cross-section for radiationless RUTHERFORD scattering through large angles and σ_{rec} the order of magnitude for the cross-section for recombination or radiative capture [cf. Eq. (75.7)]. Thus, although σ_0 decreases in absolute value with increasing p_0, its ratios to σ_R and to σ_{rec} increase. σ_0 is small compared with σ_R at all nonrelativistic energies E_0, but is larger than σ_{rec} if E_0 is much larger than the K-shell ionization potential of the atom.

We have seen that, with screening included, the quantity $\nu\sigma(\nu)$ approaches a finite, but *non*-zero, limit as $\nu \to 0$. Hence the integral $\int d\nu\, \sigma(\nu)$ diverges logarithmically at the low-frequency limit. One also finds a similar result if one keeps the direction of the final momentum $\boldsymbol{p}$ of the electron fixed (rather than integrating over it): The relative probability that the scattering of an electron from momentum $\boldsymbol{p}_0$ to $\boldsymbol{p}_0 - \boldsymbol{q}$ be accompanied by the emission of a photon of very low frequency (between ν and $\nu + d\nu$) is of the order of magnitude of $\alpha (q/m c)^2 d\nu/\nu$. The *total* number of low frequency photons which are emitted in a scattering process is thus infinite, but only of the order of one photon is emitted in the enormous fractional frequency range ν to $\nu \exp(-137\, m^2 c^2/q^2)$. This so called infrared catastrophe was discussed in Sect. 18γ in connection with radiative corrections to elastic scattering.

Another quantity of interest is the average energy loss, due to Bremsstrahlung radiation, of an electron passing through matter. This energy loss per unit length of path is

$$-\frac{dE_0}{dx} = N \int_0^{\nu_0} h\nu\, \sigma(\nu)\, d\nu, \tag{77.17}$$

where N is the number of atoms per unit volume. Using the BORN approximation (77.14) for $\sigma(\nu)$, the result of the integration gives (see [6], p. 252)

$$-\frac{1}{\log 2} \frac{dE_0}{dx} = 2N E_0 \sigma_0 = \frac{16}{3} N Z^2 \alpha \frac{e^4}{m c^2} = \frac{32}{3} N Z^2 \alpha^3 \frac{\text{Ry}}{a_0}. \tag{77.18}$$

The last expression in (77.18) holds if N is expressed in atoms per a_0^3 and length in the atomic unit a_0. Note that the energy loss per unit length is *independent* of the energy E_0 (for energies for which the nonrelativistic BORN approximation holds). In atomic units, N is of the order of 0.01 for most solids (e.g. $N = 0.009$ for Al, $N = 0.005$ for Pb). The energy loss is then of the order of $100 Z^2$ electron volts per cm in solids. We shall not discuss the energy loss due to radiationless ionization of bound atomic electrons[1], which is actually much more important at nonrelativistic energies: The ionization energy loss per unit length is of order $N Z e^4/E_0$, i.e. larger than the Bremsstrahlung energy loss by a factor of order $m c^2/Z \alpha E_0$.

γ) *Retardation*[2]. Within the framework of nonrelativistic BORN approximation, retardation effects are included rigorously in the matrix element (77.3). In the discussion of Sect. 77β, we have neglected retardation in going from (77.3) to (77.5), i.e. by replacing the photon momentum $\boldsymbol{k}$ by zero both in the

[1] See ref. [6], Sect. 37; ref. [9], Chap. 11 and ref. [10], Sect. 56.

[2] For further details see ref. [7], Chap. 7, Sect. 6.

term $V'(q)$ and in the last two denominators in (77.3). From (76.5) we find the following expression, valid only for nonrelativistic energies,

$$k = (p_0 - p)\frac{p_0 + p}{2mc} \lessapprox |\boldsymbol{p}_0 - \boldsymbol{p}|\frac{p_0}{mc} = |\boldsymbol{p}_0 - \boldsymbol{p}|\frac{v_0}{c}, \tag{77.19}$$

where v_0 is the velocity of the incident electron. Retardation affects the angular distribution of the emitted photons, but (as for the photoeffect) the effect is only of relative order v_0/c.

We discuss only two special cases, for which the angular distribution of the photons is relatively simple and the effect of retardation is relatively important: (1) The initial and final momenta $\boldsymbol{p}_0$ and $\boldsymbol{p}$ are parallel to each other. (2) The inequality $p \ll p_0$ holds (high frequency limit) and the direction of $\boldsymbol{p}$ is arbitrary. We sum the differential scattering cross-section over the two possible polarization directions. With retardation neglected, this cross-section for both cases is then [see (77.9)] proportional to $\sin^2\vartheta_0$, where ϑ_0 is the angle between $\boldsymbol{p}_0$ and $\boldsymbol{k}$, i.e. the intensity has a maximum in the plane perpendicular to $\boldsymbol{p}_0$. We now take for $V'(q)$ in (77.3) an unscreened COULOMB potential ($V' \propto q^{-2}$) and take the ratio R of the retarded matrix element (77.3) and the unretarded one (77.5). Using (77.19), expanding the ratio R in powers of v_0/c and keeping only the first two terms, we find in both cases

$$R^2 = 1 + 4\frac{v_0 + v}{c}\cos\vartheta_0, \tag{77.20}$$

where v is the electron's velocity in the final state.

The angular distribution is then given by a cross-section which is proportional to $R^2 \sin^2\vartheta_0$. The intensity thus no longer has a maximum for $\vartheta_0 = \frac{1}{2}\pi$, but for an angle $\vartheta_{0,\max}$, given by (for $v_0 \ll c$)

$$\frac{\pi}{2} - \vartheta_{0,\max} = 2\frac{v_0 + v}{c}. \tag{77.21}$$

Near the high-frequency limit ($v \ll v_0$), these nonrelativistic expressions for the angular distribution become identical with those for the photoeffect (after averaging over polarization directions) in nonrelativistic approximation (Sect. 72β). In fact, the angular distributions for the photoeffect and for Bremsstrahlung remain identical even at relativistic energies, as long as $v \ll v_0$. Thus Fig. 35 also applies to Bremsstrahlung near the high-frequency limit.

78. Calculations for low energies. As mentioned before, the BORN approximation results of the previous section break down unless both the initial and final momenta p_0 and p of the electron are large compared with the BOHR momentum of the struck atom. Neglecting only retardation and relativistic effects, SOMMERFELD[1] has obtained an exact analytic expression for the differential cross-section (76.2) for an unscreened COULOMB potential. This general expression is rather complicated and we shall only quote some of the results derivable from it (for details see [7], Chap. 7).

We discuss first the integrated cross-section (76.4). By a very ingenious method[2] SOMMERFELD's differential cross-section for a pure COULOMB potential can be integrated over all electron and photon angles. Let

$$n_0 = \frac{Z\text{ at. un.}}{p_0}, \qquad n = \frac{Z\text{ at. un.}}{p}, \qquad \frac{\nu}{\nu_0} = 1 - \frac{n_0^2}{n^2}, \tag{78.1}$$

[1] A. SOMMERFELD: Ann. d. Phys. **11**, 257 (1931).
[2] A. SOMMERFELD and A. MAUE: Ann. d. Phys. **23**, 589 (1935).

where ν_0 is the high-frequency limit (77.8). The general result for the integrated cross-section $\sigma(\nu)$ is

$$\frac{\nu\,\sigma(\nu)}{\sigma_0} = \frac{\pi^2 x_0}{(e^{2\pi n_0}-1)(1-e^{-2\pi n})}\,\frac{d}{dx}\,|F(i\,n_0, i\,n, 1, x)|^2_{x=x_0}, \tag{78.2}$$

where

$$x_0 = -\frac{4 n_0 n}{(n-n_0)^2} = -\frac{4 p_0 p}{(p_0-p)^2}, \tag{78.3}$$

and σ_0 is defined by (77.15). F is the general (*not* the confluent) hypergeometric function whose power series expansion is (for $x<1$)

$$F(a, b, c, x) = 1 + \frac{a\,b}{c}\,x + \frac{a(a+1)\,b(b+1)}{c(c+1)}\,\frac{x^2}{2!} + \cdots. \tag{78.4}$$

The general expression (78.2), which is a complicated function of the two variables n_0 and n, can be simplified for various limiting values of n_0 and n, using various properties of the hypergeometric function, such as

$$\frac{d}{dx}\,|F|^2_{x=x_0} = -2 n_0\, n\, \mathrm{Re}\,[F(1-i\,n_0, 1-i\,n, 2, x_0)\,F(i\,n_0, i\,n, 1, x_0)] \tag{78.5}$$

and

$$F(1, 1, 2, x_0) = -x_0^{-1}\log(1-x_0). \tag{78.6}$$

In the limit $2\pi n_0 \ll 1$, one finds

$$\frac{\nu\,\sigma(\nu)}{\sigma_0} = \frac{2\pi n}{1-e^{-2\pi n}}\log\left(\frac{n+n_0}{n-n_0}\right). \tag{78.7}$$

If we also have $2\pi n \ll 1$, then (78.7) reduces to the BORN approximation expression (77.14). Note, however, that (78.7) goes to a finite *non*-zero value at the high frequency limit $n \to \infty$ ($p \to 0$). ELWERT[1] finds that the following more accurate approximation to (78.2) is in error by less than about 10% for values of n_0 up to about 0.5,

$$\frac{\nu\,\sigma(\nu)}{\sigma_0} = \frac{n}{n_0}\,\frac{1-e^{-2\pi n_0}}{1-e^{-2\pi n}}\log\left(\frac{n+n_0}{n-n_0}\right). \tag{78.8}$$

(78.8) is identical with the BORN approximation result near the low-frequency limit ($n \to n_0$) and approaches the following limit as $n \to \infty$ ($\nu \to \nu_0$, $p \to 0$)

$$\frac{\nu_0\,\sigma(\nu_0)}{\sigma_0} = 2\,(1-e^{-2\pi n_0}). \tag{78.9}$$

If $2\pi n_0 \ll 1$, ELWERT'S expression (78.8) reduces to (78.7).

For values of n_0 near the upper limit of validity of (78.8), $n_0 \sim 1$, the two exponential terms in (78.8) are rather small and the ratio of (78.8) to the BORN approximation is approximately n/n_0. ELWERT has also shown that (78.8) holds even if n_0 is *not* small, as long as $n - n_0 \ll 1$. Thus the BORN approximation holds very close to the low-frequency limit even for very low initial momenta p_0 of the electron.

In the limit of $p_0 \to 0$ and *away* from the low-frequency limit, i.e. for $n_0 \gg 1 \ll n - n_0$, one can derive[2] another approximation to (78.2): One uses (78.5) and the integral representation for the general hypergeometric function F. Using the fact that $n, n_0 \gg 1$, one can simplify the contour integrals by a method similar

[1] G. ELWERT: Ann. d. Physik **34**, 178 (1939).
[2] See also J. A. GAUNT, Phil. Trans. Roy. Soc. Lond. Ser. A **229**, 163 (1930).

to the method of stationary phase (see [7], appendix Sect. 16). Using such relations as

$$\int_0^\infty dx \frac{\cos x}{x^{\frac{2}{3}}} = \Gamma\left(\frac{1}{3}\right) \sin\frac{\pi}{3}, \qquad \int_0^\infty dx \frac{\sin x}{x^{\frac{1}{3}}} = \Gamma\left(\frac{2}{3}\right) \sin\frac{\pi}{3},$$

one finds the following constant value

$$\frac{\nu\,\sigma(\nu)}{\sigma_0} = \frac{\pi}{\sqrt{3}} = 1.82, \tag{78.10}$$

valid if $n - n_0 \gg 1$, as well as $n_0 \gg 1$.

To summarize the situation: The high-frequency limit of $\nu\sigma(\nu)/\sigma_0$ is $4\pi n_0$ for $2\pi n_0 \ll 1$, increases to a maximum value of about two for n_0 of the order of unity and then approaches 1.82 as n_0 approaches infinity. The dependence on ν of $\nu\sigma(\nu)/\sigma_0$ becomes less marked as n_0 increases, except near the low-frequency limit where the function approaches $\log\left(2n/(n-n_0)\right)$ for all values of n_0. In Fig. 39 we have plotted the function $\nu\sigma(\nu)/\sigma_0$ as a function of ν for various values of n_0: "BORN" denotes the BORN approximation ($n_0 \to 0$), "hard" denotes a value of $n_0 \approx 0.04$, "medium" denotes n_0 about 0.5 and "soft" denotes an *estimated* curve for fairly large values of n_0 (of the order of 5).

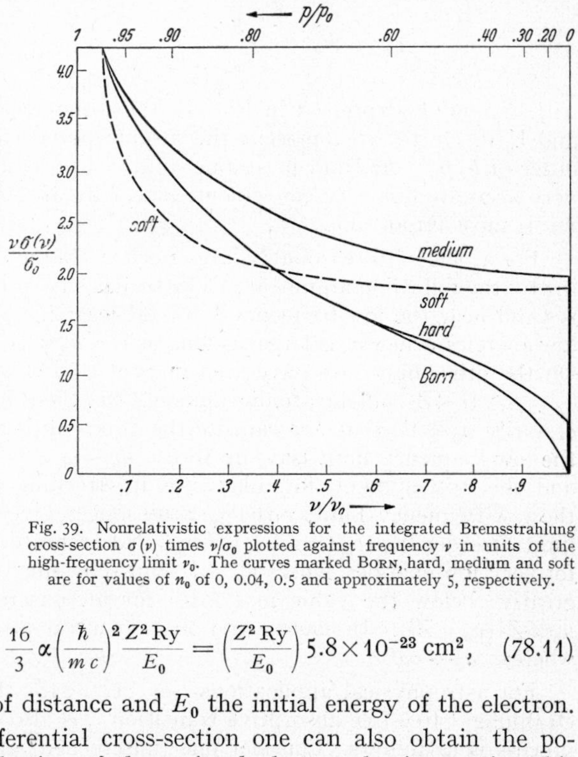

Fig. 39. Nonrelativistic expressions for the integrated Bremsstrahlung cross-section $\sigma(\nu)$ times ν/σ_0 plotted against frequency ν in units of the high-frequency limit ν_0. The curves marked BORN, hard, medium and soft are for values of n_0 of 0, 0.04, 0.5 and approximately 5, respectively.

The constant σ_0, defined by (77.15), which gives the order of magnitude of Bremsstrahlung cross-sections, can also be written as

$$\sigma_0 = \frac{16}{3} Z^2 \alpha^3 a_0^2 \frac{\mathrm{Ry}}{E_0} = \frac{16}{3} \alpha \left(\frac{\hbar}{m c}\right)^2 \frac{Z^2\,\mathrm{Ry}}{E_0} = \left(\frac{Z^2\,\mathrm{Ry}}{E_0}\right) 5.8 \times 10^{-23}\,\mathrm{cm}^2, \tag{78.11}$$

where a_0 is the atomic unit of distance and E_0 the initial energy of the electron.

From SOMMERFELD's differential cross-section one can also obtain the polarization and angular distribution of the emitted photons, by integrating this cross-section over $d\Omega_p$, the direction of the electron's final momentum (for fixed photon momentum $\boldsymbol{k}$ and polarization $\boldsymbol{j}$). For general n_0 and n, the result of this integration cannot be expressed in closed analytical form [unlike the *total* cross-section (78.2)]. However, these integrals have been carried out by semi-numerical methods for a number[1] of values of n_0 and n and analytic expressions are available in limiting cases: The measure $P = (J_\parallel - J_\perp)/(J_\parallel + J_\perp)$ is given by the BORN approximation expression (77.7), plotted in Fig. 38, if $2\pi n_0 \ll 1$. At

[1] R. WEINSTOCK, Phys. Rev. **61**, 585 (1942), ELWERT's paper, and especially P. KIRKPATRICK and L. WIEDMANN, Phys. Rev. **67**, 321 (1945), who also give numerical values for (78.2) for various values of n_0 and n.

the low-frequency limit ($\nu=0$), $P=-1$ for all values of n. If $2\pi n_0$ is not very small, P increases more rapidly with increasing ν than (77.7) for small ν and then approaches a constant value less than unity as $\nu\to\nu_0$ (high-frequency limit). For $n_0\gg 1$ (very low initial electron energy), P approaches the constant value of $\frac{3}{5}$ for all except very small frequencies ν (valid as long as $n-n_0\gg 1$). For $P=\frac{3}{5}$, the polarization is not complete, but $J_{\parallel}=4J_{\perp}$. The angular distribution of the emitted photons is given in terms of $J_{\parallel}/J_{\perp}$ by (77.10) for all values of n_0 and n.

SOMMERFELD's differential cross-section, and the total cross-section (78.2) derived from it, is valid only for an unscreened COULOMB potential. However, these formulas can be adapted to a potential of the form (76.10), which takes account of the atomic screening at least over a reasonable range of radial distances. In SOMMERFELD's formula, and in the definition (77.15) for σ_0 one simply replaces Z by $Z-s$ and defines n_0 and n (instead of 78.1) by

$$n_0=\frac{Z-s}{\sqrt{E_0-2V_0}}\,,\qquad n=\frac{Z-s}{\sqrt{E-2V_0}}\,, \tag{78.12}$$

with E_0 and E expressed in Ry. In the differential cross-section one chooses s and V_0 in (76.10) to represent the atomic potential $V(r)$ for values of r of the order of $\hbar|\boldsymbol{p}_0-\boldsymbol{p}|^{-1}$ (all in atomic units). Unfortunately this method is neither very accurate nor very convenient, especially at very low energies where screening is most important.

For atoms with reasonably large nuclear charge Z, one can account for screening by the following argument: ELWERT has shown that the BORN approximation is valid near the low-frequency limit (at least for a COULOMB potential) even at low energies, when n_0 is large, as long as $n-n_0\ll 1$ [with n_0, n defined by (78.1)]. On the other hand, we have seen in Sect. 77β that screening is unimportant if $p_0-p\gg Q\sim Z^{\frac{1}{3}}$ (all in atomic units). One then finds, *if* $n_0\ll Z^{\frac{1}{3}}$ (but not necessarily $n_0\ll 1$), that one can use the BORN approximation with screening near the low-frequency limit (say, up to $n-n_0\sim n_0\,Z^{-\frac{1}{3}}\ll 1$, i.e. $p_0-p\sim Z^{\frac{2}{3}}\,n_0^{-1}\gg Z^{\frac{1}{3}}$) and the SOMMERFELD formula without screening for larger frequencies. Near the low-frequency limit, $\nu\,\sigma(\nu)/\sigma_0$ is no longer given by (78.8), but has a finite[1] limit of order $\log(p_0/Q)\sim\log(Z^{\frac{2}{3}}/n_0)$. No accurate approximations are available for very low energies, where $n_0\gg Z^{\frac{1}{3}}$, but screening depresses the value of $\nu\,\sigma(\nu)/\sigma_0$ greatly [below the value in (78.10) for an unscreened COULOMB potential] if $n_0\gg Z^{\frac{2}{3}}\,(p_0\ll Z^{\frac{1}{3}})$. In fact, $\nu\,\sigma(\nu)$ for a neutral atom remains finite as $E_0\to 0$, whereas $\sigma_0\to\infty$.

For astrophysical applications (see Sect. 74β) the inverse process to Bremsstrahlung, "free-free absorptive transition", is also of interest. The fundamental process is as follows. Consider one (unscreened) atomic nucleus of charge Z at rest, immersed in a stream (of infinite extent) of electrons with density $\mathcal{N}$ per unit *volume* and velocity v, energy E. We are interested in the absorption cross-section $\sigma_{FF}(\nu)$ for a photon of frequency ν, presented by the combination of one nucleus plus the electron stream. In the process, one of the incident electrons makes a transition to a state of higher energy $E_0=E+h\nu$ (to obtain σ_{FF}, we integrate the differential cross-section over all directions of the final momentum of the electron). The matrix elements which enter into the formula for σ_{FF} are identical with those for the Bremsstrahlung process (transition from E_0 to E), but the various normalization factors are different.

[1] For details see P. KIRKPATRICK and L. WIEDMANN, Phys. Rev. **67**, 321 (1945).

If we average $\sigma_{FF}(\nu)$ over the angle between the momentum of the photon and that of the incident electrons, we find[1]

$$\sigma_{FF}(\nu) = \frac{\mathcal{N} v c^2}{\nu^3} \frac{E_0}{E} \frac{\nu \sigma(\nu)}{8\pi}, \tag{78.13}$$

where $\sigma(\nu)$ is the total Bremsstrahlung cross-section, defined in (76.3), (76.4). If we use the low-energy approximation (78.10) for $\sigma(\nu)$, we find

$$\sigma_{FF}(\nu) = \frac{2\mathcal{N}}{3\sqrt{3}} \frac{Z^2 e^6}{m^2 \hbar c v \nu^3} = \frac{2}{3\sqrt{3}} Z^2 \alpha \left(\frac{\mathcal{N}}{\nu^3 v}\right)_{\text{a.u.}}, \tag{78.14}$$

where the last expression holds if all quantities are expressed in atomic units (unit of frequency is 4π Ry). It is interesting to compare this expression with the low-energy approximation for $\sigma_n(\nu)$, the cross-section for the photoeffect from a shell of *bound* electrons with principal quantum number n, obtained from (71.19) and (71.20). In atomic units we have,

$$\sigma_n(\nu) = \frac{2}{3\sqrt{3}\,\pi^2} \frac{Z^4 \alpha}{\nu^3 n^3}. \tag{78.15}$$

The two cross-section are thus of the same order of magnitude, if (in atomic units) $\mathcal{N}$ is of order Z, v of order Z and n of order unity, for all Z and ν [at least in the range of ν not much larger than Z^2, where (78.14) and (78.15) are valid].

One can also *combine* expressions (78.14) and (78.15) in the following manner. We consider first the photoeffect from bound electron states with high principal quantum numbers n (total energy E negative and small compared with Z^2 Ry): If all the shells with principal quantum numbers from $n-y$ to $n+y$, say, are filled (with $n \gg y \gg 1$), then all the electronic states in the energy interval (in atomic units)

$$\Delta E = \frac{Z^2}{2(n-y)^2} - \frac{Z^2}{2(n+y)^2} = \frac{2yZ^2}{n^3}$$

are occupied. The photon absorption cross-section (78.15) from one closed shell thus represents the absorption from occupied electron states in the energy interval Z^2/n^3. We can then rewrite (78.15) in the following more general form: If a fraction ξ of all the electronic states in an energy interval ΔE are occupied, then the photon absorption cross-section from these electrons is

$$\sigma(\nu)\,\xi\,\Delta E = \frac{2}{3\sqrt{3}\,\pi^2} \frac{Z^2 \alpha}{\nu^3} \xi\,\Delta E. \tag{78.16}$$

Consider next free-free transitions from electrons with positive (but small) total energies near the energy E (momentum p, velocity v, all in atomic units). The total number of possible electronic states per unit energy interval per unit volume is then (cf. the theory of a degenerate FERMI gas)

$$\frac{8\pi}{(2\pi)^3} p^2 \frac{dp}{dE} = \frac{v}{\pi^2}.$$

If $\mathcal{N}$ free electrons per unit volume with energies in a small energy interval ΔE are present, the fraction ξ of states in this energy interval which are filled is then given by $\xi \Delta E = \pi^2 \mathcal{N}/v$. Substituting this relation into (78.14), we *also* obtain (78.16) for photon absorption from free electrons.

[1] See ref. [7], p. 566.

79. Relativistic effects[1]. If the electron is to be treated relativistically, the following changes have to be made in our previous treatment. We denote now by E_0 and E the total (including rest mass) initial and final energy of the electron, divided by c. We then have, instead of (76.5),

$$E_0 = \sqrt{p_0^2 + \mu^2}, \quad E = \sqrt{p^2 + \mu^2}, \quad h\nu/c \equiv k = E_0 - E, \tag{79.1}$$

where $\mu = mc$. We further have to use DIRAC wave functions and replace the operator $\boldsymbol{p}$ by $\mu \boldsymbol{\alpha}$ in the matrix element D, Eq. (76.2).

As discussed before, the exact DIRAC wave functions, which behave asymptotically like plane waves, for an electron in a COULOMB potential cannot be written in closed analytic form. Thus the DIRAC matrix element D cannot be evaluated analytically. The partial wave solutions (in spherical polar coordinates) of the DIRAC equation are expressible in analytic form and, in principle, D could be evaluated as an infinite sum of matrix elements which involve these solutions. Even this method is impractical, except for special cases such as extremely high energies (Sect. 79β). However, if BORN approximation is used, the calculations become relatively simple. The main results of such calculations are described below.

α) *The* BETHE-HEITLER *formula*. As in Sect. 77 we assume that $Z\alpha \ll 1$ and that the initial and final momenta p_0 and p are large compared with the BOHR momentum $Z\alpha\mu$ for nuclear charge Z. The BORN approximation to the DIRAC wave functions, which are the relativistic generalizations of (77.2), for an electron in *any* potential $V(r)$ can then be obtained analytically, if the FOURIER transform $V'(p)$ of the potential is known. By methods analogous to those leading to (77.3), one can then derive the BORN approximation to the DIRAC matrix element D. However, retardation must not be neglected since retardation effects are extremely important at relativistic energies. As in the nonrelativistic case, the same result for D can also be obtained by second-order perturbation theory, the method used by BETHE and HEITLER[2].

In the relativistic BORN approximation, the differential cross-section also depends on the initial and final spin-states of the electron as well as on the polarization direction of the photon. Summing over the final spin states and over photon polarization[3] and averaging over the initial spin-states, one obtains the BETHE-HEITLER result

$$\sigma(\nu, \Omega_p, \Omega_k)\, d\nu\, d\Omega_p\, d\Omega_k = \alpha^3 \frac{\hbar^2}{\pi^2}\, d\Omega_p\, d\Omega_k \frac{d\nu}{\nu} \frac{p}{p_0} \frac{[Z - F(q)]^2}{q^4}\, \Gamma, \tag{79.2}$$

where Γ is the expression

$$\left.\begin{aligned} \Gamma = p^2 \sin^2\vartheta \left(\frac{4E_0^2 - q^2}{4\varepsilon^2} + \frac{k^2}{2\varepsilon\,\varepsilon_0}\right) + p_0^2 \sin^2\vartheta_0 \left(\frac{4E^2 - q^2}{4\varepsilon_0^2} + \frac{k^2}{2\varepsilon\,\varepsilon_0}\right) - \\ - 2p\,p_0 \sin\vartheta \sin\vartheta_0 \cos\varphi \left(\frac{4E_0 E - q^2 + 2k^2}{4\varepsilon\,\varepsilon_0}\right) \end{aligned}\right\} \tag{79.3}$$

with

$$\boldsymbol{q} = \boldsymbol{p}_0 - \boldsymbol{p} - \boldsymbol{k}, \quad \varepsilon_0 = E_0 - p_0 \cos\vartheta_0, \quad \varepsilon = E - p\cos\vartheta. \tag{79.4}$$

---

[1] Bremsstrahlung and pair creation calculations at relativistic energies are described in more detail in ref. [7], Chap. 7, Sect. 7; ref. [6], Sects. 25 and 26; B. ROSSI aud K. GREISEN, Rev. Mod. Phys. **13**, 240 (1941) and J. ASHKIN und H. A. BETHE in E. SEGRÈ: Experimental Nuclear Physics, Vol. 1, Part II. New York; J. Wiley 1953.

[2] H. A. BETHE and W. HEITLER: Proc. Roy. Soc. Lond., Ser. A **146**, 83 (1934).

[3] Photon polarization is discussed by M. MAY and G. WICK, Phys. Rev. **81**, 628 (1951).

The screening function F is defined in (76.8), ϑ_0 (or ϑ) is the angle between $\boldsymbol{k}$ and $\boldsymbol{p}_0$ (or $\boldsymbol{p}$), φ the angle between the $(\boldsymbol{p}, \boldsymbol{k})$ and $(\boldsymbol{p}_0, \boldsymbol{k})$ planes and E, E_0, p, p_0 and k are connected by (79.1).

For nonrelativistic momenta, $p_0, p \ll \mu$, each of the three expressions in brackets in (79.3) can be expanded in powers of p_0/μ and p/μ. The leading term in each of these expansions is unity and the expression (79.3) for Γ reduces to the nonrelativistic, non-retarded expression (77.9). If terms linear in p_0/μ and p/μ are kept, and also terms linear in $k/|\boldsymbol{p}_0 - \boldsymbol{p}|$ in the expressions in (79.2) involving q [see Eq. (77.19)], the nonrelativistic retardation effects of Sect. 77γ are obtained.

If screening is neglected (F replaced by zero), the differential cross-section (79.2) with (79.3) can be integrated analytically [see [6], p. 245) over $d\Omega_p$ and also over $d\Omega_k$ for arbitrary values of p_0 and p. We shall discuss in detail only the limiting case of extremely large momenta.

For p_0 and p of the order of magnitude of μ the analytic expressions for the angular distribution of the photons and for the integrated cross-section are very involved, but the main effect is a shift in the forward direction of the angular distribution of the emitted photon and outgoing electron. For such momenta, the effect of screening is small, except near the low-frequency limit (ν and $p_0 - p$ small).

The expressions simplify somewhat in the extreme relativistic case of p_0, $p \gg \mu$. This case is of practical importance both for showers produced by the electronic component of cosmic rays in its passage through matter and for many high energy electron accelerators where the electron beam is made to strike an internal target and the emerging beam of Bremsstrahlung photons is used in experiments. For such extremely relativistic momenta the differential cross-section (79.2) is appreciably large only for small values of the angles ϑ and ϑ_0. This is due to the fact that the quantities ε and ε_0 in (79.4), as well as q, increase rapidly with increasing ϑ and ϑ_0 if p and p_0 are large. We simplify the expressions occuring in (79.2) to (79.4) by expanding E_0 and E in powers of μ/p_0 and μ/p and by making the small-angle approximation $\sin\vartheta \to \vartheta$ and $\cos\vartheta \to 1 - \frac{1}{2}\vartheta^2$. Carrying only the first two terms in the expansion in powers of μ/p_0 and μ/p, we get from (79.1)

$$E_0 = p_0 + \frac{1}{2}\frac{\mu^2}{p_0}, \quad E = p + \frac{1}{2}\frac{\mu^2}{p}, \quad k = (p_0 - p)\left(1 - \frac{1}{2}\frac{\mu^2}{p_0 p}\right). \tag{79.5}$$

From (79.4) we find

$$\left.\begin{aligned} 2\varepsilon_0 &= \frac{\mu^2}{p_0} + p_0\vartheta_0^2, \quad 2\varepsilon = \frac{\mu^2}{p} + p\,\vartheta^2; \\ q^2 &= q_{\min}^2 + (p_0\vartheta_0 - p\,\vartheta)^2 + 2p_0 p\,\vartheta_0\vartheta\,(1 - \cos\varphi) \end{aligned}\right\} \tag{79.6}$$

where

$$q_{\min} = (p_0 - p)\,\frac{\mu^2}{2p_0 p} \approx \frac{k\,\mu^2}{2p_0 p}. \tag{79.7}$$

Instead of quoting the exact results, we shall derive some simple expressions, illustrating the angular distribution of the photon and outgoing electron. We consider a fixed direction (and magnitude) of the photon momentum $\boldsymbol{k}$ for fixed $\boldsymbol{p}_0$ (ϑ_0 fixed). Let ξ be the angle which the outgoing electron momentum $\boldsymbol{p}$ makes with the fixed vector $\boldsymbol{p}_0 - \boldsymbol{k}$. Using the fact that ϑ_0 and ϑ are small, one can derive from (79.6) an alternative approximation for q,

$$q^2 = q_{\min}^2 + p^2\xi^2. \tag{79.8}$$

Now ε_0 (or ε), given by (79.6), increases rapidly with increasing ϑ_0 (or ϑ) if $\mu \ll p_0\vartheta_0$ (or $p\,\vartheta$) and the most important values of $p_0\vartheta_0$ (or $p\,\vartheta$) are of the order of μ.

On the other hand, q^2 [given by (79.8)] increases with increasing ξ for ξ larger than $k\mu^2/p_0p^2$ ($\ll \mu/p$). We shall see that the important range of values of ξ is

$$\frac{k\mu^2}{p_0p^2} \ll \xi \ll \frac{\mu}{p}(\sim\vartheta), \qquad q \ll \mu \ll k, p, p_0.$$

For $\xi \ll \vartheta$, (79.6) and (79.8) show that

$$p\vartheta \approx p_0\vartheta_0, \quad p\varepsilon \approx p_0\varepsilon_0.$$

We now replace $p\varepsilon$ by $p_0\varepsilon_0$ in (79.3) and omit q. Using (79.5) and (79.6), the expression (79.3) for Γ reduces approximately to

$$\Gamma = \frac{2p_0^3p^3\xi^2}{(p_0^2\vartheta_0^2+\mu^2)^2}$$

if $p \ll p_0$. Integrating over the azimuthal angles which correspond to ξ and ϑ_0 and substituting this expression for Γ into (79.2), we find

$$\left.\begin{aligned}\sigma(\nu,\Omega_p,\Omega_k)\,d\nu\,2\pi\xi\,d\xi\,2\pi\vartheta_0\,d\vartheta_0 &\equiv \sigma(\nu,\xi,\vartheta_0)\,d\nu\,d\xi\,d\vartheta_0\\ &= 8Z^2\alpha^3\left(\frac{\hbar}{\mu}\right)^2\frac{d\nu}{\nu}\left\{\frac{\xi^3\,d\xi}{\left[\xi^2+\left(\frac{k\mu^2}{2p_0p^2}\right)^2\right]^2}\right\}\left\{\frac{(\mu/p_0)^2\vartheta_0\,d\vartheta_0}{\left[\vartheta_0^2+\left(\frac{\mu}{p_0}\right)^2\right]^2}\right\}.\end{aligned}\right\} \quad (79.9)$$

Although (79.9) is strictly valid only if $p \ll p_0$, it gives the right order of magnitude of the cross-section for *all* values of p/p_0, as long as $\xi \ll \vartheta \ll 1$.

The angular distribution of the outgoing electron, as given by the first curly bracket in (79.9), behaves like $d\xi/\xi$ for $k\mu^2/2p_0p^2 \ll \xi$. For $\xi > \mu/p$, the approximation (79.9) breaks down and the cross-section decreases more rapidly with increasing ξ. After integrating over ξ, the first curly bracket in (79.9) reduces to an expression of the order of $\log(p_0p/k\mu) \gg 1$. The angular distribution of the photon is thus largely given by the second curly bracket in (79.9), i.e. most of the photons are emitted in a cone of semi-angle $\mu/p_0 \ll 1$ about the forward direction. The *exact* cross-section, integrated over ξ, for *arbitrary* p/p_0 (but for $p \gg \mu$, $\vartheta_0 \ll 1$) is (see [7], p. 551).

$$\begin{aligned}\sigma(\nu,\vartheta_0)\,d\nu\,d\vartheta_0 &= 4Z^2\alpha^3\left(\frac{\hbar}{\mu}\right)^2\frac{d\nu}{\nu}\,\frac{y^2\vartheta_0\,d\vartheta_0}{(\vartheta_0^2+y^2)^2}\times\\ &\times\left\{2\left[1+x^2-4x\left(\frac{\vartheta_0 y}{\vartheta_0^2+y^2}\right)^2\right]\log\left(\frac{2p_0p}{\mu k}\right)-\left[(1+x)^2-16x\left(\frac{\vartheta_0 y}{\vartheta_0^2+y^2}\right)^2\right]\right.,\end{aligned}$$

where $x = p/p_0$ and $y = \mu/p_0$. Note that the angular distribution of the photons does not depend very strongly on the ratio x. In particular, even for very low frequency ν ($x \to 1$) do most of the photons emerge in a narrow cone of semi-angle μ/p_0 around the forward direction.

By integrating the above expression over $d\vartheta_0$, one can obtain the integrated cross-section $\sigma(\nu)\,d\nu$, which we discuss below. However, one can also carry out the integrations in a different order: We again consider the initial vector momentum $\boldsymbol{p}_0$ and also the photon frequency ν (hence also p and k) as fixed. The vectors $\boldsymbol{p}$ and $\boldsymbol{k}$ for an elementary process can also be specified by giving the absolute value q and direction of the momentum transfer $\boldsymbol{q}$, defined in (79.4) (which fixes the vector $\boldsymbol{p}+\boldsymbol{k}$), as well as the azimuthal angle of the $(\boldsymbol{p},\boldsymbol{k})$ plane. Keeping the absolute value q fixed, one can carry out the angular integrations analytically[1]. The range of possible values of q extends from $q_{\min}$ ($\ll \mu$), defined

[1] This is done by H. A. Bethe, Proc. Cambridge Phil. Soc. **30**, 524 (1934). Since the screening factor F depends only on the absolute value q, the same analytic integrations hold even if screening is included (see Sect. 79β).

in (79.7), up to $p_0+p+k(\gg\mu)$. With screening neglected and for $p\ll p_0$, the dependence of the cross-section on q is given by

$$\sigma(\nu, q)\, d\nu\, dq \propto \frac{dq}{q}\left(\frac{q-q_{\min}}{q}\right)^2$$

for $q\ll\mu$, and the cross-section decreases more rapidly with increasing q for $q>\mu$. The dependence on q is qualitatively very similar for arbitrary values of p/p_0, i.e. the important range of q extends from about $2q_{\min}$ to about μ.

We finally quote the limit of the exact integrated cross-section for $p\gg\mu$, which is

$$\sigma(\nu)\, d\nu = \bar{\sigma}\frac{d\nu}{\nu}\left(1+\frac{p^2}{p_0^2}-\frac{2}{3}\frac{p}{p_0}\right)\left(\log\frac{2p_0 p}{k\mu}-\frac{1}{2}\right), \tag{79.10}$$

$$\bar{\sigma} = 4Z^2\alpha^3\left(\frac{\hbar}{\mu}\right)^2 = 4Z^2\alpha\left(\frac{e^2}{m c^2}\right)^2 = Z^2\times 2.32\times 10^{-27}\ \text{cm}^2. \tag{79.11}$$

The expression (79.10) is not valid very close to the high-frequency limit where $p\gtrsim\mu$. For $p\ll\mu$, the cross-section is of the form

$$\nu\,\sigma(\nu) = \tfrac{1}{2}(p/\mu)\,\bar{\sigma} \tag{79.12}$$

and approaches zero as $p\to 0$ $(k\to p_0-\mu)$, as does the nonrelativistic Born approximation (for corrections see Sect. 79β). After a sharp rise from $p=0$ to $p\sim\mu$, the function $\nu\,\sigma(\nu)$ increases rather slowly with increasing p and diverges logarithmically at the low-frequency limit.

β) Screening. We now have to consider the effect of screening, i.e. of the atomic form factor $F(q)$ in (79.2), which we have neglected so far. As discussed in Sects. 76γ and 77β, $F(q)\ll Z$ only if $q\gg Q$, where Q is a momentum of the order of $Z^{\frac{1}{3}}\alpha\mu$. For $q<Q$, $(Z-F)$ decreases rapidly with decreasing q. In the nonrelativistic calculations we have found that, for fixed p_0 and p, the minimum value of the momentum transfer q is approximately p_0-p. At nonrelativistic energies the effect of screening becomes relatively less important with increasing energy E_0. In the relativistic region this is *not* the case, in fact the importance of screening *increases* with increasing energy E_0: Consider fixed values of p_0 and p with $p_0, p\gg\mu$. The minimum value $q_{\min}$ of q is then given by (79.7), which is very much *smaller* than p_0-p for extremely relativistic momenta. We have seen that the important values of the photon angle ϑ_0 are of order μ/p_0. For ϑ_0 of this order, the important values of the angle ξ are of order $\vartheta\sim p_0\vartheta_0/p$ and smaller. In this range the momentum transfer q varies from $q_{\min}$ if $\xi=0$ ($q_{\min}$ is independent of ϑ_0) to $q\sim\mu$ if $\xi\sim\vartheta$. Now, for all elements, $Q\sim Z^{\frac{1}{3}}\alpha\mu\ll\mu$ and screening is unimportant for the larger values of ξ. On the other hand, if

$$\frac{\mu k}{p_0 p}\ll Z^{\frac{1}{3}}\alpha, , \tag{79.13}$$

then $q_{\min}\ll Q$ and the cross-section for $\xi\gtrsim Q/p$ in (79.9) is depressed by screening.

If we integrate this differential cross-section over $d\xi$, the angular distribution of the emitted photons is not affected very strongly by screening[1]. In the integrated cross-section, finally, a term of order $\log(\mu/q_{\min})\sim\log(p_0 p/k\mu)$ is replaced by a term of order $\log(\mu/Q)\sim\log(1/Z^{\frac{1}{3}}\alpha)$. For the limit of "complete

[1] For further details on the angular distribution see P. V. Hough, Phys. Rev. **74**, 80 (1948) and M. Stearns, Phys. Rev. **76**, 836 (1949).

screening" [i.e. if the inequality (79.13) holds] the integrated BETHE-HEITLER cross-section, using the THOMAS-FERMI values for the atomic form-factor F, is

$$\nu\,\sigma(\nu) = \bar{\sigma}\left[\left(1 + \frac{p^2}{p_0^2} - \frac{2}{3}\frac{p}{p_0}\right)\log\left(183\,Z^{-\frac{1}{3}}\right) + \frac{1}{9}\frac{p}{p_0}\right], \tag{79.14}$$

whereas (79.10) holds if the opposite inequality to (79.13) applies. For a number of intermediate values of the parameter $\mu k/p_0 p Z^{\frac{1}{3}}\alpha$, the integrated cross-section for the THOMAS-FERMI atomic form-factor has been obtained by numerical integration (see references at beginning of Sect. 79α).

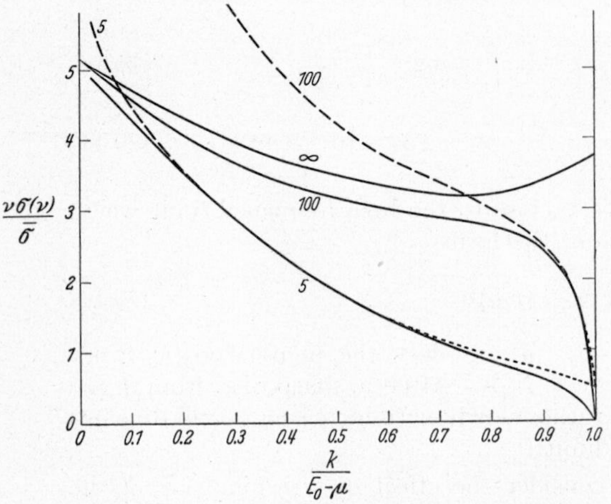

Fig. 40.

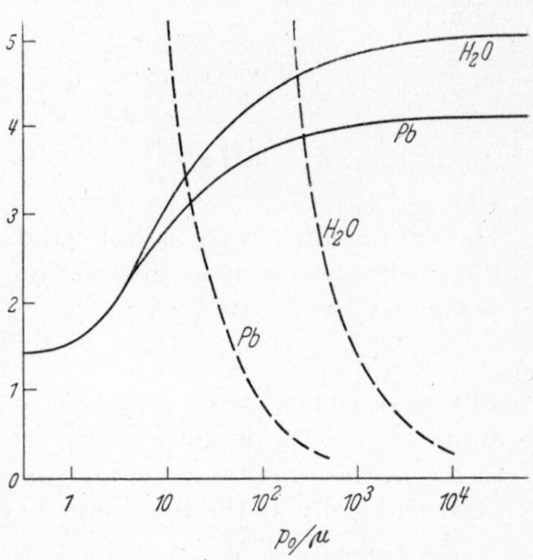

Fig. 41.

Fig. 40. The BETHE-HEITLER integrated Bremsstrahlung cross-section $\sigma(\nu)$ times $\nu/\bar{\sigma}$, plotted against photon momentum in units of the high-frequency limit The number against each curve is the primary energy E_0 in units of the rest-mass energy μ. The solid curves are for Pb ($Z=82$), the dotted curves are those with screening neglected. The solid circles near the high-frequency limit denote ELWERT's *estimated* deviations from the BORN-approximation results.

Fig. 41. Energy loss per cm divided by $N E_0 \bar{\sigma}$ is plotted against primary momentum in units of μ. The solid curves are the Bremsstrahlung energy loss, the dotted curves the ionization energy loss.

To summarize the behavior of the function $\nu\sigma(\nu)/\bar{\sigma}$ for different initial momenta p_0: With screening neglected, this function depends on p_0, but not on Z. For p_0 not much larger than μ, this function is similar to that for the nonrelativistic BORN approximation. For $p_0 \gg \mu$, the function rises sharply from zero at the high-frequency limit ($\nu=\nu_0$, $p=0$) to a value of order unity for $p \sim \mu$ and then rises only logarithmically. Screening becomes important when the inequality (79.13) holds. $\nu\sigma(\nu)$ is finite at the low-frequency limit for all values of p_0, if screening is included. If $\mu/p_0 \gg Z^{\frac{1}{3}}\alpha \ll 1$, then screening is important only near the low-frequency limit. If $p_0 \gg 137 Z^{-\frac{1}{3}}\mu$, then screening is important everywhere except near the high-frequency limit (screening sets in for $p \gtrsim 137 Z^{-\frac{1}{3}}\mu$). In Fig. 40, the function $\nu\sigma(\nu)/\bar{\sigma}$ is plotted against $\nu/\nu_0 = k/(E_0-\mu)$ for $E_0/\mu = 5$ and 100 respectively, with and without screening. The curves with screening are for $Z=82$ (Pb). The curve marked ∞ is a plot of the function (79.14) for $Z=82$ (Pb), which holds in the limiting case of $p_0 Z^{\frac{1}{3}}/137\mu \approx E_0/32\mu \to \infty$, if screening is included.

We finally mention the average energy loss $-dE_0/dx$ of an electron passing through matter due to Bremsstrahlung. This quantity is defined by the integral (77.17). General results for this quantity are discussed in [6], p. 252. We merely give two limiting cases, both for $E_0 \approx p_0 \gg \mu$ (the nonrelativistic limit of $p_0 \ll \mu$

is given by (77.18)]: We write

$$-\frac{dE_0}{dx} = N E_0 \sigma_{\rm rad}, \quad \sigma_{\rm rad} = \int\limits_0^{\nu_0} \frac{\nu}{\nu_0} \sigma(\nu)\, d\nu. \tag{79.15}$$

If $p_0 \ll 137 Z^{-\frac{1}{3}} \mu$, then screening can be neglected and one finds

$$\sigma_{\rm rad} = \left(\log \frac{2p_0}{\mu} - \frac{1}{3}\right) \bar{\sigma}, \tag{79.16}$$

where $\bar{\sigma}$ is defined by (79.11). If $p_0 \gg 137 Z^{-\frac{1}{3}} \mu$, the screening is complete and $\sigma_{\rm rad}$ tends to a limit independent of p_0,

$$\sigma_{\rm rad} = \left(\log \frac{183}{Z^{\frac{1}{3}}} + \frac{1}{18}\right) \bar{\sigma}. \tag{79.17}$$

In Fig. 41, $\sigma_{\rm rad}$ is plotted against p_0/μ for Pb ($Z = 82$) and for H_2O (mainly $Z = 8$). Apart from the logarithmic factor in (79.16) the energy loss per atom is proportional to $Z^2 E_0$. The energy loss due to ionization is proportional to Z and roughly independent of energy E_0 in the relativistic region. The radiation energy loss is one order of $Z\alpha$ smaller than the ionization loss for $p_0 \sim \mu$, the two losses are equal for p_0 of the order $137\mu/Z$ and the radiation loss is more important at larger energies still. For comparison, the ionization energy loss, divided by NE_0, is also plotted in Fig. 41.

γ) Deviations from Born *approximation.* The Bethe-Heitler cross-sections are based on the Born approximation which is accurate only if the following parameter n,

cf addenda p. 359

$$n = \frac{Ze^2}{\hbar v} = Z\alpha \frac{c}{v}, \quad \frac{v}{c} = \sqrt{\frac{E^2 - \mu^2}{E^2}} = \sqrt{\frac{p^2}{p^2 + \mu^2}}, \tag{79.18}$$

and a similar parameter n_0 for the initial momentum, is small. Close to the high-frequency limit, n is by no means small, even if n_0 is, and the Born approximation breaks down even for relativistic E_0. Especially if p_0 is not very much larger than μ, then $n \gtrsim 1$ over an appreciable part of the frequency range. Elwert[1] has given some arguments that the correct integrated cross-section $\sigma(\nu)$ is approximated fairly closely by the Bethe-Heitler expression multiplied by the factor

$$\frac{n}{n_0} \frac{1 - e^{-2\pi n_0}}{1 - e^{-2\pi n}}, \tag{79.19}$$

for fairly small values of Z [see Eq. (78.8)]. Using this factor and (79.12) one finds an expression for $\nu\sigma(\nu)$ which tends to a *finite* limit (at the high-frequency limit) of

$$\nu\sigma(\nu) = \frac{1}{2} \bar{\sigma} Z \alpha \frac{1 - e^{-2\pi n_0}}{n_0} = \frac{1}{2} \bar{\sigma} \frac{v_0}{c} (1 - e^{-2\pi n_0}). \tag{79.20}$$

In Fig. 40 the cross-sections corrected by Elwert's factor (79.19) are shown as the dotted curves (points) for Pb ($Z = 82$). Experiments[2] for $E_0 = 2\mu$ and 3μ are at least in semi-quantitative agreement with Elwert's cross-section for fairly small p if Z is not too large.

For extremely relativistic energies $E_0 \gg \mu$, Elwert's semi-empirical factor (79.19) is close to unity over most of the frequency range. For large Z this factor is not accurate and appreciable deviations from the Bethe-Heitler formula

---

[1] G. Elwert: Ann. d. Phys. **34**, 178 (1939).

[2] J. W. Motz: Phys. Rev. **100**, 1560 (1955).

could be expected; for Pb for instance, even when E_0, $E \gg \mu$, both n_0 and n are about 0.64, which is by no means small compared with unity. Approximate analytic calculations have been carried out recently, which are quite accurate for *arbitrary* values of $Z\alpha$, as long as both p_0 and p are large compared with μ: The calculation for the differential cross-section[1], with screening neglected, is based on the following arguments. The exact initial and final state DIRAC wave functions in a COULOMB field, which behave asymptotically like plane waves (plus outgoing and incoming spherical ones, respectively), can each be expressed as an infinite sum of partial wave solutions (whose analytic form is known) with all values of the orbital quantum numbers l_0 and l. We have seen that the important values of the momentum transfer q are of order μ (or less) and one finds, for the corresponding matrix element, the important values of l_0 and l are of order p_0/μ and p/μ (or larger). By neglecting only terms of relative order $(Z\alpha/l_0)^2$ and $(Z\alpha/l)^2$ in these partial wave solutions, one can sum the series over l_0 (or l) to get an analytic wave function[2] separable in parabolic coordinates, which is approximate but far more accurate than the BORN approximation wave function. Using these wave functions one can evaluate the matrix element for the differential cross-section. Since large values of l_0 and l are most important, one finds that these results are in error only by a fraction of order $Z\alpha\mu/p$, i.e. are very accurate in the extreme relativistic case even for $Z\alpha \sim 1$. These results are smaller than the BETHE-HEITLER ones at all angles, appreciably so for small q near $q_{\min}$, Eq. (79.7), and almost identical with the BETHE-HEITLER ones for larger values of q.

These "COULOMB corrections" to the BETHE-HEITLER differential cross-section are rigorously valid only for an unscreened COULOMB potential. If $p_0 \gg 137 Z^{-\frac{1}{3}}\mu$, screening is important just at small values of q, where the COULOMB corrections are appreciable and these corrections have not yet been calculated reliably[3]. However, for the integrated cross section $\sigma(\nu)$ one can use a different set of final state electron wave functions (involving outgoing spherical waves), with which the COULOMB and screening corrections occur for different ranges of q, so that the two effects are additive[4]. We merely quote a simple form of the result: The BETHE-HEITLER integrated cross-section is multiplied by a correction factor F which is, for arbitrary strength of screening,

$$F = 1 - \frac{(Z\alpha)^2}{L} g(Z\alpha) \tag{79.21}$$

where L is a factor in the general BETHE-HEITLER formula which is approximately $\log(2p_0 p/k\mu)$ for no screening and $\log(183 Z^{-\frac{1}{3}})$ for complete screening. g is a slowly varying function of $Z\alpha$ and $g \approx 1.202$ for $Z\alpha \ll 1$ and $g = 0.926$ for $Z\alpha = 0.60$ (Pb). The correct cross-section for $p \gg \mu$ is thus *lower* than the BETHE-HEITLER one (unlike the result for $p \to 0$), but F is not much smaller than unity even for large Z (e.g. $F \approx 0.91$ for $Z = 82$ and complete screening)[5].

δ) Bremsstrahlung in the field of an electron. We have discussed so far only Bremsstrahlung processes in which the recoil momentum q is taken up by the

---

[1] H. BETHE and L. MAXIMON: Phys. Rev. **93**, 768 (1954).

[2] W. H. FURRY: Phys. Rev. **46**, 391 (1934).

[3] The implication, given in the paper by BETHE and MAXIMON, that the COULOMB and screening corrections are additive, is incorrect.

[4] H. DAVIES, H. BETHE and L. MAXIMON: Phys. Rev. **93**, 788 (1954). — H. OLSEN: Phys. Rev. **99**, 1335 (1955).

[5] For references to the experimental literature see the paper by BETHE and MAXIMON; also K. L. BROWN, Phys. Rev. **103**, 243 (1956).

atom as a whole and the atom remains in its ground state (the recoil energy of the whole atom is negligible because of the large nuclear mass). Bremsstrahlung processes "in the field of an electron" are also possible, i.e. a single atomic electron absorbs the recoil momentum q and is ejected (or at least excited). For extremely relativistic momenta p_0 of the incident electron we have seen that values of q of the order of $\mu \ll p_0$ or less are most important. In such cases the recoil energy of the atomic electron is not very important and this process cannot be distinguished experimentally from "potential" Bremsstrahlung. If screening and binding is neglected, i.e. if we replace the atomic electron by a free electron initially at rest, the differential and integrated cross-sections for Bremsstrahlung in the field of the electron can be evaluated, at least approximately[1]. For $p_0 \gg \mu$ and for small momentum transfer $q \gtrsim \mu$, the differential cross-section is almost the same as from a heavy particle (fixed COULOMB field) of unit charge. For larger values of q, the cross-section for an electron is smaller than from a fixed unit charge. For very small values of q, where screening and binding effects are important, these effects depress the cross-section *less*[2] for a single atomic electron than for the process from the atom as a whole. If the integrated cross-section for these processes from the Z atomic electrons (proportional to Z) is added to the ordinary "potential" cross-section $\sigma(\nu)$ (proportional to Z^2), the result is as follows: The factor Z^2 in the "potential" formula is replaced by $Z(Z+\xi)$, where ξ is a factor slightly less than unity for $\mu \ll p_0 \ll 137\,Z^{-\frac{1}{3}}\,\mu$ and slightly larger than unity for $p_0 \gg 137\,Z^{-\frac{1}{3}}\,\mu$, where screening is important. (For nonrelativistic momenta $p_0 \ll \mu$, ξ is very small.) These electron processes are thus important only for fairly small values of the nuclear charge Z.

ε) Pair creation by photons. The calculations for Bremsstrahlung at relativistic energies are mathematically very similar to those for another process, the creation of an electron-positron pair accompanied by the absorption of a photon in the COULOMB field of a nucleus. This is a process predicted only by the DIRAC pair theory and can be thought of as an inverse process to Bremsstrahlung: The photon is absorbed instead of emitted, and the initial electron wave function is replaced by one for a negative energy state (the absence of this state is observed as a positron). The calculations of the relativistic BORN approximation (BETHE-HEITLER formula), and even of the COULOMB corrections to it, proceed in an analogous manner to those for Bremsstrahlung. Detailed discussions of pair creation will be found in the various references given in Sects. 79α and β. We merely quote some of the most important results for the integrated cross-section in BORN approximation.

Let $h\nu = kc$ be the energy of the photon incident on an atom with nuclear charge Z and let cE_0 and cE be the energies (including restmass) of the created positron and electron. We then have the equation of energy conservation,

$$k = E_0 + E. \tag{79.22}$$

The threshold for this process is thus $k = 2\mu = 2mc$. Let $\sigma(E)\,dE$ be the cross-section for pair creation processes where the electron's energy lies between E

[1] A. BORSELLINO, Nuovo Cim. **4**, 112 (1947), and Revista univ. nac. Tucuman (Argentina) A **6**, 7 (1947). See also M. L. REDHEAD, Proc. Phys. Soc. Lond. A **66**, 196 (1953), and ref. [*6*], p. 414. See also V. VOTRUBA, Phys. Rev. **73**, 1468 (1948).

[2] J. WHEELER and W. LAMB: Phys. Rev. **55**, 858 (1939). — D. BERNSTEIN and W. K. PANOFSKI: Phys. Rev. **102**, 522 (1956).

and $E+dE$, integrated over all directions of the electron and positron momenta. For $k \gg \mu$, this cross-section can be written in the form

$$\sigma(E)\,dE = \bar{\sigma}\,\frac{dE}{k}\left(1 - \frac{4}{3}\,\frac{E_0 E}{k^2}\right) L, \tag{79.23}$$

where $\bar{\sigma}$ is defined by (79.11) and L is a factor which is approximately $\log(2p_0 p/k\mu)$ if screening is unimportant and $\log(183 Z^{-\frac{1}{3}})$ if screening is complete. Note the similarity between this expression and (79.10) or (79.14). For $k \gg \mu/Z\alpha$, pair creation is a more important cause of photon attenuation than the COMPTON effect and photoeffect (see Sect. 73 and Fig. 36). Pair creation by photons and Bremsstrahlung of electrons and positrons are the causes of "soft component showers" in cosmic radiation: A photon of extremely high energy (produced, for instance, by the decay of a neutral π-meson) is absorbed in its passage through matter and creates a high energy pair. The electron and positron suffer Bremsstrahlung, giving up a reasonable fraction of their energy to the produced photons. These photons in turn produce more pairs, etc.

Appendix on spherical harmonics.

Throughout the text we have made extensive use of a number of formulae involving spherical harmonics. We give below the definitions we have used and a collection of useful formulae, most of them without proofs. Proofs will be found in, or can be derived from, the standard mathematical texts[1].

α) LEGENDRE *polynomials.* We define the LEGENDRE polynomial, $P_l(x)$, of l-th order as the l-th expansion coefficient in the following expansion (with $r<1$)

$$\frac{1}{\sqrt{1-2rx+r^2}} = \sum_{l=0}^{\infty} r^l P_l(x). \tag{A.1}$$

The variable x is to lie in the range -1 to 1. For $x=\pm 1$, we have

$$P_l(1) = 1, \quad P_l(-1) = (-1)^l. \tag{A.2}$$

$P_l(x)$ is a polynomial in x of the l-th degree, given by

$$P_l(x) = \frac{1}{2^l\, l!}\,\frac{d^l\left[(x^2-1)^l\right]}{dx^l} \tag{A.3}$$

or, more explicitly, by

$$P_l(x) = \frac{(2l)!}{2^l \cdot l!^2}\left[x^l - \frac{l(l-1)}{2(2l-1)}\,x^{l-2} + \frac{l(l-1)(l-2)(l-3)}{2\cdot 4\cdot(2l-1)(2l-3)}\,x^{l-4} + \cdots\right]. \tag{A.4}$$

The LEGENDRE polynomials and their first derivatives satisfy the following recursion relations.

$$(2l+1)\,x P_l = (l+1)\,P_{l+1}(x) + l P_{l-1}(x). \tag{A.5}$$

$$P_l = P'_{l-1} - 2x P'_l + P'_{l+1}. \tag{A.6}$$

$$(2l+1)\,P_l(x) = P'_{l+1}(x) - P'_{l-1}(x). \tag{A.7}$$

$$\left.\begin{aligned} x P'_l &= P'_{l-1} + l P_l \\ &= P'_{l+1} - (l+1)\,P_l. \end{aligned}\right\} \tag{A.8}$$

---

[1] J. MEIXNER: Spezielle Funktionen, Vol. I of this Encyclopedia. — E. W. HOBSON: Spherical and Ellipsoidal Harmonics. Cambridge 1931. — W. MAGNUS and F. OBERHETTINGER: Spezielle Funktionen der Mathematischen Physik, Chap. 4, 2nd ed. Berlin-Göttingen-Heidelberg: Springer 1948. — E. T. WHITTAKER and G. N. WATSON: Modern Analysis, Chap. 15. Cambridge 1927. See also Sect. 65 of ref. [*10*].

The LEGENDRE polynomials satisfy the following second order differential equation

$$(1-x^2)\,P_l''-2xP_l'+l(l+1)\,P_l=0 \tag{A.9}$$

or, written in terms of ϑ, where $\cos\vartheta=x$

$$\frac{1}{\sin\vartheta}\frac{d}{d\vartheta}\left(\sin\vartheta\frac{dP_l}{d\vartheta}\right)+l(l+1)\,P_l=0. \tag{A.10}$$

The first part of (A.10) is clearly r^2 times the ϑ-part of the LAPLACE-operator Δ [cf. Eq. (1.2)], written in terms of spherical polar coordinates (r,ϑ,φ). In fact, the differential equation

$$r^{2-l}\Delta\,[r^l P_l(\cos\vartheta)]=0$$

reduces, after carrying out the r-differentation, exactly to (A.10).

The LEGENDRE polynomials satisfy the orthogonality relations

$$\int_{-1}^{1} dx\,P_n(x)\,P_m(x)=\left\{\begin{matrix} 0 & \text{if } n\neq m, \\ \frac{2}{2n+1} & \text{if } n=m. \end{matrix}\right\} \tag{A.11}$$

The inverse distance between two points with polar coordinates $(r,0,0)$ and $(\varrho,\vartheta,\varphi)$ can be expressed in terms of LEGENDRE polynomials,

$$\frac{1}{\sqrt{r^2-2r\varrho\cos\vartheta+\varrho^2}}=\left\{\begin{matrix} \sum_l \frac{\varrho^l}{r^{l+1}}P_l(\cos\vartheta), & \text{if } \varrho<r, \\ \sum_l \frac{r^l}{\varrho^{l+1}}P_l(\cos\vartheta), & \text{if } \varrho>r. \end{matrix}\right\} \tag{A.12}$$

β) Associated LEGENDRE *polynomials.* For positive integers m, we define the (unnormalized) associated LEGENDRE polynomial $P_l^m(x)$ by[1]

$$P_l^m(x)=(1-x^2)^{m/2}\frac{d^m P_l(x)}{dx^m}. \tag{A.13}$$

The function P_l^m satisfies the following differential equation

$$(1-x^2)\,(P_l^m)''-2x\,(P_l^m)'+\left[l(l+1)-\frac{m^2}{1-x^2}\right]P_l^m=0. \tag{A.14}$$

We also define the *normalized* associated LEGENDRE polynomial $\mathcal{P}_{lm}$ by

$$\mathcal{P}_{lm}=\sqrt{\frac{2l+1}{2}\cdot\frac{(l-m)!}{(l+m)!}}\,P_l^m=\sqrt{\frac{2l+1}{2}\cdot\frac{(l-m)!}{(l+m)!}}\,\frac{1}{2^l\cdot l!}(1-x^2)^{m/2}\frac{d^{l+m}}{dx^{l+m}}(x^2-1)^l. \tag{A.15}$$

We further define the (unnormalized) spherical harmonic

$$\Phi_{lm}=P_l^m e^{im\varphi}, \tag{A.16}$$

which satisfies the following differential equation, written in terms of ϑ instead of $x=\cos\vartheta$,

$$\frac{1}{\sin\vartheta}\frac{d}{d\vartheta}\left(\sin\vartheta\frac{d\Phi}{d\vartheta}\right)+\frac{1}{\sin^2\vartheta}\frac{d^2\Phi}{d\varphi^2}+l(l+1)\Phi=0. \tag{A.17}$$

---

[1] The definition used by some authors differs from ours by a factor $(-1)^m$.

Note that the functions $r^l \Phi_{lm}$ and $r^{-(l+1)} \Phi_{lm}$ both satisfy LAPLACE's equation. We also define the normalized spherical harmonic Y_{lm} by

$$Y_{lm}(\vartheta, \varphi) = \frac{1}{\sqrt{2\pi}} \mathcal{P}_{lm} e^{im\varphi} \tag{A.18}$$

which satisfies the normalization condition,

$$\int_0^\pi \sin\vartheta \, d\vartheta \int_0^{2\pi} d\varphi \, |Y_{lm}|^2 = \int_{-1}^{+1} \mathcal{P}_{lm}^2(x) \, dx = 1. \tag{A.19}$$

Any two associated LEGENDRE polynomials with different lower index l, but the *same* upper index m, are orthogonal. Hence

$$\int_0^\pi \sin\vartheta \, d\vartheta \int_0^{2\pi} d\varphi \, Y_{lm}^* Y_{l'm'} = 0$$

unless both $l = l'$ and $m = m'$.

For negative m we define $\mathcal{P}_{lm}$ and Y_{lm} still[1] by (A.15) and (A.18). Many authors use instead, for negative m,

$$Y'_{lm} = \frac{1}{\sqrt{2\pi}} \mathcal{P}_{l,|m|} e^{im\varphi}.$$

The two forms are related by

$$\mathcal{P}_{l,-m} = (-1)^m \mathcal{P}_{lm}; \qquad Y'_{lm} = (-1)^{\frac{|m|-m}{2}} Y_{lm}.$$

Our definition for Y_{lm} has the advantage that the same formulae hold for positive and negative m, which is not the case for the conventional Y'_{lm}. Note, however, that $Y_{lm}^* = (-1)^m Y_{l,-m}$.

γ) Coordinate matrix elements. For evaluating matrix elements involving the coordinates (x, y, z), the following formulae are of use:

$$\left.\begin{aligned} &\sin\vartheta \, \mathcal{P}_{lm}(\cos\vartheta) \\ &= \sqrt{\frac{(l+m+1)(l+m+2)}{(2l+1)(2l+3)}} \mathcal{P}_{l+1,m+1} - \sqrt{\frac{(l-m)(l-m-1)}{(2l+1)(2l-1)}} \mathcal{P}_{l-1,m+1}, \end{aligned}\right\} \tag{A.20}$$

$$\left.\begin{aligned} &\sin\vartheta \, \mathcal{P}_{lm}(\cos\vartheta) \\ &= -\sqrt{\frac{(l-m+1)(l-m+2)}{(2l+1)(2l+3)}} \mathcal{P}_{l+1,m-1} + \sqrt{\frac{(l+m)(l+m-1)}{(2l+1)(2l-1)}} \mathcal{P}_{l-1,m-1}, \end{aligned}\right\} \tag{A.21}$$

$$\left.\begin{aligned} &\cos\vartheta \, \mathcal{P}_{lm}(\cos\vartheta) \\ &= \sqrt{\frac{(l+m+1)(l-m+1)}{(2l+1)(2l+3)}} \mathcal{P}_{l+1,m} + \sqrt{\frac{(l+m)(l-m)}{(2l+1)(2l-1)}} \mathcal{P}_{l-1,m}. \end{aligned}\right\} \tag{A.22}$$

A double application of (A.20) to (A.22) gives

$$\left.\begin{aligned} \frac{z^2}{r^2} \mathcal{P}_{lm} = \cos^2\vartheta \, \mathcal{P}_{lm} &= \sqrt{\frac{[(l+1)^2-m^2][(l+2)^2-m^2]}{(2l+1)(2l+3)^2(2l+5)}} \mathcal{P}_{l+2,m} + \\ &+ \frac{2l^2+2l-2m^2-1}{(2l+3)(2l-1)} \mathcal{P}_{lm} + \sqrt{\frac{[l^2-m^2][(l-1)^2-m^2]}{(2l+1)(2l-1)^2(2l-3)}} \mathcal{P}_{l-2,m}, \end{aligned}\right\} \tag{A.23}$$

[1] For negative m, we must use the definition on the right hand side of (A.15); the definition (A.13) would be meaningless in this case.

$$\left.\begin{aligned}\cos\vartheta\sin\vartheta\,\mathscr{P}_{lm} = &\sqrt{\frac{(l+m+3)(l+m+2)(l+m+1)(l-m+1)}{(2l+5)(2l+3)^2(2l+1)}}\,\mathscr{P}_{l+2,m+1} + \\ &+\frac{2m+1}{(2l+3)(2l-1)}\sqrt{(l+m+1)(l-m)}\,\mathscr{P}_{l,m+1} - \\ &-\sqrt{\frac{(l+m)(l-m)(l-m-1)(l-m-2)}{(2l+1)(2l-1)^2(2l-3)}}\,\mathscr{P}_{l-2,m+1},\end{aligned}\right\}\quad \text{(A.24)}$$

$$\left.\begin{aligned}= &-\sqrt{\frac{(l+m+1)(l-m+1)(l-m+2)(l-m+3)}{(2l+5)(2l+3)^2(2l+1)}}\,\mathscr{P}_{l+2,m-1} + \\ &+\frac{2m-1}{(2l+3)(2l-1)}\sqrt{(l+m)(l-m+1)}\,\mathscr{P}_{l,m-1} + \\ &+\sqrt{\frac{(l+m)(l+m-1)(l+m-2)(l-m)}{(2l+1)(2l-1)^2(2l-3)}}\,\mathscr{P}_{l-2,m-1},\end{aligned}\right\}\quad \text{(A.25)}$$

$$\left.\begin{aligned}\sin^2\vartheta\,\mathscr{P}_{lm} = &\sqrt{\frac{(l+m+4)(l+m+3)(l+m+2)(l+m+1)}{(2l+5)(2l+3)^2(2l+1)}}\,\mathscr{P}_{l+2,m+2} - \\ &-\frac{2}{(2l+3)(2l-1)}\sqrt{(l+m+2)(l+m+1)(l-m)(l-m-1)}\,\mathscr{P}_{l,m+2} + \\ &+\sqrt{\frac{(l-m)(l-m-1)(l-m-2)(l-m-3)}{(2l+1)(2l-1)^2(2l-3)}}\,\mathscr{P}_{l-2,m+2},\end{aligned}\right\}\quad \text{(A.26)}$$

$$\left.\begin{aligned}= &\sqrt{\frac{(l-m+4)(l-m+3)(l-m+2)(l-m+1)}{(2l+5)(2l+3)^2(2l+1)}}\,\mathscr{P}_{l+2,m-2} - \\ &-\frac{2}{(2l+3)(2l-1)}\sqrt{(l-m+2)(l-m+1)(l+m)(l+m-1)}\,\mathscr{P}_{l,m-2} + \\ &+\sqrt{\frac{(l+m)(l+m-1)(l+m-2)(l+m-3)}{(2l+1)(2l-1)^2(2l-3)}}\,\mathscr{P}_{l-2,m-2}.\end{aligned}\right\}\quad \text{(A.27)}$$

Eqs. (A.23) to (A.27) can be used to evaluate matrix elements of expressions quadratic in the coordinates (like x^2, z^2, xy and xz), which occur especially in the treatment of the fine structure problem. Consider, for instance the matrix-element of the expression $f(r)\,(x+iy)\,z/r^2$, where $f(r)$ is any function of radial distance r only, between any two states with the *same* value of l (quantum number of total orbital angular momentum). If the initial and final eigenfunctions are of the form

$$u_i = R_{nl}(r)\,Y_{lm}\,,\qquad u_f = R_{n'l}(r)\,Y_{lm'}\,,$$

then the matrix element, for $m' = m+1$,

$$[f(r)\,(x+iy)\,z/r^2]_{lm}^{l,m+1} = \int d\tau\, u_f^*\, f(r)\cos\vartheta\sin\vartheta\, e^{i\varphi}\, u_i\,,$$

can be written as the product of a radial integral and an integral over angles. If we write for the radial integral

$$\bar{f} = \int_0^\infty dr\, r^2 R_{n'l}(r)\, f(r)\, R_{nl}(r)\,,$$

we then obtain

$$[(x+iy)\,z\,f/r^2]_{lm}^{l,m+1} = \bar{f}\,\frac{2m+1}{(2l+3)(2l-1)}\sqrt{(l+m+1)(l-m)}\,. \qquad \text{(A.28)}$$

Similarly

$$[z^2 f/r^2]_{lm}^{lm} = \overline{f}\,\frac{2l^2+2l-1-2m^2}{(2l+3)(2l-1)} \tag{A.29}$$

and so on.

The matrix elements of products of the various components of the operator $\boldsymbol{k}$ for orbital angular momentum, on the other hand, can be obtained by ordinary matrix multiplication, using (1.10) and (1.14). We find, for instance,

$$\left.\begin{aligned}
&[k_z(k_x+i\,k_y)]_{l,m}^{l,m+1} = (k_z)_{l\,m+1}^{l\,m+1}(k_x+i\,k_y)_{l\,m}^{l\,m+1} = -(m+1)\sqrt{(l+m+1)(l-m)}\,,\\
&[(k_x+i\,k_y)\,k_z]_{l,m}^{l,m+1} = (k_x+i\,k_y)_{l\,m}^{l\,m+1}(k_z)_{l\,m}^{l\,m} = -m\sqrt{(l+m+1)(l-m)}\,,\\
&\qquad (k_z^2)_{l\,m}^{l\,m} = m^2, \qquad\qquad (\boldsymbol{k}^2)_{lm}^{lm} = l(l+1)
\end{aligned}\right\} \tag{A.30}$$

where $\boldsymbol{k}^2 \equiv k_x^2 + k_y^2 + k_z^3$.

By comparison we find[1]

$$\left.\begin{aligned}
&[(x+i\,y)\,z]_{l\,m}^{l\,m+1} = -\frac{\overline{r^2}}{(2l+3)(2l-1)}\,[k_z(k_x+i\,k_y) + (k_x+i\,k_y)\,k_z]_{l\,m}^{l\,m+1}\,,\\
&(z^2)_{l\,m}^{l\,m} = \frac{1}{3}\,\overline{r^2} - \frac{\overline{r^2}}{(2l+3)(2l-1)}\cdot 2\cdot\left(k_z^2 - \frac{1}{3}\,k^2\right)_{l\,m}^{l\,m},
\end{aligned}\right\} \tag{A.31}$$

Similar relations hold between the matrix-elements of *all* quadratic expressions of the coordinates on the one hand and quadratic expressions of the components of the orbital angular momentum on the other, for any transitions between states of the *same* orbital quantum number l. These relations can be collected together to give

$$r^2\,\delta_{ij} - 3x_i\,x_j = -\frac{\overline{r^2}}{(2l+3)(2l-1)}\cdot[2k^2\,\delta_{ij} - 3(k_i\,k_j + k_j\,k_i)]\,, \tag{A.32}$$

where $i, j = 1, 2, 3$ denote the three CARTESian coordinates x, y, z and δ_{ij} is the KRONECKER delta-symbol ($\delta_{ij} = 1$ and 0 for $i = j$ and $i \neq j$, respectively). If $\boldsymbol{a}$ and $\boldsymbol{b}$ are any two vectors which commute with $\boldsymbol{r}$, $\boldsymbol{k}$ and each other, then (A.32) can be rewritten in the form

$$\left.\begin{aligned}
(\boldsymbol{a}\cdot\boldsymbol{b})\,r^2 - 3\,(\boldsymbol{a}\cdot\boldsymbol{r})\,(\boldsymbol{b}\cdot\boldsymbol{r}) &= \sum_{ij=1}^{3} a_i\,b_j\,(r^2\,\delta_{ij} - 3x_i\,x_j)\\
&= -\frac{\overline{r^2}}{(2l+3)(2l-1)}\,[2k^2(\boldsymbol{a}\cdot\boldsymbol{b}) - 3\,(\boldsymbol{a}\cdot\boldsymbol{k})\,(\boldsymbol{b}\cdot\boldsymbol{k}) - 3\,(\boldsymbol{b}\cdot\boldsymbol{k})\,(\boldsymbol{a}\cdot\boldsymbol{k})]\,.
\end{aligned}\right\} \tag{A.33}$$

Eq. (A.33) should be considered as a matrix equation in the sense that the matrix elements of the left and right hand side are equal for any transition between two states of the *same* orbital quantum number l (for any value of l and for all combinations of principal and magnetic quantum numbers n, n', m, m').

δ) Other relations. The derivatives with respect to ϑ of the associated LEGENDRE polynomials are

$$\left.\begin{aligned}
-\frac{d P_l^m(\cos\vartheta)}{d\vartheta} &= P_l^{m+1} - \frac{m\,x}{\sqrt{1-x^2}}\,P_l^m\\
&= -(l+m)\,(l-m+1)\,P_l^{m-1} + \frac{m\,x}{\sqrt{1-x^2}}\,P_l^m
\end{aligned}\right\} \tag{A.34}$$

[1] For simplicity we write the following formulae for the special choice $f(r) = r^2$. Equivalent equations hold for *any* $f(r)$, with $\overline{r^2}$ replaced by $\overline{f}$.

where $x = \cos\vartheta$. For the normalized functions we have

$$-\frac{d\mathscr{P}_{lm}}{d\vartheta} = \sqrt{(l+m+1)(l-m)}\,\mathscr{P}_{l,m+1} - m\cot\vartheta\,\mathscr{P}_{lm}, \tag{A.35}$$

$$= -\sqrt{(l+m)(l-m+1)}\,\mathscr{P}_{l,m-1} + m\cot\vartheta\,\mathscr{P}_{lm}. \tag{A.36}$$

In the DIRAC wave equation, derivatives of the wave function with respect to the coordinates occur. These derivatives can be rewritten, using

$$\frac{\partial}{\partial z} = \cos\vartheta\frac{\partial}{\partial r} - \sin\vartheta\frac{1}{r}\frac{\partial}{\partial\vartheta},$$

$$\frac{\partial}{\partial x} = \sin\vartheta\cos\varphi\frac{\partial}{\partial r} + \cos\vartheta\cos\varphi\frac{1}{r}\frac{\partial}{\partial\vartheta} - \frac{\sin\varphi}{r\sin\vartheta}\frac{\partial}{\partial\varphi},$$

$$\frac{\partial}{\partial y} = \sin\vartheta\sin\varphi\frac{\partial}{\partial r} + \cos\vartheta\sin\varphi\frac{1}{r}\frac{\partial}{\partial\vartheta} + \frac{\cos\varphi}{r\sin\vartheta}\frac{\partial}{\partial\varphi}.$$

If f is any function of the radial distance r alone, we find,

$$\left.\begin{aligned}\frac{\partial}{\partial z}[f(r)\,Y_{lm}(\vartheta,\varphi)] = &\sqrt{\frac{(l+m+1)(l-m+1)}{(2l+3)(2l+1)}}\,Y_{l+1,m}\left(\frac{df}{dr} - l\frac{f}{r}\right) + \\ &+ \sqrt{\frac{(l+m)(l-m)}{(2l+1)(2l-1)}}\,Y_{l-1,m}\left(\frac{df}{dr} + (l+1)\frac{f}{r}\right).\end{aligned}\right\} \tag{A.37}$$

Similarly we get

$$\left.\begin{aligned}\left(\frac{\partial}{\partial x} + i\frac{\partial}{\partial y}\right)(fY_{lm}) = &\sqrt{\frac{(l+m+2)(l+m+1)}{(2l+3)(2l+1)}}\,Y_{l+1,m+1}\left(\frac{df}{dr} - l\frac{f}{r}\right) - \\ &- \sqrt{\frac{(l-m)(l-m-1)}{(2l+1)(2l-1)}}\,Y_{l-1,m+1}\left(\frac{df}{dr} + (l+1)\frac{f}{r}\right),\end{aligned}\right\} \tag{A.38}$$

$$\left.\begin{aligned}\left(\frac{\partial}{\partial x} - i\frac{\partial}{\partial y}\right)(fY_{lm}) = -&\sqrt{\frac{(l-m+2)(l-m+1)}{(2l+3)(2l+1)}}\,Y_{l+1,m-1}\left(\frac{df}{dr} - l\frac{f}{r}\right) + \\ &+ \sqrt{\frac{(l+m)(l+m-1)}{(2l+1)(2l-1)}}\,Y_{l-1,m-1}\left(\frac{df}{dr} + (l+1)\frac{f}{r}\right).\end{aligned}\right\} \tag{A.39}$$

We finally state the spherical harmonics addition theorem in our notation. Let (Θ, Φ) and (ϑ, φ) be the angle coordinates of two vectors $\boldsymbol{R}$ and $\boldsymbol{r}$ in spherical polar coordinates ,with some other vector chosen as polar axis. Let (ϑ', φ') be the polar coordinates of the vector $\boldsymbol{r}$ in a coordinate system with the vector R as polar axis, so that

$$\cos\vartheta' = \cos\Theta\cos\vartheta + \sin\Theta\sin\vartheta\cos(\Phi - \varphi). \tag{A.40}$$

The spherical harmonics addition theorem then states that

$$Y_{l0}(0)\,Y_{l0}(\vartheta') = \sum_m Y^*_{lm}(\Theta,\Phi)\,Y_{lm}(\vartheta,\varphi). \tag{A.41}$$

For the special case of $\vartheta' = 0$ we have

$$\sum_m |Y_{lm}(\Theta,\Phi)|^2 = (Y_{l0}(0))^2 = \frac{2l+1}{4\pi}. \tag{A.42}$$

Bibliography.

[1] DIRAC, P. A. M.: The Principles of Quantum Mechanics, 3rd ed. Oxford: Clarendon Press 1947.

[2] KRAMERS, H. A.: Quantentheorie des Elektrons und der Strahlung. In Hand- und Jahrbuch der Chemischen Physik, Bd. 1, Abschn. I und II. Leipzig: Akademische Verlagsgesellschaft 1938.

[3] PAULI, W.: Die Allgemeinen Prinzipien der Wellenmechanik, this Encyclopedia, Vol. V.

[4] SCHIFF, L. I.: Quantum Mechanics, 2nd ed. New York: McGraw-Hill 1955.

[5] CONDON, E. U., and G. H. SHORTLEY: Theory of Atomic Spectra. Cambridge: Cambridge University Press 1951. — Discusses mainly discrete spectra and also deals with general operator manipulation.

[6] HEITLER, W.: The Quantum Theory of Radiation, 3rd ed. Oxford: Clarendon Press 1954. — Discusses in detail the application of quantum electrodynamics to various radiation processes.

[7] SOMMERFELD, A.: Atombau und Spektrallinien, 2. Aufl., Bd. 2. Braunschweig: Vieweg & Sohn 1939. — Gives a detailed account of the quantum mechanics of the hydrogen atom (up to 1938) and also of Bremsstrahlung and the photoeffect.

[8] WHITTAKER, E. T., and G. N. WATSON: A Course of Modern Analysis, 4th ed. Cambridge: Cambridge University Press 1927.

[9] MOTT, N. F., and H. S. W. MASSEY: The Theory of Atomic Collisions. Oxford: Clarendon Press 1949. — Also contains detailed discussions of positive energy states of a DIRAC electron in a COULOMB field.

[10] Bethe, H. A.: Quantenmechanik der Ein- und Zwei-Elektronenprobleme. In Handbuch der Physik, Bd. 24/1. Berlin: Springer 1933. — This is the forerunner of the present work and contains more details on some of the older calculations and experiments.

[11] WENTZEL, G.: Einführung in die Quantentheorie der Wellenfelder. Vienna: Deuticke 1943. — An account of the older formulation of quantum field theory.

[12] SCHWEBER, S. S., H. A. BETHE and F. DE HOFFMANN: Mesons and Fields, Vol. I (Fields). Evanston: Row, Peterson & Co. 1955. — An introduction to the modern formulations of quantum field theory.

[13] JAUCH, J. M., and F. ROHRLICH: Theory of Photons and Electrons, Cambridge (Mass): Addison-Wesley 1955. — A text on modern quantum field theory and especially on quantum electrodynamics.

[14] KÄLLEN, G.: Quantum electrodynamics. This Encyclopedia, Vol. V. — A discussion of the more fundamental aspects of quantum electrodynamics.

[15] MOTT, N. F., and I. N. SNEDDON: Wave Mechanics and its Applications. Oxford: Clarendon Press 1948.

[16] RAMSEY, N. F.: Nuclear Moments. New York: John Wiley 1953. — Also gives a discussion of the ZEEMAN effect and of hyperfine structure and of relevant microwave experiments.

Addenda and Errata.

17γ. The fine structure formula for X-ray levels. On p. 88 of our text we discussed the fine structure splitting between the L_{II} and L_{III} subshells ($2P_{\frac{1}{2}}$ to $2P_{\frac{3}{2}}$) in atoms with large nuclear charge Z. This splitting has been remeasured recently[1] to an accuracy of better than one part in 10^4 for a number of atoms with Z between 74 and 94. Theoretical calculations have not reached anywhere near this accuracy: One can start with the exact DIRAC expression (17.1) for the splitting in an unscreened hydrogen-like atom. One can evaluate next the effect on the splitting due to the interaction between a $2p$-electron and all the other atomic electrons, using hydrogen-like DIRAC wave functions and the *first* order perturbation methods outlined in Sect. 43 of our text. These effects are of relative order $1/Z$ and can be evaluated for arbitrary values of $Z\alpha$. Essentially this calculation had been performed by CHRISTY and KELLER, but not to very high numerical accuracy. Terms of relative order $1/Z^2$ are still missing after such a calculation. There are two other kinds of interesting correction terms whose relative contributions to the splitting *increase* (rather than decrease) with increasing Z: One is the effect of the finite nuclear size (which increases with Z) on the energy of the $2p_{\frac{1}{2}}$-electron (whose wave function at small distances from the nucleus increases very strongly with increasing Z). The other effect is due to the variation with $Z\alpha$ of radiative corrections such as the electron's anomalous magnetic moment, vacuum polarization and the "LAMB shift proper". Except for vacuum polarization, these radiative corrections have not yet been calculated for arbitrarily large values of $Z\alpha$. For $Z \sim 90$ the nuclear size and radiative corrections are of the order of 10^{-3} of the total splitting.

18β. Covariant calculations of radiative corrections. On p. 93 of our text we quoted theoretical results for the anomalous moment g_1 of the electron, including the fourth order contribution $-2.973\ \alpha^2/\pi^2$ as calculated by KARPLUS and KROLL. The evaluation of this fourth order moment contribution involves extremely lengthy and intricate calculations and it now appears likely that KARPLUS and KROLL's numerical coefficient of -2.973 is incorrect. SOMMERFIELD[2] has recalculated this coefficient and obtained -0.328 instead of -2.973. This difficult calculation is now being redone by a number of theorists, using different methods, in order to establish the theoretical value of the fourth order moment beyond any doubt. If we accept the result of SOMMERFIELD's calculation we obtain, instead of (18.5),

$$1 + g_1 = 1 + \frac{\alpha}{2\pi} - 0.328\,\frac{\alpha^2}{\pi^2} = 1.0011596. \tag{18.5 A}$$

20β. Corrections for nuclear structure. In the text we have shown that there is a contribution to the level shift of S-states, due to the finite size of a nucleus, which is proportional to the mean square radius $\langle r^2 \rangle$ of the charge distribution inside the nucleus. We have stated that a similar but smaller spread of charge of the proton cannot yet be calculated from meson theory. This is still true but

[1] R. L. SHACKLETT and J. W. DUMOND: Phys. Rev. **106**, 501 (1957).
[2] C. M. SOMMERFIELD: Phys. Rev. **107**, 328 (1957).

experiments on high energy scattering of electrons by protons do give an experimental value for the mean square radius $\langle r^2 \rangle$ of the proton charge distribution. This value is somewhat larger than one might have suspected on purely theoretical grounds and is[1]

$$\langle r^2 \rangle = (0.77 \pm 0.10)^2 \times 10^{-26}\ \text{cm}^2 \approx 2.1 \times 10^{-10}\ a^2 \tag{20.3 A}$$

for the proton, while the equivalent quantity $\langle r^2 \rangle$ for the neutron is almost exactly zero. This spread of the proton charge contributes an amount[2] of $(+0.12 \pm 0.03)$ Mc to the shift of the $2S$-state in hydrogen.

We quoted in our text a contribution of $+0.73$ Mc to the shift of the $2S$-state in deuterium, due to the charge spread inside the deuteron (made up of one proton and one neutron). This calculation also had not taken into account the charge spread of the proton and recent experiments[3] on electron-deuteron scattering indicate that this contribution of $+0.73$ Mc for deuterium should also be increased by approximately 0.12 Mc.

21. Fine structure and the LAMB shift. The theoretical expression (21.5) for the fine structure separation $2P_{\frac{1}{2}} - 2P_{\frac{3}{2}}$ in deuterium can be written in the form

$$F = \frac{c R_D}{16} \alpha^2 \left[1 + 2g_1 + \frac{5}{8}\alpha^2 - \frac{m}{M_D}\frac{\alpha}{\pi}\right], \tag{21.5 A}$$

where g_1 is the anomalous magnetic moment of the electron. If we accept the change in the theoretical value of g_1 from expression (18.5) in the text to expression (18.5 A) in these Addenda, we have to modify the value in (21.6) for the fine structure constant to

$$\frac{1}{\alpha} = 137.0390 \pm 0.0012. \tag{21.6 A}$$

The change of the fourth order moment contribution to g_1 from $-2.973\,\alpha^2/\pi^2$ to $-0.328\,\alpha^2/\pi^2$ affects the LAMB shift markedly: The fourth order moment contributes about -0.94 Mc to the $n=2$ LAMB shift in H and in D if we use the old value of g_1, but only -0.10 Mc if we use the new one. Further, the change in the fine structure constant from (21.6) to (21.6 A) decreases the LAMB constant L in (21.8) by about 43 ppm and decreases $S_\infty^{(1)}$ by about 0.05 Mc. If we accept these changes and add the contributions due to nuclear size, discussed in Sect. 20β of these Addenda, the theoretical values in Table 3 for the LAMB shift (in Mc/sec) are changed to

H	D	He$^+$
1058.03 ± 0.15	1059.38 ± 0.15	14055 ± 3

Comparison with Table 3 shows that these changes decrease the magnitude and change the sign of the discrepancy between theory and experiment.

22. Hyperfine structure splitting. As (22.13) and the table at the bottom of p. 110 show, the ratio of the hyperfine splittings ΔE in the $1S_{\frac{1}{2}}$ and $2S_{\frac{1}{2}}$ states of any hydrogenlike atom should be 8 according to the simple FERMI formula. Accurate measurements of the hyperfine splitting in the metastable $2S_{\frac{1}{2}}$ state are now available[4] for both H and for D and the experimental ratios are

$$\left(\frac{8\Delta E_{2S}}{\Delta E_{1S}}\right)_{\text{exp}} = \begin{Bmatrix} 1 + (34.6 \pm 0.3) \times 10^{-6}\ (H) \\ 1 + (34.2 \pm 0.6) \times 10^{-6}\ (D) \end{Bmatrix}. \tag{22.13 A}$$

[1] D. YENNIE, M. LÉVY and D. RAVENHALL: Rev. Mod. Phys. **29**, 144 (1957).
[2] W. ARON and A. ZUCHELLI: Phys. Rev. **105**, 1681 (1957).
[3] J. MCINTYRE and S. DHAR: Phys. Rev. **106**, 1074 (1957).
[4] J. HEBERLE, P. KUSCH and H. REICH: Phys. Rev. **101**, 612 (1956); **104**, 1585 (1956).

There are no corrections of order α to the theoretical ratio but there is a correction of $(\frac{5}{8})\alpha^2$ from purely relativistic effects and some radiative corrections of order α^3 which have not been calculated yet. For D at least, there are appreciable corrections (about 2×10^{-4}) due to nuclear structure both in the $1S$ and $2S$ states but these corrections should be almost exactly 8 times larger in the $1S$ state so they should have little effect on the ratio. The present theoretical ratio, both for H and D, is then

$$\left(\frac{8\Delta E_{2S}}{\Delta E_{1S}}\right)_{\text{theor}} = 1 + \frac{5}{8}\alpha^2 = 1 + 33.3\times 10^{-6}. \tag{22.13 B}$$

The discrepancy between theory and experiment is seen to be only about 1 *ppm*.

We have to discuss next the effect of a change in the theoretical anomalous magnetic moment g_1 of the electron on Eqs. (22.15) to (22.20) of our text. To compound the confusion there are some misprints in some of the equations in the text: The last term $\alpha^2(\frac{5}{2}-\log 2)$ in the first line of (22.15) should have a minus sign instead of a plus sign and (22.17) should read

$$\left.\begin{aligned} \frac{\nu_{\mathrm{H}}}{c R_\infty} &= \frac{16}{3}\alpha^2\left(\frac{M_p}{M_p+m}\right)^3\left(\frac{g_p\mu_N}{g_s\mu_0}\right)\times \\ &\times(1+g_1)\left[1+g_1+\alpha^2(\log 2-1)-0.2\times 10^{-5}+\delta\right] \end{aligned}\right\} \tag{22.17 A}$$

where we have written $1+g_1$ for $g_s/2$. Further, in (22.19) we quoted the experimental value for protons in a liquid sample. For substitution into (22.17A) we need the value for free protons. This value, obtained by applying diamagnetic corrections to (22.19), is

$$\left(\frac{g_s\mu_0}{g_p\mu_N}\right)_{\text{free}} = 658.2096 \pm 0.0010. \tag{22.19 A}$$

However, in evaluating (22.20) we had used the correct expressions (22.17A) and (22.19A), and (22.20) would be correct[1] if we use the "old" theoretical value for the anomalous moment $g_1=0.0011453$. If, on the other hand, we accept the "new" value (see Sect. 18β of these Addenda) of $g_1=0.0011596$ we get, instead of (22.20),

$$\frac{1}{\alpha} = 137.0387\left(1+\frac{1}{2}\delta \pm 2\times 10^{-5}\right). \tag{22.20 A}$$

It should be noted that a comparison between (21.6A) and (22.20A) gives almost exactly the same "experimental" value for the proton structure correction δ as obtained with the "old" value of g_1: Dividing Eq. (22.17A) by (21.5A) and dropping only terms smaller than 10^{-7} we get

$$\left.\begin{aligned} &\frac{3}{256}\frac{\nu_{\mathrm{H}}}{F}\left(\frac{g_s\mu_0}{g_p\mu_N}\right)_{\text{free}} \\ &= \frac{(1+m/M_D)}{(1+m/M_p)^3}\left[1+g_1^2+\alpha^2\left(\log 2-\frac{13}{8}\right)+\frac{\alpha}{\pi}\frac{m}{M_D}-0.2\times 10^{-5}+\delta\right], \end{aligned}\right\} \tag{22.22 A}$$

where F is the fine structure separation $2P_{\frac{1}{2}}-2P_{\frac{3}{2}}$ for deuterium, discussed in Sect. 21. The anomalous moment g_1 only occurs in the very small term g_1^2 in this expression and the velocity of light c and the value of the RYDBERG constant are also not needed. Using the experimental value $(10971.59\pm 0.20)\,Mc/\text{sec}$ for F, (22.18), (22.19A) and the accurately known electron, proton and deuteron masses m, M_p and M_D, we find

$$\delta = (0.4 \pm 2.0)\times 10^{-5}. \tag{22.23 A}$$

[1] Except for another misprint: The error should read $\pm 2\times 10^{-5}$, instead of $\pm 2\times 10^{-6}$.

In our text we had stated that the proton structure correction δ cannot be calculated explicitly from presentday meson theories. In the strictest sense this is still true, but an expression has recently been derived[1] for δ in terms of just two physical parameters related to the proton structure. This theoretical expression is

$$\delta = -\frac{2\langle r\rangle_{\rm em}}{a} - 0.33\times 10^{-5}\log\frac{2K}{M_p}, \qquad (22.24\,\mathrm{A})$$

where $\langle r\rangle_{\rm em}$ is the "mean radius" of the proton, defined in a certain manner, and must be positive. $2K$ is a cut-off parameter, also related to the proton structure, which should be of the order of magnitude of M_p. Assuming $2K/M_p$ to lie between 0.1 and 10, we get from (22.23 A) an "experimental" value for $\langle r\rangle_{\rm em}$ of $(-0.1\pm 0.7)\times 10^{-13}$ cm. The correct value of $\langle r\rangle_{\rm em}$ must be positive and might be expected to be only slightly smaller than the root mean square radius of about 0.8×10^{-13} for the proton's charge distribution, given in (20.3 A) of these Addenda.

28. First order HEISENBERG's method: Misprint correction: In Table 4, Sect 28 δ p. 136, the last column should be labelled $\frac{1}{2}(\delta_p-\delta_0)$ instead of $\frac{1}{2}(\delta_0-\delta_p)$.

30. FOCK's method (excited S-states). In the text we described SMITH's calculation of the HARTREE-FOCK wave functions and the corresponding RYDBERG corrections δ for highly excited nS-states $(n\to\infty)$ of ortho- and para-helium. This calculation has been repeated recently[2], with the same method but higher numerical accuracy[3]. The theoretical and experimental values for $(-\delta)$ are

	theory	experiment[4]
ortho	0.292_9	0.297 ± 0.02
para	0.123_0	0.140 ± 0.01

The sign of the discrepancy between the theoretical and experimental results for δ is such that the actual (experimental) energy level lies lower (larger ionization potential) than the calculated one, both for ortho- and para-helium. This (rather small) discrepancy must be due to the correlation (polarization) effects between the two electrons, which are not included in the HARTREE-FOCK (HF) wave function. For *excited* states of an atom one cannot in general prove rigorously that the HARTREE-FOCK method gives an upper limit to the correct energy, but for *singly* excited discrete states $(1s, nl)$ in helium we might in fact expect this to be the case: The correct wave function for a state $(1s, nl)$ could be pictured as the HF-function U_F plus an infinite sum of product-type functions (which take account of polarization effects). It follows from the fact that the expressions in curly brackets in (30.2) vanish that the matrix element $\langle U_F^* H\psi\rangle$ vanishes, where ψ is any product wave function which contains as a factor either of the two single-particle functions u_1 or u_2. We thus might except that in the infinite sum of product functions, to be added to U_F, only those functions will occur which correspond, in some sense, to "*doubly* excited states". Since all the real doubly excited states of the helium atom have higher energies than our $(1s, nl)$ state, we might expect any second order perturbation energy which involves matrix elements to these "doubly excited functions" to give a *negative* correction to the HF-energy.

[1] A. C. ZEMACH: Phys. Rev. **104**, 1771 (1957).

[2] R. T. BRADEN: Unpublished report (Engineering Physics Dept., Cornell U., 1957).

[3] The value obtained for δ for para-helium from SMITH's wave function is approximately -1.24, not -1.60 as quoted in his paper and our text.

[4] The experimental values are extrapolations to principal quantum number $n\to\infty$ from the experimental δ_n for various n up to about 10.

32 and 33. Ground state of He and helium-like ions. The work of KINOSHITA, quoted in Sect. 32 of the text, has meanwhile been published[1]. This work on the ground state of He ($Z=2$) has been extended to include 39 parameters, but the numerical values are almost identical with those quoted in the text (from a 38 parameter function). HART and HERZBERG[2] have obtained variational wave functions with 20 parameters for a number of helium-like ions ($Z=1, 2, 3, 6, 8, 10$ and 12). Their values for the ionization potentials J are in good agreement with the interpolation formula (33.12) of our text, which was based on the work of HYLLERAAS and MIDTDAL. For $Mg^{(10+)}$ ($Z=12$), for instance, the explicit 20-parameter calculation gives $J=129.313866$ Ry while (33.12) gives 129.313894 Ry. HART and HERZBERG have also evaluated the mass-polarization corrections ε_M (see Sect. 37γ of our text) with their wave functions.

36β. Expansion in LEGENDRE polynomials. The exact wave function for any state of a two-electron atom can (in principle) be written as a superposition of central field functions (i.e. of products of two single-particle functions). For S-states of the atom the angular dependence of each central field function is simply $P_l(\cos\vartheta_{12})$ and the wave function is of the form (36.4) of our text. More work has been and is being done[3] on the evaluation of wave functions of this form (with a finite number of terms), especially for the ground state and the metastable $2S$-state of helium. Values obtained with such functions for the energy eigenvalue do not seem to converge as rapidly with the number of terms carried as with variational wave functions of the type discussed in Sect. 33 and 35. However, wave functions of such type can have some other advantages over the variational ones which employ r_{12} as one of the coordinates: First, these methods can be generalized for higher states or more complicated atoms where the variation method is not practical. Second, the various terms in a superposition of central field functions are orthogonal to each other, which the HYLLERAAS-type terms in a variational function are not, and have a more direct physical significance. Finally, such wave functions may yield more reliable expectation values of some operators (such as a high power of r_1) which weight heavily regions in position or momentum space which are unimportant for the energy expectation value and are therefore not given very accurately by the variational functions. Unfortunately no wave functions of this kind of very high accuracy are available as yet for helium.

40. Fine structure splitting of helium. We merely add a few references to those quoted in the text: New microwave techniques for measuring fine structure separations in the rather short-lived excited triplet states of helium are described in a paper by LAMB[4], who also reviews the status of theoretical fine structure calculations. Calculations of the effect of radiative corrections on the theoretical fine structure splitting are also being carried out[5]. More accurate wave functions for the excited triplet states of helium are badly needed for the accurate evaluation of the main theoretical splitting (order $Z^2\alpha^2$ Ry), before effective use can be made of accurate experiments and of higher order calculations.

[1] T. KINOSHITA: Phys. Rev. **105**, 1490 (1957).
[2] J. HART and G. HERZBERG: Phys. Rev. **106**, 79 (1957).
[3] P. O. LÖWDIN and H. SCHULL: Phys. Rev. **101**, 1730 (1956). — L. C. GREEN et al.: Phys. Rev. **104**, 1593 (1956). — D. H. TYCKO: Ph. D. Thesis, Columbia U., 1957. — E. HOLØIEN: Phys. Rev. **104**, 1301 (1956).
[4] W. E. LAMB: Phys. Rev. **105**, 559 (1957). — W. E. LAMB and T. H. MAIMAN: Phys. Rev. **105**, 573 (1957).
[5] G. ARAKI: Phys. Rev. **101**, 1410; **103**, 1906 (1956). — H. ARAKI: Progr. Theor. Phys. **17**, 619 (1957).

41. Relativistic corrections for the ground state. *β) The* LAMB *shift.* Misprint correction: In (41.7) on p. 190 of the text, the first fraction on the right-hand side should read $\frac{16}{3}$ instead of $\frac{3}{16}$.

γ) Numerical results. Details on the evaluation of $E_J - \varepsilon_M$ for He ($Z=2$) will be found in KINOSHITA'S paper[1]. There has been some slight numerical improvements in the evaluation of $E_J - \varepsilon_M$ and ΔE_J for helium-like ions of $Z>2$: The small mass-polarization term ε_M has been evaluated accurately[2], using 20-parameter wave functions for a number of ions; ε_M increases slowly from 4.9_6 cm^{-1} for Li$^+$ to 7.1_6 cm^{-1} for O$^{(6+)}$. E_J and ΔE_J have not yet been evaluated using these accurate wave functions, but all the relevant expectation values have been evaluated[3] for Li$^+$ and O$^{(6+)}$ ($Z=3$ and 8) using 10 parameter wave functions[4]. These expectation values, together with (74.9A) in Sect. 74 of these Addenda, give E_J and ΔE_J. From these results for $Z=3$ and 8 and from the more accurate ones for $Z=2$ and for $Z\to\infty$, we have constructed interpolation formulae for other values of Z. These formulae, which should be slightly more accurate than (41.11) and (41.12) of our text, are

$$E_J = \frac{1}{4}\alpha^2 Z^2 \left(Z^2 - 3.606 Z + 3.29 + 0.05\,\frac{1}{Z}\right) \text{Ry}, \tag{41.11A}$$

$$\left.\begin{aligned} \Delta E_J = -\frac{16 Z^4 \alpha^3}{3\pi}\Big[(3.745 - \log Z) - \frac{1}{Z}(5.97 - 1.31 \log Z) +\\ + \frac{1}{Z^2}(3.08 - 0.28 \log Z)\Big]\,\text{Ry}. \end{aligned}\right\} \tag{41.12A}$$

We estimate the probable errors in the numerical values in the various terms contributing to the theoretical ionization potential J_{theor} for $Z=3$ to 8 to be as follows: A few cm^{-1} in J_{NR} for all Z; from about ± 3 cm^{-1} (for $Z=3$) to ± 60 cm^{-1} (for $Z=8$) in $E_J - \varepsilon_M$; from about ± 1 cm^{-1} (for $Z=3$) to ± 20 cm^{-1} (for $Z=8$) in ΔE_J. We reproduce below the part of Table 12 for $Z>2$, using our revised values for E_J and ΔE_J. The calculated ionization potentials agree with the experimental ones to within better than the quoted experimental errors.

Table 12A. *Experimental and theoretical ionization potentials for helium-like ions* (*in* cm^{-1}).

Z ion	3 Li$^+$	4 Be^{++}	6 C$^{(4+)}$	8 O$^{(6+)}$
J_{NR}	610072	1241177	3161660	5959980
$E_J - \varepsilon_M$	$+14._6$	+98	+922	+3590
ΔE_J	$-\ 8._2$	−28	−134	−390
J_{theor}	610078	1241247	3162448	5963180
J_{exp}	610079 ± 25	1241225 ± 100	3162450 ± 300	5963000 ± 600

49δ. The absolute value of g_s. The largest contribution to the probable error in the experimental value in (49.9) for g_s comes from the measurement of the electron cyclotron frequency (in terms of the proton resonance frequency). An independent measurement of this quantity has been carried out recently[5] with slightly different results (and about the same accuracy) as the older measurement quoted in our text. The newer measurement leads to an experimental value for g_s of

$$g_s = 2(1.001165 \pm 0.000011). \tag{49.9A}$$

[1] T. KINOSHITA: Phys. Rev. **105**, 1490 (1957).
[2] J. HART and G. HERZBERG: Phys. Rev. **106**, 79 (1957).
[3] T. KINOSHITA, M. NAUENBERG and R. F. PEIERLS: Unpublished work.
[4] S. CHANDRASEKHAR and G. HERZBERG: Phys. Rev. **98**, 1050 (1955).
[5] P. FRANKEN and S. LIEBES: Phys. Rev. **104**, 1197 (1956).

The theoretical value (see Sect. 18β of these Addenda) for $g_s/2$ would be 1.001145 using the "old" KARPLUS-KROLL value of the fourth order electron moment, 1.001160 using the "new" SOMMERFIELD value.

50. The diamagnetism of helium. In the text we have shown that the diamagnetic susceptibility χ per gm mol of helium is related to $\overline{r^2}$, the expectation value of r^2 for one electron in the helium ground state. With $\overline{r^2}$ in atomic units (a^2) and χ in cm^3 we have

$$\chi = -1.585 \times 10^{-6}\, \overline{r^2}. \tag{50.5 A}$$

We had found excellent agreement between the older measurements of χ and the approximate theoretical value of $\overline{r^2} = 1.19$ obtained from the HARTREE wave function. The excellence of the agreement is somewhat fortuitous, since the latest measurements[1] of χ lead to a slightly larger value of $\overline{r^2}$, namely

$$\chi_{\text{exp}} = -(1.93_3 \pm 0.01) \times 10^{-6}, \qquad (\overline{r^2})_{\text{exp}} = (1.22_0 \pm 0.006) \quad \text{a.u.} \tag{50.6 A}$$

$\overline{r^2}$ has not yet been evaluated directly with any ground state wave function more accurate than the HARTREE function, but DALGARNO and LYNN[2] have used some semi-empirical formulae for dipole oscillator strengths to evaluate a sum [see (61.22A) of our Addenda] which, indirectly, leads to a value of about 1.22 for $\overline{r^2}$.

58. The dielectric constant of helium. In the text we have stated that the STARK effect energy $E_2 F^2$ for the helium ground state in an electric field F is related to the dielectric constant ε of helium. E_2 is defined as [see (56.1)]

$$-\frac{\alpha'}{2} \equiv E_2 = \sum_k \frac{(z_1 + z_2)^2_{0k}}{E_0 - E_k}, \tag{58.12 A}$$

where $(\,)_{0k}$ is a matrix element between the ground state and a state k, and $\alpha' \equiv -2E_2$ is called the "polarizability of helium in atomic units" ($\alpha' a^3$ is the polarizability in C.G.S. units). We saw that the polarizability can also be calculated approximately by the perturbation-variation method and that SLATER and KIRKWOOD's calculated approximate value was $\alpha' = 1.43$. More recent measurements[3] of the dielectric constant yield a slightly lower experimental value for the polarizability than the older one quoted in the text, the present value being

$$\alpha' = 1.40 \pm 0.01. \tag{58.13 A}$$

Extrapolation of refractive index measurements in helium to infinite wavelengths yields a similar value for α'.

61α. Statement of sum rules. A number of other sum rules, besides those stated in the text, have been derived by various authors[2,4]. We shall state without proof a few of these sum rules which apply to a general atom or ion: Let Z be the number of electrons, Z_c the nuclear charge, f_{n0} the oscillator strength

$$f_{n0} = +(2i/\hbar)\,(p_x)_{0n}\,(x)_{n0}$$

[1] G. G. HAVENS: Phys. Rev. **43**, 992 (1933). In evaluating HAVENS' results the more recent change in the CURIE constant for O_2 has to be taken into account.

[2] A. DALGARNO and N. LYNN: Proc. Phys. Soc. A (in print, 1957).

[3] L. ESSEN: Proc. Phys. Soc. B **66**, 189 (1953). — L. HARTSHORN: Precision Electrical Measurements. (London: H. M. Stationary Office, 1955.

[4] J. P. VINTI: Phys. Rev. **41**, 432 (1932). — H. MARGENAU: Phys. Rev. **56**, 1000 (1939). — A. DALGARNO and J. LEWIS: Proc. Roy. Soc. Lond., Ser. A **233**, 70 (1955).

and E_n the energy of the state n expressed in units of the RYDBERG (*not* in atomic units). The sum rules are

$$\sum_n f_{n0}(E_0 - E_n)^{-2} = \tfrac{1}{4}\alpha', \qquad (61.21\,\text{A})$$

$$\sum_n f_{n0}(E_0 - E_n)^{-1} = \tfrac{1}{3}\Big(\Big|\sum_i \boldsymbol{r}_i\Big|^2\Big)_{00}, \qquad (61.22\,\text{A})$$

$$\sum_n f_{n0} = Z, \qquad (61.23\,\text{A})$$

$$\sum_n f_{n0}(E_0 - E_n) = \tfrac{4}{3}\Big[\big[E_0 + \tfrac{1}{2}\sum_{i \neq j}(\boldsymbol{p}_i \cdot \boldsymbol{p}_j)_{00}\Big], \qquad (61.24\,\text{A})$$

$$\sum_n f_{n0}(E_0 - E_n)^2 = \frac{16\pi Z_c}{3}\sum_i \big(\delta^{(3)}(\boldsymbol{r}_i)\big)_{00}. \qquad (61.25\,\text{A})$$

On the left-hand sides of these equations the summation n goes over all the states of the atom, including those in the continuum, except for the ground state, i.e. $n \neq 0$. On the right-hand sides the summations i and j go over each of the Z electrons; $\boldsymbol{r}$ and $\boldsymbol{p}$ are position and momentum in atomic units; the symbol $(\ )_{00}$ denotes an expectation value for the ground state. The symbol α' in (61.21 A) is the "polarizability" of the atom, defined (for $Z=2$) in (58.12 A) of the present Addenda. As indicated in Sect. 58, the polarizability α' can (in principle) be calculated by means of the perturbation-variation method without explicit reference to transition matrix elements to excited states.

Of the above sum rules, (61.23 A) is simply the THOMAS-REICHE-KUHN sum rule (61.1); (61.22 A) is related to our sum rule (61.6); (61.25 A) is equivalent to (19.13) plus (21.1) of our text and is also restated in (74.5). The expectation values on the righthand sides of these equations are often evaluated much more easily than the sums on the left-hand sides and some of them (e.g. α') can also be obtained from experimental measurements. DALGARNO and LYNN[1], for instance, have used these sum rules, together with a few explicit calculations, to derive a semi-empirical formula for the oscillator strengths of dipole transitions from the ground state of helium to each of the various excited states (including $df/d\nu$ for the continuum, see Sect. 74γ of our text).

68. X-ray spectra. We merely add some recent references which deal with the dipole oscillator strengths and their sum rules in highly relativistic atoms[2].

73 α. Relativistic Born approximation. Misprint correction: On p. 312, equation (73.3), the factor in square brackets should read $\left[1 - \tfrac{1}{2}\gamma(\gamma - 1)(1 - \beta\cos\Theta)\right]$.

74 γ. The average excitation energy for the LAMB shift. In (74.8) of the text we stated the result of an approximate calculation of K_0, the "average excitation energy for the LAMB shift" for the ground state of He ($Z=2$). The probable error quoted in (74.8) is most probably too small[3]: The quantity $\nu^3\, df/d\nu$ for transitions to the continuum, which enters in the calculation of K_0, has its maximum at quite large frequencies ($h\nu$ about 25 times the ionization potential of He). The expressions used for $df/d\nu$ are quite reliable for moderately low values of ν and again for very large ν (where the BORN approximation applies), but they employ the approximate "full screening" wave functions for the continuum

[1] A. DALGARNO and N. LYNN: Proc. Phys. Soc. A (in print, 1957).

[2] J. S. LEVINGER, M. RUSTGI and K. OKAMOTO: Phys. Rev. **103**, 439 (1956), **106**, 1191 (1957). — G. E. BROWN and D. F. MAYERS: Proc. Roy. Soc. Lond., Ser. A **234**, 387 (1956). — I. P. GRANT: Phys. Rev. **106**, 754 (1957).

[3] P. KABIR and E. SALPETER: Phys. Rev. **108** (in press, 1957).

and may not be very accurate near the maximum of $\nu^3 df/d\nu$. The present value for He ($Z=2$) is

$$K_0 = (80.5 \pm 15)\ \mathrm{Ry}, \tag{74.8A}$$

where the ± 15 Ry is only an estimate of the probable error. This value divided by $Z^2=4$ is quite close to the hydrogenic value of 19.77 Ry. An (even rougher) calculation for Li^+ ($Z=3$) also gave a value for K_0 close to $3^2 \times 19.8$ Ry and, within the present accuracy, we adopt for the ground state of helium-like ions of charge Z

$$K_{0(z)} \approx 19.77 Z^2\ \mathrm{Ry}. \tag{74.9A}$$

78. Bremsstrahlung calculations for low energies. In our text, Eq. (78.2), we have quoted SOMMERFELD's exact nonrelativistic formula for the integrated cross-section $\sigma(\nu)$, expressed in terms of the general hypergeometric function. In our text we gave the simplified expressions to which (78.2) reduces for various limiting values of the parameters n_0 and n. Very accurate numerical evaluations of SOMMERFELD's formula (78.2) are now also available[1] for arbitrary values of n_0 and n.

79γ. Relativistic deviations from BORN approximation. In our text we have discussed the "Coulomb effects", i.e. deviations from the BETHE-HEITLER BORN approximation formula for large values of $Z\alpha$, and stated that the calculations are very difficult when these COULOMB effects and screening effects are of importance simultaneously. Calculations for the differential cross-section at high energies for Bremsstrahlung and for pair-production, including both COULOMB and screening effects, have nevertheless been performed recently[2].

Another recent paper[3] tabulates numerical values for the *un*corrected BETHE-HEITLER formula, integrated over the direction of the radiated photon only.

[1] J. M. BERGER: Phys. Rev. **105**, 35 (1957).
[2] H. OLSEN, L. C. MAXIMON and H. WERGELAND: Phys. Rev. **106**, 27 (1957).
[3] P. MCCORMICK, D. KEIFFER and G. PARZEN: Phys. Rev. **103**, 29 (1956).

Author Index.

Subject Index.

Index of Tables.